Inorganic Chemistry

BY

W. NORTON JONES, Jr.

Professor of Chemistry, McMurry College
Abilene, Texas

Philadelphia • THE BLAKISTON COMPANY • Toronto

1949

COPYRIGHT, 1947, by THE BLAKISTON COMPANY

Printing of September 1949

PRINTED IN THE UNITED STATES OF AMERICA
BY THE MAPLE PRESS COMPANY, YORK, PA.

To My Parents

BEATRICE RODDY JONES

and

WILLIAM NORTON JONES

Preface

This textbook embodies a successful method of presentation of a first-year course in college chemistry to groups composed of (1) students who had studied high school chemistry, (2) those who had not studied it, and (3) to mixed groups. Experimental presentation of this method covered several years. Among the major conclusions drawn are, first, that all groups grasp and retain the facts of chemistry best when they are presented in the light of theory, and, second, that the retention and deduction of facts is greatly improved by constant reference to the modern concepts of electronic structure and to the periodic relationship of the elements.

In view of these conclusions, atomic structure and the periodic classification of the elements are given early treatment and constant reference is made to both. The behavior of each new element or family of elements is discussed in the light of electronic configuration, and interrelationships are carefully pointed out. To impress the regular variation of properties with slight changes in electronic configuration, the elements of the third period have been chosen for first attention. In addition to showing periodic variation well, these elements are all of great practical value and serve to emphasize the practical aspects of chemistry. In addition, they give the student early experience with both typical metals and nonmetals. When consideration of these elements has been completed, attention is turned next to hydrogen, and then to the elements of a typical family of the periodic table. If the time allotted for a given course is too brief for the consideration of the table as a whole, then, by reference to the variations learned for a typical period and for a typical family, the student may predict rather closely the behavior of many elementary substances which he has not yet studied.

For two reasons, no attempt has been made to follow the meandering course of chemical history save in the cases in which historical development is necessary. *First*, the average student is often confused by this time-honored historical approach, and *second*, time limits rarely permit the presentation of both facts as currently accepted and chemical history. However, because it is important from both the cultural and the scientific standpoints for the student to know something of the men and events which have shaped a science, a number of portraits of outstanding scientists accompanied by brief sketches have been included.

In keeping with the considerations above presented, most of the essential theoretical matter has been placed in the first half of the book, interspersed, however, with descriptive chapters. For the purpose of emphasizing the importance of chemistry in the daily life of the modern world, some details of a number of industrial processes have been incorporated in these descriptive chapters. These serve to emphasize similarities and differences between commercial and laboratory accomplishment of identical reactions. Also included in the descriptive chapters are sections which deal with the uses of elements and their important compounds.

The use of numbered sideheads should permit the instructor whose time is limited to note necessary deletions with a minimum of difficulty. Similarly, their use will permit those who desire to reorder the sequence of topics to make assignments with ease. Also with these ends in view, many of the chapters—especially those in the latter half of the text—are organized so that they may be omitted or reordered without causing serious consequences, for the early presentation of theory insures the coverage of fundamentals. Additional time, then, may be devoted to description or to those topics which the individual instructor considers most worthy of attention. Once the fundamental theory is thoroughly understood, the interested student can continue with the descriptive material unassisted.

Repetition is a necessary part of the learning process, hence a conscious effort has been made to introduce each concept and then to return to it for further development wherever such a procedure seemed at all possible. For the same reason, reference is made again and again to many topics and principles, and an effort has been made to incorporate adequate cross-references, which students should be encouraged to use.

References to both books and periodicals appear at the end of each chapter, since the student should be encouraged to gain contact with the literature in each of his fields of study. A series of Exercises appears in the Appendix; these include questions, problems, and equations to be balanced. In the problems, emphasis has been placed on the standard calculations of chemistry. Solution of problems by the student is of special importance, for there is usually no better test of the understanding of principles than the necessity for applying them in the solution of problems. Problem solution also supplies the student with an opportunity to reason, a process in which many freshmen are sadly deficient.

The author wishes to express his appreciation to his publishers for their many helpful suggestions, and to Dean Ernest H. Bader for his advice and encouragement. He also acknowledges a debt to former teachers, to the authors of many text and reference books, and to all of those individuals who either directly or indirectly have contributed to the preparation of this textbook. Special acknowledgment is due the author's wife, Roberta J. Jones, without whose constant efforts and untiring assistance the book could not have been prepared. To the various individuals and organizations who have furnished illustrative material and have permitted its use, the author is grateful. Thanks will also be due to those kind enough to suggest any changes or inclusions they may deem necessary.

W. NORTON JONES, JR.

Hesperus, Colorado

Contents

Introduction to Chemistry

1. Science and Philosophy

Since some time in the far distant past, man has been at home upon this planet which we call the Earth. During this period, he has acquired a body of knowledge concerning himself, his fellow man, his local environment, his world, and even his universe. This knowledge, acquired bit by bit down through the centuries, is generally divided into two broad fields known, respectively, as *science* and *philosophy*. His findings concerning nature and its modes of operation are grouped under the heading of science, while his findings concerning the beliefs, the ideas, and the moral and mental behavior of his fellow mortals are classified as philosophy. It is the province of science, then, to deal with the finite and its behavior, and the province of philosophy to deal with the intangible values of life. These two broad fields of learning complement each other, and, as surely as nature presents two aspects, if man would fully understand his surroundings and his relation to them he must seek the aid of both science and philosophy in his quest.

2. The Divisions of Science

At first, man's knowledge of nature consisted of such facts as he had learned by casual observation. Although generally useful, these facts were totally unrelated and constituted no organized body of information. As the years passed, man's understanding increased until he knew a great many facts about many different aspects of nature. To facilitate the organization and use of these facts, science was divided first into two branches—*physical science* and *biological science*. The former dealt with the behavior of inanimate objects, the latter with the behavior of the matter of living organisms and their products. Later, as still more material became available, further subdivision was made. Astronomy, geology, physics, and chemistry are prominent subdivisions of physical science, while zoology, botany, medicine, and physiology are numbered among the subdivisions of biological science. These subdivisions are commonly called sciences, and all are concerned with the behavior of finite bodies according to natural laws, but each is concerned with its own special approach to the problem and no one of them can proceed without the aid of the others. There is, then, only one science whose divisions are both arbitrary and artificial.

Science is not static; each passing year sees man's store of facts increase, with the result that further subdivisions are made within the sciences, yet at the same time the dependence of each of the sciences upon the others increases. Without the chemist the physicist would be lost, and vice versa, and without these two the astronomer, the physician, the geologist, and all the other scientists could make little progress.

3. Matter and Energy

Two categories are easily recognized in nature. We are all conscious of the numerous material objects about us—of trees, houses, furniture, automobiles, other human beings, animals, etc.; in short, we are conscious of *matter*, which may be defined as *anything that occupies space*.

In addition to matter, though, we are aware also of a second manifestation of nature—we see people and animals moving; we see machines doing work; we feel the heat given off by stoves or radiators; and we see the light emitted by burning matter or by heated objects such as a red-hot stove or a heated light-bulb filament. This second manifestation we call *energy*, which may be defined as *the ability to do work*.

Under all ordinary circumstances, matter and energy, while often associated, are two entirely different aspects of nature, but within relatively recent times it has been shown that in changes which involve huge quantities of energy there may actually be minute accompanying changes in mass. This concept of energy will be of little concern to us, however, since no such conversions are possible under ordinary laboratory conditions.

4. The Science of Chemistry

Naturally, the first concern of the student undertaking the study of that branch of science known as chemistry is to know just what chemistry is. By way of arriving at an answer to this question, we should first reëmphasize the fact that each of us is at home in a world which is filled with a wide variety of material objects; further, each of us is aware that this vast array of objects represents a considerable number of materials. We recognize iron, wood, sand, clay, copper, starch, cotton, etc., as being present in many familiar objects. Cloth is easily identified, and linen cloth is easily distinguished from cotton cloth.

Furthermore, we are all familiar with the fact that a piece of cloth burns easily, that a discarded piece of iron soon changes to a heap of reddish powder, that milk upon standing gradually becomes sour—in short, we are familiar with the fact that materials may undergo changes. These observations, then, point to the most general definition of chemistry: *Chemistry is that branch of science which deals with the composition and properties of matter, and with the changes which it will undergo.*

We also recognize the fact that it is possible to facilitate or to retard changes in the nature of matter. Cloth does not burn unless its temperature is first raised considerably above room temperature*; milk does not sour so readily if it is kept cool; a piece of iron does not rust so easily if it is kept painted, or covered with oil, or kept dry; liquid gasoline burns, but vaporized gasoline when mixed with air explodes. From these considerations it follows, then, that if chemistry is concerned with the changes matter will undergo, it must perforce be concerned with the conditions which foster or hinder these changes.

When changes in matter occur, it is common knowledge that there are accompanying energy changes. We make use of the heat energy that is evolved when wood and coal change into gases and ashes to heat our homes and to provide motive power for industry. Opposed to reactions of this type there are others which absorb energy in the form of heat when they occur. A change accompanied by the evolution of heat is described as *exothermic*, while one in which heat is absorbed is called *endothermic*. Since changes of energy accompany changes of matter, chemistry cannot ignore them but must perforce include them in its field.

Finally, then, we may say that the particular domain of chemistry is the study of the composition and properties of matter, the changes which matter will undergo, the conditions under which such changes will take place, and the energy changes which accompany them.

5. *The Development of Chemistry*

The oldest records of man's activity tell us that he worked with metals, that he made wine, vinegar, soap, and glass, and that he prepared medicinals from animal, plant, and mineral materials. The first people to become notably proficient in these arts were the inhabitants of Egypt's Nile Valley—a land which, because of its black alluvial soil, was known in Arabic as *al Khem*. In other lands, practitioners of the arts of *al Khem* came to be known as *alchemists*.

In those early days, knowledge of the behavior of matter consisted of

* Throughout this text, the phrase "about 20° C." will be used to designate a temperature corresponding to that of a normal room.

isolated facts which were completely uncorrelated and which were applied wholly by rule of thumb. As the years went by, more information was acquired slowly, bit by bit, and attempts were made by both Greek and Hindu philosophers of the pre-Christian era to arrive at explanations of the nature and behavior of matter. Information upon which they could base their conclusions was scant, and, since they were thinkers rather than experimentalists, their achievements in the realm of chemistry were in no wise comparable with their achievements in the fields of mathematics and metaphysics. One of their chief contributions, however, was the idea that all of the numerous types of matter were composed of a relatively few simple types of matter in various combinations.

Knowledge of the changes that a few varieties of matter would undergo, coupled with the conclusions of the early philosophers, soon led to the idea that, under proper conditions, all types of matter should be interconvertible. If this were true, then lead, iron, and other less valuable materials should be convertible into gold. Gold and the hope of securing gold have ever been prime initiators of action; this case was no exception. Experimentation flourished as never before as men sought to prepare the valuable metal. Ultimately, there developed the idea that gold could be prepared easily enough if only the proper material could be developed with which to touch the baser material to be converted. In time, this magical substance which so many sought to prepare came to be known as the *Philosopher's Stone*, search for which continued through the early years of the Christian era, throughout the Middle Ages, and into the earlier years of the Renaissance period.

During the same era, there developed the idea that there should be an equally magical substance which, when taken by a human, would make him eternally youthful. This substance was known as the *Elixir of Life*. In the days following the discovery of America, men of action such as Ponce de Leon sought it by exploration, believing that it would be found in a natural spring, but the sedentary alchemist sought to prepare it in his laboratory. Many important discoveries were made during the long search for these two wonder-working substances. Some of these discoveries were made public; many others undoubtedly were buried in the private and secret shorthand of jealously guarded notebooks or were discarded in disappointment so that rediscovery at a later date was necessary.

The practice of alchemy fell into disrepute toward the end of the Middle Ages, partially because so much labor had produced neither gold nor eternal youth, and partially because many of its practitioners had become charlatans claiming magical powers which, of course, they did not possess. Alchemical ideas were still in vogue, however, and in the thirteenth century the Encyclopaedists prepared compilations of all available alchemical thought and findings. The end of alchemy began with the attacks made upon it in the sixteenth century by the Swiss physician, Theophrastus Bombastus von Hohenheim, who

AN ALCHEMICAL LABORATORY. A reproduction of a painting made in 1648 by David Teniers the Younger. (Courtesy, Fisher Scientific Co.)

is more commonly known by his pseudonym, Philippus Aureolus Paracelsus. Paracelsus insisted that the ideas of the ancient alchemists should be accepted only when experimentation proved their truth, and he advocated the use of chemical substances in the treatment of human ailments.

By the end of the sixteenth century, sufficient facts, entirely free of the aura of magic which had surrounded the work of the alchemists, had been made available for the first systematic treatises on chemistry to appear, and in the seventeenth century modern chemistry as we know it began with the work of the Englishman, Robert Boyle. Boyle was the first worker to devote a major portion of his time to chemical investigations; the first worker to make careful measurements of the quantities of materials used and produced in his work; and the first to keep meticulous records of his findings. His advice to chemists— "First to doubt, then to enquire, and then to discover"—is still wise counsel.

Boyle is generally called the Father of Modern Chemistry, for his ideas on chemical investigation were widely accepted and applied. The search for exact information which began with him continues today. In the intervening period, sufficient data have been collected to permit the formulation of a number of generalities concerning the nature and behavior of matter. The study of these generalities, together with certain descriptive material, will occupy us in this course. Chemical research today is proceeding more rapidly than ever before, with the result that our knowledge of the subject is still increasing. Consequently, the last word on chemistry will not be written for a long time to come.

6. The Scientific Method

Chemistry as a science began to develop only when, with the definite aim of ascertaining facts about the behavior of matter, man began to experiment and to record his findings. When he did this, he began to apply what is generally termed the *scientific method*. The first step in the application of this method is the accumulation of experimental data. These data may be obtained by both the observation of naturally occurring phenomena and the observation of especially designed and planned experiments; and they should be as complete and as accurate as possible. Often data appear to be totally unrelated, but when sufficient have been obtained, and especially when experiments have been so planned that their data tend to relate to data of other observations, it is possible to develop generalizations concerning the behavior of matter under the specified conditions. This development of generalizations from correlated data is the second step in the application of the scientific method.

7. Scientific Laws

When a large number of observations which confirm each other have been made concerning the behavior of nature, the scientist summarizes his findings in a statement which is called a *scientific law*, which is defined as *a statement of some uniform, or constant, mode of behavior of nature*. The law of universal gravitation is a good example of a natural, or scientific, law. No one has ever observed an example of a body operating contrary to it, so the conclusion is that it must be true.

8. *Hypotheses*

After a law has been established, we are next concerned with the question: why is it true? or, what is the explanation for the behavior which it sets forth? There may not be enough corollary information available at the moment to establish definitely the true explanation, but from the few facts known it may be possible, with the aid of the imagination, to establish a plausible explanation. Such an explanation is known as a *hypothesis*, and is often hardly more than a well-founded guess.

9. *Theories*

As other facts which bear on the explanation in question are ascertained, they may either substantiate or disprove the hypothesis. If the new information does not agree with the imaginary solution, this solution is discarded, but if it successfully withstands the tests imposed upon it by all additional discoveries, it is eventually advanced to the status of a *theory*, which is *an explanation of natural behavior which has withstood the test of time and is used to coördinate, to correlate, and to interpret natural laws*. Often a theory will suggest further experiments to be performed.

The Greek philosophers as early as 450 B.C. developed the hypothesis that all matter is made up of very tiny particles which they called atoms. All observations made within the past 2400 years confirm this idea, so today we speak of the atomic theory.

A theory differs from a law in that it makes use of concepts which are not directly susceptible of experimental proof. This statement implies that theories can be wrong, and such has occasionally been the case. Each new discovery tests a theory; if the theory cannot meet the test, it must be discarded or modified. Generally accepted theories are used as if they were entirely true, but it is tacitly understood that change or even abandonment of a theory may be necessary at any time.

10. *Chemistry an Exact Science*

Since the days when Robert Boyle first began to weigh and to measure in various ways the materials used in his experiments, devices with which to make such measurements have developed to the point that today even very tiny differences may be determined with great accuracy. Many of the laws, theories, and hypotheses of chemistry are now expressible in mathematical terms as a result of the development of these better instruments and of the development of better techniques for the accomplishment of quantitative work. A science whose laws, theories, and hypotheses may be so expressed is said to be an *exact science*. Hence, in the main, chemistry is an exact science, since many of the relationships encountered in it may be expressed mathematically. The aim of much present-day research is to extend quantitative exactness to the remaining relationships which at the moment are known only qualitatively. As these gaps in our knowledge are filled, undoubtedly some theories may be discarded, others may need to be altered, and still others may be expressed in simpler form; hence, the work of the theoretical chemist, like that of chemists who deal with other phases of the science, is far from complete.

11. Chemistry in the Modern World

The publicity given chemistry during World War II makes it figure in the public mind as never before. Everyone is aware that, without the development of processes and plants for the preparation of magnesium, aluminum, high-test gasoline, synthetic rubber, nylon, and many other fundamental necessities of modern warfare, our record in the struggle in all likelihood would have been vastly different. Less spectacular, but even more essential, is the part chemistry plays in the daily life of every man. At the outset, man is composed of matter which functions to maintain life as the result of one of the most complicated systems of intricate, interdependent chemical equilibria which may be cited. Without the chemical conversion of food, the life of the body would be brief. Without the chemical process commonly termed the burning of fuel, human life in cold countries would be virtually impossible, and without the chemical production which goes on in the plant and animal world, food and clothing would be lacking.

Many of the ordinary objects which we use and upon which we have grown to depend would not be available without chemistry. If chemistry had not made possible the refining of ores and oils and the vulcanizing of rubber, the modern automobile which is propelled by the combustion of a fuel would not be possible. Clothes would be drab were it not for synthetic dyes. Had not the chemist made possible the production of fundamental materials, or discovered necessary processes, moving pictures and the radio would be unknown; the plastics which are so widely used would never have existed; large-scale production of paper and ink would be impossible; and the anesthetics and antiseptics which have been such a blessing to the human race still would be in the limbo of things unknown and unsuspected. In short, man, at least as we know him, would not be here at all were it not for the operation of chemical processes, and his life would

ROBERT BOYLE

(1627–1691, *British*)

Because of his quantitative approach to the experiments which he performed, Boyle is frequently
credited with being the father of modern chemistry. In this role he is usually introduced to students
early in their elementary courses. His investigations were divided between the fields of chemistry and
physics. He played a prominent part in the revival of the atomic theory, and is noted especially for his
work on the physical behavior of gases and for his definition of the term "element." He was the
seventh son and fourteenth child of the Earl of Cork.

9

be as limited as that of prehistoric man were it not for the discoveries and applications made by chemists down through the ages.

12. The Divisions of Chemistry

The work of the chemist involves several distinct processes. First, he must discover or detect existing materials. Second, by purification he must separate impurities from the materials in question so that he may be sure there are no contaminants which might be a source of error in his findings. Third, he must analyze his samples both quantitatively and qualitatively to determine their composition. Fourth, he must seek to find means of synthesizing or preparing the substance under investigation. Fifth, he must determine the chemical behavior of his subject, and from that behavior suggest uses for it. Sixth and last, as he obtains more data on the behavior of matter in general, he must formulate laws and theories which become the foundation for further application of the science.

The two major divisions of chemistry are *inorganic* and *organic*. *Inorganic chemistry is the study of those materials which have their origin in mineral matter, while organic chemistry is the study of those materials which contain carbon, many of which are produced by living organisms.* The six processes mentioned in the preceding paragraph well represent the major subdivisions of these two divisions. Analytical chemistry detects, answering the questions "what?" and "how much?"; synthetic chemistry develops preparations; applied chemistry puts acquired information to work; descriptive chemistry catalogs the information for future reference; and theoretical chemistry develops the explanations for the observed facts.

Other descriptive terms which suggest the connection in which chemical information is being used are sometimes applied. As examples of such use we may cite biological chemistry, pharmaceutical chemistry, physiological chemistry, electrochemistry, etc.

13. The Future of Chemistry

The future of chemistry is practically unlimited. When they note the size of textbooks on the subject or consider the achievements of modern-day chemistry, students often think that surely the field must be on the verge of exhaustion. The truth is that the modern-day chemist is like an explorer who has set foot on a strange and wondrous continent, and who, having penetrated a few miles inland, has made many remarkable discoveries which give promise of even more wonderful things to come in the thousands of miles which stretch before him. For the adventurous a still unexploited frontier exists in chemistry. Much pioneering remains to be done. The fruits of this pioneering can mean much to both the pioneer and the human race. The motto of one large company is "better things for better living through chemistry." The developments of past years attest the truth of this motto, and the promise is that future developments will bear it out even more forcefully.

14. Purpose

If a student is to acquire a real knowledge of the workings of chemistry rather than an array of assorted details related to it, there are certain fundamental laws and theories whose operation he must understand thoroughly, as well as certain useful descriptive material which he should acquire. It shall be the purpose of this text to set forth as clearly and as logically as possible those fundamental concepts and to apply them repeatedly in explaining and unifying the descriptive material to be presented.

There is only one chemistry; hence, whether a student is preparing for continued work in chemistry or whether his aim is a career in an allied field of science or the acquisition of information to broaden his outlook, if he would know chemistry there are certain basic concepts which he must master. The majority of students who take courses in beginning chemistry do not become practicing chemists upon graduation from college or university; nevertheless, the value of the experience should not be discounted. The scientific method whose operation is set forth in such courses is generally applicable to the experiences of life. Anyone should find his course along any pathway of life made both easier and more rewarding by observing carefully and accurately, by organizing and correlating his observations, and by reasoning logically. Incidentally, people who have developed such an orderliness of mind are in demand to fill positions of every variety.

Finally, man usually enjoys most the things with which he is most familiar; thus, the student who obtains a knowledge of the nature and behavior of the infinite variety of matter which surrounds him is likely to derive the most pleasure and enjoyment from it.

(See Appendix for Exercises)

COLLATERAL READINGS

Flipper and Morris: Helpful aids in the study of chemistry, *J. Chem. Education*, **22,** 276 (1945).

Goldblatt: *Collateral Readings in Inorganic Chemistry*, New York, D. Appleton-Century Co., 1937.

Harrow: *Eminent Chemists of Our Time*, 2d ed., New York, D. Van Nostrand Co., 1927.

Haynes: *Chemical Pioneers*, New York, D. Van Nostrand Co., 1939.

——: *This Chemical Age*, New York, Alfred A. Knopf, Inc., 1942.

Heimerzheim: Some hints on how to study, *J. Chem. Education*, **20,** 508 (1943).

Jaffe: *Crucibles*, New York, Simon and Schuster, 1930.

Leonard: *Crusaders of Chemistry*, New York, Doubleday, Doran & Co., Inc., 1930.

Manuel: How to study chemistry, *J. Chem. Education*, **12,** 579 (1935).

Moore: *History of Chemistry*, New York, McGraw-Hill Book Co., 1939.

Sedgwick and Tyler: *A Short History of Science*, New York, The Macmillan Co., 1939.

2

The Varieties and Subdivisions of Matter

1. Introduction

If one stops to think of the many kinds of matter with which he comes in contact in just one day, he cannot fail to be impressed with the infinite variety exhibited. Even the ancients, who knew far fewer types of matter than we do, were impressed with the variety which their world showed. The result of the meditation of the early Greek philosophers was the promulgation of the idea that all of the many different kinds of matter were made up of a relatively few simpler types of matter, just as many different structures may be made from bricks, steel, and mortar. The ideas of these ancient scholars as to what were these few simpler, fundamental forms of matter are today outmoded and better dealt with in a history of chemistry than in a textbook upon the fundamentals of chemistry, but the conception of simplicity in the composition of matter has persisted down through the centuries and is today well substantiated by the work of the experimental chemist. In this chapter it shall be our purpose to set forth some of the present-day ideas upon the composition of matter; still other of these ideas will be presented in later chapters.

2. Properties

Everyone recognizes his friends when he meets them by means of certain distinguishing traits or characteristics possessed by each of those individuals. In a similar fashion, everyone recognizes and easily identifies many varieties of matter by certain characteristics which each of them possesses. In scientific work, however, the term *property* is preferred to the word *characteristic* when matter is being described. The whiteness, the sweetness, the solubility of sugar are all properties of that particular variety of matter.

Properties fall into two categories: *physical* and *chemical*. *Physical properties are those characteristics of matter which are discernible or detectable with the physical senses*, either with or without the aid of certain mechanical devices which make detection either easier or more exact. Physical properties, hence, are continuous;

they may be ascertained at any time during the existence of the particular sample of matter in question. Chemical properties, on the other hand, are not continuous. That wood leaves ashes when it burns is common knowledge, but to demonstrate that a given piece of wood will form an ash the wood must be burned, and once the burning is complete the demonstration of this property of wood is at an end. Chemical properties, then, are manifest only when a change in the composition of the matter in question is occurring, and are useful for describing the changes which are undergone by that substance. In short, *chemical properties may be defined as the changes in composition matter will undergo when subjected to specific changes in conditions.*

3. Conditions

The properties of a given variety of matter are specific, and are therefore true of all samples of the same kind of matter. All massive silver has a bright luster and is fairly hard, but not all silver comes in the form of fifty-cent pieces nor is it all at the same temperature. *Such attributes of a sample of matter as are variable as a result of the action of either the will of man or chance are called conditions, or experimental conditions.* Prominent among these are temperature, pressure, size, and shape, save in the case of naturally occurring crystals.

Conditions, even though variable and not inherent in the matter itself, cannot be neglected, for they influence properties, making it necessary for properties to be described as having been observed under a certain set of conditions. For instance, water below its freezing point exists as hexagonal crystals, but between its freezing and boiling points it is a thin liquid, and above the latter point it exists as a gas. Iron when cooled shrinks so that at 10° 1 cu. in. of iron contains more matter than does 1 cu. in. of iron at 50°. Chemical properties, too, depend upon conditions. A stick of wood at about 20° C. has no tendency to change to ash, but a heated stick of wood usually bursts into flame and begins to undergo change. The greater the pressure applied to a mixture of gasoline vapor and air, the more violent the change which results when the mixture is ignited.

The properties of a substance determine its value, but it is properties and conditions together which determine its use.

4. Chemical and Physical Changes—The States of Matter

An iron rod held in the fire long enough increases its energy content until it becomes too hot to hold in the unprotected hand, and some of its properties vary somewhat with this change of conditions. Nevertheless, the rod is still iron, and when it has cooled to its original temperature its properties are just as they were before the heating occurred. The heating and subsequent cooling of the rod are examples of a *physical change*. A physical change may result in a more or less temporary alteration of a few of the properties of a substance, but no change in composition results from it and most of the altered properties usually regain their former value when original conditions are reëstablished.

Changes of this type are numerous, and many of them are familiar to everyone. As an example we may cite the behavior of ice when it is heated. At first the ice melts, then upon further heating the liquid water ultimately boils, forming gaseous water (or steam, as it is commonly called). Upon cooling the steam, the process is reversed, with ice finally resulting if the cooling is continued sufficiently. The substance present in every instance was water, as is shown by reversing the process and as can be shown by other tests. This experiment points to the fact that *there are three physical states in which a substance may exist*, and that in which state it does exist at a given time depends largely upon the conditions under which it is existing at that time.

If the same iron rod mentioned above now is placed in a container of hydrochloric acid, it will be noted that bubbles begin to form on the rod and to rise to the surface of the liquid. If the rod is left in the acid for some time, the evolution of gas will continue, and upon examination the rod will be found to have diminished in mass or to have disappeared altogether. The liquid in the container, if examined, will be found to have a greenish color now as contrasted with its original lack of color, and on evaporation a mass of greenish crystals will be obtained. The iron has disappeared, forming these crystals which have totally different properties. This is an example of a *chemical change*. A chemical change results in a permanent change of properties because there is an alteration of composition, with the formation of a new substance or new substances.

A chemical change is usually called a chemical reaction, or simply a *reaction*. The substances which enter into a chemical reaction are called *reactants*.

5. *Mass and Weight*

Since matter is the concern of chemistry and since chemistry has been described as an exact science, it immediately becomes evident that the chemist often must know how much matter he is working with. *Mass is the measure of the amount of matter in a given sample or a given body*. The mass of a given body is invariable, regardless of where it may be or under what conditions it may exist. *Weight*, on the other hand, is variable from place to place on the earth's surface, for *weight is a measure only of the earth's gravitational attraction upon the matter in the sample*. Since the earth is not exactly round, and since the surface of the earth is not smooth, the distance between the centers of the earth and a given mass varies from place to place on the earth's surface, and, as a consequence, the weight of the object varies. It is mass, rather than weight, in which the chemist is interested.

6. *Common Physical Properties*

Chemical properties are manifest only during a change in the composition of matter, but physical properties are more easily ascertained, and hence are more commonly used in the identification of most materials. Some of the commoner physical properties are odor, taste, color, form, melting point, boiling point, state at about 20° C., solubility, density, hardness, ductility, malleability, electrical conductivity, and thermal conductivity.

Odor, *taste*, and *color* are such well-known qualities that they require no comment.

A substance is said to have *form* when, in its solid state, it exists as crystals of one of the 32 crystal classes. Crystals are geometric solids which are bounded by characteristic plane surfaces intersecting at definite angles. All solids which are noncrystalline are said to be without form, or *amorphous*.

The *melting point* is that temperature at which a substance passes from the solid to the liquid state. This temperature is definite and characteristic for every crystalline substance. For such substances the melting point and the freezing point have the same numerical value.

The *boiling point* is that temperature at which a liquid changes into the gaseous state under existing conditions of pressure. More specifically, it is that temperature at which the vapor pressure of the liquid is just equal to the external pressure acting upon the liquid.

Room temperature in buildings where the temperature is properly controlled is usually about 70° F. or 21° C. Thus the *state* of a substance at room temperature depends upon the relation of the melting point and the boiling point of the substance to the temperature of the room.

Solubility is another property which varies with temperature, since most substances are more soluble in hot liquids than in cold. It is usually defined as the number of units of mass of the substance which will dissolve in a fixed number of units of mass of the solvent at a specified temperature.

Density is defined as the mass of a substance per unit of its volume. Since the volume of most substances varies with temperature while mass does not, the temperature at which density is measured must always be stated.

Hardness is that property of matter which offers resistance to forces which would dent it, scratch it, or wear it away by rubbing or grinding.

Ductility is the name given to the ability to be drawn into wires which certain types of matter possess.

Malleability is the term applied to the ability of certain substances to be hammered or pounded into thin sheets or foils.

Electrical conductivity refers to the ability certain substances have of permitting electric currents to flow through them. The opposite of electrical conductivity is *electrical resistance*.

Thermal conductivity is the property of permitting the flow of heat.

7. Materials and Substances

The words *material* and *substance* have different connotations for the chemist. Wood is easily recognized by nearly everyone, and the term wood suggests a certain type of matter, yet a block of hickory and a block of pine are easily distinguished. Their colors are different, their hardness is different, and various other properties are different; yet they have certain properties in common which make them, like most samples of wood, easily recognizable as such. *Varieties of matter* like wood or cheese *which are recognizable as being a certain type of matter, but which do not have identical properties, are called materials.*

Samples of silver or salt are also easily identified by their properties, but all samples of pure silver have identical properties, as do all samples of pure salt. *Types of matter all samples of which have identical properties are called substances.* These definitions show that all substances are also materials, but all materials are not substances.

8. Mixtures

Most materials have variable properties because they are *heterogeneous*— that is, they are mixtures of substances. It is easy to see that some mixtures are such, but not so easy to see that this is the case with others. It is very easy to see that grains of corn and grains of wheat in the same container constitute a mixture, but it is not so easy to see that salt and sugar have been mixed, in which case a hand lens or microscope is needed to permit the eye to see that a mixture exists, but the sense of taste readily establishes the existence of such a mixture. The recognizable components of a mixture are referred to as *phases*, hence the two mixtures mentioned above are two-phase systems.

9. Solutions

The most complete mixture which may be encountered is the solution. The solution appears to be entirely *homogeneous* to the eye; this is true even when the eye has the assistance of the best of microscopes. Since solutions are homogeneous, they constitute one-phase systems. The particles which are mixed in the solution are so tiny that they have never been seen, yet even though a solution of salt in water looks like water, it does not taste like water,

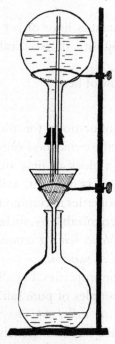

and upon evaporation of the water the salt is recovered in an unaltered form. Since the components of a solution are recoverable, the process of solution must be a physical one. The components are called the *solute* and the *solvent*. The solvent is thought of as being the component in which the solute dissolves. Sometimes it is difficult to say which is which, as in the case of a 50-50 solution of alcohol and water.

10. The Separation of Mixtures

Mixtures may be separated—some easily, some with difficulty. Corn and wheat grains are easily separated, either by simply picking out the grains of one kind or by using a perforated plate through which the wheat kernels may fall, but through whose holes the corn grains will not pass. A mixture of the two optical modifications of tartaric acid is much more difficult and much more tedious to resolve. Generally, the ease or difficulty of the separation depends upon the similarity or dissimilarity of the substances mixed, and upon the size of the particles in the mixture.

DEVICE FOR AUTOMATIC FILTRATION. The liquid to be filtered feeds slowly from the left tube of the upper flask into the funnel. Repeated fillings of the funnel are thus obviated. Insoluble material collects on the filter paper in the funnel. (Courtesy, Hackh-Grant: "Chemical Dictionary," Philadelphia, The Blakiston Company.)

There are several methods for separating mixtures and those special mixtures which are termed solutions. For the most part, these methods are physical in nature. Various ones of them will be introduced in later chapters.

11. Compounds and Elements

Mixtures may be separated into components which may be either mixtures themselves, and hence heterogeneous, or specific, homogeneous substances. In the former case, however, separation may be continued until substances are obtained. Each of these resulting substances will fall into one of two categories.

Substances which, as a result of a chemical change, can be broken down into two or more simpler chemical entities, or substances, are called compounds. Compounds, as has been stated, are homogeneous and possessed of specific physical and chemical properties, but one of their chemical properties is this ability to decompose into simpler substances as the result of certain chemical changes. Compounds are, therefore, complex, and they constitute by far the larger class of chemical substances.

Substances which cannot be broken down into simpler chemical substances by chemical means are called chemical elements, or simply elements. It is essential to include the term "by chemical means" in the above definition since there are certain elements which do undergo changes spontaneously and certain others which may be made to undergo changes as the result of a physical bombardment. Other definitions of the term "element" will be given in later chapters. Substances which meet the conditions of the definition just given are not numerous. At present their number is usually said to be only 92, although four additional unstable elements have recently been prepared. From the interaction of these 96 simple varieties of matter, all of the several hundreds of thousands of other compound substances and materials result.

12. *The Abundance of the Elements*

Some of the elements occur free in nature and were apparently known by prehistoric man; others which are easily obtained by the decomposition of their compounds were discovered during the alchemical period either by alchemists or by artisans; still others were discovered during the chemical period, inaugurated by Robert Boyle, with several of them having been discovered in the twentieth century. It is the present belief of many chemists that there is little likelihood of the discovery of any more naturally occurring elements. The properties of 90 of the 92 elements whose discovery was reported prior to World War II are known rather well, but the remaining two which are of more recent discovery and which were named virginium and alabamine by their discoverer, Professor Allison of the Alabama Polytechnic Institute, have never been prepared in sufficient quantity for satisfactory study. Concerning the four artificially prepared elements discovered during the War years by Seaborg and his associates and for which the names neptunium, plutonium, americium, and curium have been proposed, little information has yet been made available.

The elements do not have an equal distribution in that portion of the earth's structure which man has been able to explore. The relative quantities of the 10 most abundant elements in the outer 10 miles of the earth's crust, in the seas, and in the atmosphere have been estimated by two Government scientists to be as follows:

Element	Per Cent	Element	Per Cent
Oxygen	49.52	Sodium	2.64
Silicon	25.75	Potassium	2.40
Aluminum	7.51	Magnesium	1.94
Iron	4.70	Hydrogen	0.88
Calcium	3.39	Titanium	0.58

This compilation shows that the 10 most abundant elements account for more than 99 per cent of the earth's crust and atmosphere. Among the 82 elements which make up the remaining fraction of a per cent are many useful substances such as copper, carbon, sulfur, and tin—all important in modern economy. Two

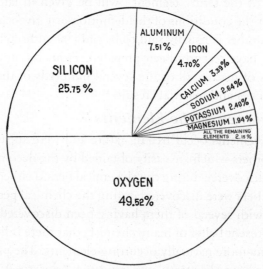

GRAPHICAL REPRESENTATION OF THE PERCENTAGE OF
THE COMMONER ELEMENTS IN THE EARTH'S CRUST.

elements alone, oxygen and silicon, account for approximately three-fourths of our familiar material world. This is not strange since sixteen-eighteenths by weight of all water is oxygen, 21 per cent by volume of the air is free oxygen, and most of the rock, sand, clay, and just "dirt" are compounds which contain both oxygen and silicon.

A systematic study of the elements enables us to correlate what would otherwise be a vast jumble of assorted facts into a well-integrated knowledge of the behavior of matter in general.

13. Analysis and Synthesis

The methods by which the composition of mixtures, solutions, and compounds is established are those of *analysis* and *synthesis*. Analysis is a destructive method which brings about a separation of mixtures and solutions and a decomposition of compounds; on the other hand, synthesis is a process of building up the more complex from the simple.

Analysis is divided into a number of branches, some of whose names indicate what the aim of the analysis is, while others indicate the method by which the analysis proceeds. Qualitative analysis simply seeks to determine what the components are, while quantitative analysis seeks to determine the quantities involved. Proximate analysis may determine the amounts of materials or compound substances present, while ultimate analysis determines the quantity of the elements present in a mixture or a compound.

Synthesis, while important in its own right as a process by which many useful materials are prepared, is often used in the laboratory in conjunction with analysis in the establishment of composition. If, for instance, a given substance upon analysis yields copper and chlorine and a substance with identical properties can be made by the reaction of copper with chlorine, there can be little doubt of the composition of the compound.

14. The Discontinuity of Matter

The results of chemical investigation established the idea of a limited number of elementary substances formulated by the early Greek philosophers, albeit in a modified form. In their meditations upon the nature of matter, this same school of ancient philosophers arrived at a second conclusion which merits consideration. As early as the fifth century B.C., Democritus advanced the idea that matter is not continuous but is made up of tiny particles which in a solid are packed closely together, in a liquid are less closely associated, and in a gas are rather far from each other. These tiny particles were termed *atoms*. A box full of baseballs offers a firm surface upon which a second box or surface can easily be supported, yet the large spaces between the balls are readily observed. The atoms of the philosophers were conceived of as being something like baseballs in that they were pictured as round, hard, and closely packed in solids, but they were also pictured as being infinitely small so that they packed very closely together, giving an effect of continuity in solids.

The idea of atoms persisted down through the centuries, being mentioned by later Greek philosophers of the pre-Christian era as well as by thinkers of later times. Sir Isaac Newton is on record as having thought in the seventeenth century that there must be atoms, but it remained for John Dalton, an English schoolmaster born in the last half of the eighteenth century, to make definite assumptions concerning the atomistic nature of matter which could be tested experimentally. Dalton apparently conceived the idea of his suppositions in

1803. In the main, the assumptions he made have been proved by experimentation to be correct, but in certain particulars he erred. As the result of the work inspired by his views on the subject, we now look upon matter as being discontinuous—that is, as being composed of small discrete particles. Just what are the present views upon these particles will be presented in succeeding chapters.

15. Molecules

A cube of salt whose edge is 1 in. has all of the properties peculiar to and characteristic of salt. Now suppose that by some mechanical means this cube is cut in half. Upon examination of the two pieces, it will be readily seen that each still has all of the properties of salt, since the division of the original cube involved only a physical process. If one of the halves is now divided again, the resulting pieces will be found to possess all the properties of salt. Suppose, now, that our senses become acute to the extent that we may see the tiniest of tiny particles, and suppose, also, that we have acquired ultra instruments with which to continue the subdivision of the salt. Conceivably, then, we may continue the splitting of each increasingly smaller particle until at last we have arrived at a particle which, upon being split, yields two pieces neither of which shows the characteristic properties of salt. Thus, presumably, there is a tiny particle of salt which cannot be further divided without ceasing to be salt. This, then, gives us our concept of a molecule (a Latin word meaning *little mass*). *The molecule is the tiniest quantity of a substance that possesses all of the specific properties of that substance.*

16. Atoms

Salt is a compound substance composed of the elements sodium and chlorine. In the preceding imaginary process of division, we arrived at the salt molecule, which is the smallest particle having all the properties of salt, and found that upon its division there result two particles neither of which shows the properties of salt. One of these particles has properties which identify it with sodium, the other has properties which identify it with chlorine. *The small particles of elements which combine to form the molecules of compound substances are called atoms*—or, to say the same thing another way, *the smallest particle of an element which will enter into a chemical reaction is called the atom.*

All experimental evidence points to the existence of atoms, but, since they are so tiny that even with the aid of the electron microscope no one has yet seen one, the concept of matter being composed of them is referred to as the *atomic theory.*

Naturally, since atoms of elementary substances enter into chemical

JOHN DALTON
(1766–1844, English)

At the age of 12 years, Dalton became a schoolteacher, a profession he was to follow for the major portion of his long life. An interest in the weather made him a close observer and a taker of voluminous notes. From his interest in water and water vapor thus developed, there stemmed the experiments which resulted in his formulation of the laws of evaporation. His greatest contribution to chemistry was the development of testable assumptions which served to establish the atomic theory. To him goes credit for much of the fundamental work upon which the laws of mass relationships are based. In so far as is known, he was the first to state the law of multiple proportions. He continued to teach and to conduct experiments throughout his life.

reactions, the smallest unit of an elementary substance is the atom, but in the case of many elements it has been found that the atoms group themselves into elementary molecules. For instance, investigation has revealed that the element chlorine normally exists in the form of diatomic molecules, as do hydrogen and various other elements. When we speak of the properties of chlorine as we know it in the laboratory, we are speaking of the properties of chlorine molecules (the smallest particle that has all of the properties of chlorine), and not of the properties of chlorine atoms. For the purpose of reaction, the molecules of these elements of this variety release their atoms so that they may enter directly into reactions with other atoms, released from other elements, to form compound molecules. An explanation for the existence of elementary molecules will be given in due course.

17. Ions

In the preceding section it was stated that the splitting of a salt molecule gave rise to particles which had properties which identified them with sodium and chlorine, respectively. These particles in this case are identical with sodium and chlorine atoms save that they possess an electrical charge which ordinary atoms do not have, and which makes these charged atoms different in properties from ordinary atoms. Atoms are always of zero net electrical charge, and many atoms combine with other atoms to form molecules without acquiring a charge, but in some instances atoms do acquire electrical charges which in some cases are positive and in others negative. *Electrically charged atoms, or an electrically charged group of atoms which act together as a whole, are called ions.* It is a well-established fact that electrical charges are attracted by other charges of unlike sign, and under proper conditions particles of unlike charge will travel toward each other. It is this ability of ions to travel under proper conditions which is responsible for their name, for *ion* in Greek means *I go.*

18. Symbols

Many an alchemist kept the records of his work in a private system of shorthand lest his secrets be discovered. The early chemists continued to use similar systems because of the saving of time in making records, with economy rather than secrecy as their aim. Because there was no general system of signs and symbols in use, much confusion resulted when chemists consulted the writings of other scientists. To do away with this source of irritation and this hindrance to the circulation of chemical thought, the Swedish chemist, Berzelius, proposed that the first letter and one other, if necessary, of the Latin name of an element be generally used as the symbol for that element. His proposal was adopted and is generally used throughout the world today. Thus, C is the symbol for carbon, Ca for calcium, Cu for copper (cuprum), H for hydrogen, He for helium, Ag for silver (argentum), Na for sodium (natrium), etc.

SILVER   GOLD   COPPER   IRON   MERCURY   LEAD   SULFUR

OLD SYMBOLS USED FOR THE REPRESENTATION OF A FEW OF THE COMMON ELE-MENTS. Such symbols were in common use until Berzelius proposed the use of modern symbols in 1808.

A symbol has other significance, too, but for the moment it is sufficient to say that in chemistry *a symbol stands first for the name of an element and second for one atom of that element.* For a list of the elements and their symbols, consult the table on the inner side of the back cover.

19. Formulas

Molecules are conceived of as being made up of several atoms which may be of like or unlike nature. Hence, if a symbol stands for one atom of an element, several symbols of like or different kinds must be used to represent a molecule. These aggregates of symbols which represent the composition of a molecule are called *formulas*. Chlorine was referred to as diatomic, hence its formula is Cl_2, a small subscript written on the right being used to indicate the presence of more than one atom of the same kind. The formula for salt (sodium chloride), which contains one atom of sodium and one atom of chlorine, is NaCl, and the formula for table sugar is $C_{12}H_{22}O_{11}$. If it is desired to write of several molecules of the same kind, a coefficient indicating the desired number is placed before the molecular formula; thus, three molecules of salt would be 3NaCl, indicating three molecules each composed of one atom of sodium and one atom of chlorine.

A formula, too, has other significance, but again for the moment it is sufficient to say that *a formula stands for the chemical name of a compound (except in the case of the formula of an elementary molecule) and for one molecule of that compound.*

20. Conclusion

Formulas for a great many compound substances have been established as the result of calculations based upon many, many hours of laboratory work carried on by thousands of workers down through the years. Why the atoms of certain elements combine with the atoms of certain other elements, and why these atoms combine in the numbers they do rather than in some other ratios, and why most of these combinations are stable will be explained later.

(*See Appendix for Exercises*)

COLLATERAL READINGS

Coward: John Dalton, *J. Chem. Education*, **4,** 22 (1927).

Goldblatt: *Collateral Readings in Inorganic Chemistry*, New York, D. Appleton-Century Co., 1937.

Gregory: *A Short History of Atomism*, New York, Walter J. Black, Inc., 1931.

Handbook of Chemistry and Physics, Cleveland, Chemical Rubber Publishing Co. New edition each year.

Jaffe: *Crucibles*, New York, Simon and Schuster, 1930.

Lange: *Handbook of Chemistry*, Handbook Publishers, Inc. Frequent editions.

Weeks: *The Discovery of the Elements*, 5th ed., Mack Printing Co., 1945.

3

Measurement and Calculation

1. Introduction

It has been pointed out that modern chemistry did not have its beginning until investigators began to measure and to record the results of their measurements, and that, as a result of such quantitative work, chemistry is today classed as an exact science. It is obvious from these two facts that, among the skills which the chemist must acquire, are those associated with the correct operation of the various measuring devices which he must employ. Faulty operation usually yields faulty results, and, since the whole structure of modern chemistry is based upon results obtained in the laboratory, faulty results inevitably lead to false interpretations and a mass of misinformation which is of little value.

When measurement was first begun by men of inquiring minds, the instruments at their disposal were of the crudest kind, and the units of measurement used varied so from country to country that experimental work performed in one country often meant little in another. Today, measuring devices have improved to the point that tiny quantities may now be measured with a high degree of accuracy, and units which enjoy international usage have been defined.

2. Comparison

The problem of measurement is essentially one of comparison of a quantity of unknown value with one of known value. The relative size of the quantity to be measured and the degree of accuracy with which its dimensions must be ascertained often determine both the means employed to make the measurement and the units in which the results are to be expressed. Also, the method employed and the conditions under which the measurements are made may greatly affect the accuracy of the results obtained. For instance, if one wished to ascertain the length of a sheet of writing paper, he would probably compare this dimension with an ordinary ruler. The result would be expressed in terms of the major divisions on the ruler—say, for instance, as 8½ in. If, on the other hand, we wished to measure the distance between two cities, we would certainly not choose the inch as the unit nor the desk ruler as the instrument of our comparison. Again, if the length of the sheet of paper had to be known to the nearest one-thousandth of an inch, the desk ruler again would not be chosen, since its smallest graduation is usually no smaller than $\frac{1}{16}$ in. A more delicate and more exact instrument would have to be employed; our method of applying this new instrument would have to be much more careful; and the conditions of temperature, etc., which might affect either the subject or the instrument during the process would have to be carefully considered.

The steps in the securing of a measurement, then, are in general three: (1) The choice of a unit of comparison suitable for the subject and for the accuracy required, (2) the selection of a suitable device followed by its application, and (3) the proper interpretation of the results obtained in view of the method employed and the conditions under which the work was performed.

3. The Measurements of Chemistry

To understand the quantitative relationships which exist between various kinds of matter, the chemist, primarily interested in matter and the changes which matter undergoes, must measure the quantities of matter with which he works; that is, since mass is the measure of the quantity of matter, he must measure mass. This is the one type of measurement which the chemist makes most frequently, hence the measuring device employed in this determination, the balance, is his most useful instrument of measurement.

Instruments other than the balance are also used by the chemist. Since for every chemical change there is always an accompanying energy change which often has to be taken into account, the calorimeter and the thermometer are often employed.

The microscope is useful for examining small samples of matter, as it is in reading certain other instruments. When equipped with a micrometer stage, it is useful for measuring very small distances.

The chemist usually employs graduated cylinders, burets, pipets, and volumetric flasks for the measurement of volumes of liquids, and the gas buret, or eudiometer, for the measurement of volumes of gases.

Since the pressure of the atmosphere which prevails during an experiment is often of concern to the chemist, the barometer is useful to him for measuring this pressure. He often uses instruments called manometers to determine gas pressures inside closed systems.

The analytical chemist and the physical chemist employ more measuring devices than do most other chemists. They use colorimeters, turbidimeters, polarimeters, refractometers, and a number of electrical devices which they borrow from the realm of physics. Few of these specialized devices are employed in elementary chemistry, so descriptions of them will not be given save in special instances, and reference will be made to descriptions in other texts.

4. Systems of Measurement

In general, our oldest units of measure resulted from some set of familiar objects having been chosen as standards of comparison. In the English system, which is commonly used in the United States, the foot betrays its origin in its name; the yard is said to have been originally the distance from the end of King Henry I's nose to his thumb when his arm was extended; and the relationship between units of length, volume, and mass are irregular in the extreme. Because of these irregularities within systems and between the systems of different nations, a new and simpler system was devised. This system is known as the *metric system*, and it has been universally adopted for scientific work. Because of its simplicity, it is used also in the general commerce of many countries. It is a decimal system, like our money system, so that calculations within the system are easily and rapidly made. Furthermore, the units of mass, volume, and length within the system are interrelated in a simple fashion which further facilitates calculations involving units of several kinds.

For general scientific work there is the *C.G.S.* (centimeter-gram-second) *system*, or *metric-absolute system*, in which all of the units of measurement save those of temperature and heat are interrelated. This is the system most frequently employed by the physicist, since he has a wide variety of measurements to make. The second is generally employed in scientific work as the unit of time.

5. The Metric System

Since in elementary chemistry the metric system is that most generally employed, it warrants early attention.

The fundamental unit of the metric system is the *meter*, which is a unit of length. A meter is the distance between two scratches on a platinum-iridium bar kept at the International Bureau of Weights and Measures near Paris. Since changes of temperature produce changes in the length of a metal rod, the standard meter bar must be kept at constant temperature. Two copies of the standard meter bar are kept at the U.S. Bureau of Standards in Washington, D. C. The units of length derived from the meter are:

$$1 \text{ millimeter} = \tfrac{1}{10} \text{ centimeter} = \tfrac{1}{1000} \text{ meter}$$
$$1 \text{ centimeter} = \tfrac{1}{10} \text{ decimeter} = \tfrac{1}{100} \text{ meter}$$
$$1 \text{ decimeter} = \tfrac{1}{10} \text{ meter}$$

1 meter = 39.37 in.
1 dekameter = 10 meters
1 hectometer = 10 dekameters = 100 meters
1 kilometer = 10 hectometers = 1000 meters

The millimeter and centimeter are the units most frequently used in chemical work. Relationships between metric and English units of length are:

1 inch = 2.54 centimeters
1 meter = 39.37 inches
1 kilometer = 0.621 mile

For measuring extremely short distances, two other units are frequently employed. One of these is the *micron* (μ) which is one-millionth of a meter or 0.001 of a millimeter. The millimicron is, of course, 0.001 of a micron. The other unit is the *Ångström unit* (A.) which is one ten-billionth of a meter or one hundred-millionth of a centimeter.

The unit of mass in the metric system is the *gram*. The gram was originally intended to be the mass of 1 cc. of water at 4° C., its temperature of greatest

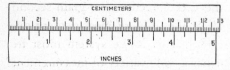

INCHES VS. CENTIMETERS. Five inches is equal to about 12.7 centimeters.

density. Subsequent determinations show that the original determinations were very slightly in error so that the relationship is not exact, though for all practical purposes the error may be neglected. Because of this error, the gram is defined as the mass of a metal cylinder kept at the International Bureau of Standards, copies of which are also kept in Washington. Multiples of the gram and their relationship to various English units are given in the following table.

1 milligram = $\frac{1}{1000}$ gram
1 centigram = $\frac{1}{100}$ gram
1 decigram = $\frac{1}{10}$ gram
1 gram = 0.0353 oz. (avoir.)
1 dekagram = 10 grams
1 hectogram = 100 grams
1 kilogram = 1000 grams = 2.2 lb.

The milligram, the gram, and the kilogram are the most important of these units to the average chemist.

The unit of volume in the metric system is the *liter*. The liter is defined as the volume occupied by 1 kg. (1000 g.) of water at its temperature of greatest density, 4° C. The liter was originally intended to be equal to 1000 cc., but because of the error mentioned above this relationship is slightly incorrect, and for that reason it is more accurate to speak of the thousandth part of a liter as a milliliter rather than as a cubic centimeter. Multiples of the liter and their relationship to various English units are given in the following table.

$$1 \text{ milliliter} = \tfrac{1}{1000} \text{ liter} = 0.034 \text{ fl. oz.}$$
$$1 \text{ centiliter} = \tfrac{1}{100} \text{ liter}$$
$$1 \text{ deciliter} = \tfrac{1}{10} \text{ liter}$$
$$1 \text{ liter} = 1.06 \text{ qt.}$$
$$1 \text{ dekaliter} = 10 \text{ liters}$$
$$1 \text{ hectoliter} = 100 \text{ liters}$$
$$1 \text{ kiloliter} = 1000 \text{ liters}$$

Of these units, those most commonly employed by chemists are the milliliter and the liter. In expressing large volumes, the chemist often uses cubic meters. A cubic meter is very nearly equal to 1000 l.

6. *Units Employed in Thermometry*

A thermometer is a device used to determine not the quantity, but the quality, of heat in a body. Two bodies of unequal size may have the same temperature; the bigger contains more heat, but the quality of the heat in each is the same. Thermometers take many forms, the commonest of which is the mercury-bulb variety which makes use of mercury's property of expanding as its temperature increases. Several systems of thermometric units are in common use. The U.S. Weather Bureau reports temperatures in terms of the Fahrenheit scale, while most scientific workers employ the Centigrade scale.

On the Fahrenheit scale, the freezing point of water is designated as 32° and the boiling point of water as 212°. On the Centigrade scale, the freezing point of water is called 0° and its boiling point 100°. Thus, 180 divisions on the Fahrenheit scale are equal to 100 divisions on the Centigrade scale, and $1° F = \tfrac{5}{9}° C$. To convert temperatures from one scale to the other, the following formulas, in which F stands for the reading of the Fahrenheit thermometer and C for the reading of the Centigrade, are useful:

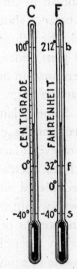

A COMPARISON OF A FEW POINTS ON THE CENTIGRADE AND FAHRENHEIT SCALES. (Courtesy, Foley, A. L.: "College Physics," 3d ed., Philadelphia, The Blakiston Company.)

$$C = \tfrac{5}{9}(F - 32) \qquad \text{and} \qquad F = \tfrac{9}{5}C + 32$$

7. Calorimetric Units

In the metric system, the unit of heat measurement is the *calorie*, which is defined as the quantity of heat required to raise the temperature of 1 g. of water from 15° to 16° C. The unit of heat measurement in the English system is the *British thermal unit*, which is defined as the quantity of heat required to raise the temperature of 1 lb. of water from 59° to 60° F.

8. The Balance

The difference between mass and weight has been pointed out, as has the fact that it is the mass of a sample of matter in which the chemist is interested. To determine mass, a *balance* is employed. The balance is an instrument used for comparing known masses with unknown masses. In essence, the balance consists of a beam suspended at its midpoint on a knife edge, with a pan or platform attached in some suitable fashion to each end of the beam. When the pans of the balance bear equal loads, the beam assumes a horizontal position, as is shown by an attached pointer which moves along a fixed scale. Naturally, the balance should be adjusted to assume this same position when it bears no load. The influence of gravity is made negligible by placing equal masses on the two pans, since it will be the same on both masses regardless of where the determination may be made. A spring balance, on the other hand, measures the attraction of gravity for a body, and hence its weight, rather than its mass.

Some balances are much more sensitive than others; that is, some will detect smaller differences in mass than will others. This sensitivity depends upon several factors. In the first place, the sensitivity increases as the length of the beam increases, and secondly, the sensitivity increases as the mass of the object placed on the pan increases, but this increase in mass of the object must be well within the load limit of the machine. Thirdly, the sensitivity increases as the weight of the beam decreases, and fourthly, it increases as the distance between the point of support of the beam and the center of gravity of the movable portion of the balance decreases. With these factors established, it is relatively easy to choose a balance which is suitable for every job.

In the average chemical laboratory there are usually three varieties of balances available to the student. The least accurate of these is the *platform balance*, which usually has porcelain platforms and a rider moving on a calibrated scale which is divided into tenths of a gram. This balance is so constructed that it gives readings which are correct to only 0.1 g. Hence, to obtain readings which are correct to 1 per cent, one would have to weigh samples of 10 g. or more, because $0.1 / 10 \times 100 = 1.0$ per cent.

The *pulp balance* consists of an upright support upon which is mounted a light beam to whose ends light metal pans are attached by means of stirrups. The pulp balance may or may not be protected by a glass case. It is of finer construction and is more sensitive than the platform balance, and reads correctly

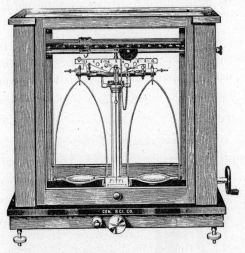

A CHEMICAL BALANCE. This balance is of the "Chainomatic" type. A 1-g. counter is the smallest required for use with it. Fractions of a gram are read by noting the position of the rider on the beam and the length of the chain attached to the beam as indicated on the horizontal scale above the beam. (Courtesy, Central Scientific Co.)

to one one-hundredth of a gram. Samples as small as 1 g. may be weighed on it without incurring an error in excess of 1 per cent, since $0.01 / 1 \times 100 = 1.0$ per cent.

The *analytical balance* is of still finer craftsmanship. In general, it is made on the same pattern as the pulp balance, but it reads correctly to about $\frac{1}{10.000}$ g.; as a consequence, as little as one one-hundredth of a gram of material may be weighed without the incurrence of an error in excess of 1 per cent, since $0.0001 / 0.01 \times 100 = 1.0$ per cent. The analytical balance is always kept in a glass case, which, in turn, is kept in a special balance room where the temperature can be kept constant and where adequate supports to insulate the balance from vibrations are provided. Hot or cold objects are never placed on such a balance, and the glass case is always closed before final readings are made since air currents might influence its final point of equilibrium.

There are even more delicate balances known as *microbalances,* by means of which weighing to $\frac{1}{1,000,000}$ of a gram may be made. Such delicate instruments are used only in advanced chemical work.

It must be remembered that every balance has its load limit and should not be loaded beyond this limit, since to do so may be to damage the machine permanently.

The object to be weighed is always placed on the left pan or platform of a balance, and the known counters placed on the right. More detailed information on the construction, use, and maintenance of balances is usually provided in the laboratory manuals whose procedures require their use.

9. The Calorimeter

The calorimeter consists essentially of two covered metallic cups, one of which is small enough to fit inside the other. The material which is either to

VARIOUS TYPES OF CALORIMETERS. From left to right: an electric calorimeter, a calorimeter cup, a vacuum jacketed calorimeter, and a Dewar flask calorimeter. (Courtesy, Central Scientific Co.)

liberate or to absorb energy, after having had its mass determined, is placed in the inside cup. The larger cup generally contains water. If the mass of the water is known and its temperature is taken before and after the energy change, the amount of energy gained or lost can be calculated since water gains one calorie of energy per gram for each degree of rise of the temperature as measured on the Centigrade scale.

There are many types of calorimeters, the more accurate of which are those that are completely insulated from the surrounding conditions and which have parts whose heat-absorbing qualities have been quantitatively established.

10. The Microscope

The microscope is an instrument which, by a combination of lenses arranged according to the principles of physical optics, permits man to see objects which are far too small for him to see with the naked eye. It is an instrument which is useful in many sciences and which, although more frequently used in a qualitative way, can also be used quantitatively for the making of measurements of length. The chemist frequently finds it of use in the study of crystals and other small bodies.

The microscope was invented in the seventeenth century by Anton van

THE ELECTRON MICROSCOPE. (Courtesy, Hercules Powder Co., Inc.)

Leeuwenhoek, whose original scope was capable of magnifying an object some 200 times. This invention opened up a whole new field for investigation, and was directly responsible for many important discoveries. Modern optical microscopes are capable of magnifying as much as 2000 times.

Although 2000 times seems like very high magnification, it is still not sufficient to render an atom or molecule visible to the human eye. At present, there is a hope that man may yet see particles of the order of magnitude of an atom. This hope has arisen from the development within recent years of the electron microscope. For some years it has been known that an object which has a diameter less than the wavelength of light cannot be seen by means employing light. The fact that electrons in motion set up a vibration whose wavelength is much shorter than that of visible light led to the development of the electron microscope, which has already permitted the taking of pictures of particles much smaller than the smallest visible with the aid of the optical microscope. The possibilities for further development of this new device hold much promise, so that it may become an even more important tool of the chemist than it is now.

For details of the operation and the theories involved in the operation of these microscopes, the student should consult physics texts and specialized publications on these subjects.

11. Instruments Used for Measuring Liquid Volumes

It is often necessary for the chemist to measure the volume of liquids to be used in his work. The commonest instrument so used is the *graduated cylinder*, on whose side are marked scratches corresponding to milliliters or multiples of milliliters. The cylinder is provided with a lip so that its contents may be poured readily into another container. Scratched in the glass of the cylinder will be the temperature (usually 20° C.) at which it contains the quantity indicated by its graduations. Since some of the liquid contained in the vessel usually adheres to its walls, it will not deliver exactly the quantity which it contained.

The *volumetric flask* is frequently used in the preparation of solutions. Like the graduated cylinder, it too is calibrated to contain a fixed volume. This volume is indicated by a scratch around the neck of the flask, and its value and the temperature of calibration are usually etched on the wall of the flask. Many volumetric flasks are provided with glass stoppers so that solutions prepared in them may be mixed thoroughly without loss of material.

The *buret* and the *pipet* are both calibrated to deliver a certain volume rather than to contain a certain volume. Since the volume they deliver is the quantity measured, they are used a great deal in quantitative analysis and other quantita-

Jacobus Henricus van't Hoff
(1852–1911, Dutch)

Van't Hoff well may be regarded as one of the founders of what is now referred to as physical chemistry. He studied in Germany and France and finally took his degree at the University of Utrecht. He held a number of professorial appointments in Holland, and from 1896 until his death he held a research professorship in Berlin. His contributions include work upon the effect of heat upon reaction velocity, the effect of heat upon systems in equilibrium, a theory of stereochemical isomerism, and information upon the colligative properties of solutions. In the latter connection his work upon osmotic pressure was of especial importance. He was awarded the Nobel Prize in 1901.

Antoine-Laurent Lavoisier
(1743–1794, French)

The most notable contribution of Lavoisier to chemistry was his clarification of the nature of combustion. It was he who first pointed out that combustion is in essence a union of the burning substance with oxygen and that the mass of the products of combustion are equal to the mass of material burned plus the mass of the oxygen involved in the process. This knowledge dealt a death blow to the older phlogiston theory and laid the groundwork for the rapid advance in chemical knowledge which followed. Lavoisier also helped to bridge the gap between chemical processes and life processes and made many other contributions to chemical knowledge. He also played an important part in the political and administrative affairs of the kingdom. Because of his political activity, he was guillotined during the French Revolution.

37

tive work. The buret is a glass tube of regular bore, open at the top end and closed with a stopcock or other easily regulated delivery device at the lower end. Its length is divided into units of 0.1 ml. so that by subtracting the initial reading from the final reading the volume of liquid delivered may be had. The pipet is a glass tube open at both ends but drawn to a fine tip at the lower one.

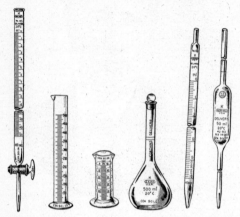

Some pipets are of uniform bore otherwise, but many have bulbs in their middles. On the neck of the pipet is a scratch which is the mark to which it must be filled to deliver the quantity etched on its side. The Mohr pipet is calibrated like a buret. The pipet is filled by suction. Since both pipets and burets are made of a material which shrinks and expands with changes in temperature, they are calibrated to deliver the stated volume only at the indicated temperature.

INSTRUMENTS USED FOR THE MEASURING OF LIQUID VOLUMES IN SCIENTIFIC LABORATORIES. From left to right they are: a buret, a graduated cylinder, a graduated cylinder with double scale and two lips, a volumetric flask, a Mohr pipet, and a transfer pipet. (Courtesy, Central Scientific Co.)

In reading all such devices, the eye should be exactly on a level with the mark to be read, otherwise the phenomenon known as parallax will cause an erroneous figure to be recorded. A liquid in a tube usually has a convex or concave surface, known as a *meniscus*. Most liquids wet glass, and therefore have a concave meniscus. When transparent liquids are measured, it is the custom to read the bottom of the meniscus, but in the case of opaque liquids the top of the curve must of necessity be read.

12. The Barometer

The *barometer* is a purely physical instrument, but the chemist often makes use of it to determine the exact pressure of the atmosphere at the time of his experimentation. Barometers are of two types, the *aneroid* and the *mercurial*. The mercurial is the type most commonly used in laboratories. Essentially it is a glass tube, closed at one end, from which all the air was removed before the unsealed end was placed in a dish of mercury. The atmosphere from where the dish is located up to the place where there ceases to be any atmosphere rests on the exposed surface of the mercury, forcing a column of it to rise in the evacuated tube to such a height that the weight of the column of mercury is just equal to the weight of the column of air. From this it will be seen that, since a barometer on a high mountain has less air above it than a barometer at sea level, the former contains a shorter column of mercury than the latter. The pressure of the atmosphere, then, is directly proportional to the height of the column of mercury in it, and as a consequence the barometer is usually read in terms of the height of the column rather than in terms of pressure units. Most chemistry laboratory barometers are graduated both in centimeters and in inches, and are equipped with a device called a *vernier* which permits readings of the order of 0.01 cm. The operation and theory of operation of verniers are set forth in many laboratory manuals of both chemistry and physics.

For a number of reasons, mercury is used in barometers in preference to other liquids. A few of these reasons are: it is dense, requiring only a short tube to measure the greatest atmospheric pressure; it has a low coefficient of thermal expansion, requiring little correction for temperature changes; it does not evaporate easily, hence it does not have to be replaced; nor does it create much gas pressure in the closed tube. At sea level, under normal atmospheric pressure, the mercury in a barometer stands at a height of 76 cm., which is about 30 in.; a water barometer under identical conditions stands at a height of about 33 ft.

13. Calculations in Chemistry

The making of measurements in numerical terms immediately suggests that these measurements will be used in calculations. A knowledge of higher mathematics is absolutely necessary for advanced work in chemistry, especially in theoretical chemistry, but in elementary chemistry only a knowledge of arithmetic and of simple algebra is required. Most of the problems of elementary chemistry can be solved, if that method seems more clear, by the application of the

A MERCURIAL BAROMETER. (Courtesy, Central Scientific Co.)

principles of ratio and proportion, with x standing for the unknown term. The use of ratio and proportion suggests the need for multiplication and division, both of which processes can be accomplished much more quickly by the use of logarithms or by the use of the slide rule than by long multiplication and division.

When using a number of mathematical quantities in a calculation, the student should bear in mind that the result of such a calculation is no more accurate than the least accurate figure employed in obtaining it. A helpful rule to follow in tabulating data and in using them is that the number of significant figures set down should contain only one doubtful digit. For instance, suppose the result of a weighing made on a pulp balance is found to be 1.036 g. Since the pulp balance is known to be accurate only to the nearest hundredth of a gram, this figure should be recorded as 1.04 g. since 0.036 is nearer to 0.04 than it is to 0.03.

Study of a text which deals at some length with the rules usually employed in the mathematical treatment of scientific data will be of value to all students of the mathematical sciences.

(See Appendix for Exercises)

COLLATERAL READINGS

Black: *Introductory Course in College Physics*, New York, The Macmillan Co., 1941.

Hamilton and Simpson: *Quantitative Chemical Analysis*, Chaps. III and IV, New York, The Macmillan Co., 1937.

Handbook of Chemistry and Physics, Cleveland, Chemical Rubber Publishing Co. New edition each year.

de Kruif: *Microbe Hunters*, Chap. I, New York, Harcourt, Brace and Co., 1926.

Lange: *Handbook of Chemistry*, Handbook Publishers, Inc. Frequent editions.

Smith: *The Elements of Physics*, New York, McGraw-Hill Book Co., 1938.

The Structure of the Atom

1. Introduction

Like the early Greek philosophers, Dalton looked upon the atom as being a small, hard, indestructible particle of matter which was the simplest building stone of nature. In 1859, Plücker's discovery that gases at very low pressure will permit continuous flow of electricity initiated a series of discoveries which have led to the belief that the atom itself is a complex structure composed of still more fundamental units, which in various combinations make up the known varieties of atoms. A knowledge of the composition and constitution of the various atoms is essential if one would understand why certain atoms behave as they do while others have a totally different behavior. This knowledge constitutes the foundation upon which modern chemistry is built, and serves as the basis for the unification of principles governing chemical change. Its importance cannot be emphasized too strongly.

2. Evidence for the Complexity of the Atom

The majority of the evidence for the complexity of the atom was collected by physicists and chemists during the period between 1879 and 1911. Much of this evidence was derived from a study of cathode rays, which were investigated by Sir William Crookes and others; a study of canal rays or positive rays, which were discovered in 1886 by Goldstein; a study of x-rays, which were discovered in 1895 by Röntgen; a study of the spontaneous disintegration of radioactive elements, evidence of which was first observed by Becquerel in 1896; a study of the data obtained by Rutherford in "scattering experiments"; and other studies and investigations which were suggested by observations made in connection with the discoveries and observations listed above. Details of these studies which are responsible for our present-day views upon the complexity of the atom are extremely interesting, but, since most of the work is of a physical nature, the student is referred to other texts for accounts of it.

3. The Units of Which Atoms Are Built

No one has yet seen an atom, let alone the still smaller units of which atoms are made, but, as a result of conclusions reached by the many investigators who have studied the complexity of atoms, chemists now believe that the atoms of the different elements are all made essentially of two simple types of units which have been named *protons* and *electrons*. The proton is a very tiny but relatively heavy particle which bears one charge of positive electricity. It has practically the same mass as the hydrogen atom, whose mass is 1.662×10^{-24} g. or 1.008 atomic weight units,* and is identical with the positively charged hydrogen ion. Its diameter is 1×10^{-13} cm. Although the electron is much lighter than the proton, it has a larger size, but is still a very tiny

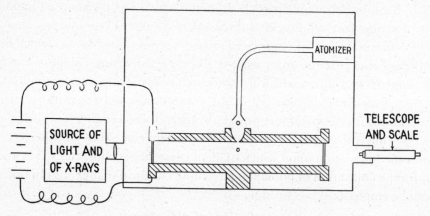

Millikan's Apparatus for the Measurement of the Charge on an Electron. By use of this apparatus, Millikan was able to show that the electrical charges gained or lost by the oil droplets suspended in air between the two charged plates were either equal to, or were multiples of, a definite value which was taken to be the unit electrical charge and the charge borne by one electron.

particle. As a result of the work of Dr. R. A. Millikan, performed in 1909, we know that the electron bears a charge of electricity equal in size to that of the proton but opposite in sign, and that its mass is $\frac{1}{1838}$ of that of the proton. Thus the mass of the electron would be 9.1×10^{-28} g. or 0.00055 atomic weight unit. Its diameter is 2.5×10^{-13} cm.

Some comparisons bring the extremely small size of these particles into sharper focus. The average straight pin has a head whose diameter is 0.1 cm. If one divides 0.1 cm. by 2.5×10^{-13} cm., the diameter of the electron, he finds that it would require 400 billion electrons laid side by side in a row to reach across a pinhead. Furthermore, it has been calculated that, if a proton

* An atomic weight unit is an arbitrary unit of mass whose value is equal to one-sixteenth of the mass of the oxygen atom. Further information concerning the unit and its choice will be given in section 3 of Chapter 8.

were as big as a pinhead, a pinhead on the same scale would be as large as the sun.

4. *The Structure of the Atom*

The proton bears one unit of positive electricity and the electron bears one unit of negative electricity, and, since all atoms are neutral in charge, it seems reasonable to assume that in an atom there must be equal numbers of protons and electrons. From his "scattering experiments" in which he bombarded thin metallic foils with high-speed particles of positive charge, Rutherford found that many of the positively charged particles were sharply deflected as if they had come near large charges of like sign, and he was thus able to show that within matter there are highly concentrated positive charges. Today, the atom is looked upon as consisting of a positively charged nucleus surrounded at a distance by a sufficient number of electrons to balance the positive charge on the nucleus. These electrons are believed to be held within the atom by the electrical attraction of unlike charges, and they are further believed to move in orbits about the nucleus as a center and to spin on their axes as they move about their orbits. The atom may thus be likened to a solar system in extreme miniature, and, far from being a hard, solid body, is in reality mostly made up of the empty space which exists between the small nucleus and the small electrons in their orbits. The distances between the planetary electrons and the nucleus are relatively great as compared with the size of these particles. It has been estimated that, in general, the diameter of the electron is about one fifty-thousandth of that of the atom as a whole, or that, if the proton were as large as a pinhead, the atom would be more than half the size of a standard baseball diamond.

5. *Atomic Numbers*

It was believed that a given atom should contain equal numbers of electrons and protons, and that the protons are all contained in its nucleus. Rutherford, as a further result of his "scattering experiments," arrived at the conclusion that at least a portion of the electrons must also be in the nucleus. Since the weight of the electron was known to be negligible as compared with that of the proton, since the weight of the proton was known to be approximately 1 (1.008) atomic weight unit, and since many atomic weights were well established, it was possible to calculate the number of protons, and hence the number of electrons, in many atoms. There still remained, however, the question of how many of the electrons were in the nucleus and how many were in the orbits of the known atoms.

The answer to this question was provided in 1913 by the young English physicist, H. G. J. Moseley. By the use of x-ray tubes in which the different elements were used successively as targets, he was able to show that there existed a definite arithmetical progression in the characteristic lengths of the waves emitted and that order numbers showing their positions in the series could be assigned to the elements. These numbers were taken to indicate the *net* positive charge on the nucleus (the net positive charge is the number of protons minus the number of electrons) and hence also the number of planetary electrons. These order numbers are known today as *atomic numbers*. The atomic number of hydrogen is 1, that of oxygen 8, that of sodium 11, etc.

Moseley's scientific work was terminated by his joining the British army when World War I began and by his subsequent death in 1915 during the Gallipoli Campaign, but it has since been established by Chadwick that the atomic numbers are equal to the net nuclear charge as was originally assumed. For a list of the elements and their atomic numbers, see the inside of the back cover of this book.

6. *The Nucleus*

Since the proton weighs 1838 times as much as the electron, and since the protons are all in the nucleus, it follows that the mass of the atom is concentrated in the nucleus. Those physical properties of the atom which are dependent upon mass are determined, therefore, by the nucleus. Further, since the weight of the proton is approximately 1 (1.008) atomic weight unit, it follows that the weight of an atom expressed in atomic weight units gives the number of protons contained in that atom. The weight of sodium, for instance, is given as 22.997; this would indicate that the nucleus of the sodium atom contains 23 protons. But 23 × 1.008 yields a number which is slightly larger than 22.997. This same diminution in mass is noted in the case of nearly all of the other elements, and is explained by Harkins as due to what he terms the "packing effect." It is a well-known principle of physics that the closer two bodies are to each other, the greater will be the attraction they have for each other. Harkins believes that when protons, which have a highly concentrated mass or high density, are packed together as closely as they are in an atomic nucleus, a small part of their mass is converted into energy to permit the exceedingly strong attraction which they have for each other. In an earlier chapter it was pointed out that under very extraordinary circumstances it was believed that mass might be converted into energy. According to the equation set forth by Einstein,

$$-dm = dE / c^2,$$

in which $-dm$ is the small amount of mass converted when the quantity of energy dE is liberated, and c is the speed of light, 3×10^{10} cm. per sec. Since c^2 would be a very large number, 9×10^{20}, it is apparent that, though the energy liberated were relatively large, the change in mass would still be small.

With the number of protons in the nucleus given by the atomic weight expressed in atomic weight units, and with the net nuclear charge given by the atomic number, it is a simple matter to calculate the number of electrons contained in the nucleus: *at. wt.* $- \epsilon = $ *at. no.*, where ϵ stands for the number of nuclear electrons. A more useful form of this equation is at. wt. $-$ at. no. $= \epsilon$.

7. Groupings Within the Nucleus

If a watch is wound up, it runs down; if a pail of hot water is set aside, it cools; and if a ball is placed on an incline, it rolls down as far as it may. These phenomena are all examples of a well-recognized scientific principle; namely, that every system which is left to itself (that is, free from outside influences) will change toward a condition in which it possesses less available energy. This law being general applies, then, to atomic nuclei also, and as a consequence of its operation the protons and electrons of the nucleus apparently arrange themselves into definite groupings within the nucleus. A study of the decomposition products of those elements which disintegrate spontaneously, the radioactive elements, revealed that alpha particles were evolved; and later, when atomic nuclei were broken down by physical means, alpha particles were also detected among the fragments. This led to the belief that alpha particles are present in the nuclei of all atoms save those of hydrogen which do not contain sufficient protons and electrons to form an alpha particle.

Later investigations established the presence in the nucleus of particles of virtually the same mass as the proton but of no electrical charge. Because of their neutral charge, these particles were named *neutrons*, and it is now believed that they are made of one electron and one proton very closely associated, which would account for both their mass and their lack of charge.

It is now believed that all of the electrons contained in an atomic nucleus are associated each with a proton to form neutrons. Since the number of protons in the nucleus is in excess of the number of electrons, there will always be an excess of protons left after as many neutrons as possible have been formed.

It is further believed, since the alpha particle is shown by experiment to be among the fragments resulting from the destruction of all nuclei which contain sufficient electrons and protons to form them, that the neutrons and excess protons in the nucleus become associated in the proper numbers to form as many alpha (α) particles as possible. The *alpha particle* was so named when its identity was not known; today, it is known to be identical with the helium nucleus or helium ion. It consists of 4 protons and 2 electrons, or of 2 neutrons and 2 protons. Any neutrons and protons left over after the formation of the

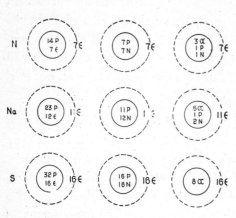

maximum number of alpha particles are looked upon simply as being present in the nucleus and associated closely with the alpha particles.

As an example, consider the atom of nitrogen, whose atomic weight is 14 and whose atomic number is 7. Since the weight is 14, there will be 14 protons in the nucleus. From the relationship, at. wt. − at. no. = ϵ, it is evident that there are $14 - 7$ or 7 electrons in the nucleus. From 7 electrons and 14 protons there are possible 7 neutrons, which leaves 7 protons.

THE NUCLEAR ORGANIZATION OF THE ATOMS OF NITROGEN, SODIUM, AND SULFUR.

Since an alpha particle contains 2 neutrons and 2 protons, there would be in the nitrogen nucleus 3 alpha particles with 1 proton and 1 neutron left over. In symbols the nucleus would be represented thus: $(3\alpha, n, p)$ or $(\alpha_3 np)$. For sodium, whose atomic weight is 23 and whose atomic number is 11, the nucleus would be represented first as $(23p, 12\epsilon)$ then as $(5\alpha, 2n, p)$ or $(\alpha_5 n_2 p)$.

8. The Extranuclear Electrons

As stated previously, the atomic number gives not only the net positive charge on the atomic nucleus, but also, since atoms are neutral in charge, the number of electrons outside the nucleus, the *extranuclear* or *planetary* electrons. From the investigations of Niels Bohr and other scientists, it is now believed that these outside electrons move about the nucleus as a center and that each extranuclear electron is characterized by being possessed of a definite quantity of energy; thus the electrons are said to exist in energy levels. For some electrons this amount of energy is larger than for others, but the amounts are definitely fixed and no electron may have an energy intermediate between these fixed amounts. The case of a ball lying on a table may be cited as an analogy. The ball on the table-top has a definite potential energy. If it falls off it must fall to the floor, where it comes to rest and has another, but a different, potential energy. It cannot have potential energies intermediate between these two values unless some outside agency intervenes to halt it in mid-air between table-top and floor.

In accordance with the principle cited above—that nature prefers systems whose available energy is as low as possible under the circumstances—the number of electrons which may have these various definite quantities of energy is limited. Only 2 electrons in a given atom may have the lowest amount of energy, 8 may have the next smallest amount, 18 the next, and so on. If numbers, beginning with 1 for the lowest energy level, are assigned to the various levels, then *the number of electrons that may exist in any level is given by the formula $2n^2$, where n stands for the level number.* Thus the fifth level might contain a maximum of 50 electrons, since 2×5^2 is 50.

9. *The Ionization of Gases*

At the beginning of this chapter, the cathode ray was mentioned. The cathode ray is produced in a simple glass tube into whose ends are sealed metallic electrical terminals. When the gas in the tube is pumped out until very small quantities of it remain and the current is turned on, the gas begins to glow as a "ray" passes from the negative terminal (cathode) to the positive (the anode). This ray has been shown to be a stream of electrons. As the voltage, which is a measure of the electrical pressure existing between the two electrodes, is increased, naturally this stream of electrons moves faster and therefore hits harder. It has been shown experimentally that the glow mentioned above does not appear if very low voltages are first turned on. As the voltage is increased, a value is presently

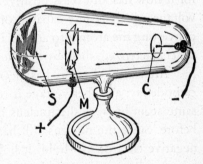

A CATHODE RAY TUBE. The shadow cast by the anode shows that the rays travel in straight lines. (Courtesy, Foley, A. L.: "College Physics," 3d ed., Philadelphia, The Blakiston Company.)

reached at which the glow begins, but a continued increase of voltage causes the glow to disappear, only to reappear at a second higher voltage. Further increases of voltage produce similar results, but the values of the voltages at which the glow reappears get closer and closer together until a value is finally reached above which all voltages cause the glow to continue.

In his study, Bohr made the above observations with hydrogen gas, which contains the lightest of all atoms, consisting of only one proton and one planetary electron. His interpretation of these observations is as follows: At first the voltage is so low that the electrons in the beam are not moving rapidly enough to hit the planetary electron of an atom with which they come in contact hard enough to give it enough energy to permit it to move into the next higher energy level. A further increase in energy to another fixed value is then necessary to move the electron to the next higher level, and so on. As the electron gets farther away from its nucleus, the attraction between them diminishes until finally the electron has acquired enough energy to fly completely away from the nucleus, and hence out of the atom. Naturally, any voltage larger than that which gives the electron enough energy to fly away will be large enough to produce a similar result. As an analogy, consider a rock on a string swung in a circle by the hand. As the hand moves faster, the rock acquires more energy, moving faster too. Ultimately, it may acquire enough energy to break the string (i.e., the attraction to the hand), upon doing which it flies off into space.

An atom containing an electron which has gained enough energy to move into a higher energy level is said to be an *excited atom*. An atom which has lost an electron—that is, one of its negative charges—is no longer neutral in charge, for it now has an excess positive charge of one. It has become an *ion*, and the voltage which is just capable of removing an electron from an atom, or of converting the atom into an ion, is called the *ionizing potential*. The energy levels are characterized, then, by the energy required to remove an electron from them.

After one electron has been removed from an atom by means of the cathode ray, a higher voltage is required to remove a second electron from the same atom because the nucleus now has one less electron to hold than it did before. Since the nucleus still has the same net positive charge but one fewer negative electrons to hold, it holds its remaining electrons more tightly, and hence more energy is required for the second removal. This means that a higher ionizing potential is required for the removal of each successive electron withdrawn from an atom in the gaseous state.

10. The Emission of Energy by Excited Atoms

All of the foregoing does not explain, however, why the gas in the tube glows, for the emission of light is an emission of energy rather than an absorption of energy such as has been discussed. Consider, however, the behavior of an excited atom when it moves out of the line of fire of the cathode ray's stream of electrons. In this atom, the electron has enough energy to be in a level higher than its normal one. As soon as it is removed from the stress which produced this abnormal condition, the electron returns to its normal position either in one jump or stepwise through the intervening levels, giving up the energy which it had acquired as a result of the collision. This energy manifests itself as a radiation seen as light, or may be too short to be seen, in which case it is manifest as ultraviolet radiations which can be photographed. The amount of energy given off when an excited planetary electron returns to its normal level is called a *quantum*, and for this reason an energy level is often called a *quantum level*.

The quantum is a variable quantity, since naturally, if an electron falls from the fourth level to the first, it gives up more energy than if it had fallen from the second to the first. If one ties a rope by one end to a fixed object, he will note that the harder he agitates the free end (that is, the more energy he puts into it), the shorter will be the transverse waves generated in the rope. So it is with light waves: the greater the energy that goes into their formation, the shorter will be the waves produced, and hence the greater the number of the waves that can pass a given point in a second, i.e., the greater the frequency. The eye sees light of certain frequencies as certain colors, but the human eye cannot see frequencies either greater or less than those producing the colors. It is the radiations produced by the return of electrons to their normal energy levels in many

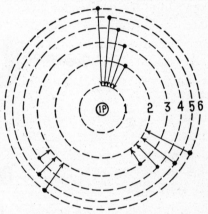

DIAGRAM SHOWING HOW THE ELECTRON MAY MOVE TO LOWER LEVELS IN AN EXCITED HYDROGEN ATOM. In the normal hydrogen atom, the electron belongs in the first energy level. It may move to a higher level by the absorption of energy and by emission of this absorbed energy it may return to lower levels either stepwise or by longer jumps. Ultimately, the electron should return to its normal position. Some of the possible jumps which the excited electron may make are indicated above.

atoms of the same kind which produce the characteristic pattern of colored lines called a *spectrum*, which one may see when these radiations are viewed through a spectroscope. It is also these radiations from gases of various kinds which one sees in the so-called "neon" signs

11. Sub-energy Levels

The electrons in any one energy level were spoken of above as if they all possessed exactly the same quantity of energy; such, however, is not the case. According to Pauli, no two extranuclear electrons in a given atom possess exactly the same quantity of energy, although those electrons in a given energy level do have very nearly the same energies. Within a given *main quantum level*, however, it is possible to distinguish *sub-levels* on the basis of these slight differences.

A given main level always has as many sub-levels as the number of the main level. Thus main level number 1 has one sub-level, main level number 2 has two sub-levels, and so on. The lowest main energy level is given the number one, but the lowest sub-level within a main level is given the number zero. *The*

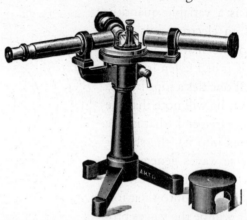

A PRISM SPECTROSCOPE. Light entering through the tube at the right is resolved by the triangular prism into a spectrum which may be viewed through the small telescope at the left. The third tube at the back contains a measuring scale. (Courtesy, Hackh-Grant: "Chemical Dictionary," Philadelphia, The Blakiston Company.)

formula for calculating the number of electrons in a given sub-level is $2(2l + 1)$ where l is the number of the sub-level. By substituting in this formula, it can be seen that the sub-zero level always contains 2 electrons, the sub-one level 6, the sub-two level 10, and so on.*

A knowledge of these sub-levels is necessary for an understanding of the chemical behavior of the atoms of a number of elements to be studied later. Still further classifications of the electrons of a main quantum level are made, but, since they will not be useful in the discussions to be presented in this text, they will not be set forth here.

* For example, the phosphorus atom contains 15 extranuclear electrons distributed among the first three main energy levels as follows: 2, 8, 5. In turn, these 15 electrons would be distributed among the sub-levels (2; 2, 6; 2, 3), whence it might be expected that the three electrons of the 3_1 level might be involved in reaction more readily than the remaining two valence electrons of the 3_0 level. Such is, indeed, the case, and the matter will be discussed more fully in later chapters.

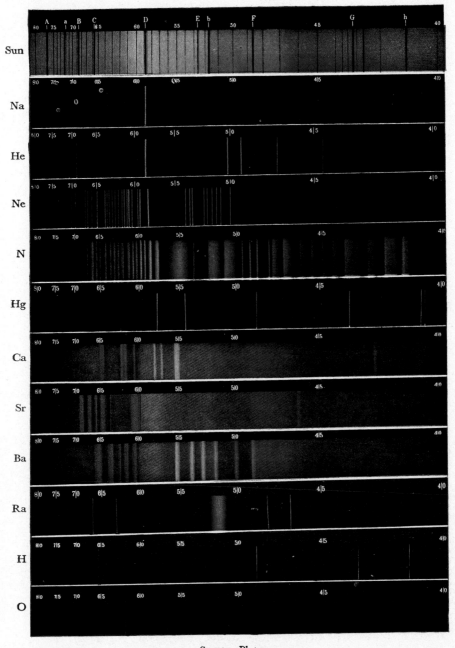

Spectra Plate.
(Modified from Hofman "Lehrbuch der Anorganischen Chemie,"
Friedr. Vieweg & Sohn.)

12. *Isotopes*

One of the assumptions made by Dalton in his atomic hypothesis was that all of the atoms of a given element are identical. Modern investigations of atomic structure have proved that this assumption is not true for all elements. It is not even true for the simplest element, hydrogen, nor for the third element, lithium; in fact, there are relatively few elements for which it is true.

Investigation has revealed that there are two varieties of lithium atoms whose atomic numbers and chemical properties are identical, but whose weights are 7 and 6, respectively. Since their atomic number is 3, this means that one has the structure (6p, 3ϵ)3ϵ and the other the structure (7p, 4ϵ)3ϵ where the numbers and symbols outside the parantheses represent the extranuclear electrons. Such *atoms whose atomic numbers are identical but whose atomic masses are different are called isotopes.*

DIAGRAMS OF THE NATURALLY OCCURRING ISOTOPES OF LITHIUM.

Since the chemical behavior of such atoms is identical, it may be concluded that the chemical properties of atoms depend only on the extra-nuclear electrons. Further investigation has established that it is, in general, only the outermost of these electrons (those in the highest energy levels) which determine chemical behavior.

It is the existence of isotopes which explains, also, why so many of the atomic masses of the elements are fractions instead of whole numbers. For instance, the atomic mass of lithium has been found to be 6.94 atomic weight units. This figure, however, is the average mass of a lithium atom, and is the figure that would be given if the sample of lithium investigated contained 94 per cent of atoms of mass 7 and 6 per cent of atoms of mass 6. Fortunately for all those who need to employ atomic masses, nature always produces those elements which are isotopic with an invariable percentage of each isotope present. No one has ever succeeded in finding a sample of lithium in which the atomic species 6 and 7 were ever present in any ratio save 6 to 94, respectively. In the case of lead, which has many isotopes, they are always present in such ratios that the average atomic mass of a lead atom is always found to be 207.22.

13. *Radioactive Elements*

Radioactive elements are those which spontaneously disintegrate into simpler atomic species with the evolution of energy. The most notable of these are the seven heaviest naturally occurring elements, though there are isotopes of other elements which are also radioactive. When such elements decompose, they

ERNEST, LORD RUTHERFORD
(1871–1937, British)

Although he was born in New Zealand, Rutherford's work was done principally in Canada and in England, where for many years he was professor of experimental physics at Cambridge University. His great contributions to physical science have been the proof of the spontaneous disintegration of radium into simpler elements, the investigation of the nature of atomic nuclei, and the discovery of artificial transmutation of the elements. His work, while essentially physical in nature, has been of great interest and value to chemists, since much of our knowledge of the atom derives from it. In 1908 he was awarded the Nobel Prize in chemistry, and in 1931 he was created a baron by the British Crown.

ROBERT A. MILLIKAN
(1868–   , American)

A physicist who has made many original contributions to knowledge, Millikan is best known to students of chemistry for his classical work on the electron. He is also known for his work on light and x-rays, and for his studies of cosmic rays. After being graduated from Oberlin College and receiving his Ph.D. degree at Columbia University, he studied at the Universities of Berlin and Göttingen in Germany and then returned to the United States to serve for many years as professor of physics at the University of Chicago. From 1921 to 1945 he served as chairman of the Executive Council at the California Institute of Technology and as director of its physical laboratories.

yield alpha (α) particles, beta (β) particles, and gamma (γ) rays, though one variety of atom yields only one variety of particle along with the γ rays. The alpha particles gain electrons from the air to become helium atoms and the beta particles are simply electrons. The gamma ray is a very short electromagnetic wave, shorter than an ordinary x-ray, which results from the evolution of energy no longer used to hold the emitted particles in the atom. Most radioactive elements continue their disintegration, which man is powerless to alter, until an isotope of lead is formed. The particles which are emitted come from the nucleus of the disintegrating atom.

Since it is the heaviest elements which show the property of radioactivity most pronouncedly, it would appear that perhaps they disintegrate because their nuclei have become so heavy that they break apart under their own weight. A further possibility suggested is that at one time there were more than 92 elements, but that as time went on these still heavier elements decomposed into simpler ones. A more complete consideration of radioactive substances and of nuclear changes produced by physical means will be undertaken in a later chapter.

DIAGRAMS REPRESENTING THE ORBITS OF THE VARIOUS ELECTRONS IN SEVERAL DIFFERENT ATOMS. Note the difficulty encountered in representing the more complex atoms, such as radium. At the present time, atomic models are seldom used. (Courtesy, Wendt & Smith: "Matter and Energy," Philadelphia, The Blakiston Company.)

14. Atomic Models

Electrons have been spoken of as moving in orbits about the atomic nucleus. Such mechanical models are rather easy to picture for the simpler atoms whose planetary electrons are few, but for the more complex atoms, which have many extranuclear electrons, such models are not so easy to picture, nor do they satisfactorily explain all observed properties. Apparently, as the electrons move within the atom, they set up a wave motion so that some of the properties of the electron appear to be those of a particle while others appear to be those of a wave. As a result of their attempts to reconcile this apparent duality of the nature of the electron, Heisenberg and Schrödinger developed what is called the *wave mechanics*, by whose application they abandon mechanical models of the atom in favor of mathematical equations which express the energetic relationships of the electrons within the atom. By this method, then, no particular point in space is assigned to any electron, but each electron is looked upon as possessing a definite amount of energy so that the idea of energy levels for the extranuclear electrons is entirely acceptable even though the idea of orbits for these electrons is now outmoded save in the mechanical models of the simpler atoms.

15. *Properties of the Atoms* (*Summary*)

All atoms are composed of electrons and protons.

The proton has a mass of about 1 at. wt. unit and a charge of 1 unit of positive electricity.

The electron has a mass of $\frac{1}{1838}$ of the proton and a charge of 1 unit of negative electricity.

The nucleus of the atom contains all of the protons and some of the electrons.

The number of protons in the nucleus is given by the mass of the atom.

The number of electrons in the nucleus is given by the at. wt. minus the at. no.

The nuclear protons and electrons group themselves into as many neutrons as possible, then into as many alpha particles as possible.

The number of electrons outside of the nucleus is also given by the atomic number.

The extranuclear electrons exist in definite energy levels, the maximum number of electrons which may exist in a given main level being given by the formula $2n^2$ where n is the number of the level, the lowest being numbered 1.

The electrons within a given main energy level are divided into sub-levels, the maximum number of electrons which may exist in any sub-level being given by the formula $2(2l + 1)$ where l is the sub-level number which may be 0, 1, 2, 3, 4, etc.

The voltage necessary to remove an electron from the atom is called the ionizing potential.

Energy is emitted by atoms when excited electrons within the atom return to lower energy levels.

The mass of the atom depends upon the number of its protons.

The size of the atom depends upon the number and distribution of the extranuclear electrons.

The stability of the atom depends principally upon the stability of the nucleus. Radioactive atoms may eject either α or β particles along with γ-rays.

The physical properties which depend upon mass are determined by the atomic nucleus. The emission of x-rays is determined by the extranuclear electrons nearest the nucleus, and still other physical properties are determined by the outermost extranuclear electrons.

Chemical properties are determined by the outermost extranuclear electrons.

(See Appendix for Exercises)

COLLATERAL READINGS

Aston: The story of isotopes, *Science*, **82**, 235 (1935).

Briscoe: *The Structure and Properties of Matter*, New York, McGraw-Hill Book Co., 1935.

Collins: *How to Understand Chemistry*, New York, D. Appleton-Century Co., 1934.

Conn: *The Nature of the Atom*, New York, Chemical Publishing Co., 1939.

Darrow: Nuclear chemistry, *J. Chem. Education*, **12**, 76 (1935).

Gamow: *Mr. Tompkins in Wonderland*, New York, The Macmillan Co., 1940.

——: *Mr. Tompkins Explores the Atom*, New York, The Macmillan Co., 1944.

Kendall: *At Home Among the Atoms*, New York, D. Appleton-Century Co., 1929. Cathode ray tube, *J. Chem. Education*, **31**, 369 (1926).

Millikan: *Electrons* (+ *and* −), *Protons, Photons, Neutrons and Cosmic Rays*, Chicago, University of Chicago Press, 1935.

Rice: *Electronic Structure and Chemical Binding*, New York, McGraw-Hill Book Co., 1940.

Soddy: *Interpretation of the Atom*, New York, G. P. Putnam's Sons, 1932.

HENRY GWYN JEFFREYS MOSELEY
(1887–1915, English)

Few great scientists of modern times have had a shorter career or have had a more profound influence upon scientific thought than Moseley. The most noteworthy of his contributions resulted from his studies of the x-ray spectra of the elements known at that time. From these he was able to assign to each element an order number (atomic number) which is presumably the same as the net positive charge on the atomic nucleus and also the same as the number of extranuclear electrons in the atom. His work not only clarified periodic relationships of the known elements and their isotopes, but also it greatly stimulated the search for new elements. His promising career was brought to an end during the Gallipoli Campaign of World War I while he served with the British Army.

NIELS HENRIK DAVID BOHR
(1885–   , Danish)

Bohr is regarded by many as the founder of the modern atomic theory, and certainly his theory of the hydrogen atom and the origin of spectra as published in 1913–1915 in The Philosophical Magazine has had a profound influence on all subsequent work and thought in that field. The Bohr theory has also been of great value in the study of the chemical and physical properties of atoms and in their periodic relationships. In 1911 Bohr received the doctor's degree from the University of Copenhagen, after which he studied with J. J. Thomson and Rutherford in England. In 1916 he became professor of physics at his alma mater, and, in 1920, director of the newly founded Institute of Theoretical Physics at that institution— a position which he still holds. During World War II he worked on the atomic bomb project in the United States. In 1922 he was awarded the Nobel Prize in physics, and in addition has received many other medals and honors.

Atomic Structure as Related to Chemical Change

1. The Inert Gases

Between the years 1894 and 1900, six elements, all of which are gases and all of which are chemically inactive, were discovered. All of the other known elementary substances enter into chemical reactions, but no reaction has been found into which these gases will enter. It was because of their inactivity as well as because of their scarcity that they were so long in being discovered. Collectively, they are known as the *inert gases*, and their names are helium, neon, argon, krypton, xenon, and radon.

Table 1

ELECTRON DISTRIBUTION AMONG THE ENERGY LEVELS IN THE INERT GASES

Name	Symbol	At. No.	First Energy Level	Second Energy Level	Third Energy Level	Fourth Energy Level	Fifth Energy Level	Sixth Energy Level
Helium	He	2	2	. .	. .	. .	. .	. .
Neon	Ne	10	2	8	. .	. .	. .	. .
Argon	A	18	2	8	8	. .	. .	. .
Krypton	Kr	36	2	8	18	8	. .	. .
Xenon	Xe	54	2	8	18	18	8	. .
Radon	Rn	86	2	8	18	32	18	8

Of all the known varieties of atoms, then, those of the inert gases must be the most stable. This idea immediately raises the question: what is it that makes them most stable? The answer to this question was sought, naturally, in the structure of these atoms. Upon investigation, it was found that, outside of being composed of protons and electrons like all other atoms, the only thing these atoms had in common was eight electrons in their outermost energy level, save in the case of helium which had only two. Helium has an atomic number of 2 and hence can have only two electrons, which are both in the first main level, completing it. Since these are the only known atoms which contain such outer electronic arrangements, the natural conclusion was that eight electrons in the outermost, or highest, energy level of the atoms, save in the case of the first energy level, confer upon the atom the greatest degree of chemical stability.

2. Why Atoms Undergo Changes

It was pointed out in the preceding chapter that one of the fundamental laws governing natural behavior is that a system which is left to itself always changes in such a fashion as to decrease its available energy. Since energy is the ability to do work, it follows, then, that the system with the least energy is the one which will do the least work, and is, therefore, the one which is least likely to undergo further change; in other words, such a system has attained the maximum of stability. This law is generally spoken of as the *Second Law of Thermodynamics*, hence further reference will be made to it by that title.

If an outer electronic arrangement like that of the inert gases represents the greatest degree of chemical stability, and if all systems react in such a manner as to attain the greatest degree of stability possible under existing conditions, then again it follows that atoms undergo the chemical changes they do to attain as nearly as possible to the structure of the inert gas which has already a structure most like their own. This follows, of course, so that they may have the stability such a structure confers. To be sure, such changes are not always entirely successful, varying as they do with external conditions and with the nature of the atoms involved; but a structure as near the ideal as possible is attained. It is this tendency of the atoms to attain greater stability which accounts for their ability to enter into chemical reactions.

3. How Atoms Undergo Changes

The methods by which the outer electrons of an atom may be redistributed so as to attain a structure similar to that of an inert gas are three: (1) An atom may lose electrons to another atom or other atoms; (2) it may gain electrons from another atom or other atoms; or (3) it may share electrons with another atom or other atoms, which are also seeking stability. Of these three methods, the one open to a given atom will depend upon a number of factors, chief among which are the structure of the other atoms with which it is to react and the relative quantities of work which would be required in the various methods. Nature usually chooses the process which involves the performance of the least work for its accomplishment. A few examples will illustrate these points.

Since the electrons involved in a chemical change are usually those of the outermost energy level, Prof. Gilbert N. Lewis of the University of California proposed a convenient schematic method of representing these electrons and their relationships in chemical reactions. His proposal was that the symbol of the element be used in such instances to represent all of the atom except the electrons of the outermost level, and that this portion of the atom be termed the *kernel*. The electrons of the outermost level he represented by dots placed around the symbol. The sodium atom which has the structure (5α, 2n, p)2ϵ, 8ϵ, ϵ would by Professor Lewis's system be represented as Na·, and the chlorine atom which has an atomic number of 17, and hence has 17 extranuclear electrons which would be distributed 2, 8, 7, would be represented by $\overset{..}{\underset{..}{:Cl}}$· This system of notation will facilitate further discussion.

When sodium and chlorine are placed in the same vessel, they react to form the compound substance sodium chloride. This reaction occurs as a result of the sodium giving up its one electron in the third main level to the chlorine which needs only one electron to go with its seven to give it eight in its outermost level. As a consequence of this gain and loss, the sodium now has eight electrons in its outermost level with the same electronic arrangement as neon, the inert gas which just precedes it, and chlorine has now the same electronic arrangement as argon, the inert gas which immediately follows it. Conceivably, the sodium might have gained seven electrons to go with its one or chlorine might have lost its seven to become like neon, but since the gain or loss of seven involves the performance of much more work than the gain or loss of one, nature chooses the latter process; hence, in general, atoms tend to assume

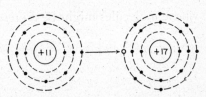

DIAGRAMMATIC REPRESENTATION OF THE REACTION OF AN ATOM OF SODIUM WITH AN ATOM OF CHLORINE. An electron is transferred from the sodium atom to the chlorine atom so that after the transfer each may have eight electrons in its outermost energy level.

the configuration of the nearest inert gas. As a result of the loss of one electron with its negative charge from the neutral sodium atom, there now exists a sodium ion which bears an excess positive charge of one. The chlorine atom gained an electron, hence it is now a chlorine ion bearing an excess charge of one unit of negative electricity. As a result of these equal but unlike charges, the sodium and chlorine ions attract each other, and, as a result of this attraction, the crystals of salt are built up of sodium and chlorine ions.

Magnesium has the electronic configuration 2, 8, 2, hence to attain the neon structure of 2, 8, it would have to lose two electrons. If the magnesium is reacting with chlorine, one magnesium atom will have to react with two chlorine atoms since one chlorine atom requires only one electron to become like argon in its electronic configuration. The magnesium ion will then bear a charge of 2+ and be capable of attracting two chlorine ions each of which has a charge of 1−.

Carbon, whose atomic number is 6, has the electronic configuration 2, 4; hence, for carbon to attain an inert gas structure, it might either lose four to become like helium or gain four to become like neon in its structure. As a consequence of this possibility of making two changes either of which would involve four electrons, it usually makes neither, but rather shares its four electrons with other atoms. For instance, it might share its four electrons with four chlorine atoms, each of which needs one electron, which might in turn permit the carbon to share in their electrons. As a result, there would be formed a compound whose molecules might be represented thus by the Lewis notation:

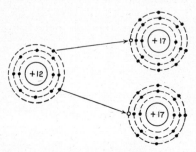

DIAGRAMMATIC REPRESENTATION OF THE REACTION OF A MAGNESIUM ATOM WITH ATOMS OF CHLORINE.

$$
\begin{array}{c}
\overset{\cdot\cdot}{:}\text{Cl}\overset{\cdot\cdot}{:} \\[2pt]
\overset{\cdot\cdot}{:}\text{Cl}\overset{\times}{}\text{C}\overset{\times}{}\text{Cl}\overset{\cdot\cdot}{:} \\[2pt]
\overset{\cdot\cdot}{:}\text{Cl}\overset{\cdot\cdot}{:}
\end{array}
$$

Carbon tetrachloride is not prepared by direct union of its elements, but it is, nevertheless, a well-known compound. It will be seen that by sharing electrons none of the atoms involved actually attains an inert gas structure, as is the case when electrons are gained or lost, but all of the atoms involved approach closely to the inert gas structure. From this discussion it will also be noted that the atoms whose electronic configurations already approach most nearly to those of inert gases are those which most readily gain or lose electrons.

Atoms of the same kind may also share electrons. It has previously been mentioned that many of the elementary gases exist in diatomic molecules; this results from the same tendency to attain stability that has been under discussion. When chlorine atoms are placed together, it is possible for them to approach an inert gas structure by each atom entering into a mutual sharing with another atom. The molecule formed is represented thus:

$$: \overset{..}{\underset{..}{Cl}} : \overset{..}{\underset{..}{Cl}} :$$

Sometimes, instead of each of the two atoms furnishing one electron of the shared pair, one atom may furnish both electrons of the shared pair; such is presumed to be the case when sulfur, $\overset{oo}{\underset{8}{S}}{}_{8}$, reacts with oxygen, $:\overset{..}{O}$, to form sulfur dioxide. The compound has the formula $: \overset{..}{O} \overset{oo}{\underset{8}{S}} \overset{..}{\underset{..}{O}} :$ in which the sulfur apparently furnishes the electrons of both shared pairs of electrons, but in which the oxygen atoms approach more closely to the inert gas structure than does the sulfur. Later it will be seen that, as a result of the sulfur not yet having attained to an inert gas structure, this compound will undergo further reactions which tend to rectify this matter.

From the foregoing discussion, it is shown that the atoms of the elements undergo reaction only by transferring electrons or by sharing them with other atoms.

4. Valence

Valence is defined as *a measure of the combining capacity of atoms.* As has been shown in the preceding section, the combining power of a given atom is determined by the number of electrons which it will lose, gain, or share; hence the valence of an atom may be defined as the number of electrons which it loses, gains, or shares. The valence of elements is always considered to be zero even though the atoms of the element may have formed elementary molecules. Since the electrons which an atom loses, gains, or shares are usually in the outermost energy level, these electrons are usually referred to as the *valence electrons*.

5. Types of Union

The ways in which atoms seek to attain inert gas electronic structures are three, as a consequence of which there are three types of chemical union, or three types of chemical bonds. The first of these is *electrovalence*.

Electrovalence results from an actual transfer of electrons such as is effected in the cited case of the reaction of sodium with chlorine. In this case, electrically charged ions are formed which exert an electrical attraction for each other as a result of their bearing unlike charges. *Positive electrovalence* results from a loss of electrons, and, according to the definition of valence, is numerically equal to the number of electrons lost. Hence, sodium would have a valence of +1 in sodium chloride while magnesium would have a valence of +2 in magnesium chloride. The maximum positive valence which an atom may exhibit is given by the number of electrons in the outermost level, save in the cases of a few metals which may lose in addition one or more electrons from the next lower level when that level is incomplete and hence unstable. *Negative electrovalence* results from the gain of electrons and is numerically equal to the number of electrons gained; thus the valence of chlorine in the two chlorides just mentioned is −1. The maximum negative valence which an atom may exhibit is the difference between the number of valence electrons and eight. Atoms do not always, however, exhibit the maximum valences which may be predicted for them on this basis. As has already been mentioned, a negative valence of seven might be predicted for sodium, but sodium never shows this valence since the loss of one electron involves less work than a gain of seven. In general, atoms which have only a few valence electrons usually lose electrons and show a positive electrovalence, while atoms which lack only a few electrons of having eight in their outermost levels usually gain electrons and show a negative electrovalence. Under abnormal conditions, some atoms will exhibit valences which they do not normally show. Elements whose atoms normally develop a positive valence are for the most part, metals, while elements whose atoms develop a negative valence under normal conditions are nonmetals.

Covalence is the term applied to the type of bond formed when atoms combine as a result of each of them furnishing one electron of a shared pair. In this case, no ions are formed, and hence no particles of unlike electrical charge are developed. On the contrary, molecules are formed that are the building units of which the solid forms of such compounds are constructed. The valence, or covalence, of an atom which forms such compounds is given by the number of electrons which the atom shares. In the cited case of the compound formed by carbon and chlorine, the carbon exhibits a valence of 4 (without any sign), while the chlorine exhibits a valence of 1. Elements which characteristically form covalent compounds are those which have approximately half as many valence electrons as are required to give an inert gas structure to their molecules. These elements, for the most part, are nonmetals. Of course, any element which combines with them is also exhibiting covalence; hence it is possible for many of the elements which commonly exhibit electrovalence, such as chlorine, to show also covalence.

The molecules of some covalent compounds are quite symmetrical, like those of carbon tetrachloride, whose structure was represented as

$$: \overset{\cdot\cdot}{C}l :$$
$$: \overset{\cdot\cdot}{C}l \overset{\cdot\times}{\times} \overset{\cdot\cdot}{C} \overset{\cdot\cdot}{\times} Cl :$$
$$: \overset{\times}{C}l :$$

while others are unsymmetrical, like those of water, which are represented thus:

$$H \overset{\cdot}{\circ} \overset{\cdot\cdot}{O} :$$
$$\overset{\circ}{H}$$

In symmetrical molecules the electrical charges are apparently evenly distributed, but in unsymmetrical molecules the electrical charges are not equally distributed. For instance, in the case of the water molecule, since the oxygen has a heavier more highly charged nucleus than does hydrogen, the electrons are drawn more closely to the oxygen nucleus than to that of hydrogen. This makes the oxygen end of the molecule more negative and the hydrogen end of the molecule more positive. Such molecules will become oriented in an electrical field just as will a compass needle. As a consequence of this behavior, these compounds are described as *polar* and their molecules, in which the charges are separated, are called *dipoles*. The farther the charges are separated, the more polar is the compound. Compounds which are symmetrical do not behave in this manner and are described as being *nonpolar*. The properties of polar and nonpolar compounds often differ to a considerable extent, with this difference being most prominent when the comparison is made with the substances in the liquid state. The polarity of polar substances is measured in terms of their *dielectric constant*, which is defined as the capacity of an electrical condenser with the substance to be measured between its plates divided by the capacity of the same condenser with a vacuum between its plates.

Coördinate valence, or *coördinate covalence*, are the names applied to the third type of chemical bond. Such a bond results when one atom supplies both electrons of a shared pair. Sulfur dioxide, $: \overset{\cdot\cdot}{O} \overset{\circ\circ}{} \overset{\cdot\cdot}{S} \overset{\cdot\cdot}{O} :$, was given as an example of a compound resulting from this type of union. It is usually elements which normally form covalent compounds and which have unused electron pairs that form coördinate compounds. Naturally, the atoms with which they combine in such a manner are also involved in the coördinate linkage.

All three types of union are exhibited in certain compounds, while simpler compounds will contain only one or two types of linkage.

6. Oxidation and Reduction

The union of oxygen with other elements has long been known. This process was termed, naturally enough, *oxidation*. When the electronic nature of chemical reactions came to be understood, it was noted that when oxygen combines with another element the valence of the other element is always increased. By extension of this idea, oxidation is now considered to be *any process by which the valence of an atom is increased*. In the case of atoms which develop an electrovalence, those which acquire a positive valence are showing an increase in valence which is occasioned by a loss of electrons, hence *oxidation may be defined also as any process in which an atom loses electrons*.

As has already been noted, whenever there is a loss of electrons by an atom of one variety, there must be a gain of electrons by atoms of another variety; or, for an increase in valence by one atom, there must be a decrease in valence for another. Hence, oxidation is always accompanied by an opposite process. This process is termed *reduction;* it may be defined as *any process by which valence is decreased or any process by which electrons are gained*. Since oxidation and reduction invariably occur simultaneously, it is proper to refer to any reaction in which they occur as an oxidation-reduction reaction.

The substance which causes another to become oxidized is called the *oxidizing agent*. The substance which causes another to become reduced is a *reducing agent*. In the case of the reaction between sodium and chlorine, the sodium becomes oxidized by the chlorine and the chlorine becomes reduced by the sodium; hence, the chlorine is the oxidizing agent while the sodium is the reducing agent. Oxygen and many of the nonmetals are good oxidizing agents, while hydrogen and the metals are, in general, good reducing agents.

7. Oxidation Numbers and the Zero Valence Rule

In the case of atoms which show electrovalence, oxidation and reduction result from a transfer of electrons. The extent of the oxidation or reduction undergone by such atoms is best expressed by giving the difference in electrovalence numbers of the atom before and after the change. In the case of covalent and coördinate compounds, there has been no transfer of electrons, and hence there are no electrovalence numbers with their positive and negative signs. But, to simplify the relationships involved in oxidation and reduction and to unify the methods of calculating the changes involved in such processes, arbitrary assumptions generally have been adopted so that positive and negative valence numbers may be assigned to atoms which are actually exhibiting no such valences. These numbers are usually called oxidation numbers or ionic-valence numbers, and they are most useful in calculations involving oxidation and reduction and in classifying certain compounds and their properties. In general, the oxidation number may be thought of as representing the net electrical charge on the atom.

Oxidation numbers are assigned to the atoms of covalent and coördinate compounds by a consideration of the atoms present, their relationship to each other, and the properties of the compound in question. To understand this assignment of numbers more fully, however, the student should be acquainted with the *zero valence rule*. Since neither electrovalent nor covalent compounds are electrically charged under ordinary conditions, it is natural to assume that the valence charges in those compounds just balance each other. This consideration is the source, then, of the statement that *in any chemical compound the algebraic sum of the valence charges, or numbers, must be zero*. This is the zero valence rule; in its light the oxidation numbers may be assigned.

Let us consider the oxidation number of sulfur in sulfuric acid, whose formula is H_2SO_4. In the majority of known ionic hydrogen compounds, hydrogen shows a valence of $+1$ while oxygen, with very few exceptions, possesses an oxidation number of -2. In H_2SO_4 the two hydrogens must account for $2(+1)$ valence charges while four oxygens account for $4(-2)$ valence charges, and according to the zero rule $+2 + x + (-8)$ must equal zero, whence $x - 6 = 0$ and $x = +6$. The oxidation number of sulfur in this compound must be $+6$. In the compound NaH_2PO_2, P has an oxidation number of $+1$ since Na, as has been shown, has a valence number of $+1$, hydrogen $+1$ and oxygen -2. Accordingly, $(+1) + (+2) + x + (-4) = 0$ and $x - 1 = 0$, whence $x = +1$.

As an extension of the zero valence rule, it will be readily understood that *when compounds enter into oxidation-reduction reactions, the net change in oxidation numbers undergone by all of the compounds involved in the reaction must be zero*, since the loss in electrons by one compound must be just equaled by the gain in electrons of the other compound or compounds.

Study of the individual elements will show that many elements exhibit more than one oxidation number. This situation is to be expected, since it has already been demonstrated that a given atom may either lose, gain, or share electrons, depending upon the nature of the substances with which it reacts and the conditions under which the reaction occurs.

8. Coördination Numbers

Another type of number is often useful in classifying facts about the various elements and their compounds; this is the *coördination number*. In most molecules there is one atom or ion about which the other constituents of the molecule are grouped. The number of atoms, ions, or molecules grouped around that central atom or ion is the coördination number of the molecule. Thus, in the compound

$$
\begin{array}{c}
\overset{\cdot\cdot}{:}\text{Cl}\overset{\cdot\cdot}{:} \\
\overset{\cdot\cdot\ \ \cdot\times\ \ \cdot\cdot}{:\text{Cl}\overset{\times}{\cdot}\text{C}\overset{}{\cdot}\text{Cl}:} \\
\overset{\cdot\cdot\ \ \times\ \ \cdot\cdot}{:\text{Cl}:} \\
\overset{\cdot\cdot}{}
\end{array}
$$

carbon is the central atom and the coördination number of carbon in this compound is 4. The coördination number has no connection with oxidation and reduction considerations. Further reference to this number will be made in later chapters.

9. Intermediate Steps of Reactions

Reactions have previously been spoken of as resulting from the transfer or sharing of electrons by atoms. While this is the most important consideration to be taken concerning reactions, they do not occur nearly so simply as this might indicate. For instance, when solid sodium and gaseous chlorine unite to form sodium chloride (salt), the most important change is the transfer of an electron from sodium atoms to chlorine atoms, but before this can take place there are other changes involved, and at least one process follows this transfer. These changes in the complete process are (1) the separation of individual sodium atoms from a piece of sodium containing many atoms, (2) the separation of Cl_2 molecules into chlorine atoms, (3) the removal of an electron from each sodium atom, (4) the addition of an electron to each chlorine atom, and (5) the building of solid particles of salt as a result of the attraction of positive sodium ions for negative chlorine ions.

The final result of such a series of changes is the same as if it had been achieved by one suitable process; hence, unless the chemist is especially interested in the various steps of a process, he may for convenience look upon them as representing only one process, the whole being equal to the sum of its parts.

10. *Types of Reactions*

Reactions (chemical changes) result from the efforts of the atoms to attain the most stable electronic structure possible under existing conditions. The patterns which these reactions take are relatively few. *There are four common types of reactions*, three of which are: (1) *combination:* the union of two or more substances (either elements or compounds) to form a single more complex substance; (2) *decomposition:* the breaking up of a complex substance into two or more simpler substances; and (3) *displacement* or *replacement:* the replacement of an element in a compound by a more active element. The above definitions reveal that combination and decomposition are the reverse of each other. The reactions may all be classed as oxidation and reduction also, since in all displacements there are changes of oxidation number and since in all combinations and decompositions involving elements there are changes of oxidation number. The fourth type of reaction will be discussed later, as will be the more complex varieties of oxidation and reduction.

11. *Characteristics of Reactions*

Besides wanting to know of what type a given reaction may be, the chemist wants to know (1) what the *products* of the reaction may be; (2) under what *conditions* the products form most readily and in greatest yield and what effect a change of conditions has on the nature of the products; (3) what the *speed* of the reaction is, and how the speed is altered by a change in conditions; (4) what the direction and magnitude of the *energy change* accompanying the reaction are; and (5) what the extent is to which the reaction goes; that is, are all of the reactants converted to products or is some of the original material left, and, if so, what *per cent* of it. All of these factors should be considered in the study of every chemical change.

12. *Formulas*

In Chapter 2 it was stated that a formula represents the composition of a molecule of the substance under consideration. From the discussions presented in this chapter it should now be evident why a given substance always has a fixed and invariable formula. It is evident that the smallest particle which could have the properties of sodium chloride would contain one ion of sodium and one of chlorine, because to attain stability one sodium atom must lose one electron and one chlorine atom must gain one electron. The formula for magnesium chloride is $MgCl_2$ because one magnesium atom has to lose two electrons while one chlorine atom can gain only one electron. Here again is illustrated the working of the zero valence rule. From these considerations, it will be seen why a knowledge of the electronic structure of the atoms and a knowledge of their valence numbers will permit the calculation of the formulas of hundreds of compounds which otherwise would have to be memorized.

13. *Equations*

Equations are the result of the chemist's application of his shorthand to the expression of the changes which occur during a chemical transformation. It has been shown that a symbol represents an atom, a formula represents a molecule, and special derivations of these represent the outer electronic structure of atoms, ions, etc. By combining these various representations of chemical entities with mathematical symbols, equations are produced. By agreement, the substances entering into a reaction (the reactants) are always written in the left member of the equation and the products in the right member, and the two members are joined by an arrow representing the direction of the reaction rather than with the conventional equal sign of mathematics. In writing equations which involve compounds and/or elements known to exist in molecular form, *molecular formulas are always used* to represent those substances. Symbols are used to represent all other elements. Thus, to represent the reaction between tin and chlorine, one writes

$$Sn + Cl_2 \rightarrow SnCl_4$$

but, since this is not an equality, coefficients are introduced as in algebraic equations to rectify the situation, and the completed equation becomes

$$Sn + 2Cl_2 \rightarrow SnCl_4$$

This equation then states that one atom of tin will combine with two molecules of chlorine to produce one molecule of tin tetrachloride.

In the case of sodium chloride, one commonly writes

$$2Na + Cl_2 \rightarrow 2NaCl$$

but, since ions of sodium and of chlorine are produced, one might more properly write

$$2Na + Cl_2 \rightarrow 2Na^+ + 2Cl^-$$

or, in terms of the Lewis notation,

$$2Na^{\times} + :\overset{..}{\underset{..}{Cl}}:\overset{..}{\underset{..}{Cl}}: \rightarrow 2Na + 2 \overset{..}{\underset{..}{\times Cl}}:$$

As an example of a case of *decomposition*, one might write

$$2HgO \rightarrow 2Hg + O_2 \uparrow$$

while an example of *displacement* is

$$Zn + CuSO_4 \rightarrow ZnSO_4 + Cu$$

or

$$Zn + Cu^{++} + SO_4^{--} \rightarrow Cu + Zn^{++} + SO_4^{--}$$

which shows that since zinc is more active than copper it will displace copper from its compounds. If an upward-pointing arrow is written by a product it indicates that that product is a gas, while a line inserted under a symbol or formula indicates that the substance so distinguished is a solid. All other symbols or formulas occurring in equations bearing these marks are presumed to be either liquids or in solution.

It will be noted that an equation tells nothing of the conditions, speed or extent of the reaction, or of the energy involved in it. Conditions of temperature or pressure are frequently written over or under the arrow; the energy liberated or absorbed is frequently written in the right member with either a plus or a minus sign as the case warrants; speed is seldom indicated in an equation; and the extent of the reaction is indicated qualitatively by using a double arrow. In the equation

$$N_2 + 3H_2 \rightleftharpoons 2NH_3$$

the double arrow indicates that nitrogen and hydrogen do not combine completely to form ammonia; the longer arrow pointing to the left indicates that very little ammonia is formed with respect to the quantities of nitrogen and hydrogen present. Further significance of these double arrows will be discussed in a later chapter.

14. The Nomenclature of Binary Compounds

Binary compounds are those which are made up of only two elements, like NaCl or CCl_4. Some of these compounds are ionic in nature, like NaCl; others are covalent, like CCl_4, but the system of naming is the same in both instances. In writing formulas, the symbol for the more positive element (the one which attracts electrons less and hence has the greater tendency to form positive ions) is written first, as in NaCl. In naming binary compounds, this element is named first, being given its usual elementary name, while the more negative element is named last, with the ending *-ide* having replaced the ending of its elementary name. Thus NaCl, the compound of sodium and chlorine, is named sodium chloride; Na_2S is sodium sulfide; $MgBr_2$ is magnesium bromide.

Prefixes are sometimes added to indicate the number of atoms of one variety which are in a given atom. *Di-* indicates two; *tri-*, three; *tetra-*, four; *penta-*, five; *hexa-*, six; *hepta-*, seven; and *octa-*, eight. Phosphorus forms two chlorides, PCl_3 and PCl_5, hence they are named phosphorus trichloride and phosphorus pentachloride, respectively. Carbon forms only one chloride, CCl_4, which is called carbon tetrachloride, but most of the chlorides of elements which form only one chloride do not have these prefixes in their names.

(See Appendix for Exercises)

COLLATERAL READINGS

Briscoe: *The Structure and Properties of Matter*, New York, McGraw-Hill Book Co., 1935.
Buehler: Electronic theory of valency, *J. Chem. Education*, **10**, 741 (1933).
Conn: *The Nature of the Atom*, New York, Chemical Publishing Co., 1939.
Gamow: *Mr. Tompkins in Wonderland*, New York, The Macmillan Co., 1940.
——: *Mr. Tompkins Explores the Atom*, New York, The Macmillan Co., 1944.
Hildebrand: *Principles of Chemistry*, Chap. XVI, New York, The Macmillan Co., 1941.
Kendall: *At Home Among the Atoms*, New York, D. Appleton-Century Co., 1929.
Lewis: *Valence and the Structure of Atoms and Molecules*, New York, Chemical Catalog Co., 1923.
Meitner: The nature of the atom, *Fortune*, **33**, No. 3, 137 (1946).
Rice: *Electronic Structure and Chemical Binding*, New York, McGraw-Hill Book Co., 1940.
Soddy: *Interpretation of the Atom*, New York, G. P. Putnam's Sons, 1932.

The Periodic Classification
of the Elements

1. The Distribution of Extranuclear Electrons in the Atoms

The work of Moseley showed that the known elements might be arranged in a series of increasing order numbers, and Chadwick definitely established that these order numbers represented both the net charge on the atomic nuclei and the number of extranuclear electrons of the atoms. This means, then, that each element has atoms which differ from the atoms of the element just before it in the series by having one more net positive charge on the nucleus and one more extranuclear electron. Viewing the elements arranged in the order of their increasing atomic numbers, one finds that at recurring intervals he encounters elements which have similar chemical properties. As has already been pointed out, chemical properties for the most part are governed by the extranuclear electrons of the highest occupied energy level of the atom, hence atoms which have similar chemical properties must have them because of similar outer electronic structures.

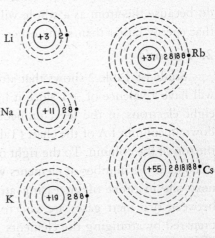

DIAGRAMMATIC REPRESENTATION OF THE STRUCTURES OF THE ATOMS OF THE ELEMENTS OF THE I A FAMILY. Note that the atoms of each element contain but one electron in their outermost energy levels.

That there should be similar outer electronic structures among the atoms is to be expected, since it has been shown that the number of electrons which may exist in a given energy level is limited. Starting off with only one electron in the first energy level, and proceeding to more complex structures as the first level is completed, the next electron which adds will do so in the second level, giving again a structure of one electron in the outermost level. Every element, then, which has one electron in its outermost level will closely resemble in chemical behavior the other atoms which have only one electron in the outermost level.

If a table be prepared to show the distribution of the extranuclear electrons of the atoms of the 96 known elements, elements whose atoms have similar structures may be readily identified, and a chart may be made in which elements whose atoms have similar structures may be placed in the same vertical columns. In preparing such a table of electron distributions, the formulas set forth in Chapter 4 for calculating the maximum numbers of electrons which may exist in a given main energy level and in a given sub-level should be reviewed.

Table 2 shows the electronic distributions in the atoms of the 96 elements mentioned above as given to us by the scientists who have worked with this phase of subatomic physics. It is generally assumed, and in many instances proved by mathematical calculations, that the electrons occupy the energetic positions in a given atom that they do because of the operation of the Second Law of Thermodynamics; in other words, the electrons have the energies they do because the atom as a whole will possess less available energy if they have that energy rather than some other.

2. Periods

Study of Table 2 shows that after each inert gas there is an element which will have a valence of $+1$ since it has one electron in its outermost level with eight electrons in the level immediately underneath. These elements are set down in column I A of the chart (Table 3) with the element of lowest number at the top of the column. To the right of this column are placed sufficient columns to contain the number of elements which occur between one inert gas and the next one in order of increasing atomic numbers. The elements which exist between two inert gases are said to constitute a period, and hence the table prepared by arranging the elements in periods is the *Periodic Chart*, or *Periodic Table*.

By examining the structures set forth in Table 2, it will be seen that the periods are of unequal length; period number one contains only the two elements hydrogen and helium; periods two and three contain eight elements each; periods four and five contain 18 elements each; period six contains 32 elements; and period seven contains only 10 elements, four of which are the recently discovered, artificially prepared elements previously mentioned.

Table 2

ELECTRONIC DISTRIBUTIONS OF THE ELEMENTS

Period	Element	At. No.	Main Level 1	Main Level 2		Main Level 3			Main Level 4				Main Level 5				Main Level 6				Main Level 7
			Sub-levels																		
			1_0	2_0	2_1	3_0	3_1	3_2	4_0	4_1	4_2	4_3	5_0	5_1	5_2	5_3	6_0	6_1	6_2	6_3	7_0
1	H	1	1																		
	He	2	2																		
2	Li	3	2	1																	
	Be	4	2	2																	
	B	5	2	2	1																
	C	6	2	2	2																
	N	7	2	2	3																
	O	8	2	2	4																
	F	9	2	2	5																
	Ne	10	2	2	6																
3	Na	11	2	2	6	1															
	Mg	12	2	2	6	2															
	Al	13	2	2	6	2	1														
	Si	14	2	2	6	2	2														
	P	15	2	2	6	2	3														
	S	16	2	2	6	2	4														
	Cl	17	2	2	6	2	5														
	A	18	2	2	6	2	6														
4	K	19	2	2	6	2	6	..	1												
	Ca	20	2	2	6	2	6	..	2												
	Sc	21	2	2	6	2	6	1	2												
	Ti	22	2	2	6	2	6	2	2												
	V	23	2	2	6	2	6	3	2												
	Cr	24	2	2	6	2	6	5	1												
	Mn	25	2	2	6	2	6	5	2												
	Fe	26	2	2	6	2	6	6	2												
	Co	27	2	2	6	2	6	7	2												
	Ni	28	2	2	6	2	6	8	2												
	Cu	29	2	2	6	2	6	10	1												
	Zn	30	2	2	6	2	6	10	2												
	Ga	31	2	2	6	2	6	10	2	1											
	Ge	32	2	2	6	2	6	10	2	2											
	As	33	2	2	6	2	6	10	2	3											
	Se	34	2	2	6	2	6	10	2	4											
	Br	35	2	2	6	2	6	10	2	5											
	Kr	36	2	2	6	2	6	10	2	6											

Table 2 (Continued)

Period	Element	At. No.	Main Level 1	Main Level 2		Main Level 3			Main Level 4				Main Level 5				Main Level 6				Main Level 7
			1_0	2_0	2_1	3_0	3_1	3_2	4_0	4_1	4_2	4_3	5_0	5_1	5_2	5_3	6_0	6_1	6_2	6_3	7_0
5	Rb	37	2	2	6	2	6	10	2	6	..	..	1								
	Sr	38	2	2	6	2	6	10	2	6	..	..	2								
	Y	39	2	2	6	2	6	10	2	6	1	..	2								
	Zr	40	2	2	6	2	6	10	2	6	2	..	2								
	Cb	41	2	2	6	2	6	10	2	6	4	..	1								
	Mo	42	2	2	6	2	6	10	2	6	5	..	1								
	Tc	43	2	2	6	2	6	10	2	6	6	..	1								
	Ru	44	2	2	6	2	6	10	2	6	7	..	1								
	Rh	45	2	2	6	2	6	10	2	6	8	..	1								
	Pd	46	2	2	6	2	6	10	2	6	10	..	..								
	Ag	47	2	2	6	2	6	10	2	6	10	..	1								
	Cd	48	2	2	6	2	6	10	2	6	10	..	2								
	In	49	2	2	6	2	6	10	2	6	10	..	2	1							
	Sn	50	2	2	6	2	6	10	2	6	10	..	2	2							
	Sb	51	2	2	6	2	6	10	2	6	10	..	2	3							
	Te	52	2	2	6	2	6	10	2	6	10	..	2	4							
	I	53	2	2	6	2	6	10	2	6	10	..	2	5							
	Xe	54	2	2	6	2	6	10	2	6	10	..	2	6							
6	Cs	55	2	2	6	2	6	10	2	6	10	..	2	6	..	..	1				
	Ba	56	2	2	6	2	6	10	2	6	10	..	2	6	..	..	2				
	La	57	2	2	6	2	6	10	2	6	10	..	2	6	1	..	2				
	Ce	58	2	2	6	2	6	10	2	6	10	1	2	6	1	..	2				
	Pr	59	2	2	6	2	6	10	2	6	10	2	2	6	1	..	2				
	Nd	60	2	2	6	2	6	10	2	6	10	4	2	6	..	..	2				
	Il	61	2	2	6	2	6	10	2	6	10	5	2	6	..	..	2				
	Sm	62	2	2	6	2	6	10	2	6	10	6	2	6	..	..	2				
	Eu	63	2	2	6	2	6	10	2	6	10	7	2	6	..	..	2				
	Gd	64	2	2	6	2	6	10	2	6	10	7	2	6	1	..	2				
	Tb	65	2	2	6	2	6	10	2	6	10	8	2	6	1	..	2				
	Dy	66	2	2	6	2	6	10	2	6	10	10	2	6	..	..	2				
	Ho	67	2	2	6	2	6	10	2	6	10	11	2	6	..	..	2				
	Er	68	2	2	6	2	6	10	2	6	10	12	2	6	..	..	2				
	Tm	69	2	2	6	2	6	10	2	6	10	13	2	6	..	..	2				
	Yb	70	2	2	6	2	6	10	2	6	10	14	2	6	..	..	2				
	Lu	71	2	2	6	2	6	10	2	6	10	14	2	6	1	..	2				
	Hf	72	2	2	6	2	6	10	2	6	10	14	2	6	2	..	2				
	Ta	73	2	2	6	2	6	10	2	6	10	14	2	6	3	..	2				
	W	74	2	2	6	2	6	10	2	6	10	14	2	6	4	..	2				
	Re	75	2	2	6	2	6	10	2	6	10	14	2	6	5	..	2				
	Os	76	2	2	6	2	6	10	2	6	10	14	2	6	6	..	2				
	Ir	77	2	2	6	2	6	10	2	6	10	14	2	6	7	..	2				
	Pt	78	2	2	6	2	6	10	2	6	10	14	2	6	9	..	1				
	Au	79	2	2	6	2	6	10	2	6	10	14	2	6	10	..	1				
	Hg	80	2	2	6	2	6	10	2	6	10	14	2	6	10	..	2				
	Tl	81	2	2	6	2	6	10	2	6	10	14	2	6	10	..	2	1			
	Pb	82	2	2	6	2	6	10	2	6	10	14	2	6	10	..	2	2			
	Bi	83	2	2	6	2	6	10	2	6	10	14	2	6	10	..	2	3			
	Po	84	2	2	6	2	6	10	2	6	10	14	2	6	10	..	2	4			
	At	85	2	2	6	2	6	10	2	6	10	14	2	6	10	..	2	5			
	Rn	86	2	2	6	2	6	10	2	6	10	14	2	6	10	..	2	6			

Table 2 (Continued)

Period	Element	At. No.	Main Level 1	Main Level 2		Main Level 3			Main Level 4				Main Level 5				Main Level 6				Main Level 7
			Sub-levels																		
			1_0	2_0	2_1	3_0	3_1	3_2	4_0	4_1	4_2	4_3	5_0	5_1	5_2	5_3	6_0	6_1	6_2	6_3	7_0
	Fa	87	2	2	6	2	6	10	2	6	10	14	2	6	10	..	2	6	..	..	1
	Ra	88	2	2	6	2	6	10	2	6	10	14	2	6	10	..	2	6	..	..	2
	Ac	89	2	2	6	2	6	10	2	6	10	14	2	6	10	..	2	6	1	..	2
	Th	90	2	2	6	2	6	10	2	6	10	14	2	6	10	1	2	6	1	..	2
	Pa	91	2	2	6	2	6	10	2	6	10	14	2	6	10	2	2	6	1	..	2
7	U	92	2	2	6	2	6	10	2	6	10	14	2	6	10	3	2	6	1	..	2
	NP	93	2	2	6	2	6	10	2	6	10	14	2	6	10	4	2	6	1	..	2
	Pu	94	2	2	6	2	6	10	2	6	10	14	2	6	10	5	2	6	1	..	2
	Am	95	2	2	6	2	6	10	2	6	10	14	2	6	10	7	2	6	..	..	2
	Cm	96	2	2	6	2	6	10	2	6	10	14	2	6	10	7	2	6	1	..	2

3. The Periodic Chart

One form of the periodic chart is the arrangement of the elements of the periods in horizontal lines with the elements of succeeding periods which have properties similar to those of elements of preceding periods placed in the same vertical columns with those elements. A number of forms of this chart have been proposed from time to time, but that presented herewith (see Table 3) is one of the most generally useful for the student of chemistry.

The main purpose of the chart is to assist in the correlation of information concerning the properties of the elements; hence, the chart which does this most clearly is the chart which is most useful. One of the charts which presents the greatest number of facts about each element is that originally prepared by Henry D. Hubbard and revised by Meggers and published in a form for classroom use.

4. The Periodic Law

Elements with similar properties exist at fixed intervals in the chart, as has been pointed out, simply because these elements have similar outer electronic configurations. This information is contained in the statement known as *the periodic law, which states that the properties of the elements are periodic functions of their atomic numbers.*

5. The First Period

The first period contains only two elements because the first energy level is filled when it contains only two electrons. Thus it is that the second element of the series is an inert gas, helium. The first element, hydrogen, is peculiar in

Table 3

A Modern Form of the Periodic Chart of the Elements, Including a Table of Oxidation Numbers* many of its properties, and as a result presents some difficulties when one attempts to assign it a place in the periodic system. As a consequence of being the lightest of known elements, it has physical properties which are different from those of sodium and the other elements which have only one electron in the outermost level. Hydrogen is also peculiar in that, although it has only one electron which it might be expected to lose, it also lacks only one electron of having the helium structure and might, therefore, be expected to gain one electron. Occasionally hydrogen does gain an electron to become like helium, forming thus the H^- ion, but in the majority of its reactions it loses its one electron, which leaves only its nuclear proton, the ion H^+. Because of its tendency to lose an electron rather than to gain one, hydrogen is usually placed in the first column with sodium and the other alkali metals, though its physical properties and many of its chemical properties are quite different from those of these metals. When hydrogen gains an electron or when it forms covalent compounds, its properties are much more like those of chlorine and the halogens than like those of the alkali metals. This last consideration explains why in some charts, like the one given, hydrogen is placed between columns I and VII with lines drawn to both.

6. The Second and Third Periods

The second period begins with the metal lithium, which contains one electron in the second energy level. The elements which follow it add one electron at a time until the second level is completed, when eight electrons are present. The element which completes the second energy level and also the second period is the inert gas neon. Thus the second period contains eight elements, with each element having one more electron than the one before it and as a result showing a valence which is different from that of the other elements of the period. Since lithium is much more like helium in its structure than it is like neon, it always reacts by losing one electron, never by gaining. Study of the individual elements will show that, outside of the differences already cited for hydrogen, the differences that exist between the elements of period two and the elements of similar structure of period three, are the greatest that exist between successive elements in a given column of the table.

With sodium, the third energy level begins to contain electrons and the third period begins. Sodium, with its one outer electron, shows properties very similar to those of lithium. Following sodium, electrons add one at a time so that when eight electrons have added another inert gas has been reached and the period is ended. In the case of the second and third periods, if their atoms which have more than two outer electrons are to react to show a maximum positive valence, they must lose electrons from both the sub-zero and sub-one levels. Also to be noted is the fact that those atoms which contain more than four outer electrons are more likely to gain electrons, or to share electrons, than they are to lose them.

7. The Fourth and Fifth Periods: Transition Elements

The third period comes to an end when the inert gas argon containing eight electrons in the third energy level is reached, but, since the third energy level may contain 18 electrons, it is obvious that the third level is not also completed. The next electron which adds does not add to the 3_2 level but skips to the 4_0 level, giving rise, as seen in Table 2, to another atom similar in behavior to that of lithium and sodium; this is the potassium atom. The next electron to add also goes into the 4_0 level, causing calcium to be similar in behavior to magnesium. The third electron to add, however, does not add in the 4_1 level; it goes into the vacant 3_2 level to start filling it up, thus giving rise to an electronic configuration unlike any encountered thus far. This element to attain a stable configuration first would have to lose its two 4_0 electrons and then its one 3_2 electron. It could thus show a valence of $+2$ and a valence of $+3$ of which the $+3$ valence would form the more stable compounds. *Elements which, like scandium, may lose valence electrons from two main energy levels are called transition elements.*

The next several elements following scandium are also transition elements since they too are gaining their additional electrons in the 3_2 level and hence must lose electrons from two levels to attain an inert gas structure. All of the transition elements are metals and electron-losers, and, as more electrons are added in the 3_2 level, the maximum positive valence of these metals increases for a time. Since these transition elements all occupy a position intermediate between the regular elements which will lose two and three electrons, respectively, from their fourth main level, the latter members of the transition series should decrease in valence. This decrease in valence is begun with the group of three elements of very similar properties—iron, cobalt, and nickel—which are placed in the VIII B column. Following these elements is the element copper, which ends the transition series of the fourth period. Following copper is zinc, which has the structure 2, 8, 18, 2 and thus completes the third energy level so that the next electron added will go into the fourth energy level to give an element of the regular series which will closely resemble aluminum in its chemical properties.

The six elements which follow zinc add one electron at a time in the 4_1 level until a fourth inert gas, krypton, is reached, thus ending the period.

The fifth period begins with rubidium, whose electron has added in the 5_0 level, skipping the 4_2 and 4_3 levels to do so. The second element of this period also adds its electrons in the 5_0 level, then the next several elements add their electrons back in the 4_2 level in a fashion similar to that in which the fourth period was built up. As a consequence of these electrons adding back in the 4_2 level, there is formed another series of transition elements whose structures and properties are similar to those of the transition elements of the fourth period. When the 4_2 level has been filled, then additions are made in the 5_1 level, giving rise to six more regular elements and ending the period with the inert gas, xenon, which has the usual eight electrons in its highest level. The 4_3 level remains still unfilled.

8. The Sixth Period

The sixth period starts like the fourth and fifth periods with the first two electrons skipping the 5_2 level to add in the 6_0 level and with the third electron adding in this period falling back into the 5_2 level to start filling it just as was the case with the transition elements of periods four and five. Lanthanum, then, has properties similar to those of scandium and yttrium. The fourth electron which adds in this period, however, does not continue to add in the 5_2 level in an analogous fashion to the further additions in periods four and five; rather, this fourth electron goes back to the 4_3 level to start filling it up. The next 13 electrons which add also go, in general, into the 4_3 level, finally completing it. As a consequence of this addition of electrons to an empty inside sub-level, the resulting 14 elements have atoms whose outer electronic configurations are similar. Since chemical properties are dependent largely upon outer structure, these 14 elements should have almost identical chemical properties and such has been found to be the case. These elements constitute a special group of transition elements, all of which apparently should occupy one space in the periodic chart, or should be placed in a specially extended chart. Since they cannot be stacked up like a deck of cards with lanthanum on the bottom and lutecium on top, and since an extended chart would be inconveniently long, they are usually placed in a separate series at the foot of the chart. These elements are known collectively as the rare earth metals. Their name indicates that they are not plentiful in the earth's crust.

After the completion of the 4_3 level with the rare earths, further addition of electrons takes place in the 5_2 level until it is completed. This series of additions gives rise to elements which resemble the other transition elements of periods four and five. When the 5_2 level is completed, the next six electrons are added in the 6_1 level, giving elements whose atoms have structures similar to those of the regular elements, and the sixth period ends with radon when the sixth main energy level has eight electrons.

9. The Seventh Period

The seventh period barely gets started before the end of the series of elements is reached. The first two of these elements add their new electrons in the 7_0 level, skipping the 6_2 level, and are hence similar in properties to sodium and magnesium, respectively. The next addition takes place in the 6_2 level giving the element actinium so formed a structure and chemical properties similar to lanthanum, yttrium, and scandium. Further additions then take place in the until now empty 5_3 level, so that the remaining seven elements form a series of special transition elements of the type of the rare earth metals of period six. These elements also are given a special place at the foot of the table, and the catalog of known elements comes to an end in the midst of this series. All of the elements of this period are radioactive, and, with the exception of uranium, are quite rare.

10. The Variation of Properties Within a Period

As one passes from left to right across either period two or period three, each successive element has atoms which have one more positive charge on the nucleus and one more electron in their outermost energy level. As a consequence of this gradual change in mass, charge, and number of valence electrons, the elements of these periods show an equally gradual change in properties. The elements in column I A are metals and are violent electron-losers, since they have but one to lose, and hence for the most part form only electrovalent compounds. The elements of column II A are also metals and electron-losers, but their electrons are less readily lost since the charge on the nucleus which attracts them is growing larger. In a similar manner, gradual changes take place from element to element as one crosses the periods, with the elements becoming steadily less metallic until the last several elements in the period are definitely nonmetallic and are strong electron-acceptors. In the middle of the period are elements whose fundamental nature is less well defined and whose compounds are, for the most part, covalent.

In the longer periods, there exists between the regular elements of columns II A and III A the series of transition elements whose properties change even more gradually than do those of the regular elements—so gradually, in fact, that all of the transition elements are metals. This is to be expected since they occupy spaces between two of the regular metallic elements. The columns in which these elements are placed are given numbers identical with those of the columns in which the regular elements are placed, but B is used with these numbers to distinguish them from those of the regular columns, which are marked A. The elements in a given column are spoken of as a family; thus we have the I A family, the VI B family, etc. The column numbers, with only a few exceptions to be noted later, indicate the *maximum* positive valence which the elements in that column may exhibit, but they do not tell what other valences may be shown. However, in the case of the A numbers greater than 4, if the number be subtracted from 8 the minimum valences of the elements of those families is given.

The elements of any given pair of A and B families—for instance, the II A and II B families—are best not put in the same column because, while they may exhibit the same maximum valences, they have very few other properties in common. These other differences arise from the fact that in many instances when the valence electrons are lost different underneath structures are left exposed. When magnesium loses two electrons, eight electrons are left in an outer level, while when zinc loses two electrons, 18 electrons are left in the outer level. From this it may be inferred that if eight electrons in an outer main level may not be established, then 18 electrons in an outer main level is the next most desirable situation. The relative sizes and charges of the ions in the two sub-families also account for some of the differences of properties.

11. The Ionic Radius

The three attributes of the atom which determine its properties in the compounds which it forms are (1) the charge which it acquires in its compounds, (2) the structure which it assumes in its compounds, and (3) its particle size in those compounds. The manner in which the maximum charge of the ions of the elements of a given period vary across that period has been discussed, and reference has been made in the preceding section to the fact that, though two ions may have the same charge, their other properties may vary considerably with the electronic structure of the remaining outermost energy level. There remains to be discussed variation of ionic size among the atoms of the periodic chart. Because atoms are assumed to be spherical, their radii will be taken as a measurement of their respective sizes.

Since the elements of a given column of the periodic chart exhibit the same valences (i.e., have the same ionic charges) and since the external structures of these ions are the same, the variations which occur among similar compounds of these ions must be due to the difference in size of the ions formed. Naturally, the one of these ions which contains electrons in the greatest number of main levels will be the largest of the group. The importance of the size of the particles which are formed as a result of reaction is coming to be better understood as investigations in this field increase.

Our knowledge of ionic radii comes largely from x-ray studies of crystals which contain the particles in question and from an application of the principles of wave mechanics in the calculating of these dimensions. In Table 4 are given the radii of the ions of a number of the elements expressed in terms of Ångström units. Actually, ions of many of the elements which form only covalent compounds are not known, but, just as it was convenient for purposes of comparison in the case of oxidation-reduction to assign oxidation numbers, or ionic valence numbers, so also in this case it is convenient for purposes of comparison to list the radii of those same imaginary ions to which valence numbers were assigned. The radius of an ion of a certain charge and structure can be calculated whether the ion actually exists or not. It will thus be seen that some of the values given in Table 4 are for ions which actually exist while others are for hypothetical ions. Furthermore, the values given are not precise, yet they serve very well to show the general trend of variations of this kind in the periodic arrangement of the elements.

From a study of Table 4, it is seen that as one passes from left to right across a given period of the Periodic Chart, the ionic radii decrease as the charge on the ion increases, and, conversely, as the charges decrease the radii increase. The radius of an atom decreases as its valence charge increases because, as the number of extranuclear electrons is decreased by their removal from the neutral atom, the net positive charge on the nucleus remains the same. This permits the remaining extranuclear electrons to be attracted more strongly and hence pulled in more closely to the nucleus. Table 4 also reveals that, as one passes from top to bottom down any column, the ionic radius increases, and that, in a given period, the element which forms an ion containing 18 electrons in its outermost energy level will have a smaller radius than the element which forms an ion of the same charge but with eight electrons in its outermost level. An examination of the ionic radii of the trivalent ions of the rare earth metals shows a slight decrease from left to right in the table. This decrease in radius accounts for the fact that, though the ions of all these metals have similar charges and similar external structures, they exhibit slight differences in properties which permit their separation from mixtures of their compounds. The chemical properties of a molecule depend to a large extent upon the forces between the atoms which compose it. These attractive forces depend largely upon the sizes of the atoms and upon the charges which they bear.

Table 4

CHART OF ATOMIC AND IONIC RADII AND IONIC POTENTIALS (SQ. RT.)

Legend:

At. Radius	H 0.37
+ Ionic Radius	H^+
+ √Ionic Pot.	
− Ionic Radius	H^- 2.08
− √Ionic Pot.	−0.69

Category groupings across the chart: **Light Metals** (I A–II A), **Heavy Metals** (III B–II B), **Nonmetals** (III A–VII A), **Inert Gases** (VIII A).

Each cell lists: atomic radius · cation (ionic radius / √ionic potential) · anion (ionic radius / √ionic potential).

I A	II A	III B	IV B	V B	VI B	VII B	VIII B	VIII B	VIII B	I B	II B	III A	IV A	V A	VI A	VII A	VIII A
																	He 0.53
Li 1.50 / Li^+ 0.06 / 1.29	Be 1.12 / Be^{+2} 0.31 / 2.54											B 0.7(ca.) / B^{+3} 0.2 / 3.87	C 0.77 / C^{+4} 0.15 / 5.16 ; C^{-4} 2.60 / −1.24	N 0.7 / N^{+5} 0.11 / 6.71 ; N^{-3} 1.71 / −1.32	O 0.68 / O^{+6} 0.09 / 8.16 ; O^{-2} 1.40 / −1.19	F 0.60 / F^{+7} 0.07 / 10.00 ; F^{-1} 1.36 / −0.86	Ne 1.60
Na 1.84 / Na^+ 0.95 / 1.02	Mg 1.60 / Mg^{+2} 0.65 / 1.76											Al 1.43 / Al^{+3} 0.50 / 2.45	Si 1.17 / Si^{+4} 0.41 / 3.13 ; Si^{-4} 2.71 / −1.22	P 1.17 / P^{+5} 0.34 / 3.83 ; P^{-3} 2.12 / −1.18	S 0.87 / S^{+6} 0.29 / 4.55 ; S^{-2} 1.84 / −1.04	Cl 1.06 / Cl^{+7} 0.29 / 5.20 ; Cl^{-1} 1.81 / −0.74	A 1.91
K 2.31 / K^+ 1.33 / 0.87	Ca 1.97 / Ca^{+2} 0.99 / 1.42	Sc 1.51 / Sc^{+3} 0.81 / 1.92	Ti 1.45 / Ti^{+4} 0.68 / 2.43	V 1.30 / V^{+5} 0.59 / 2.92	Cr 1.25 / Cr^{+6} 0.52 / 3.39	Mn 1.18 / Mn^{+7} 0.46 / 3.90	Fe 1.18 / Fe^{+2} 0.74 ; Fe^{+3} 0.52 / 3.90	Co 1.27 / Co^{+2} 0.82 ; Co^{+3} 0.67 / 2.12	Ni 1.25 / Ni^{+2} 0.82 / 1.56	Cu 1.24 / Cu^{+2} 0.96 ; 0.78 / 1.60 / 1.44	Zn 1.28 / Zn^{+2} 0.74 / 1.64	Ga 1.24 / Ga^{+3} 0.62 / 2.20	Ge 1.22 / Ge^{+4} 0.53 / 2.75	As 1.22 / As^{+5} 0.47 / 3.26 ; As^{-3}	Se 1.16 / Se^{+6} 0.42 / 3.78 ; Se^{-2} 1.98 / −1.00	Br 1.13 / Br^{+7} 0.39 / 3.92 ; Br^{-1} 1.95 / −0.715	Kr 1.98
Rb 2.44 / Rb^+ 1.48 / 0.82	Sr 2.15 / Sr^{+2} 1.13 / 1.33	Y 1.58 / Y^{+3} 0.93 / 1.79	Zr 1.58 / Zr^{+4} 0.80 / 2.24	Cb 1.43 / Cb^{+5} 0.70 / 2.66	Mo 1.36 / Mo^{+6} 0.62 / 3.11	To	Ru 1.32 / Ru^{+4} 0.65 / 2.48	Rh 1.32 / Rh^{+3} 0.69 / 2.09	Pd 1.34 / 0.69 / 2.09	Ag 1.37 / Ag^+ 1.26 / 0.70	Cd 1.44 / Cd^{+2} 0.97 / 1.44	In 1.57 / In^{+3} 0.81 / 1.93	Sn 1.51 / Sn^{+4} 0.71 / 2.37	Sb 1.45 / Sb^{+5} 0.62 / 2.84	Te 1.44 / Te^{+6} 0.56 / 3.27 ; Te^{-2} 2.21 / −0.95	I 1.35 / I^{+7} 0.50 / 3.74 ; I^{-1} 2.16 / −0.68	Xe 2.18
Cs 2.62 / Cs^+ 1.69 / 0.77	Ba 2.17 / Ba^{+2} 1.35 / 1.21	La 1.86 / La^{+3} 1.15 / 1.61	Hf 1.59 / Hf^{+4} 0.79 / 2.25	Ta 1.46 / Ta^{+5} 0.71 / 2.65	W 1.37 / W^{+6} 0.65 / 3.05	Re 1.37 / Re^{+7} 0.65 / 3.05	Os 1.34 / Os^{+4} 0.67 / 2.45	Ir 1.35 / Ir^{+4} 0.66 / 2.46	Pt 1.35 / Pt^{+4} 0.66 / 2.46	Au 1.38 / Au^+ 1.37 / 0.70	Hg 1.44 / Hg^{+2} 1.10 / 1.35	Tl 1.71 / Tl^{+3} 0.95 / 1.78	Pb 1.75 / Pb^{+4} 0.84 / 2.18	Bi 1.55 / Bi^{+5} 0.74 / 2.60	Po	At	Rn

As the various elements are studied, ionic radii will be used along with the structure and charge of atoms and ions to correlate the properties of the elements and the compounds which they form.

12. The Ionic Potential

At this juncture, it will be convenient to define a quantity which will be useful in later discussions; this quantity is the *ionic potential*, which relates the charge on an ion and its radius. The ionic potential (ϕ) is defined as the ratio of the charge on an ion (its valence) (z) to its radius (r) expressed in Ångström units: $\phi = z/r$. Since this quantity combines both charge and radius, it may then be used with structure in the study of the behavior of the various ions. It is especially valuable in the study of ions which have attained an inert gas structure.

Since ϕ for the ions of higher charge is often a fairly large number, the square root of ϕ is more frequently used for purposes of comparison. Values for $\sqrt{\phi}$ for a number of ions are given together with the atomic and ionic radii in Table 4.

Under no circumstances is the ionic potential to be confused with the ionizing potential of gases (cf. section 9, Chapter 4).

13. The Varieties of Elements

In general, the elements fall into two main categories: metals and nonmetals. The metals are those which have the bright luster and other characteristics which are usually associated with such substances as iron, silver, zinc, and tin, while the nonmetals are those substances which do not have the characteristics of metals. By far the greater number of elements are metals, since the transition elements are all metals. The elements are usually still further subdivided into five groups, three of which are metallic and two of which are nonmetallic. Classified as *light metals* are the very active elements of groups I A and II A. The *heavy metals* include those elements which are in the middle of the table and which extend well into its lower right corner. The *rare earth metals*, as has been stated, occupy a special place at the bottom of the table but really belong in the III B column with lanthanum, or, better still, in an even more extended form of the table. The *inert gases* occupy the last column on the right, and the *nonmetals* occupy places extending from the third column of the second period to the right and diagonally downward to the right; in general, if one except the inert gases, they may be said to occupy the right side of the chart and its upper right corner.

14. History of the Periodic Chart

The first attempts at classifying the elements were made long before any-thing was known of the structure of the atom. One of the first attempts was that of the British physician, Prout, who in 1815 suggested that the atoms of all the elements might be made up of different numbers of hydrogen atoms. This idea was discredited when more accurate determinations of atomic weights showed that most atoms do not have weights which are exact multiples of the weight of hydrogen. As has been shown previously, however, atomic nuclei are today considered to be made up largely of protons which are hydrogen nuclei, hence Prout's ideas which were often laughed at in his own day today stand largely vindicated.

The next attempt at a correlation of the properties of the elements came in 1817 when Döbereiner pointed out that there were a number of groups of three elements, which he called triads, whose three members had similar properties and whose middle member had an atomic weight which was roughly the average of the weights of the other two members. No relationships between the various triads were suggested, because many of the elements which might have sug-gested their relationship were not known at that time.

Although further attempts were made to extend existing ideas of classifica-tion, no great success was achieved until after 1858, when, as the result of Cannizzaro's application of Avogadro's law, approximately correct atomic weights were established for the known elements. During the 1860's, great progress was made in the development of schemes of classification. John A. R. Newlands, an Englishman, was one of the first of this period to propose a classification. He suggested that the elements be arranged in order of their increasing atomic weights, but, because he did not recognize that there might be still undiscovered elements, he had considerable difficulty in getting the right element in the right place. His ideas also met with considerable scorn of the type found in the question of a member of the Royal Society who asked Newlands if he had ever thought of arranging the elements alphabetically. Credit for observ-ing that the short periods contain seven active elements, however, does belong rightly to Newlands.

Others who suggested systems of classification during the 1860's were De Chancourtois, Lothar Meyer, and Mendelejeff. The best of these classifications was that of the latter, and was first proposed in 1869. Mendelejeff recog-nized that many elements were not known at that time, hence he was able to leave blank spaces in his chart for them, and by noting the family relationships of the blank spaces he was able to predict the properties of the missing elements and to make suggestions as to the type of minerals in which they might be found. His chart thus gave a great impetus to element hunting. Mendelejeff arranged his elements in the order of increasing atomic weight, save for three instances in which similarities of family properties definitely indicated that the weight order should not be followed.

In 1913, Moseley's work, which established the atomic numbers, also established the true order in which the elements should go. It might be added that this order agreed with Mendelejeff's order based on properties, where these disagreed with weight. Moseley's work also established the modern form of the periodic law which has already been stated.

The establishment of the electronic structures of the atoms has made even more clear our knowledge of the fundamental relationship of the simple forms of matter. As a result of this knowledge, still more elements have been discovered, until today we know practically all of them, or so it is generally believed.

Since the days of Mendelejeff, other workers have proposed a number of different forms for the periodic chart, but, for the most part, these are only variations of the form he used. The modern periodic chart contains much more information about each element than did his table, but in essence it is the same and the chances are that for many years to come the periodic chart will remain a monument to the insight and analytical powers of this great Russian chemist.

15. *Uses of the Periodic Chart*

The principal use of the periodic chart at present, as in the years which have elapsed since Mendelejeff first proposed it, is as an aid in classifying and correlating information concerning the elements and the compounds which they form. Other classifications and other considerations are often necessary for the complete understanding of the elements, but there is no one unifying agent which is quite so generally useful as the periodic chart.

Because it does show so clearly many of the relationships which exist between elementary substances, metallurgists, physicists, engineers, and other scientific workers have found the chart useful. For instance, metallurgists have found the relationships shown for the metals particularly useful in their attempts to prepare new alloys of specific properties.

In the past, the chart has also served other purposes. Reference has already been made to the fact that the blank spaces left in the Mendelejeff table served as a great inspiration and guide to the discovery of the unknown elements. Other

Dmitri Ivanovitch Mendelejeff
(1834–1907, *Russian*)

A chemist of great originality and boldness and a writer of no mean ability, Mendelejeff made contributions to all branches of chemistry, but he is best known as the originator of the periodic classification of the elements in essentially the same form in which it is used today. While previous attempts at classification of the elements had been made, Mendelejeff's work was unique in that he realized that not all of the elements had been discovered and that many of the accepted atomic weights of the then known elements were not correct. The promulgation of his ideas greatly stimulated both the search for new elements and work on atomic-weight determination. He served as professor of chemistry at the University of Saint Petersburg and later as Director of the Imperial Bureau of Weights and Measures. His book, *The Principles of Chemistry*, is considered a chemical classic and is a storehouse of suggestions of problems to be investigated.

Jöns Jakob Berzelius
(1779–1848, *Swedish*)

One of the giants of chemical history is Berzelius. He was famed as teacher, author, and investigator. Shortly after his graduation from the University of Upsala, he became a member of the faculty of the famous school of medicine of Stockholm, a post which he held until his death. He was the first chemical investigator to establish the atomic weights of the then known elements with any degree of accuracy, and in so doing he laid the foundation for the science of quantitative analysis. Among his achievements are the discovery of the elements cerium, selenium, silicon, thorium, and zirconium. He was a famous teacher who drew students from all over Europe, and was among the first to illustrate his lectures with experimental demonstrations. His textbook, entitled *"Lehrbuch der Chemie,"* was translated into German and many other languages, and the yearbook entitled *"Jahresbericht der Chemie,"* which he founded in 1821 and edited until his death, was widely read. In 1836, upon the day of his marriage, he was created a baron by the King of Sweden.

elements also owe their discovery to the chart. In his original table, Mendelejeff left no space for the inert gases whose existence was not even suspected, but, when the first of these elements was discovered, known family relationships of the other elements suggested that there should be a family of such elements—a supposition which research soon vindicated. The positions of the various elements in the chart have served as a guide to the proper atomic weights for those elements whose weights were in doubt, thus assisting in the establishment of more exact atomic weights. Some of the predictions of Mendelejeff concerning properties of elements not known in his day proved to be so nearly correct, even to atomic weight, as to appear almost uncanny. With the aid of the chart, though, such predictions are perfectly natural and normal.

16. Weaknesses of the Chart

Although the periodic classification of the elements brings into sharp focus the extreme orderliness of nature, it also calls to attention the fact that there are some apparent discrepancies in nature which cause irregularities in even the best of the periodic charts. The form in which the chart is presented in Table 3 offers fewer irregularities than does the Mendelejeff form of the table, but there are irregularities even in this form.

The difficulty which causes the greatest concern is the placing of the element hydrogen. Hydrogen is an important element which forms many compounds, and, therefore, cannot be ignored. It shows valences which resemble those of both the alkali metals and the halogens, but in its other properties it resembles the elements of neither group very closely. Even when solidified, it does not resemble a metal at all. Its position in the table, then, is always a problem, and no matter where it is put the position does not emphasize its properties and relationships very well.

The second great weakness of the table is that it serves well only to emphasize the maximum valence state of an element with a secondary emphasis on the minimum valence state. Intermediate states of valence can be brought into the picture only by coupling the electronic structure with the position of the element in the chart, and then relationships with other elements of the same valence state are not brought out too sharply. In this connection, there are a few cases in which elements do show higher valences than the number of the column in which they find themselves. For instance, the electronic structures of the atoms of copper, silver, and gold indicate that these elements should go in the I B column, but, while these elements do show a valence of $+1$, they also show higher valences. The rare earth metal, cerium, which is usually put in column III B, in addition to showing a valence of +3 also shows one of +4.

Another difficulty encountered in relating valence numbers to column numbers is found in column VIII. The inert gases which occupy the VIII A column have no compounds, and hence no valences, while the VIII B column is occupied by three groups of three transition metals each, whose valences are for the most part 2, 3, and 4, with a valence of 8 shown only by osmium and ruthenium.

The rare earths also present a problem in chart making. It has been seen that their atoms all have similar outer electronic structures and as a consequence are usually considered to occupy the same place in the table as lanthanum. Strictly speaking, however, the long form of the table should be made still longer so that these elements might be placed in a row in order of their increasing atomic numbers between lanthanum and hafnium, thus indicating that their properties are not wholly identical due to the slight variations which they undergo as their atomic nuclei and radii change. Since these elements are very rare, this discrepancy does not, in general, cause too much trouble.

A last irregularity to be mentioned is that which caused trouble for Mendelejeff and others who arranged the elements in order of increasing atomic weights. In general, atomic weight increases as atomic number increases, but in the four cases of argon and potassium, cobalt and nickel, tellurium and iodine, and thorium and protoactinium, the weight order is reversed. Since the modern classifications are based upon atomic numbers, this matter is not too serious; nevertheless, it is an example of a type of irregularity to be met.

Despite these weaknesses, however, the periodic chart still remains one of the chemist's most useful devices. Its importance to the student who would gain a practical working knowledge of chemical substances can scarcely be emphasized too greatly.

(See Appendix for Exercises)

COLLATERAL READINGS

Babor: A periodic table based on atomic numbers and electron configuration, *J. Chem. Education*, **21**, 25 (1944).

Foster: The periodic table, *J. Chem. Education*, **16**, 409 (1939).

Jaffe: *Crucibles*, New York, Simon and Schuster, 1930.

Lange: *Handbook of Chemistry*, Handbook Publishers, Inc. Frequent editions.

Luder: Electron configuration as the basis of the periodic table, *J. Chem. Education*, **20,** 21 (1943).

Midgley: From the periodic table to production, *Ind. Eng. Chem.*, **29,** 241 (1937).

Moore: *History of Chemistry*, New York, McGraw-Hill Book Co., 1939.

Wagner and Booth: A new periodic table, *J. Chem. Education*, **22,** 128 (1945).

Weeks: *The Discovery of the Elements*, 5th ed., Mack Printing Co., 1945.

7

Sodium and Its Compounds

1. Introduction

It has previously been shown that the chemical behavior of an element depends largely upon the number and distribution of its valence electrons, and that the number of these valence electrons increases one by one from one element to the next in a given period. Starting with this chapter and continuing through the next several descriptive chapters, the elements of a representative period will be studied, with the purpose of associating the accompanying changes in properties with the structural changes that take place from atom to atom. Since the variation of properties of the regular elements of a period are of the same general character for all periods, when they have been learned for one period they may be applied, with due regard for the starting point, to the other periods. A consideration of variations within the long periods which contain transition elements and within a given family must of necessity come later.

For the purpose of this study, the third period has been chosen. There are several reasons for this choice. The third period was chosen in preference to either the first or second periods because the former contains only two elements and because the latter, while containing eight elements, is not entirely representative since its atoms are below average size. Furthermore, the elements of the third period are all of long-established practical use. Its atoms show very well the properties which are characteristic of their respective structures.

During this study of the elements of the third period, attention will also be given to the diminishing atomic and ionic radii of the particles involved in the changes undergone by these substances.

2. Sodium

The first element of the third period is sodium, whose compounds salt, soap, glass, lye, etc., are so important to man in his everyday life. The sodium atom contains one more extranuclear electron than does the inert gas, neon, hence its structure is already very close to that of an inert gas and as a result of this condition its reactions are relatively simple. Sodium is a metal, and, as a consequence of the simplicity of its chemical behavior, it is almost ideal for demonstrating the chemical properties which are in varying degrees character-istic of all metals. Because of its softness and its extreme reactivity, sodium is, however, of little value for the manufacture of articles.

3. Physical Properties

Sodium is a silvery metal with a bright luster. It is a light metal with a density of only 0.97 g. per ml., which is less than that of water. It is so soft that it is easily cut with a knife. The melting point of the metal is 97.5° C., which is 2.5° lower than the boiling point of water at sea level; its boiling point is 880° C. The vapor of sodium is blue in color, and, when introduced into a flame or into an electrical discharge tube, gives a characteristic orange-yellow glow which when viewed through a good spectroscope appears as two distinct yellow lines.

Solutions of other metals in the liquid metal mercury are known as *amalgams*. Sodium dissolves readily, sometimes violently, in mercury to form sodium amalgam, which is used both in the laboratory and industrially. The amalgam is preferred to sodium for many reactions because it is less reactive than the pure sodium.

Sodium also dissolves in liquid ammonia to give a blue solution whose color gradually fades as the sodium reacts with the ammonia.

Because the outermost electron of the sodium atom is so loosely held, the metal makes an excellent conductor of electricity, but, because of its extreme reactivity, it is seldom used for this purpose. It has been suggested, however, that sodium might be so used by enclosing a wire of it in a protective tube of some cheaper and less active substance.

4. The Ionizing Potential

One of the important physical properties of an element is its ionizing potential. As was pointed out in Chapter 4, the ionizing potential of an ele-mentary substance is the voltage required to remove a valence electron from an atom of that substance in the gaseous state. (Do not confuse "ionizing poten-tial" with the "ionic potential" discussed in Chapter 6.) Naturally, the more tightly the valence electrons of an atom are held, the harder they will have to be hit by the bombarding stream of electrons to be knocked out of their atom, and the higher the voltage will have to be to give the bombarding particles the necessary energy. Conversely, only a low voltage will be required to remove an electron which is not strongly attracted to the atomic nucleus. The physical laws of attraction tell us that the attraction between two masses, whether they be charged or uncharged, varies inversely with the square of the distance between them; hence, it follows that an electron in an outer level of an atom of large radius is more easily removed than is an electron in an atom of comparable nuclear charge but of small radius.

Table 4 reveals that sodium has the largest atomic radius of any of the active elements of the third period, and hence should have the lowest ionizing

Table 5

IONIZING POTENTIALS (IN VOLTS) OF THE ELEMENTS OF PERIOD III (REMOVAL OF ONE ELECTRON)

Na	Mg	Al	Si	P	S	Cl
5.12	7.61	5.96	8.12	10.9	10.30	12.95

potential. This it has, as can be seen from Table 5. Furthermore, since all of the other elements of period three have to lose more than one electron to attain

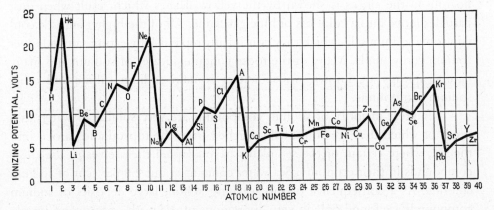

THE IONIZING POTENTIALS OF THE FIRST 40 ELEMENTS PLOTTED AGAINST THE ATOMIC NUMBER.
Note the repetitive pattern.

an inert gas structure, sodium again requires less energy to become an ion than they do. The ionizing potential of sodium is 5.12 v. (volts). Numerical values of the ionizing potentials of a majority of the other elements are tabulated in the succeeding chapters in which the various periodic families are discussed.

The foregoing considerations show that sodium will be the most active electron-loser of period three, and that, as a consequence of the ease with which it loses electrons, it will enter readily, even violently, into reactions in which it may lose its one outermost electron.

This change may be represented by the equation:

$$Na_{(g)} + energy \rightleftarrows Na_{(g)}^+ + \epsilon$$

where the symbol (g) indicates the gaseous state, ϵ stands for an electron, and the backward-pointing arrow indicates that when the source of energy is removed the electron may recombine with the sodium ion to form the neutral sodium atom with the liberation of a quantity of energy equal to that required to bring about the forward process.

The ionizing potentials of various elements thus serve as a means of comparing their relative chemical activities.

5. The Natural Occurrence of Sodium

By *occurrence* of an element is meant the state of combination in which it occurs and its distribution in nature. Sodium is so active that it is never found free in nature, but always in combination with other elements. Its compounds are so widely distributed that they are contained in even the tiny dust particles floating in the air, as is shown by the yellow flashes which result when dust particles move into a colorless or blue gas flame. All of the higher animals contain some sodium salts which they continually replenish by eating salt and other sodium compounds. Many of the rocks contain silicates of sodium and many natural springs are known whose waters contain sodium sulfate and other sodium compounds.

The great majority of sodium compounds are very soluble in water, as a result of which they are continually leached from the topsoil and carried into the sea, where certain of the sea plants have adapted themselves to use these compounds in their economy. Sea water contains about 2.8 per cent of sodium chloride. As a consequence of this leaching action, large deposits of sodium compounds are found only in very dry regions of the earth or at a considerable distance underground. The geologists tell us that practically all of these deposits have resulted from the drying up of inland seas whose waters were laden with sodium compounds. Some of these were subsequently covered by wind, earthquakes, and the operation of other natural phenomena.

In the very dry Atacama desert of northern Chile, there is an immense deposit of sodium nitrate ($NaNO_3$) which contains smaller quantities of other sodium salts. In the deserts of southern California there are deposits of sodium carbonate (Na_2CO_3), as there are also in the deserts of Egypt, which latter deposits were apparently being worked long before historical times. In Utah, salt ($NaCl$) is obtained commercially by the evaporation of the waters of the

Great Salt Lake, and there are salt industries in the states of Kansas, Louisiana, Michigan, Ohio, and New York. In fact, salt is widely distributed through the continents, with workable deposits found in many countries. These salt deposits constitute the principal source of sodium and sodium compounds.

A GREAT UNDERGROUND SALT MINE. Pillars of salt have been left to help support the ceiling. (Courtesy, International Salt Co., Inc.)

6. The Preparation of Sodium

Elementary sodium was unknown until 1807, when the English chemist, Sir Humphry Davy, first obtained it by decomposing molten sodium hydroxide (NaOH) by means of an electric current. Since sodium goes into combination with other substances so actively, it stands to reason that it will not easily forsake those combinations to go back into its elementary state. More exactly, since sodium liberates large quantities of energy as heat when it combines, to decompose its compounds large quantities of energy must be poured back into them. No sufficient source of energy was available until the discovery of electricity was made. Other methods of preparing the metal have been discovered since, but electrolysis is still the most commonly used method. (*Electrolysis* is the name applied to any reaction brought about by use of an electric current.)

Sodium may be prepared by the electrolysis of molten sodium chloride. The anode (positive pole) of the electrolytic cell is usually made of carbon and

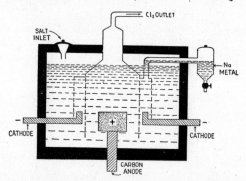

CROSS-SECTION OF THE DOWNS CELL USED FOR THE PRODUCTION OF METALLIC SODIUM. The cell is circular and the electrolyte is molten sodium chloride.

the cathode (negative pole) of iron. Chlorine gas, liberated at the anode, is led through a series of pipes to a compressor which forces it into steel cylinders for storage and shipment. Molten sodium collects at the cathode. Lighter than the molten salt, it rises to the top inside a special shield to protect it from air. Thence it overflows into a special container from which it is removed to be cast into bars. Because of its extreme reactivity, both with water and with oxygen, sodium has to be kept submerged in oil, with which it does not react. In the laboratory it is usually kept submerged in a tightly corked bottle of kerosene. Fortunately, its density is greater than that of kerosene. The melting point of sodium chloride is 805° C., but by the addition of small amounts of other compounds this figure is lowered to about 600° C., which temperature must be maintained throughout the electrolysis. Usually, small amounts of calcium are produced along with the sodium, but since the melting point of calcium is several hundred degrees higher than that of sodium, it solidifies first and can be strained out of the still molten sodium.

Sodium is also prepared by the electrolysis of molten sodium hydroxide. In this process, oxygen is liberated at the anode while both sodium and hydrogen are set free at the cathode. All three of these products are of commercial value, and the atmosphere of hydrogen around the molten metal helps protect it from the air. The hydrogen and oxygen are much less difficult to manage than is the hot chlorine of the other process, which is extremely reactive.

Upwards of 10,000 tons of sodium are produced annually in the United States in normal years. During times of war this figure is greatly exceeded.

7. *Chemical Properties*

Since sodium has only one electron to lose, and since this electron is so loosely held, it never shows any valence but $+1$ in its compounds, all of which are ionic. As a result of the extreme ease with which sodium loses its electron, it will react with a great variety of substances which are capable of accepting electrons. The reactions into which it can enter are of two types; namely, combination and displacement.

8. *Combination Reactions*

The best electron-acceptors are those elements whose atoms lack only a few electrons of having eight in their outermost levels. Such elements are those in the right side of the periodic chart, i.e., the nonmetals. It is with these elements that sodium combines most vigorously. As has been shown, the atoms with the largest atomic radii are the best electron-losers, hence the atoms with the smallest atomic radii must be the best electron-acceptors. By this standard, sodium should combine more readily with chlorine than with any other element of the third period, and more readily with fluorine than with any other element in the table, and such is the case. Spontaneous reactions which may be violent occur when sodium is placed in the presence of either of these gaseous nonmetals. The Second Law of Thermodynamics tells that spontaneous reactions proceed only in such a direction as will liberate energy, hence we should expect heat to develop when these reactions occur. Again such is the case. Large quantities of heat are set free and flames are usually developed.

$$2Na_{(s)} + Cl_{2(g)} \rightarrow 2NaCl_{(s)} + 195,800 \text{ cal.}$$

The symbols (s) and (g) are used here to denote solid and gas, respectively. With less willing electron-acceptors the quantities of heat liberated are smaller. The heat involved in the formation of one molecule of a given substance is known as its *molecular heat of formation*. The molecular heat of formation of sodium chloride would therefore be 195,800 / 2 or 97,900 cal.

Sodium combines with all of the other nonmetals save the inert gases. It even combines with hydrogen, but the two elements must be heated together to 400° C., or more, to effect the union. The sodium atom having a larger atomic radius than the hydrogen atom holds its electron less strongly and hence is able to force the hydrogen to accept it. The compound formed is sodium hydride, NaH, in which hydrogen is the negative ion as a result of its having attained the helium structure upon the addition of the extra electron. That the

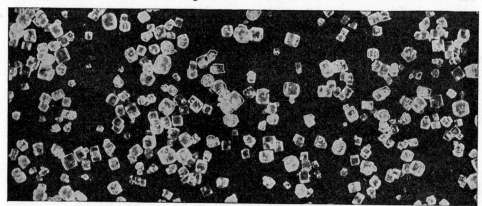

CUBIC CRYSTALS OF SODIUM CHLORIDE. (Courtesy, American Museum of Natural History.)

hydrogen really exists as a negative ion in this case can be shown by electrolyzing the molten sodium hydride whose hydrogen is set free at the anode rather than at the cathode, as is the case with most hydrogen compounds when so treated. A compound which is formed from elements both of whose atoms tend to lose electrons should not be expected to be stable—an expectation which might also be based upon the fact that heat was absorbed in the formation of the compound. This instability is readily exhibited when the hydride is placed in water with which it reacts to form sodium hydroxide and hydrogen according to the following equation:

$$NaH + HOH \rightarrow NaOH + H_2 \uparrow$$

Other combination reactions of sodium will be mentioned in later sections.

9. The Electrode Potential

When electrovalent compounds—i.e., those made up of ions of opposite charge—are dissolved in water, the individual ions are freed from the attractions of the other ions which held them in place in the solid and thus become free to move about independently in the solution. If, now, two metallic electrodes which are connected to the positive and negative terminals of a source of direct current are placed in the solution, the positive ions are attracted to the negative pole and the negative ions to the positive pole of this simple electro-

lytic cell, provided the difference in volt-age, or potential, between the electrodes and the solution is sufficiently large. This voltage varies for different ions, for solu-tions of different concentration of the same ions, and for the same solution of a given ion under different conditions. *The voltage required, however, to deposit electro-lytically a given ion at a specified concentration under specified conditions is known as the elec-trode potential of that ion.*

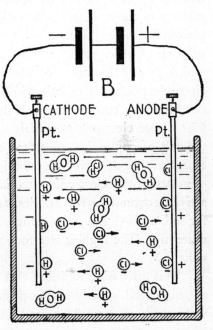

If positive ions of a given element are to be deposited as the free element on a cathode, it is evident that the ions must be converted back into atoms. Such ions were made by removing electrons from atoms, hence at the cathode electrons must be added to the ions to make them again into atoms. The electrons necessary for this purpose are taken from the cath-ode. Because positive ions are attracted to the cathode, they are often referred to as *cations*.

AN ELECTROLYTIC CELL. The small arrows indicate the direction of movement of the ions. (Courtesy, Foley, A. L.: "College Physics," 3d ed., Philadelphia, Pa., The Blakiston Company.)

At the same time that the cations are traveling to the negative pole, the negative ions, *anions*, are traveling to the positive pole, *anode*, where they give up to the anode their extra electrons which make them ions, thus being set free as atoms of the free element again. The electrons given up flow around through the outside circuit—i.e., the metallic conductor—to the cathode, where they are used to make atoms of the cations as they arrive there. It is because of this behavior that an ionic substance in solution, or in the molten or liquid condi-tion, is able to carry a current. Such substances are termed *electrolytes;* when an electrolyte conducts a current there is always a chemical reaction at each electrode as a result of which the electrolyte is eventually completely used up, or decomposed.

It is to be expected that an atom such as sodium, which easily loses electrons, will not take an electron back readily. In such a case, work has to be done to force the electron back into the atom. The voltage required to cause this electron to go back is proportional to the work done, and hence serves as a measure of the ease with which the electron is replaced. As a standard of comparison for the ease with which various ions in solution will accept electrons, a solution of hydrogen ions under certain specified conditions has been chosen arbitrarily and its electrode potential fixed by agreement as 0.00 volt. The electrode potentials of other ions have then been determined under similar conditions by comparison with the arbitrarily chosen hydrogen standard. All ions whose electrode potentials are greater than that of hydrogen are more difficult of conversion to atoms than is the hydrogen ion, and hence their atoms are more active electron-losers than is hydrogen. Conversely, those elements whose electrode potentials are less than that of hydrogen are more active electron-acceptors and less active electron-losers. The electrode potential for sodium is +2.71 volts, which, by comparison with the chosen standard, is quite high. The highest electrode potential is that of cesium, which is +3.02 volts.

This discussion indicates that ionizing potentials and electrode potentials are, in general, measures of opposing tendencies; the former measures the ease with which an atom becomes an ion, while the latter measures the ease with which an ion becomes an atom. In general, then, an element which has a high ionizing potential will have a low electrode potential, and *vice versa*. This comparison must not be made on the basis of the numerical values involved, however, without reference to their respective places in their respective series, for one set of measurements is made on material in the gaseous state, the other on material in liquid solution, and different standards of comparison are used in the two cases. An element which occupies a high place in one series will, however, occupy a correspondingly low place in the other.

10. *The Activity Series and Oxidation-reduction*

The elements arranged in order of decreasing electrode potentials are known as the *activity series* or as the *electromotive force series*. This series, then, has the most active electron-losers at its top and the most active electron-acceptors at its bottom. A comparison of the voltages listed for any two elements will serve to indicate the kind of behavior they will exhibit toward each other in solution and the degree of readiness with which such behavior will be exhibited. Theoretically, any element should be able to force any element below it in the series to accept electrons; actually, two such elements may have tendencies that are so nearly the same in kind and magnitude that under ordinary circumstances no such reaction will occur. By consulting the accompanying table,

Table 6

THE ACTIVITY SERIES

Reduced State	Oxidized State	Electrode Potential in Volts
Cs	Cs$^+$	+3.02
K	K$^+$	+2.92
Na	Na$^+$	+2.71
Ba	Ba^{++}	+2.90
Sr	Sr^{++}	+2.89
Ca	Ca^{++}	+2.87
Mg	Mg^{++}	+2.34
Al	Al^{+++}	+1.67
Be	Be^{++}	+1.70
Mn	Mn^{++}	+1.05
Zn	Zn^{++}	+0.76
Cr	Cr^{++}	+0.71
S^{--}	S	+0.51
Cd	Cd^{++}	+0.40
Fe	Fe^{++}	+0.44
Co	Co^{++}	+0.28
Ni	Ni^{++}	+0.25
Sn	Sn^{++}	+0.14
Pb	Pb^{++}	+0.13
H	H$^+$	0.00
Sb	Sb^{+++}	−0.10
Sn^{++}	Sn^{++++}	−0.15
Bi	Bi^{+++}	−0.20
As	As^{+++}	−0.30
Cu	Cu^{++}	−0.34
OH$^-$	O$_2$ + H$_2$O	−0.40
As^{+++}	As^{+++++}	−0.50
I$^-$	I$_2$	−0.53
Fe^{++}	Fe^{+++}	−0.75
Sb^{+++}	Sb^{+++++}	−0.75
Hg	Hg$^+$	−0.80
Ag	Ag$^+$	−0.80
Hg$^+$	Hg^{++}	−0.91
Br$^-$	Br$_2$	−1.06
Cl$^-$	Cl$_2$	−1.36
Au	Au$^+$	−1.68
F$^-$	F$_2$	−2.85

Left margin labels (vertical): *Increasing tendency to act as reducing agents* — *Increasing tendency to become oxidized* — *Not reduced by hydrogen* — *Reduced by hydrogen* — *Reduced by heat only*

Right margin labels (vertical): *Metals displace hydrogen from cold water* — *Metals displace hydrogen from steam* — *Metals react with acids to displace hydrogen* — *Metals react with oxygen to produce oxides* — *Metals form oxides indirectly* — *Increasing tendency to become reduced* — *Increasing tendency to act as oxidizing agents* it will be seen that all of the metals above hydrogen in the series displace hydrogen, but not from all hydrogen compounds under the same conditions.

Oxidation has been defined as the losing of electrons and reduction as the gaining of electrons. This statement means that at the head of the activity series are the elements which are most easily oxidized and are hence the best reducing agents. As one proceeds down the table, the elements show a greater tendency to go into the reduced state or less tendency to go into the oxidized state, hence the most easily reduced substances and therefore the best oxidizing agents are at the foot of the table. Consultation of the activity series shows clearly why the terms oxidizing agent and reducing agent are only relative. Hydrogen is below sodium in the series so it will oxidize sodium, forming sodium hydride,

$$2Na + H_2 \rightarrow 2NaH$$

but hydrogen will reduce chlorine (or chlorine will oxidize hydrogen) because chlorine is still lower in the series than hydrogen,

$$Cl_2 + H_2 \rightarrow 2HCl$$

A given substance thus is best said to be an oxidizing agent or a reducing agent only when the substance upon which it is to show such action is mentioned.

11. Displacement Reactions

Sodium stands high in the activity series and hence is capable of entering into many displacement reactions as well as into many combination reactions. The particles of matter are possessed neither of mind nor of moral sense, as a consequence of which the dominance of the strong over the weak and the active over the inactive is the rule. Because of its great activity, or its strong tendency to lose electrons, sodium is capable of displacing less active electron-losers from their compounds by forcing them to take the electrons it wishes to lose and thus become atoms again while it is converted simultaneously into its ions. When sodium metal is heated with zinc chloride the following reaction occurs:

$$2Na_{(s)} + ZnCl_{2(s)} \rightarrow 2NaCl_{(s)} + \underline{Zn_{(s)}}$$

Little use is made of most of these displacement reactions of sodium, though for several decades prior to the discovery of the Hall process for preparing aluminum this metal was made by displacement from its chloride by sodium:

$$AlCl_3 + 3Na \rightarrow Al + 3NaCl$$

A few of the rarer metals are still prepared by the reduction of their oxides or chlorides with sodium as the reducing agent. Sodium as a displacing agent is also used in the preparation of tetraethyllead, which is used as an anti-knock compound in gasoline.

The most important displacement reaction of sodium is with water. While water is on the whole a covalent compound, it does break up into a very, very few *hydrogen* and *hydroxyl* ions according to the following equation:

$$HOH \rightleftharpoons H^+ + OH^-$$

When sodium is dropped into water it displaces the hydrogen ions from the solution by forcing them to accept the electrons which the sodium atoms wish to lose:

$$2Na + 2H^+ + 2OH^- \rightarrow 2Na^+ + 2OH^- + H_2 \uparrow$$

The hydrogen gas escapes, leaving the Na^+ and OH^- ions in the solution. Before the addition of the sodium to the water, the latter will show no effect on litmus paper, but after the action of the sodium the solution will turn red litmus paper blue. If the remaining water be evaporated away, there remains a colorless solid of the formula NaOH, which is called sodium hydroxide. The heat developed by this reaction is often sufficient to cause the hydrogen being evolved to burst into flame. If sodium is dropped into hot water, or into hydrogen compounds which furnish more hydrogen ions than does water, or if the piece of sodium dropped into cold water is very large, the reaction may be violent, throwing out chemicals which burn the skin and eat holes in clothing. It is because of this reaction with water that sodium must be protected from the moisture of the air by being kept under kerosene.

Sodium dissolved in mercury so that its action will be less violent is often used in the laboratory to react with water or alcohol to liberate hydrogen in solutions where it is used as a reducing agent. It is also so used in the manufacture of certain medicinals, dyes, and compounds of considerable value.

Sodium does not displace most of the less active metals from solutions of their compounds in water, because most of these metals are more active than hydrogen. As a result, the sodium will displace the less active hydrogen from water before it will the more reactive metals from their salts. This, again, is an example of nature taking the course of least resistance.

12. Sodium Oxide and Peroxide

If sodium metal is subjected to a preliminary heating, it will combine vigorously with the oxygen of the air, liberating large quantities of heat:

$$4Na + O_2 \rightarrow 2Na_2O + 236,800 \text{ cal.}$$

Industrially, this reaction is carried on in an iron vessel which may be cooled with water and in which the intake of air may be controlled to prevent over-heating and to prevent the formation of sodium peroxide.

If the sodium oxide is warmed further in an excess of oxygen—preferably a stream of pure oxygen gas—a second compound of the formula Na_2O_2 is formed:

$$2Na_2O + O_2 \rightarrow 2Na_2O_2$$

This compound contains sodium, which appears to have an oxidation number of $+2$, $(2x - 4) = 0$, but this is only apparent since in this compound the oxygen atoms are sharing an electron with each other:

$$\text{Na} \circ \overset{..}{\text{O}} :$$
$$\text{Na} \circ \overset{..}{\underset{..}{\text{O}}} :$$

Compounds in which oxygen atoms are attached to each other in this fashion are known as *per-* compounds. Na_2O_2 is sodium peroxide.

Both sodium oxide and sodium peroxide react vigorously with water to form sodium hydroxide. The latter compound also liberates oxygen when it reacts with water. Because of this behavior, it is frequently used as an oxidizing agent as well as for the generating of small quantities of oxygen:

$$Na_2O + HOH \rightarrow 2NaOH \quad \text{and} \quad 2Na_2O_2 + 2HOH \rightarrow 4NaOH + O_2 \uparrow$$

A compound which reacts with water to form one new compound is known as the *anhydride* of the new compound, hence sodium oxide is the anhydride of sodium hydroxide. As will be shown in the next section, sodium hydroxide belongs to the class of compounds known as bases. For this reason, sodium oxide is known also as a *basic anhydride*.

13. *Sodium Hydroxide*

The hydroxide and the chloride of sodium are two of its most important compounds. Pure sodium hydroxide is a colorless solid which may be purchased in the form of sticks, pellets, or flakes. Its melting point is 318.4° C., and it dissolves readily in water with the evolution of large amounts of heat. It is *hygroscopic*—that is, when left exposed to the air it will absorb moisture. In a very few minutes pellets of the solid become wet, and if left exposed long enough they absorb sufficient water to dissolve themselves completely. The compound, when left exposed to the air, also reacts with the carbon dioxide

(CO_2) contained in the latter, to form sodium carbonate:

$$2NaOH + CO_2 \rightarrow Na_2CO_3 + H_2O$$

As a consequence of this behavior, sodium hydroxide is nearly always contaminated with sodium carbonate. Carbonate-free solutions may be prepared by dissolving the hydroxide in alcohol, in which the carbonate is not soluble, filtering, and diluting the alcoholic solution with distilled water. A second method involves the preparation of a concentrated aqueous solution of the hydroxide. The carbonate is not soluble in such a solution, and will gradually adhere to the walls of the containing vessel. Eventually, the concentrated solution may be poured off and diluted.

In aqueous solution, sodium hydroxide has a bitter taste, a soapy feel, and the ability to turn red litmus paper blue. These properties all result from the ionization of the compound which produces sodium ions and hydroxyl ions, and are characteristic of the hydroxyl ion:

$$NaOH_{(s)} \rightarrow Na^+ + OH^-_{(in\ sol.)}$$

Compounds which have such properties are known as *bases*, and those which possess them to a marked degree like sodium hydroxide are called *alkalies*. A shortening of the term alkali gives rise to the name *lye*, by which the housewife knows sodium hydroxide; commercially, it is known as *caustic soda*. Alkalies are very active chemicals which will attack a wide variety of materials, including clothing and skin. They cause painful burns which are difficult to heal.

14. The Preparation of Sodium Hydroxide

Because sodium hydroxide is used in large quantities in many industries, it is prepared commercially in large quantities. Two processes are used mainly: the lime-soda process and the electrolytic process.

The lime-soda process is much the older of the two processes, having been used by the ancient Egyptians long before the Christian era. It consists of heating a slight excess of slaked lime, calcium hydroxide, with a 20 per cent solution of sodium carbonate

$$Na_2CO_3 + Ca(OH)_2 \rightarrow 2NaOH + \underline{CaCO_3}$$

The calcium carbonate forms as a solid. Solids which are formed as a result of reactions which occur in solution are called *precipitates*. The precipitate of calcium carbonate is allowed to settle to the bottom of the container; the solution of sodium hydroxide is drawn off; the precipitate is washed to remove further sodium hydroxide; and the aqueous solutions are combined and evaporated to give the commercial caustic.

The above reaction introduces the fourth type of chemical reaction. The equation shows that the positive sodium and calcium ions have simply exchanged partners. Such reactions are called *metatheses*, or *double decompositions*, and are a characteristic behavior of ionic compounds. A more complete discussion of metatheses will be given in Chapter 17. It may be noted in this connection that solutions of sodium hydroxide react by metathesis with solutions containing ions of the heavy metals to precipitate the insoluble hydroxides of these metals:

$$Cu^{++} + 2NaOH \rightarrow 2Na^+ + \underline{Cu(OH)_2}$$

The *electrolytic* process for the manufacture of soda lye is, in its essence, the electrolytic decomposition of brine, a strong solution of sodium chloride in water. Such a solution contains high concentrations of sodium and chloride ions from the salt and low concentrations of hydrogen and hydroxyl ions from the water:

$$NaCl_{(s)} \rightarrow Na^+ + Cl^-_{(in\ sol.)};$$
$$H_2O \rightleftharpoons H^+ + OH^-$$

When electrodes are placed in this solution and the current turned on, the activity series table indicates that hydrogen will be discharged at the cathode in preference to the more active sodium. From the activity series it would appear that oxygen rather than chlorine would be liberated at the anode, since the OH^- ion requires a lower voltage for its displacement than does the chloride ion. This will be the case for solutions whose concentration of sodium chloride is low, but for more concentrated solutions chlorine is liberated in preference to oxygen. As a consequence of this action, the solution in the cell becomes a solution of sodium hydroxide due to the sodium and hydroxyl ions which are left behind when the hydrogen and chloride ions are removed. The overall equation for this reaction is:

$$2NaCl + 2H_2O \rightarrow 2NaOH + H_2\uparrow + Cl_2\uparrow$$

When all of the chloride ions have been removed, the aqueous solution is evaporated to obtain the solid sodium hydroxide. The chlorine and hydrogen gases which are evolved are collected and compressed into steel cylinders since they are both in demand commercially.

From a practical standpoint, the design of the electrolytic cell used in this process is of the greatest importance. It must be constructed so that the two gases which are produced do not mix with each other; so that the chlorine gas produced does not have opportunity to recombine with the sodium hydroxide solution; and so that the portion of the solution in which the sodium hydroxide concentration has reached the proper value may be withdrawn from the solution

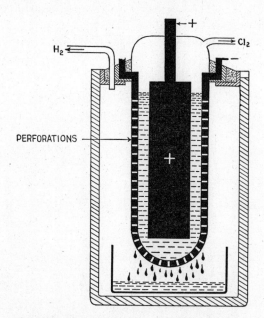

CROSS-SECTION OF THE NELSON CELL USED FOR THE COMMERCIAL PREPARATION OF SODIUM HYDROXIDE. Brine is electrolyzed and hydrogen and chlorine are produced as by-products. The solution of sodium hydroxide passes through an asbestos sheet supported by the perforated cathode and is collected in the bottom of the cell.

which still contains chloride ions. Several cleverly designed cells are in use commercially. Among these are the Nelson cell, the Castner cell, the Whiting cell, the Vorce cell, etc. Students who are interested in the details of construction and operation of these various cells are referred to the various comprehensive texts of industrial chemistry.

The cost of operation of the electrolytic process is greater than that of the soda-lime process, but the value of the by-products of the former process helps to make it profitable. Cheaper electric power is another factor in increasing its use.

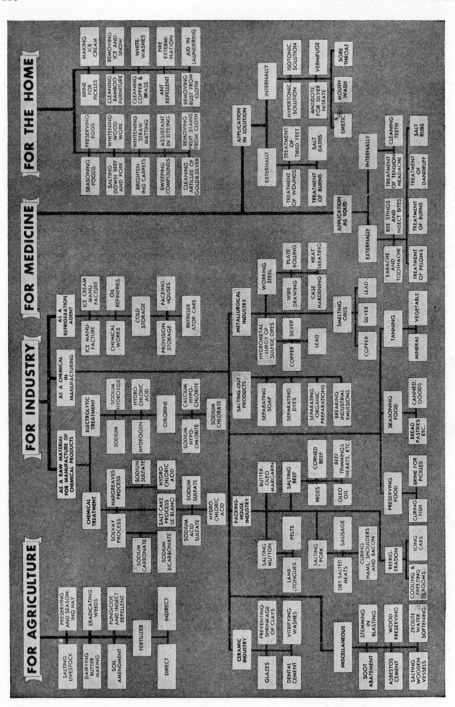

The Uses of Sodium Chloride. (Courtesy, International Salt Co., Inc.)

15. *The Uses of Sodium and Its Important Compounds*

Sodium metal is used as a reducing agent. It is also used in the laboratory for removing water and alcohol from covalent compounds with which it does not react. Industrially, it is used in the production of synthetic rubber and other polymeric compounds. It is also used in the preparation of sodium oxide, sodium peroxide, sodium cyanide, tetraethyllead, and certain bearing metal alloys. It finds further use for the removal of air bubbles from mixtures of molten metals in the preparation of light metal alloys and in the manufacture of sodium vapor electric lamps which are used for the lighting of bridges and highways.

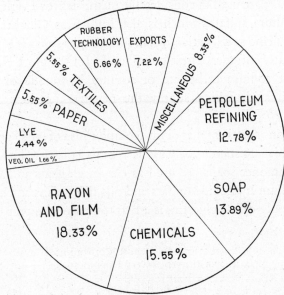

DISTRIBUTION BY USES OF THE DOMESTIC PRODUCTION OF
SODIUM HYDROXIDE.

Sodium chloride is of first importance as the naturally occurring substance from which most other sodium compounds and a number of chlorine compounds are prepared. Besides this use and its household uses, sodium chloride finds a host of other uses which are too numerous to be listed here.

Sodium hydroxide is used in great quantities for the manufacture of rayon and other fibers, for the manufacture of a wide variety of chemicals, for the manufacture of soap, for the refining of petroleum products, for the manufacture of pulp and paper, for the reclaiming of rubber, and for many lesser uses.

Sodium carbonate (Na_2CO_3) and sodium bicarbonate ($NaHCO_3$) are used in great quantities. Among processes which use them are, for the former, the manufacture of glass, chemicals, soap, cleaners, water softeners, paper, etc.; for the latter, the manufacture of sodium carbonate and chemicals, the baking of bread, medicinal uses, and a host of household uses. Sodium bicarbonate is known to the housewife as baking soda, while the carbonate is known to her as washing soda. Some of the carbonate is obtained from natural deposits, but the major quantity of both of these compounds is manufactured by processes which will be discussed later.

Sodium nitrate, sodium sulfate, sodium phosphate, and a number of other sodium compounds are used in considerable quantities for a variety of purposes. For instance, sodium sulfate, which is also known as Glauber's salt, is used somewhat in medicine as a laxative, while sodium phosphate (Na_3PO_4) is often employed as a water softener. These compounds, for the most part, are made by the treatment of sodium carbonate or sodium hydroxide or other sodium compounds with acids which supply the negative portions of the desired compounds.

The common soaps are sodium compounds of the general formula RCOONa, in which R stands for various groups composed of hydrogen and carbon. The commoner soaps are used as cleaning agents and are prepared by the action of sodium hydroxide on fats and oils from plant and animal sources. Glycerol, commonly called glycerin, is a by-product of the preparation of soap.

Table 7

PRODUCTION OF SODIUM COMPOUNDS
IN THE UNITED STATES DURING 1938

	Tons
Chloride	9,000,000
Carbonate	2,800,000
Hydroxide	900,000
Bicarbonate	140,000
Phosphate	125,000
Nitrate	3,000

16. Analytical Tests

The great majority of sodium compounds are very soluble in water. This property, which accounts in part for the wide usefulness of these compounds, renders testing for them rather difficult, since one of the commonest methods of establishing the presence of a given element is to precipitate from solution some characteristic insoluble compound of the element. Among the least soluble salts of sodium is its orthoantimoniate ($Na[Sb(OH)_6]$) which can be precipitated from moderately concentrated solutions of sodium salts by the addition of a solution of potassium orthoantimoniate:

$$K[Sb(OH)_6] + Na^+ \rightarrow \underline{Na[Sb(OH)_6]} + K^+$$

Fortunately, however, a precipitation test is not necessary for sodium, since it and its compounds, even in minute traces, color the bluish gas flame a bright yellow. A clean platinum wire dipped in a solution of a sodium compound, then held in the flame, will impart a bright orange-yellow color to it. Since sodium is present in traces in nearly everything and since this test is capable of detecting as little as 10^{-10} g. of the element, the brilliance of the flame and its duration must be taken into account in reporting the findings of such a test. The color imparted to the flame by sodium results from the fact that the electron of sodium is so loosely held that even the relatively low energy of the burner flame is sufficient to excite the atom. When the excited electrons return to their normal levels, electromagnetic waves of the characteristic wavelength are emitted.

(*See Appendix for Exercises*)

COLLATERAL READINGS

Creighton and Koehler: *Electrochemistry*, Vol. II, New York, John Wiley & Sons, Inc., 1944.

Davy: *The Decomposition of Fixed Alkalies and Alkaline Earths*, Chicago, University of Chicago Press, 1928.

Furnas: *Roger's Industrial Chemistry*, Vol. I, New York, D. Van Nostrand Co., 1943.

Hansley and Carlisle: The production of sodium hydride and some of its reactions, *Chem. & Eng. News*, **23,** 1332 (1945).

Latimer and Hildebrand: *Reference Book of Inorganic Chemistry*, New York, The Macmillan Co., 1941.

Sadtler: *Chemistry of Familiar Things*, Philadelphia, J. B. Lippincott Co., 1937.

Weeks: *Discovery of the Elements*, 5th ed., Mack Printing Co., 1945.

Chemistry in Industry, Chemical Foundation.

FRANCIS WILLIAM ASTON
(*1877–1945, English*)

Aston was another physicist whose scientific contributions, while physical in nature, have been of great importance in the field of chemistry. The most notable of his contributions was the invention of the device known as the *mass-spectrograph*, by whose use he was able to resolve isotopic mixtures, thus establishing that most of the elements as commonly known are not made up of atoms of a single species but are mixtures of atoms whose chemical properties are identical but whose masses are different. For this achievement he was awarded the Nobel Prize in chemistry in 1922.

8

Mass Relationships

1. Stoichiometry

Thus far, our discussions have concerned the nature of matter and the nature of chemical reactions. In this chapter it shall be our purpose to consider the mass relationships which exist in chemical changes. The study of chemical changes from the quantitative standpoint is known as *stoichiometry*, and from such studies have come the data upon which most of our modern theories of chemical science are based.

2. The Conservation of Mass

The most fundamental of all the laws governing the behavior of mass, or of matter, is the statement that *matter can be neither created nor destroyed*. This generalization is known as the *law of the conservation of mass, or matter*. Early scientific workers assumed that this law existed, but later workers have proved its existence. Landolt in 1908 and Manley in 1913 established the law, in so far as chemical changes are concerned, by a series of reactions which they carried out in sealed tubes. The tubes were weighed both before and after the reactions had occurred, and no differences of mass were noted within the limits of accuracy of the most sensitive balances used.

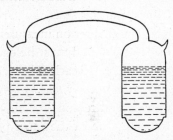

DIAGRAM OF THE APPARATUS USED FOR THE DEMONSTRATION OF THE VALIDITY OF THE LAW OF THE CONSERVATION OF MASS FOR ORDINARY CHEMICAL REACTIONS.

This law means simply that for any specified quantity of reagents taking part in a reaction, an equal quantity of products must be obtained.

As mentioned above, it is now believed that mass and energy are interconvertible. In chemical reactions, however, the quantities of energy involved are so small in comparison with the quantities of matter taking part in the reactions that no changes in mass are detectable. Thus, for all chemical reactions the law of the conservation of mass holds perfectly, and even in those subatomic changes in which there is a slight diminution of mass, this mass is not exactly lost since it continues to exist as energy.

It is the law of the conservation of mass which makes possible the writing of chemical equations. If matter were destroyed during a reaction, then it would not be possible to say that a given number of molecules of reagent would produce a specific number of molecules of products which bear a definite mass relationship to each other.

3. Relative Atomic Weights

The early chemists were quick to realize that, since all matter is made up of a relatively small number of different kinds of atoms, if they would understand the mass relationships involved in chemical compounds and chemical changes they must know the weights of these various constituent atoms. In the early days of chemistry, no means were available for determining the exact mass of an object so small as even the largest atom, but means were available for determining the relationships which existed between the masses of the known atoms. The great analytical chemists were the men who established these relationships as a result of much painstaking laboratory work; outstanding among these men are Berzelius of Sweden, Stas of Belgium, and Richards of the United States.

The chapter on measurement showed that, whenever a comparison is to be made, a standard must be chosen. For the purpose of comparing the masses of the atoms with each other, *the standard chosen was the oxygen atom to which was assigned arbitrarily and by agreement a mass of 16.0000 atomic weight units.* There were several reasons for choosing oxygen and for assigning to it a weight of 16.0000. One of the most practical of these reasons was that by so doing the hydrogen atom, the lightest atom, would have a weight of approximately 1 unit, since its mass is about one-sixteenth that of the oxygen atom. On the basis of this standard, the atomic weights of the atoms expressed in atomic weight units have been worked out. For instance, since the sulfur atom weighs approximately twice as much as the oxygen atom, its weight would be 2×16 or 32 (approximately)—the exact value is 32.06.

At the present time, the weights of individual atoms are known in terms of grams, but since these weights are so very small, as will be shown later, it is more convenient to use the older relative atomic weights which are expressed in numbers greater than one. It is these relative atomic weights which are commonly given on periodic charts and in tables of atomic weights.

4. Gram-atomic Weights

It is convenient to speak of the atom in theoretical considerations, but in the case of actual manipulation in the laboratory the atom is far too small to be used. Even the tiniest quantity of an elementary material which might conveniently be used in the laboratory contains billions of atoms, hence for practical purposes it is necessary to establish the term *gram-atomic weight* or *gram-atom*. The gram-atom is sufficient of an element to weigh as many grams as there are units in its relative atomic weight. Thus, the gram-atom of oxygen is 16.0000 g. of oxygen, the gram-atom of carbon is 12.00 g. of carbon, and the gram-atom of sulfur is 32.06 g. of sulfur.

The gram-atom is used so much in practical work that, in addition to the other meanings already cited for the symbol, it has come to represent also one gram-atom of the element for which it stands.

5. *Mass Relationships in Chemical Compounds*

It is now necessary to recall two of the characteristics of atoms which were discussed in previous chapters. In Chapter 4, it was pointed out that all the atoms of some elements are of the same mass, while other elements have atoms of two or more different masses (isotopes) but in such naturally occurring proportions that the average mass of the atoms of any given isotopic element is always the same. *The average weight, then, of the atoms of any element is always a constant.*

We know that the atoms of two elements will always combine in definite ratios, which are determined by the electronic configurations of the atoms in question. For instance, one atom of sodium always combines with one atom of chlorine, never with two or three, while one atom of magnesium always combines with two atoms of chlorine.

THE LAW OF DEFINITE PROPORTIONS. The atoms of a given element always have the same average weight, and the pattern which the atoms of two elements may follow in forming a given compound is limited by the electronic configurations of the two kinds of atoms. From this it follows that the weight relationship of the elements in a given compound should be constant. Because the same atoms always combine in a fixed pattern to give a certain compound, it may be said that a fixed mass of sodium hydride will always yield by reaction with water a certain definite mass of sodium hydroxide.

As a consequence of these two characteristics of atoms, it follows that a given compound will always be composed of the same elements whose atoms will bear a fixed numerical relationship to each other, and that the elements in the compound will bear a definite weight relationship to each other. This statement combines *the law of constant composition* and the *law of definite proportions; a given compound always contains the same elements in the same ratio by weight.*

Sodium chloride always contains sodium and chlorine atoms in the ratio of 1:1. The sodium atom weighs 22.997 at. wt. units; the chlorine atom weighs 35.457 at. wt. units; therefore, according to the law of the conservation of mass, the sodium chloride molecule weighs 22.997 + 35.457 or 58.454 at. wt. units, and 22.997/58.454 or 39.3 per cent of salt will always be sodium and 35.457/58.454 or 60.7 per cent of salt will always be chlorine. Synthesis and analysis confirms this statement.

6. The Law of Multiple Proportions

It was previously shown that sodium and oxygen form two different compounds. Sodium oxide, Na_2O, contains approximately 46 units of sodium to 16 units of oxygen, while sodium peroxide, Na_2O_2, contains approximately 46 units of sodium to 32 units of oxygen. In both instances, the weight of sodium is the same but the weights of oxygen (16 and 32) stand to each other in the ratio of 1:2.

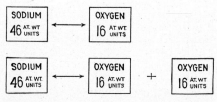

There are many pairs of elements which form more than one compound. In general, two elements will react in such a fashion as to permit each element to attain the greatest stability, but sometimes, as a result of the conditions under which the reaction occurs, compounds of intermediate stability will result rather than the compound of greatest stability. *In all such series of compounds formed by pairs of elements, it is found that for a fixed weight of one of the elements the weights of the second element will stand to each other in the ratio of small whole numbers.* This is *the law of multiple proportions.* It should be noted that the ratio exists between the weights of *one* of the elements. This relationship should be expected by the student, for it is a direct result of the fact that only whole atoms may take part in reactions.

THE LAW OF MULTIPLE PROPORTIONS. Despite the fact that the masses of the sodium and oxygen atoms are 46 and 16, respectively, the reactions between these atoms occur between whole numbers of atoms and hence the relationship is one of small whole numbers, and for a fixed mass of one of the elements the masses of the other element will stand to each other in a ratio of small whole numbers.

The chlorides of phosphorus show this relationship well:

PCl_3 31.02 at. wt. units of phosphorus; 3(35.457) at. wt. units of chlorine
PCl_5 31.02 at. wt. units of phosphorus; 5(35.457) at. wt. units of chlorine

Thus for a fixed weight of phosphorus the weights of chlorine stand to each other in the ratio of $3:5$ as a result of the existence in the two compounds of whole numbers of atoms.

7. The Derivation of a Formula

The formulas of many chemical compounds are now known. These formulas represent a great amount of work by chemists. The same type of work must be performed upon each new compound that is discovered so that its formula may be made available to all who may be interested. To establish the formula of a compound, the chemist must have the following pieces of information: (a) A knowledge of the elements present in the compound, (b) the percentage of each element in the compound, (c) the molecular weight of the compound, and (d) the atomic weight of each element present.

The first three of these pieces of information are obtained by laboratory work—the first by the use of the principles of qualitative analysis, the second by the use of the principles of quantitative analysis, and the third by the actual measurement of molecular weights using methods to be discussed in succeeding chapters. The fourth bit of information is obtained from a chart whose values were determined by actual laboratory work.

Suppose that by laboratory work the following information has been derived: (a) The compound contains 79.87 per cent of carbon and 20.13 per cent of hydrogen, and (b) the molecular weight of the compound is 30.05 at. wt. units.

The procedure for calculating the formula from such data is: (a) Divide each percentage by the atomic weight of that element. (b) Reduce the ratio of numbers obtained to the ratio of small whole numbers thus obtaining the atomic ratios in the molecule. (c) Select the multiple of this ratio whose weight corresponds to the determined molecular weight. This is the correct molecular formula. Applying these steps to the data obtained above,

(a) $79.87 / 12.00 = 6.65$ $20.13 / 1.008 = 19.97$

(b) $6.65 : 19.97 = 1 : 3$, therefore the simplest formula is CH_3

(c) the weight of CH_3 is $12 + 3(1.008)$ or 15.024, but the determined molecular weight is 30.05

therefore the formula must be C_2H_6. The ratio obtained in step *a* must be reduced to a ratio of small whole numbers in step *b* because molecules contain only whole numbers of atoms. This reduction is usually most easily effected by dividing all the numbers of the ratio by the smallest number, after which operation a ratio of small whole numbers usually may be obtained by inspection.

A second example of such a calculation is given below for emphasis. A certain compound contains 32.38 per cent of sodium, 22.57 per cent of sulfur, and 45.05 per cent of oxygen, and its molecular weight is 142.06. What is the formula of the compound?

(a) $32.38 / 23 = 1.41$ (b) $1.41 / 0.705 = 2$

$22.57 / 32.06 = 0.705$ $0.705 / 0.705 = 1$

$45.05 / 16 = 2.815$ $2.815 / 0.705 = 4$

(c) Na_2SO_4 is the formula, since the determined molecular weight corresponds to the weight of the simplest formula.

8. Gram-molecules

Just as a gram-atomic weight of an element is that quantity of it whose weight in grams is equal numerically to its atomic weight as expressed in atomic weight units, so a *gram-molecular weight* is that quantity of a substance whose weight in grams is numerically equal to its molecular weight as expressed in atomic weight units. The gram-molecular weight is also known as a *gram-molecule*, but it is more often referred to simply as a *mole*. The gram-molecule of sodium sulfate is 142.06 g. of that substance. The mole of methane (CH_4) is 16 g. This quantity, like the gram-atom, is used a great deal in practical chemical work.

9. Calculation of Reacting Proportions

The calculation which the chemist makes more often than any other is that of the mass relationship existing between the quantities of reactants and products. Such calculations are possible only when the chemical relationship between the various components of a reaction are known. There are two common methods of making such calculations.

A. THE EQUATION METHOD. Suppose that it is desired to know the quantity of sodium hydroxide which can be prepared by the action of 1 g. of sodium metal on water. It is much easier to calculate the answer to this problem than it is to go into the laboratory and prepare the sodium hydroxide and weigh it; in calculating such a problem, however, one is using information which other laboratory chemists have supplied.

To solve this problem by the equation method, one writes first the equation for the reaction:

$$2Na + 2HOH \rightarrow 2NaOH + H_2 \uparrow$$

By reference to the table of atomic weights it is possible to calculate the molecular weights of the substances represented in the equation, and by the use of the molecular weights and the coefficients employed in balancing the equation it is possible to arrive at the weight relationships which exist between the reagents and the products of the reaction. Thus,

$$2(23) + 2(18) \rightarrow 2(40) + 2$$
$$2Na + 2HOH \rightarrow 2NaOH + H_2,$$

using approximations of the atomic weights to facilitate calculation in the example. It is seen from this use of weights that 46 units (or grams, if one thinks in terms of gram-atoms and gram-molecules) will react with 36 units, or grams, of water to produce 80 units, or grams, of sodium hydroxide and 2 units, or grams, of hydrogen. To solve the stated problem, one may now say that if 46 g. of sodium will produce 80 g. of sodium hydroxide, then 1 g. of sodium will produce a proportionate quantity of sodium hydroxide. Problems of this type may be solved by means of ratio and proportion with x or some other letter standing for the anticipated unknown result, or they may be solved by simple arithmetic.

By proportion:

$$\underset{2Na}{\overset{46 \text{ g.}}{}} + 2HOH \rightarrow \underset{2NaOH}{\overset{80 \text{ g.}}{}} + H_2 \uparrow$$
$$1 \text{ g.} \qquad\qquad x \text{ g.}$$

whence $46 x = 80$ g. and $x = 80 / 46$ g. or $x = 1.74$ g.

This solution demonstrates that only the weights of the substances involved in the problem need be set down.

For a second example, take the problem: how many grams of oxygen will be required to react with 5 g. of sodium and how much sodium peroxide will be produced if all the sodium is converted to that compound?

$$\underset{2Na}{\overset{46 \text{ g.}}{}} + \underset{O_2}{\overset{32 \text{ g.}}{}} \rightarrow \underset{Na_2O_2}{\overset{78 \text{ g.}}{}}$$
$$5 \text{ g.} \quad x \text{ g.} \quad y \text{ g.}$$

$$46 x = 5(32)$$
$$x = 160 / 46$$
$$x = 3.48 \text{ g. of oxygen required}$$

$$46 y = 5(78)$$
$$y = 390 / 46$$
$$y = 8.48 \text{ g. of } Na_2O_2 \text{ produced}$$

Five grams of sodium and 3.48 g. of oxygen should yield 8.48 g. of product, which is the case in the above calculation. These calculations are in agreement with the operation of the law of the conservation of mass.

B. THE FACTOR METHOD. The equation method is much the safer and more apparent method for beginners in chemical work, but for those who have acquired a fair knowledge of chemical reactions, the factor method is, in general, more satisfactory because it is quicker while equally accurate. The factor method involves the use of the formulas of only the known and unknown substances mentioned in the problem. Thus, in the first example given above, one would use only the formulas of sodium and sodium hydroxide. The formula of the substance of known quantity is written as the denominator of a fraction; the formula of the substance of unknown quantity is written as the numerator of the fraction. In the original example, one would then have $NaOH/Na$. This factor must next be balanced; in this case, however, the factor is already balanced because a knowledge of this reaction tells the experienced student of chemistry that all of the sodium in this reaction is converted to sodium hydroxide and common sense advises that in such a case surely one atom of sodium produces one molecule of sodium hydroxide which contains but one atom of sodium to the molecule. Next the weights corresponding to these formulas are used in a similar fraction, and lastly the known and unknown weights of the problem are combined in a similar fraction which is set equal to the fraction obtained from the factor; thus,

$$NaOH/Na = 40/23 = x/1, \text{ whence } x = 1(40/23) \text{ or } 1.74 \text{ g.}$$

a value which is in agreement with the value obtained by the equation method. The immediately foregoing calculations show that, if the factor is set up according to the specified convention, the solution is obtained by multiplying the numerical value of the factor by the known quantity of the problem. The speed of the method is evident, but the need for a knowledge of chemical behavior is equally obvious.

Solving the second example given above by this method, one has

$$O_2/2Na = 32/46 = x/5 \text{ or } x = 5(32/46), \text{ whence } x = 3.48 \text{ g.}$$

and

$$Na_2O_2/2Na = 78/46 = y/5 \text{ or } y = 5(78/46), \text{ whence } y = 8.48 \text{ g.}$$

In these examples, the need for balancing the factor is better demonstrated.

To prepare one mole of Na_2O_2, surely two Na atoms are required for each O_2 molecule.

10. Avogadro's Number

When one takes a gram-atomic weight of an element, he is taking a quantity of the element which contains a great many individual atoms. Since the atoms of each element are all of the same average atomic weight, and since the gram-atomic weight is directly proportional to the average atomic weight, it can be seen that in the gram-atomic weight of any element there is exactly the same number of atoms that is contained in the gram-atomic weight of any, and every, other element.

By similar reasoning, this number is the same as the number of molecules in a gram-molecular weight of any substance which exists in the molecular condition.

As a mark of honor to the Italian scientist, Avogadro, this number (usually represented by the letter N) is known as *Avogadro's number*, although the numerical value of N was not known in Avogadro's day. It is only within relatively recent years that this value has been determined. There are several ways of arriving at this value; one of the simplest is as follows: In 1833 the English scientist, Michael Faraday, discovered that the quantity of an element liberated by electrolysis is proportional to the quantity of electricity passed through the material which contains that element. By experimentation it was found, for instance, that one gram-atomic weight of sodium, approximately 23 g., was liberated from molten sodium chloride by the passage of 96,500 coulombs of electricity. (A *coulomb* is an ampere-second. A current of 5 amp. acting for 10 sec. would produce 5×10 or 50 coulombs of electricity.) Now, to convert one sodium ion, Na^+, into a sodium atom, one electron must be added to the ion. The charge on an electron as determined by Millikan is 1.59×10^{-19} coulombs. If one now divides the number of coulombs required to put one electron on every atom in a gram-atomic weight of sodium by the coulombic value of one electron, the number of atoms receiving an electron will be given. This number as so determined is 6.06×10^{23}.

$$N = 96{,}500 \big/ 1.59 \times 10^{-19} = 6.06 \times 10^{23}*$$

* Very large and very small numbers are most conveniently expressed as powers of 10. Thus, 200 is $2 \times 10 \times 10$ or 2×10^2, and 4.5×10^4 is $4.5 \times 10 \times 10 \times 10 \times 10$ or 45,000; this latter number could also be expressed as 45×10^3 or 0.45×10^5. The number 0.00034 is best expressed as 34×10^{-5} or 3.4×10^{-4}. These numbers are derived from 34 divided by 10^5 and 3.4 divided by 10^4, respectively. It is much more convenient to write 6.023×10^{23} than it is to write 602,300,000,000,000,000,000,000. To multiply exponential numbers, one multiplies the coefficients and adds the exponents, thus:

More accurate determinations of the numerical value of Avogadro's number made recently, and by other methods than that given above, reveal its value to be 6.023×10^{23}. The student should add this figure to his supply of working information, since it represents the number of atoms of an element in a gram-atomic weight of that element and the number of molecules in a mole of any substance.

11. Absolute Atomic Weights

Once Avogadro's number has been determined, it is very easy to calculate the average mass of the atoms of any element. To do this, one simply divides the gram-atomic weight by 6.023×10^{23}. Such calculations reveal that the hydrogen atom has a mass of 1.67×10^{-24} g., the oxygen atom a mass of 26.5×10^{-24} g., and the sodium atom a mass of 37.9×10^{-24} g. The smallness of these values is one of the principal reasons for the continued use of relative atomic weights in preference to absolute atomic weights in all ordinary chemical work.

12. Equivalent Weights of Elements

The number of atoms of one variety which will react with one atom of another variety is determined by the valences of the two varieties of atoms, that is, upon the number of electrons which each must lose, gain, or share. For instance, when the sodium atom reacts with the chlorine atom, it loses one electron while the latter gains one electron. These two atoms are equivalent to each other in reactive power because the reaction of each involves only one electron. Since the gram-atomic weights of elements are directly proportional

$$(4 \times 10^6) \times (3 \times 10^3) = 12 \times 10^9$$
$$(4 \times 10^6) \times (2 \times 10^{-4}) = 8 \times 10^2, \text{ and}$$
$$(3 \times 10^{-3}) \times (5 \times 10^{-2}) = 15 \times 10^{-5}$$

To divide exponential numbers, one divides the coefficients and subtracts the exponents, thus:

$$(12 \times 10^7) \div (6 \times 10^3) = 2 \times 10^4$$
$$(12 \times 10^7) \div (4 \times 10^{-4}) = 3 \times 10^{11}, \text{ and}$$
$$(8 \times 10^{-5}) \div (4 \times 10^{-3}) = 2 \times 10^{-2}$$

To add and subtract exponential numbers, the numbers must first be converted to the same powers of the base, in this case to the same powers of 10. The coefficients are then added or subtracted in the usual manner, and the result is expressed in terms of the same power of the base.

$$(1.8 \times 10^4) + (2.2 \times 10^5) = (1.8 \times 10^4) + (22 \times 10^4) = 23.8 \times 10^4$$
$$(1.6 \times 10^3 + 3.2 \times 10^2) - 80 \times 10^{-1} = (16 \times 10^2 + 3.2 \times 10^2) - 0.08 \times 10^2$$
$$= 19.2 \times 10^2 - 0.08 \times 10^2 = 19.12 \times 10^2$$

to their atomic weights, 22.997 g. of sodium is equivalent in reactive power to 35.457 g. of chlorine. When the magnesium atom reacts with chlorine, it loses two electrons, and hence must have two chlorine atoms to accept these electrons. Theoretically, then, a half of a magnesium atom would be equivalent in reactive power to one chlorine atom, and, since things equivalent to the same thing are equivalent to each other, the half magnesium atom would be equivalent to one sodium atom. It is not possible to divide a magnesium atom, but it is possible to divide a gram-atomic weight, and one may say that 24.32 g. /2 or 12.16 g. of magnesium is equivalent in reactive power to 35.457 g. of chlorine and to 22.997 g. of sodium.

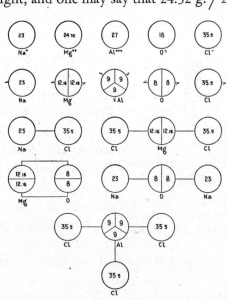

As said before, for every comparison there must be a standard. For the comparison of equivalent weights, the standard chosen has been one gram-atomic weight of hydrogen. Hydrogen reacts with oxygen according to the equation:

$$2H_2 + O_2 \rightarrow 2H_2O$$

from which it follows that one atom of hydrogen is equivalent in reactive ability to one-half atom of oxygen, whence 1.008 g. of hydrogen must be equivalent to 16.0000 /2 or 8.0000 g.

EQUIVALENT WEIGHTS.

of oxygen. Thus *the gram-equivalent weight of an element is that weight of it which combines with, liberates, or will in any wise do the same chemical work as 1.008 g. of hydrogen, or 8.0000 g. of oxygen.*

When hydrogen reacts, it does so by losing, gaining, or sharing one electron per atom. When 1.008 g. of hydrogen is chosen for a standard, this is an amount of material sufficient to involve 6.023×10^{23} electrons when reaction occurs, and hence any quantity of material which also involves 6.023×10^{23} electrons in reaction will be equivalent to it. Since magnesium furnishes two electrons per atom, a gram-atomic weight of it would furnish $2(6.023 \times 10^{23})$ electrons, and hence its gram-equivalent weight would be 24.32 /2 or 12.16 g. From this it is seen that the gram-equivalent weight of an element is easily calculated by dividing the gram-atomic weight by the valence: $E = A/V$. Therefore, the equivalent weight is not only equivalent in the sense of doing equal work or providing equal chemical activity, but it is also *equi-valent* in that it is the quantity of an element which provides the same

quantity of valence as another equivalent weight. It is the quantity which provides 6.023×10^{23} units of valence, as does one gram-atomic weight of a monovalent element, hence it is the quantity which represents one unit of valence.

By actual experimentation, it has been found that 96,500 coulombs of electricity are required to liberate by electrolysis 1.008 g. of hydrogen from solutions containing hydrogen ions. This quantity of electricity must, then, be the quantity required to put one electron on each of the 6.023×10^{23} hydrogen atoms, and hence the quantity required to restore that many electrons to any variety of atoms. This quantity of electricity also removes that many electrons from the negative ions which arrive at the anode, hence it is also possible to say that *the equivalent weight of an element is that quantity of it which is liberated by the passage of 96,500 coulombs of electricity through solutions of its ions.*

An equivalent weight of one element will react with exactly one equivalent weight of any other element with which it is capable of combining, or it will liberate one equivalent weight of any element which it is active enough to displace. This is the advantage of using equivalent weights.

APPARATUS FOR THE LABORATORY PREPARATION OF HYDROGEN.

13. *Equivalent Weights and Atomic Weights*

Equivalent weights are easily measured by the methods of quantitative analysis. For example, a 1.0000-g. sample of a compound of potassium and oxygen may be found to contain 83.01 per cent potassium and 16.99 per cent oxygen by weight. By setting up the ratio $83.01/16.99 = x/8$, the equivalent weight of potassium in terms of the definition may be found. Calculation reveals that this value, x, is 39.09 g. To get the atomic weight, however, we must have the valence, for if $E = A/V$, then $A = EV$. Often the valences of new elements were not known, hence the determination of an atomic weight often posed quite a problem in the days when chemists were seeking to establish the atomic weights which we today take so much for granted.

14. The Law of Dulong and Petit

In the year 1819 two Frenchmen, Dulong and Petit by name, discovered a means of assisting chemists to determine by what factor to multiply their equivalent weights in order to arrive at the atomic weights of the elements in question. By a study of the elements of known atomic weight, they discovered that if one multiplies the atomic weight by the specific heat of the element in the solid state, a value is obtained which is virtually a constant for all elements so treated. They found this constant to be approximately 6.2. Another way of saying the same thing is that *for nearly all elements in the solid state, the atomic heat is approximately constant at 6.2 cal.*

$$\text{at. wt.} \times \text{specific heat} = \text{at. heat} = 6.2 \text{ cal.}$$

from which

$$\text{at. wt.} = 6.2 \text{ cal.} / \text{sp. heat}$$

Since the specific heat (the number of calories required to raise the temperature of 1 g. of the substance 1° C.) of most solids is readily measured with the aid of a calorimeter, it is apparent that the *approximate atomic weight* of such an element may be calculated easily. It must be emphasized, however, that *this value is only approximate.*

This approximate value served well, nevertheless, to provide a fair estimate of the atomic weight. Suppose that the equivalent weight of an element was found to be 16.15 g. and its specific heat in the solid state was found to be 0.0937 cal.

$$6.2 \text{ cal.} / 0.0937 = 66.12 \text{ g.} = \text{approx. at. wt.}$$

From this, it is apparent that the atomic weight should be in the neighborhood of 66 g. The exact atomic weight is given by $V \times 16.15$. Now four is the value for V which will give an exact atomic weight nearest 66, hence the valence of the element in the compound investigated must be 4 and the true atomic weight must be 4×16.15 or 64.60 g.

Since the specific heat of an element varies some with the temperature at which it is measured, the atomic heat will also vary with the temperature. This is one of the reasons why only an approximate value is obtained for the atomic weight when 6.2 cal. is used as the atomic heat. Most solid elements give satisfactory results when their specific heats are measured at average room temperature; the elements boron, carbon, and silicon, however, give satisfactory re-sults only when their specific heats are measured at much higher temperatures.

The law of Dulong and Petit is little used today, but it was of great assist-ance to chemists in the days when atomic weights were being established.

15. Atomic Weights and Mendelejeff's Periodic Chart

In Chapter 6 it was pointed out that when Mendelejeff prepared his periodic chart he left vacant spaces for unknown elements, and that, in general, he ar-ranged the elements in his chart in the order of increasing atomic weights. Later, when a new element was discovered whose properties showed that it belonged in a certain vacant place, the weights of the elements on either side of this place indicated that the weight of the new element should fall between them. Thus, again the analyst was assisted in choosing the proper valence value that, when multiplied by the determined equivalent weight, would give a value for the exact atomic weight which would place it in the indicated range.

16. Equivalent Weights of Compounds

The equivalent weights of compounds are easily calculated. Since some compounds may enter into both oxidation-reduction and metathetical reac-tions, such compounds will not necessarily have the same equivalent weight in both types of reactions; nor will a given compound always have the same equivalent weight in all of its oxidation-reduction reactions unless it always undergoes the same valence change. Examples will make these points more clear.

A. IN OXIDATION-REDUCTION REACTIONS. Consider the following dis-placement:

$$\underline{Zn} + CuCl_2 \rightarrow \underline{Cu} + ZnCl_2$$

The copper changes in valence from $+2$ in copper chloride to zero in the free copper; thus, the copper from one molecule of copper chloride is gaining two electrons. A half molecule would be able, then, to gain one electron, hence the equivalent weight of copper chloride in this reaction would be g. mol. wt. $/2$ or 134.48 g. $/2$.

In the reaction $2KMnO_4 + 16HCl \rightarrow 2KCl + 2MnCl_2 + 10Cl_2 + 8H_2O$, it can be seen by applying the zero valence rule to $KMnO_4$ and to $MnCl_2$ that the oxidation number of the manganese atom changes from $+7$ in the former to $+2$ in the latter. Each molecule of potassium permanganate is thus capable of producing an oxidation number change of $7 - 2$ or 5. Its equivalent weight as an oxidizing agent in this reaction is, therefore, its gram-molecular weight divided by 5.

In the reaction $2KMnO_4 + 3C_2H_4 + 4H_2O \rightarrow 3C_2H_4(OH)_2 + 2KOH + 2MnO_2$, each manganese atom changes its oxidation number from $+7$ to $+4$, and each molecule of $KMnO_4$, since it contains one atom of manganese, is, therefore, producing an oxidation number change of $7 - 4$ or 3. The equivalent weight of $KMnO_4$ in this reaction would thus be obtained by dividing its gram-molecular weight by three.

Fortunately, the common valence changes shown by most compounds are limited, as a consequence of which the possible equivalent weights of any specific compound are also limited.

B. IN METATHETICAL REACTIONS. In metathetical reactions there are no changes of valence; the two compounds involved as reagents simply exchange partners, consequently a given partner brings into the new compound the same valence it had in the old. The gram-equivalent weight of a compound participating in such a reaction is obtained by dividing its gram-molecular weight by either the total valence of its positive ions or the total valence of its negative ions, since, according to the zero valence rule, these two values must be numerically equal.

In the reaction represented thus

$$KMnO_4 + H_2SO_4 \rightleftarrows KHSO_4 + HMnO_4$$

the $KMnO_4$ produces a K^+ ion and an MnO_4^- ion; therefore, the metathetical gram-equivalent weight of $KMnO_4$ is given by dividing its gram-molecular weight by 1.

In the reaction

$$BaCl_2 + H_2SO_4 \rightarrow \underline{BaSO_4} + 2HCl$$

barium chloride produces a Ba^{++} ion and two Cl^- ions, hence its metathetical gram-equivalent weight is obtained by dividing its gram-molecular weight by 2. The H_2SO_4 molecule furnishes $2H^+$ ions and one SO_4^{--}, hence its metathetical gram-equivalent weight is also obtained by dividing its gram-molecular weight by 2.

The foregoing discussion indicates that the metathetical gram-equivalent weight of a compound is that weight of the compound which contains one equivalent weight of each of its ions.

17. *Millimolecular and Milliequivalent Weights*

Since gram-molecular weights and gram-equivalent weights are relatively large masses, it is often convenient in actual practice in the laboratory to use considerably smaller quantities. For measuring these smaller quantities, it is desirable to have smaller units of comparison. The millimolecular weight and the milliequivalent weight serve in this capacity. *The millimolecular weight is one-thousandth of a mole; the milliequivalent weight, or milliequivalent, is one-thousandth of an equivalent weight.* The millimolecular weight is usually referred to as a *millimole.*

18. *The Law of the Conservation of Energy*

Experimentation has shown that, in all ordinary chemical reactions, the law of the conservation of mass holds true. In Chapter 5 it was pointed out that energy changes accompany all chemical changes. Again, careful experimentation has led to the conclusion that *energy can be neither created nor destroyed in all such ordinary reactions.* This statement is known as the *law of the conservation of energy.*

According to this law, energy may be transferred from one object, or one kind of matter, to another, and from one variety of energy to another, without loss. All measurements involving ordinary machines, ordinary processes, and ordinary chemical changes attest the truth of the statement. Energy, of course, may be rendered into unavailable states in which it will not do work, just as water after it has flowed downhill is no longer able to do work. The energy is no more destroyed than is the water.

An extension of reasoning along the line of the indestructibility of energy leads to the conclusion that the energy content of the universe is constant. For a long time this was held to be true, but in Chapter 4 a study of radioactive changes within atoms suggested that matter and energy are interconvertible. At first glance, this statement appears to contradict both the law of the conservation of mass and the law of the conservation of energy, but, if one reviews the modern concept of the structure of atoms, he sees that all matter built up as it is of electrically charged electrons and protons is essentially electrical in nature. Electricity as a form of energy which furnishes light, heat, and power is familiar to all. Matter and energy, then, appear to be but two manifestations of the same thing—indestructible but interconvertible. In view of this situation, perhaps the two laws should be combined into a *law of the conservation of mass-energy.*

It should be remembered, however, that for all ordinary processes the two laws hold independently as stated.

(See Appendix for Exercises)

COLLATERAL READINGS

Findlay: *The Spirit of Chemistry*, New York, Longmans, Green & Co., 1934.
Harrison: *Atoms in Action*, New York, William Morrow and Co., 1939.
Kendall: *At Home Among the Atoms*, New York, D. Appleton-Century Co., 1929.
Any standard textbook of general chemistry.

SIR WILLIAM CROOKES
(*1832–1919, English*)

Crookes was both physicist and chemist, and is most widely known because of his experiments with electrical discharges in highly evacuated tubes. From these experiments he developed his so-called "theory of radiant matter," from which the modern electronic theory has evolved. By means of the spectroscope he discovered the element thallium, and he is the inventor of the radiometer and the spinthariscope. In 1859 he founded *Chemical News*, which he continued to publish until his death. His career in the sciences was both long and productive.

JOHN WILLIAM STRUTT, LORD RAYLEIGH
(*1842–1919, English*)

Lord Rayleigh was a famous physicist who served both at Cambridge University and at the Royal Institution in London. He did much painstaking work upon the combining volumes, compressibilities, and densities of gases. As a result of his observation that the densities of atmospheric nitrogen and nitrogen obtained by the decomposition of ammonium salts were not identical, the discovery of argon was made by Sir William Ramsay, who asked Rayleigh's permission to investigate the problem. Rayleigh also did work on the electrochemical equivalent of silver, and made contributions to the physical fields of acoustics and optics. He was the recipient of many honors, including the Nobel Prize in physics, which was awarded him in 1904.

9

The States of Matter

I. GASES

1. Introduction

It is common knowledge that matter may exist in three physical states—solid, liquid, or gas. The change of a given variety of matter from existence in any one of these states to existence in another is a purely physical change. In general, the chemist is not concerned with physical changes, but because he is concerned with matter, because he must work with matter in all states, because he finds that the particular state in which a given variety of matter exists may have much to do with its reactivity, and because he must make calculations which are based upon changes of state, it is necessary for him to have a thorough knowledge of the states of matter and of the physical laws which govern the behavior of matter in the various states.

That all matter is believed to be composed of small particles called molecules has already been stated. The question to be answered, then, is: If all matter is composed of molecules, what is the essential difference between the states of matter? The answer to this question is that the essential difference between these states is the relative quantities of energy possessed by the molecules in the different states. The question is answered more fully by the *kinetic molecular theory*.

2. Gravitational Attraction vs. Escaping Tendency

The law of universal gravitation is one of the fundamental laws of physics. It states that every body attracts every other body with a force that is directly proportional to the product of the masses of the two bodies and inversely proportional to the square of the distance separating their centers. This means that the greater the masses of the two bodies, the greater will be their attraction for each other, and the greater the distance between them, the less will be their attraction for each other. Thus, particles even as tiny as molecules have an attraction for each other, and this attraction is greatest when the molecules are very close together.

Opposing this tendency of particles to be pulled together is an equally universal tendency for them to separate. If a bottle of strong ammonia water be opened in one corner of a room whose air is undisturbed, it will not be long until ammonia may be smelled in the diagonally opposite corner of the room. Mothballs will soon lend their odor to an entire room; gasoline, water, and alcohol evaporate; and a crystal of bluestone at the bottom of a tall jar of still water soon sends streamers of blue *upward* through the water. This tendency of particles of matter to separate is generally referred to as the *escaping tendency*, which indicates that molecules have the ability to move away from others of their kind; that they are *kinetic* rather than *static*.

The ability of molecules to move is directly dependent upon their energy, which, in turn, is related to their temperature. The greater the temperature of a molecule, the greater its energy, and hence the greater its ability to do the work of moving, even against the gravitational attraction of other molecules. Whether a given system, or group, of like molecules will exist as a solid, liquid, or gas depends upon the relative strength of these two opposing tendencies. If the *kinetic energy*, energy of motion, of the particles is in excess of the gravitational attraction between them, then this energy will carry the molecules relatively far from each other—that is, to distances which are large as compared with the diameters of the molecules, and the molecules will exist in the gaseous state. The compressibility of a gas is taken as proof of the fact that in this state the particles are relatively far from each other, with considerable unoccupied space in between. In the liquid state, gravitational attraction exceeds the escaping tendency, and in the solid state, the forces of gravitation are so far in excess of those of the escaping tendency that each particle is bound into a definite place in a rigid whole by the mutual attraction which it and its fellows have for each other. These latter states exist, then, when the kinetic energy of the molecules is less than the energy of attraction between them, and, as was stated in section 1, the essential difference between the states of matter is a difference of relative energies. By increasing the kinetic energies of molecules by the application of heat, one may cause them to pass from solid, to liquid, to gas, provided no chemical decomposition occurs before these changes may take place.

3. The Kinetic Molecular Theory

Because the distances between molecules in a gas are large enough for gravitational attraction to be negligible, the gaseous state is by far the simplest for study, and hence will be considered before the liquid and solid states. Observation shows that all gases, regardless of their chemical composition, have similar physical behavior when subjected to similar physical stresses. The kinetic molecular theory is of considerable help in understanding the physical nature and behavior of all matter, but especially so for gases, to which it shall be applied in this section. In a later chapter, its application to liquids and solids will be discussed. The fundamental assumptions of the theory as applied to gases, and some of the factual evidence upon which these assumptions are based, are given in the following table:

Table 8

Assumptions	Evidence
1. Gases are composed of molecules.	This evidence is largely indirect.
2. The distances between molecules of a gas at ordinary temperatures and pressures are large as compared with the diameters of the molecules.	Gases have low densities. Gases are very compressible.
3. The molecules of a gas are always in motion, (a) colliding frequently with each other, and (b) colliding with the walls of the containing vessel.	Gases diffuse spontaneously either into a vacuum or into another gas. Gases diffuse more rapidly into a vacuum than they do into another gas. Gases exert pressure upon the walls of a container.
4. The molecules of a gas are perfectly elastic, rebounding from collisions without a loss of kinetic energy.	Gases never settle or cease to exert a constant pressure so long as the temperature remains constant.
5. The molecules of a gas exert no appreciable attraction for each other at ordinary pressures, but they do exert an attraction for each other under large pressures.	Gases are very slightly cooled when they expand into a vacuum. At sufficiently low temperatures gases may be liquefied by pressure alone.
6. Molecules of a gas move in all directions with all possible speeds but with a definite average speed for a fixed temperature.	Equal pressure is manifest on all walls of a container. As a result of collisions velocities are constantly changing. It can be shown that some of the particles do not travel as rapidly as others.
7. Hot molecules move more rapidly than do cooler ones.	A gas under constant pressure expands when heated.
8. Light molecules move more rapidly than do heavy ones.	All gases under the same conditions exert the same pressures, therefore the lighter ones must move faster since the striking power of a moving particle is proportional to its momentum which is a product of mass × velocity.
9. In even a small volume of gas there are a great number of molecules.	Molecules, since they are so small, have only small individual masses, yet even a small volume of gas has a finite weight.

The foregoing discussion denotes that the existence of the gaseous state and of many of the physical properties of that state are dependent upon the kinetic energy of the particles in the state. The kinetic energy of a particle of mass m and velocity u is given by the equation

$$k.e. = \tfrac{1}{2} mu^2$$

The velocity u is dependent upon temperature. For a given temperature the lightest molecule will have the greatest velocity (see 8, above) though its average kinetic energy will be the same as that of other gases at the same temperature (see 8, Table 8). Molecules of hydrogen gas at room temperature are calculated to have an average velocity of about one mile per second; heavier molecules will, of course, have lower velocities. This does not mean that a hydrogen molecule will travel a mile in a straight line in a second. As a matter of fact, it will not travel far before it will strike another hydrogen molecule or the container wall, bouncing back to make another collision, etc. The distance a molecule will travel before it hits another, and hence the number of collisions it will make in a second, depends upon both the speed at which it is traveling and the relative distance between molecules, which in turn is dependent upon the outside pressure forcing them together. This average distance that a molecule travels before it collides is known as its *mean free flight*. For most molecules under ordinary room conditions of temperature and pressure, the mean free flight is about 1.67×10^{-6} cm. When the hydrogen atom is traveling at the rate of a mile a second, this means that it makes about 9.64×10^{10} collisions per second, which is roughly the number of times a normally beating heart would beat in 2545 years. The mean free flight of a molecule traveling into a vacuum is, of course, considerably increased.

4. Gas Laws—the Perfect Gas

The gas laws are those generalizations which describe the relationships which exist between the pressure, temperature, and volume of a stated quantity of gas. These laws when applied to large changes of conditions do not yield absolutely accurate results because gases under extreme conditions do not behave quite as they do under moderate conditions. The gas laws are described as being based upon a "perfect gas"—that is, a gas which would behave under all conditions as it does under conditions approaching those of the average laboratory. For all changes that may be encountered in the average laboratory, and for all changes that do not involve extremes of either temperature or pressure, the gas laws permit calculations whose results are sufficiently accurate for all practical purposes.

5. Boyle's Law

So far as is known, Robert Boyle was the first investigator to study quantitatively the relationship which exists between the volume of a gas and the external pressure which is exerted upon it. Common knowledge states that when the pressure upon a gas is increased, the volume of the gas becomes smaller; presumably this knowledge was common in Boyle's day, but it remained for him to establish experimentally the mathematical relationship which existed and to state his findings in the form of a law. He found that if the pressure upon a given volume of gas was doubled, its volume decreased by half provided that there was no change in temperature, and that if the pressure was trebled, the volume shrank to one-third of its former value. These findings were published in 1662 and are summarized in the statement known as *Boyle's law: At constant temperature, the volume of a gas varies inversely as the pressure exerted upon it*. The law may be stated mathematically as a proportion

$$V_1 / V_2 = P_2 / P_1$$

where V_1 and P_1 represent the original volume and pressure respectively, and V_2 and P_2 represent the final volume and pressure respectively. From the proportion it can be shown that

$$V_2 = V_1 \times (P_1 / P_2)$$

or that the final volume is equal to the original volume times a fraction given by the values of the two pressure terms. According to the law, an increase in pressure should cause a decrease in volume; hence, when P_2 is larger than P_1 the ratio P_1 / P_2 will be a simple fraction (a number less than 1) which when multiplied by V_1 will give a value for V_2 which is less than V_1, but when P_2 is smaller than P_1 the ratio will be an improper fraction (a number larger than 1) which when multiplied by V_1 will give a value for V_2 which is greater than V_1. This mathematical statement is thus seen to agree in operation with the principle stated in words.

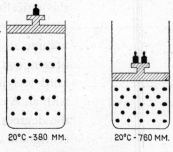

20°C - 380 MM.   20°C - 760 MM.

BOYLE'S LAW.

Pressure is usually stated in terms of millimeters of mercury, as shown in Chapter 3 in the discussion of the barometer. Very large pressures are sometimes stated in atmospheres. The relationship between these two types of units are

$$1 \text{ atm.} = 760 \text{ mm. of mercury}$$

In any calculation, both pressures must be expressed in the same units.

6. Charles' Law

That a gas will expand when heated and contract when cooled is also common knowledge, but again the exact numerical relationship between the increase

in temperature and the corresponding increase in volume is not so apparent and had to be determined experimentally. This determination was made independently by both Charles and Gay-Lussac, both of whom found that if a given volume of gas under a constant external pressure and at a temperature of 0° C. was cooled to −1° C. the volume of the gas shrank by $\frac{1}{273}$ of its original volume, and that if it was cooled to −10° C. it shrank by $\frac{10}{273}$ of its original volume at 0° C. Theoretically, then, if the gas was cooled to −273° C. it should shrink by $\frac{273}{273}$ of its original volume, and hence there would be no matter left. Now actually all gases will condense to a liquid and then freeze to a solid before −273° C. is reached; actually these liquids and solids have a volume and do not disappear. This is one reason why the gas laws do not give accurate results under extreme conditions and why they are said to hold absolutely true only for a perfect gas—i.e., one which is imaginary and would vanish at −273° C. This temperature has also a second significance: theoretically, at least, it is the temperature at which all molecular activity should cease. This concept of a point where volume and activity should vanish gives rise to a new scale of temperature known as the absolute, or Kelvin (in honor of Lord Kelvin) scale. Temperatures on this scale are written with an A or K following the numerals. On the Kelvin scale the degrees are of the same magnitude as are degrees on the centigrade scale, but zero on this scale is 273° below the zero of the centigrade scale. Any temperature on the centigrade scale may thus be converted to its equivalent on the Kelvin scale simply by adding 273 to the value of the centigrade reading. The application of the law relating volumes and temperatures is greatly simplified by the use of temperatures stated in terms of the absolute or Kelvin scale. This law, first stated in 1801, is generally known as *Charles' law;* it states that *at constant pressure the volume of a gas varies directly as the absolute temperature.* This statement may also be expressed in the form of a ratio

$$V_1 / V_2 = T_1 / T_2$$

COMPARISON OF THE ABSOLUTE AND CENTIGRADE THERMOMETRIC SCALES. (Courtesy, Foley, A. L.: "College Physics," 3d ed., Philadelphia, The Blakiston Company.)

whence

$$V_2 = V_1 \times (T_2 / T_1)$$

In this case, when T_2 is larger than T_1, the fraction T_2 / T_1 will be larger than 1 and hence V_2 will be larger than V_1, but when T_2 is smaller than T_1, the fraction will be simple and V_2 will thus be smaller than V_1. These cases both agree with the law as stated. (The capital T is conventionally used to indicate temperatures on the absolute scale.)

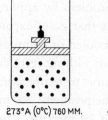 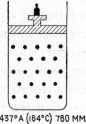

273°A (0°C) 760 MM.   437°A (164°C) 760 MM.

CHARLES' LAW.

7. Gay-Lussac's Law

The pressure in automobile tires, whose volumes are very nearly constant when well inflated, increases considerably on a hot summer day, while on a cold morning it is found to be considerably decreased. The numerical relationship between temperature and pressure at constant volume may be derived from a consideration of Boyle's and Charles' laws, or it may be worked out experimentally. In both manners, it may be shown that *at constant volume the pressure exerted by a gas varies directly as the absolute temperature*. This statement is generally known as *Gay-Lussac's law*. It may be stated as a proportionality thus:

$$P_1 / P_2 = T_1 / T_2$$

8. The General Gas Law

In chemical work, one is generally interested in the variation of the volume of a gas with both temperature and pressure, in which case both the law of Boyle and the law of Charles would apply. In section 5, the relationship

$$V_1 / V_2 = P_2 / P_1$$

was given, while in section 6 the relationship

$$V_1 / V_2 = T_1 / T_2$$

$$\frac{U_1}{U_2} = \frac{P_2}{P_1} \cdot \frac{T_1}{T_2}$$

was given. By combining these two statements one obtains the statement that

$$V_1 / V_2 = (P_2 / P_1) \times (T_1 / T_2)$$

whence

$$V_2 = V_1 \times (P_1 / P_2) \times (T_2 / T_1)$$

9. The Solution of Problems by Use of the General Gas Law

Problems which involve the change of volume with changes of temperature and pressure may be solved simply by substitution of values in the immediately foregoing formula, but, since the formula must be memorized, this is not too good a method. In general, substitution in a formula is not so desirable as is the solution of a problem by application of reason based upon experience. Since everyone knows that gases expand when heated or released from pressure and contract when cooled or compressed by greater pressure, gas law problems are very easily solved without recourse to a formula if one remembers to change the given temperatures to temperatures on the absolute scale.

Consider the problem: 200 ml. of a gas at a temperature of 0° C. and a pressure of 570 mm. of mercury is heated to a temperature of 91° C. and subjected to a pressure of 950 mm. of mercury. What will be the volume of the gas under these new conditions?

First, 0° C. is 273° K., 91° C. is 364° K., and the unknown new volume may be represented by x. The new volume, x, must of necessity equal the old volume, 200 ml., with some mathematical process having been performed upon it. The gas is being heated from 273° K. to 364° K. and therefore must expand, whence the 200 ml. must be multiplied by a fraction which will make it expand numerically; this fraction must be $364/273$. The gas is having its pressure changed from 570 mm. to 950 mm. When pressure increases, volume decreases, hence in this case the 200 ml. must be multiplied by a fraction which is less than one in order to make it decrease mathematically as reason says it must in actuality. This fraction would be $570/950$, and the final statement would be

$$x = 200 \times {}^{364}\!/_{273} \times {}^{570}\!/_{950}$$
$$x = 160 \text{ ml.}$$

Even when substitution in the formula is employed, a careful check should be made to insure that the ratios employed are in agreement with relationships which both the laws and common sense tell one must exist.

10. Standard Conditions

Many combinations of temperature and pressure are possible, hence for the purpose of comparison it was necessary to agree upon one temperature and pressure of reference. The temperature chosen was 0° C., while the pressure chosen was the normal atmospheric pressure at sea level; namely, 760 mm. of mercury. These conditions are usually termed *standard conditions*, and are often abbreviated S.T.P. (standard temperature and pressure). Calculation of gas volumes from observed temperature and pressure in the laboratory to S.T.P. is an oft-repeated operation in practical chemical work.

11. Dalton's Law of Partial Pressures

When matter exists in the gaseous state, there are such relatively large spaces between the molecules of the gas that molecules of another gas may be forced into these vacant spaces. When this occurs, the pressure in the container will now be the sum of the pressures of the two gases, provided they do not react chemically, since pressure depends upon the total number of molecules striking the walls of the container. John Dalton verified this fact by experimentation, and in 1801 summarized his findings in the statement that *in a gaseous mixture, each gas exerts its pressure independently so that the total pressure of the mixture is equal to the sum of the pressures exerted by the individual gases.*

In the laboratory, it is a common practice to collect gases which are not very soluble in water by permitting them to bubble upward into an inverted bottle of water standing in a trough of water, as indicated in the accompanying diagram. Some water evaporates into the bottle so that it ultimately contains a mixture of the gas being collected, plus water vapor. In the liquid state, at a given temperature, a liquid will evaporate into a confined space

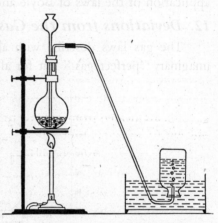

APPARATUS FOR THE LABORATORY COLLECTION OF A GAS BY DISPLACEMENT OF A LIQUID.

only until a definite pressure is established. The value of this pressure of water vapor at various temperatures may be obtained by consulting the Appendix, in which a table summarizes this information which was obtained, as is all such information, by experimentation.

When the water has been forced from the collecting bottle until the water levels in the bottle and in the trough are even, then the pressure in the bottle and the external pressure must be equal. The external pressure which is obtained by reading the barometer is equal to the pressure of the gas and the water vapor in the bottle. If the vapor pressure of the water for the working temperature is obtained from the table and subtracted from the barometric pressure, the difference must then be the pressure of the collected gas.

It must be emphasized that, whenever a gas is collected by displacement of a volatile liquid, such a calculation must be made to obtain the pressure of the gas alone, and it must be further emphasized that before any measurements or calculations are made, the liquid levels inside and outside the bottle must be equalized.

Consider the case of 200 ml. of a gas collected over water at 25° C. and at a barometric pressure of 585.0 mm. of mercury. The measurement of the volume of the gas was made only after the water levels were equalized. The table of vapor pressures in the Appendix shows that the vapor pressure of water at 25° C. is 23.76 mm., hence the true pressure exerted by the 200 ml. of collected gas is 585.0 − 23.76 or 561.2 mm. This value could then be used in the application of the laws of Boyle and Charles.

12. Deviations from the Gas Laws

The gas laws describe with absolute accuracy only the behavior of an imaginary "perfect gas," but for all ordinary calculations they give results of

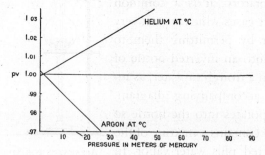

DEVIATIONS FROM BOYLE'S LAW. The behavior of the "Ideal gas" is indicated by the horizontal line. Helium and argon both deviate from the ideal, but in opposite directions.

sufficient accuracy. For extremely accurate calculations and for calculations which involve extreme conditions, several corrected formulas have been proposed, the most widely used of which is that of van der Waals. It corrects for the fact that the pressure as read is too small because the attraction of the molecules for each other is reducing it, and it also corrects for the fact that the molecules of a gas actually have a volume whereas a perfect gas should have molecules whose volume should vanish at the absolute zero. This equation can be found in any textbook of physical chemistry, but its use and further discussion of it are beyond the scope of this text.

13. *Avogadro's Law*

Since all gases, regardless of the masses of their molecules, undergo the same volume changes for all ordinary changes of temperature and pressure, one is led to believe that light molecules must move faster than heavy ones, and that, as a consequence, all gaseous particles must have the same kinetic energy for a specified temperature. It is a demonstrable fact that equal volumes of two gases under the same condition of temperature exert equal pressures; if, now, the individual molecules composing these two gases have identical kinetic energies, it follows that in the two volumes of gases there must be equal numbers of molecules. This consideration, along with others, led the Italian scientist Avogadro in 1811 to state that *equal volumes of gases under the same conditions of temperature and pressure contain the same number of molecules*. This principle can also be proved mathematically. Like all gas laws, this one is not absolutely accurate for all gases under all conditions, but in the main it works very well under ordinary conditions and is quite useful.

14. *The Gram-molecular Volume*

In Chapter 8, it was shown that one gram-molecular weight of any substance contains 6.023×10^{23} molecules. According to Avogadro's law, then, a gram-molecular weight of any substance *in the gaseous state* should occupy the same volume as a gram-molecular weight of any other substance provided they were measured under the same con-ditions of temperature and pressure. If for the conditions we specify standard conditions—namely, 0° C. and 760 mm. of mercury—the volume occupied by a gram-molecular weight of any substance is found to be 22.4 l.; this volume is known as the *gram-molecular volume*, usually abbreviated G.M.V. Since Avo-

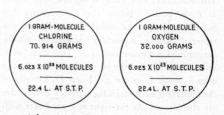

THE RELATIONSHIP OF GRAM-MOLECULES, MOLECULES, AND THE GRAM-MOLECULAR VOLUME.

gadro's law is subject to slight deviations, the weight of 22.4 l. of a gaseous substance at S.T.P. is not always exactly equal to the molecular weight of that substance. In most instances, however, the value so obtained is quite near the true value, and when used with the equivalent weights, as were the approximate atomic weights obtained by the application of the law of Dulong and Petit, it permits the calculation from the equivalent weights of the true molecular weights.

15. *Determination of the Molecular Weights of Volatile Substances*

If a substance is already a gas, or if it may be changed into the gaseous state by heating, its molecular weight may be determined by application of several of the foregoing principles. The two methods employed most frequently are those of Dumas and Victor Meyer. In the former method, a hollow glass bulb of known volume is filled with the gas in question, temperature and pressure are noted, and the mass of the gas in the bulb is obtained by subtracting the mass of the evacuated glass bulb from the mass of the bulb when filled with the gas. The volume under the observed conditions is recalculated to S.T.P., and by proportion, or otherwise, the mass of 22.4 l. of the gas at S.T.P. is calculated. The method of Victor Meyer consists of weighing accurately a small sample of the substance in question and of introducing this sample into a tube where it may be heated until it becomes a gas. A volume of air equal to the volume of gas formed is forced from the tube and caught over water in a gas buret which measures its volume. By correcting the pressure for water vapor, recalculating the volume to S.T.P., and calculating by proportion the mass of

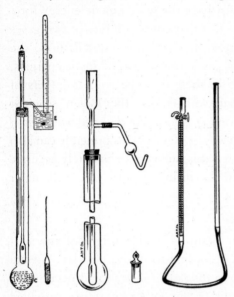

THE APPARATUS OF VICTOR MEYER. The liquid at C is boiled. When the temperature has become constant, a weighed sample of the material whose molecular weight is to be determined is introduced at A. This material is volatilized at B and the air displaced is collected over a liquid E in the gas buret D. Details of the apparatus and weighing capsules and bottles are also shown. At the right is a gas buret with leveling tube for adjustment of the pressure exerted on the contained gas. (Courtesy, Davies: "Fundamentals of Physical Chemistry," Philadelphia, The Blakiston Company.)

22.4 l. of the gas at S.T.P., its molecular weight is obtained. By either of these methods, the molecular weight of the substance in the gaseous state alone is determined; one is, therefore, forced to make the assumption that the molecular weight of the substance in either the liquid or solid state is the same. These methods, as pointed out, do not yield an absolutely accurate molecular weight, but the figures thus obtained are usually sufficiently accurate to permit the calculation of formulas as outlined in section 7 of Chapter 8.

An example will illustrate the calculations mentioned above. A sample of an unknown substance weighing 0.125 g. displaces, when vaporized, 33.6 ml. of air, which is caught over water at a temperature of 22° C. and a pressure of 699.8 mm. What is the molecular weight of the substance?

$$\text{vp. of water at } 22° \text{ C.} = 19.8 \text{ mm.}$$
$$699.8 - 19.8 = 680.0 \text{ mm. (pressure of air displaced)}$$
$$\text{Volume of air displaced at S.T.P.} = 33.6 \times {}^{273}\!/_{295} \times {}^{680}\!/_{760}$$
$$= 27.8 \text{ ml.}$$
$$27.8 \text{ ml. of the gas at S.T.P. has a mass of } 0.125 \text{ g.}$$
$$27.8 \text{ ml.} / 22400 \text{ ml.} = 0.125 \text{ g.} / x \text{ g.}$$
$$x = 100.7 \text{ g., the gram-molecular wt. of the substance}$$

16. Gay-Lussac's Law of Combining Volumes

An examination of the equations representing a wide variety of chemical reactions will show that the numbers of the molecules of the various reagents participating in these reactions are usually small, and that these numbers usually bear a simple numerical relation to each other. For instance, two molecules of hydrogen combine with one molecule of oxygen to form water:

$$2H_2 + O_2 \rightarrow 2H_2O$$

while one molecule of hydrogen unites with one of chlorine to form hydrogen chloride:

$$H_2 + Cl_2 \rightarrow 2HCl$$

According to Avogadro's law, the volumes occupied by gases are directly proportional to the number of molecules they contain, provided measurement is made under identical conditions, hence the volumes of gases participating in chemical reactions should stand to one another in the same ratio as the numbers of their molecules in the balanced equations. This leads to the statement known as *Gay-Lussac's law of combining volumes: the volumes of gases taking part in a chemical reaction stand to each other in the ratio of small whole numbers, provided the volumes are measured under identical conditions.* It is for this reason that equations are always considered to be written for S.T.P. unless otherwise stated. It must be noted that this law applies *only to the volumes of gases.* In the first equation above, two volumes of hydrogen react with one volume of oxygen, while in the second equation, one volume of hydrogen reacts with one of chlorine. If these formulas are interpreted as indicating moles, then 44.8 l. of hydrogen will react with 22.4 l. of oxygen, but 22.4 l. of hydrogen will react with 22.4 l. of chlorine.

Historically, Gay-Lussac's law, which was first stated in 1808, precedes that of Avogadro, and was in part an inspiration for the latter. Gay-Lussac based his statement upon experimental work rather than upon theoretical considerations.

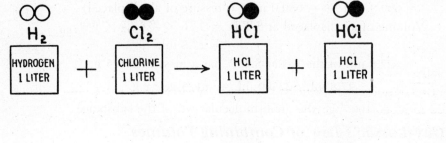

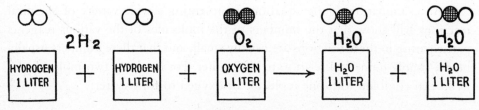

GAY-LUSSAC'S LAW.

17. Calculation of Reacting Volumes

In Chapter 8, it was shown how weight relationships might be calculated by the use of either the equation or the factor method. Similar calculations involving the volume relationships of gases, but only of gases, may also be made.

A. THE EQUATION METHOD. Consider the problem: What volume of chlorine at S.T.P. will be required to react with 5 g. of sodium? As in weight relationship problems, write the equation for the reaction, but this time, instead of writing gram-molecular weights for the two substances involved, write gram-molecular weights for the one spoken of in terms of mass and gram-molecular volumes for the one spoken of in terms of volume, thus

$$2(23) \text{ g.} \qquad 22.4 \text{ l.}$$
$$2Na \; + \; Cl_2 \rightarrow 2NaCl$$

By using this data with the data given in the problem, and by using a letter to represent the unknown, one may calculate the desired information.

$$46 \text{ g.} \qquad 22.4 \text{ l.}$$
$$2Na + Cl_2 \rightarrow 2NaCl$$
$$5 \text{ g.} \qquad x \text{ l.}$$
$$46 x = 5(22.4) \text{ l.}$$
$$x = 2.43 \text{ l. or } 2430 \text{ ml., at S.T.P.}$$

Suppose, now, that the question had asked what volume of chlorine at 20° C. and 740 mm. would react with 5 g. of sodium. The calculation would be made just as before, until the 2.43 l. at S.T.P. was obtained, then this volume would have to be recalculated to the stipulated conditions by application of the general gas law.

Now consider a problem of this type: What weight of sodium will be required to produce 3 l. of dry hydrogen at 23° C. and 710 mm. by action upon water? Since equations are usually written for S.T.P. before the volume of hydrogen may be used in a calculation based upon the data furnished by an equation, it must of necessity be recalculated to S.T.P.

$$V(S.T.P.) = 3 \text{ l.} \times {}^{273}\!/_{296} \times {}^{710}\!/_{760}$$
$$= 2.58 \text{ l.}$$
$$2(23)\text{g.} \qquad\qquad\qquad 22.4 \text{ l.}$$
$$2Na + 2HOH \rightarrow 2NaOH + H_2$$
$$x \text{ g.} \qquad\qquad\qquad\qquad 2.58 \text{ l.}$$
$$22.4 x = 46(2.58) \text{ g.}$$
$$x = 5.3 \text{ g.}$$

These latter examples are given to emphasize the facts that only volumes of gases at S.T.P. may be determined by use of the data given by equations and that only volumes of gases at S.T.P. may be used in connection with data from equations. This is true of all such problems save those which involve the volumes of two gases; if these are measured under the same conditions, calculations may be made directly without conversion to S.T.P. This is possible because of the operation of Avogadro's Law.

B. The Factor Method. The factor method of solving problems of the type discussed above is very similar to the factor method as outlined in Chapter 8 for solving mass relationship problems. The formulas of the two substances involved in the problem are combined into a fraction with the substance of known value in the denominator; the factor is balanced after the fashion already described; the correct multiple of the gram-molecular weight is set down for the substance whose mass is mentioned in the statement of the problem and the correct multiple of the gram-molecular volume is set down for the other substance; these figures are combined into a proportion with the data given in the problem, and the proportion is then solved in the usual manner. Here, again, only volumes at S.T.P. may be used in or determined directly from the calculation, save in the case of two gases under the same conditions of temperature and pressure.

For an example, consider the problem: What volume of dry oxygen gas at S.T.P. would be required to prepare 6.5 g. of sodium oxide by direct union of the elements?

$$O_2 \big/ 2Na_2O = 22.4 \text{ l.} \big/ 2(62) \text{ g.} = x \text{ l.} \big/ 6.5 \text{ g.}$$

$$x = 6.5 \times 22.4 \big/ 124$$

$$x = 1.17 \text{ l. of oxygen}$$

18. Choice of Units in Problems Involving Mass and Volume

In problems of the type, discussed in section 9 of Chapter 8, the gram was used as the unit of mass, but, since molecular weights are based upon atomic weights which are strictly relative, any other unit might be used. Kilograms, metric tons, ounces, pounds, or tons serve equally well, provided the units are used in the same pattern in both ratios of the proportion.

In problems which involve gas volumes alone, any units of volume desired may be used throughout the calculation, provided the same care is taken in establishing the ratios as was mentioned above.

Problems such as those considered in section 17, which involve relationships between mass and gas volumes, however, must have the mass expressed in grams and the volumes in liters, or multiples of liters, or the mass may be expressed in ounces and the gas volumes in cubic feet. This latter combination of units is possible because their ratio is the same as that of the gram and the liter, since the ounce contains 28.3 g. and the cubic foot contains 28.3 l. Many chemical problems related to engineering are often expressed in terms of English units, hence it is well worth the student's while to know that, if the molecular weight of a substance is expressed in ounces, its molecular volume at S.T.P. will be 22.4 cu. ft.

19. The Density of Gases

Density is defined as the mass per unit volume of a substance. It is apparent, from the laws of Charles and Boyle, that the volume of a fixed mass of gas varies with both the temperature and the pressure, hence the density of the gas will also vary with these conditions. It is necessary, for that reason, to state the temperature and pressure under which the density of a gas was determined. Because of this variation, for purposes of comparison it is customary to record the density of gases at S.T.P.

The densities of gases when expressed in grams per milliliter, or even in grams per liter, are very slight when compared with the similarly expressed densities of liquids and solids, because the molecules of a gas are so far from each other with respect to their own diameters.

There is a common tendency to compare the densities of gases with the density of that commonest of gases with which all are familiar—air. However, air is a mixture of gases rather than a compound, and hence has no molecular weight. There is nothing to prevent one from determining experimentally the mass of 22.4 l. of air at S.T.P.—this is found to be approximately 29 g. By comparing the molecular weights of other gases with 29, one has a ready means of saying whether a given gas is heavier or lighter than air, and hence whether it will rise or sink in air. The molecular weight of O_2 is 32; that of carbon dioxide, CO_2, is 44; that of ammonia, NH_3, is 17; therefore the first two gases are heavier than air under the same conditions, while the last one is lighter.

20. *The Critical Temperature of Gases*

Gravitational attraction and the escaping tendency always oppose each other in a gas. By increasing the pressure on a gas, its molecules are forced closer together and the force of gravitational attraction is increased. If this force becomes greater than the kinetic energy of the molecules, which gives them their ability to separate, then the gas will condense to a liquid, but if the kinetic energy of the molecules still exceeds this force of attraction, then the substance remains in the gaseous state. Conceivably, then, there is a definite temperature for each substance at which the kinetic energy of its molecules is just equal to the maximum gravitational attraction of the molecules when they have been pressed together as close as is practicable under laboratory conditions. A slight addition of pressure at this temperature should cause liquefaction to take place, but beyond this temperature no amount of pressure would enable the gravitational attraction to exceed the energy of motion. Hence, beyond this temperature, no amount of pressure would convert the gas to a liquid. *This characteristic temperature of a substance in the gaseous state beyond which no amount of pressure will suffice to liquefy it is known as the critical temperature of that substance.* The minimum pressure required to liquefy a gas at its critical temperature is known as its *critical pressure*. In order to liquefy a gas at a temperature below its critical temperature, it is usually necessary only to compress the gas to a pressure slightly in excess of the pressure it is exerting at its existing temperature. This last statement demonstrates that gases which have critical temperatures well above room temperature are rather easily liquefied, while those whose critical temperatures are well below room temperature must first be cooled to their critical temperatures and then must have exerted upon them pressures in excess of their critical pressures. Achieving the requisite low temperatures and high pressures presents mechanical and other practical difficulties which greatly increase the cost of liquefaction.

21. Henry's Law

Many gases dissolve in liquids. In some cases there is a reaction between the gas and the liquid, but in many other cases the gas simply dissolves in the liquid, forming a homogeneous mixture of the two. In cases of this latter type, it has been found that *if the temperature remains constant, the solubility of a gas in a liquid varies directly with the pressure of the gas in contact with the liquid.* This statement is known as *Henry's law.* When the pressure on such a solution is diminished, as when soda water runs from a fountain tap, gas escapes from the solution until the amount left in solution is proportional to the new lowered pressure.

Gases are ordinarily measured by volume rather than by weight, hence it is customary to state the volume of gas at S.T.P. which will dissolve in one volume of the liquid when the solution is prepared at a specified temperature and pressure. It is necessary to state the temperature of the liquid because a gas is generally less soluble in hot liquids than in cool ones. The solubility of oxygen in water at 20°C. and at one atmosphere is found to be 0.03 ml. of oxygen referred to S.T.P. (cf. section 10) per ml. of water.

22. Graham's Law

It has been mentioned that, if one releases a quantity of ammonia gas in one corner of a large room, he will soon smell ammonia in the diagonally opposite corner even though there are no air currents in the room. This spontaneous intermingling of gases to form mixtures which in time become uniform is called *diffusion.* All gases, regardless of the mass of their molecules, have the ability to diffuse, but the speedier molecules diffuse more rapidly. Section 13 pointed out that, at a specified temperature, all gases have the same kinetic energy. The kinetic energy of gas a will be $\frac{1}{2} m_a u_a^2$ and the kinetic energy of gas b will be $\frac{1}{2} m_b u_b^2$, where m represents mass and u represents velocity. Then for a given temperature

$$\tfrac{1}{2} m_a u_a{}^2 = \tfrac{1}{2} m_b u_b{}^2$$

whence

$$m_a u_a{}^2 = m_b u_b{}^2$$

and dividing both members by $m_b u_a{}^2$

$$m_a / m_b = u_b{}^2 / u_a{}^2$$

and

$$\sqrt{m_a / m_b} = u_b / u_a$$

The definition of density shows that density and mass are directly proportional, therefore, substitution of density for mass may be made in the immediately preceding equation, yielding the equation

$$\sqrt{d_a / d_b} = u_b / u_a$$

which states that *at a given temperature the rates of diffusion of two gases are inversely proportional to the square roots of their densities*. This was first determined experimentally by Graham in 1832, and is known as *Graham's law*. Chlorine is roughly 35.5 times as dense as hydrogen, therefore according to Graham's law hydrogen should diffuse nearly six times as fast as chlorine since $\sqrt{35.5}$ is almost six.

(*See Appendix for Exercises*)

COLLATERAL READINGS

Cartledge: *Introductory Theoretical Chemistry*, Boston, Ginn & Co., 1929.

Foster: *Romance of Chemistry*, New York, D. Appleton-Century Co., 1937.

Getman and Daniels: *Outlines of Physical Chemistry*, New York, John Wiley & Sons, Inc., 1943.

Haynes: *Chemical Pioneers*, New York, D. Van Nostrand Co., 1939.

Hildebrand: *Principles of Chemistry*, New York, The Macmillan Co., 1941.

Holmyard: *Makers of Chemistry*, New York, Oxford University Press, 1937.

Jaffe: *Crucibles*, New York, Simon and Schuster, 1930.

Moore: *History of Chemistry*, New York, McGraw-Hill Book Co., 1939.

10

Chlorine and Chlorides

1. Introduction

The element of the third period whose chemical behavior contrasts most strongly with that of sodium is chlorine. This contrast, and its occurrence with sodium in sodium chloride, decided its choice as the second element for study. In succeeding chapters, the elements falling in the third period between sodium and chlorine will be studied in order that the gradual change of properties from those characteristic of sodium to those characteristic of chlorine may be observed.

Chlorine is an important element from both a practical and a theoretical standpoint. Reference to the periodic chart shows that its atomic number is 17 and that its extranuclear electronic distribution is 2, 8, 7. As a consequence of this electronic configuration, it should have a very strong tendency to enter into reactions which will permit it to gain one electron, thereby acquiring the outer configuration of the inert gas argon. This tendency to gain one electron gives it a chemical nature exactly opposed to that of sodium, and the strength of this tendency, due in part to the rather small radius of the chlorine atom, makes it very reactive and thus desirable as a commercial reagent.

Chlorine and the other members of the VII A family strongly tend to gain electrons from metallic electron-donors with which they react to form compounds of the type of sodium chloride, salt, hence they are collectively called *halogens*. The term halogen is derived from two Greek words and means *salt-former*.

2. Physical Properties

At room temperature and pressure, chlorine exists as a gas of a yellowish-green color. This color is responsible for its name which is derived from the Greek word *chloros*, meaning such a color. Its critical temperature is 144° C., hence it is rather easily liquefied, though at 20° C., which is about average room temperature, 6.62 atmospheres are required to do the job. The boiling point of liquid chlorine under standard pressure is − 34.7° C., hence a pressure just slightly in excess of one atmosphere is sufficient to liquefy the gas when cooled to that temperature. (Cf. section 20, Chapter 9.) The freezing point of the liquid is $-102.1°$ C. The density of the gas at S.T.P. is 0.00322 g. per ml., or 3.22 g. per l. Multiplying 3.22×22.4 l. gives the value of the gram-molecular weight, 72.13 g., which is roughly two times the gram-atomic weight of 35.457. This is evidence that the molecule of chlorine contains two atoms,

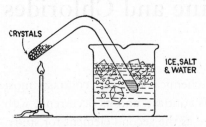

CRYSTALS

ICE, SALT & WATER

FARADAY'S LIQUEFACTION OF CHLORINE. The gas pressure created by the evaporation of the crystals is sufficient to cause liquefaction of chlorine at the temperature of the bath.

Cl_2. It agrees well with the ideas based on atomic structure, which predict that two chlorine atoms should share electrons in their efforts to attain a stable outer structure of eight electrons each, thus,

$$: \overset{..}{Cl} : \overset{..}{Cl} :$$

The gram-molecular weight as obtained by use of the gram-molecular volume is thus shown to be considerably in excess of 70.914 g., which is the true value of the molecular weight as based upon the accurate atomic weight. This, in turn, is based upon accurate equivalent weights as determined experimentally. Ordinarily, such wide deviations between the gram-molecular weights as determined by the two methods occur only in the cases of substances like chlorine, which have high critical temperatures and are easy to liquefy. This ease of liquefaction indicates that the gravitational forces among the molecules are large; therefore the molecules are not occupying the volume they should. When more molecules occupy a smaller space than they should, the weight of 22.4 l. of such a gas will naturally be slightly too large. The lower the critical temperature, the less likely there is to be a deviation in this direction. Chlorine is an isotopic mixture of atoms whose weights are 35 and 37 respectively. The average weight of the atoms in the mixture is 35.457. The solubility of chlorine in water saturated with the gas under one atmosphere of pressure is 4.5 ml. of the gas in 1 ml. of water at $0°$ C., and 2.2 ml. of the gas in 1 ml. of water at $20°$ C. referred to S.T.P.

3. Occurrence

Chlorine is so active chemically that it is never found free in nature, but is usually found in combination with metals. The most important of these natural metallic chlorides is that of sodium. The occurrence of salt beds and salt wells was discussed in Chapter 7 in connection with sodium. Sea water contains about 2.8 per cent salt, and, since the chlorides of most metals (especially those of the active metals) are soluble, a number of other metallic chlorides are also found in sea water, whose content of chloride ion is about 2 per cent. The salt deposits of Stassfurt, Germany, which were left by the drying up of a prehistoric inland sea, contain considerable quantities of potassium and magnesium chlorides. The mineral known to the geologist as *chlorapatite*, having the formula $3Ca_3(PO_4)_2.CaCl_2$, is also found in considerable quantities in various parts of the world. In addition, there are found small quantities of the naturally occurring chlorides of barium, strontium, copper, mercury, bismuth, lead, and silver.

In quantity of occurrence and in importance as a source of chlorine, sodium chloride is preëminent.

In the human organism, the blood contains about 0.25 per cent of chloride ion while the digestive juices of the stomach contain from 0.2 to 0.4 per cent of dissolved hydrogen chloride.

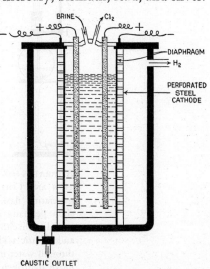

4. Preparation

Although free chlorine had been prepared by earlier workers, the Swedish chemist, Scheele (1774), because of his work with the gas and because of his records of that work, is usually credited with its discovery. It remained, however, for Sir Humphry Davy to demonstrate in 1810 that chlorine was an element. The greater portion of industrial chlorine is

CROSS-SECTION OF A VORCE CELL. The Vorce cell is one of several different specially designed cells used to prepare sodium hydroxide, hydrogen, and chlorine by the electrolysis of brine.

prepared today by the electrolysis of brine, by which process hydrogen and sodium hydroxide are also prepared. (Cf. section 14, Chapter 7.) Some is also prepared by the electrolysis of molten sodium chloride and the molten chlorides of other active metals in the preparation of the free metallic elements. (Cf. section 6, Chapter 7.) In a normal year, the United States usually produces in excess of 400,000 tons of free chlorine.

Before the use of the electrolytic method was common, considerable quantities of chlorine were produced by the *Deacon process*, which consisted of the oxidation of hydrogen chloride:

$$4HCl + O_2 \rightleftharpoons 2H_2O + 2Cl_2$$

All of the hydrogen chloride and oxygen cannot be converted to water and chlorine, because chlorine and water have a tendency to react to reproduce the original reagents but, at a temperature of about 450° C., approximately two-thirds of the original reactants will be converted into the desired products. This process finds little commercial use at present.

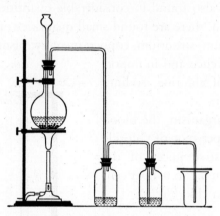

APPARATUS FOR THE LABORATORY PREPARA-
TION AND COLLECTION OF CHLORINE. The
generating flask may contain either potassium permanganate or manganese dioxide
mixed with either hydrochloric acid or salt
and sulfuric acid. The evolved gas is passed
through water in the first wash bottle to remove hydrogen chloride and through sulfuric acid in the second wash bottle to remove
water vapor.

In the laboratory, chlorine is usually prepared by the same method employed by Scheele; this consists of heating a strong aqueous solution of hydrogen chloride with manganese dioxide in a flask equipped with a thistle tube for the addition of more of the solution and a delivery tube for the escape of the gas. The gas is bubbled through a wash bottle containing concentrated sulfuric acid, which removes accompanying water vapor, and is caught in an upright bottle because it is heavier than air and will thus displace the air upward. A cardboard cover for the container tends to prevent the mixing of air and chlorine by diffusion.

$$MnO_2 + 4HCl \rightarrow MnCl_2 + Cl_2 \uparrow + 2H_2O$$

Potassium permanganate may be used instead of manganese dioxide in the preparation described above, but, since it is more expensive than the dioxide, it is less frequently employed for the purpose.

$$2KMnO_4 + 16HCl \rightarrow 2KCl + 2MnCl_2 + 5Cl_2 \uparrow + 8H_2O$$

The action of sulfuric acid (H_2SO_4) upon salt or other metallic chlorides will liberate hydrogen chloride, hence such a combination may be substituted for hydrogen chloride in the two foregoing reactions:

$$2NaCl + 3H_2SO_4 + MnO_2 \rightarrow MnSO_4 + 2NaHSO_4 + Cl_2 \uparrow + 2H_2O$$

When considerable quantities of chlorine are needed in the laboratory, a cylinder of it is usually provided.

5. Chemical Properties

In its outermost energy level, the chlorine atom has seven electrons. The nucleus of the chlorine atom bears a larger charge than does that of the sodium atom, so these outer electrons of the third level are pulled in more closely than is the outer sodium electron. The chlorine atom is thus smaller than the sodium atom and its electrons are held more tightly, rendering the removal of an electron from the chlorine atom more difficult. To remove one electron from a chlorine atom in a cathode ray tube requires a potential of approximately 13 v.— i.e., its ionizing potential is approximately 13 v. The addition of an electron to the chlorine atom, however, is an exothermal process which proceeds readily. These considerations indicate that chlorine will readily enter into ionic reactions by which it may gain electrons. With elements which do not lose electrons readily, it may approach a stable arrangement of eight by sharing one of its electrons with an atom of those elements; thus it may form covalent compounds as well as ionic ones. Compounds formed in these manners represent by far the greater number of inorganic chlorine compounds. The remaining electrons in the outer level, or valence level, if conditions are right, may now establish coordinate links with various other atoms to form a variety of rather complex chlorine compounds in which the oxidation number of the chlorine atom has a positive value. The chemistry of chlorine is, therefore, much more complicated than is the relatively simple chemistry of sodium. In this chapter, only the binary compounds of chlorine formed by the gaining or sharing of one electron will be discussed, with the more complex compounds being saved for a later chapter. In all of these simpler binary compounds, chlorine exhibits an oxidation number of -1. The types of reactions into which it may enter to acquire this oxidation number are combination and displacement.

A. COMBINATION REACTIONS. Chlorine will combine directly with all metals and with all of the nonmetals save the inert gases, fluorine, oxygen, nitrogen, and carbon. Even the noble metals, such as platinum and gold, are attacked when heated. Binary compounds of chlorine with carbon, oxygen, or nitrogen may be prepared readily by indirect methods; of these, only carbon tetrachloride is of practical importance. For the most part, the metals have configurations which permit them to lose electrons more or less readily, so that most of the metallic chlorides are formed by a transfer of electrons and are hence

ELECTROLYTIC CELLS USED IN THE COMMERCIAL PRODUCTION OF CHLORINE. (Courtesy, The Mathieson Alkali Works, Inc.)

ionic compounds. The formulas of the various metallic chlorides formed are determined by a consideration of the number of electrons the metallic atom may lose as compared with the ability of the chlorine atom to gain one electron. The zero valence rule must obtain. As stated above, the usual valence of the metals of the A columns is given by the column number. The metals of the B families, for the most part, show several valences, and may, therefore, form several chlorides, but the one in which the metal exhibits its highest valence is most likely to form by direct union. These reactions between chlorine and a metal are all pronouncedly exothermic. All of the metallic chlorides are solids save the tetrachlorides of tin, lead, and titanium, and all save those of silver, lead, and mercurous mercury possess a fair degree of solubility in water.

The nonmetals, which, like chlorine, have a tendency to gain electrons, form compounds with chlorine which in the pure condition are covalent rather than ionic. Some of the nonmetals form several different chlorides. Sulfur, for instance, forms the chlorides SCl_2 and S_2Cl_2, while oxygen forms four different binary compounds with chlorine. With iodine the compound ICl is formed, and with bromine the similar $BrCl$ is formed. Among the nonmetals, hydrogen reacts most readily with chlorine. No reaction occurs if the two gases are mixed in the dark and kept in the dark, but when ultraviolet light from either the sun or an artificial source reaches the mixture, the reaction is instantaneous and violent. As might be expected from the violence of the reaction, the combination is highly exothermic:

$$H_2 + Cl_2 \rightarrow 2HCl + 2(22,000) \text{ cal.}$$

The compound formed, however, is covalent.

B. DISPLACEMENT REACTIONS. Chlorine has been shown to be a strong electron-taker. It will take electrons which they have gained from elements which are less strong in this respect. Metals displace less active metals, and, in a like fashion, nonmetals displace less active nonmetals. The activity series provides in both cases a measure of these tendencies. By consulting the activity series, it will be seen that chlorine will displace bromine from solutions of bromide ions and iodine from solutions of iodide ions:

$$Cl_2 + 2I^- \rightarrow 2Cl^- + I_2$$

This might also have been predicted from a consideration of the relative positions of chlorine, bromine, and iodine in the periodic chart; since bromine and iodine are below chlorine in the same column, they should have larger ions whose outermost electrons are less strongly held than are those of chlorine. Chlorine will also displace the sulfide ion from solution.

Chlorine reacts by displacement with many organic compounds which have hydrogen attached to carbon, as in the case with methane represented below:

$$CH_4 + Cl_2 \rightarrow CH_3Cl + HCl$$

Chlorine dissolved in water reacts with it gradually in a displacement of the hydroxyl ion of the water with the formation of HCl. The other chlorine atom of the chlorine molecule reacts with the displaced hydroxyl group to form the compound $HOCl$, hypochlorous acid, whose properties will be discussed later, with the mechanism of the above reaction, in the chapter devoted to the more complex compounds of chlorine. Hydrogen chloride and hypochlorous acid react in solution to produce water and chlorine so that neither reaction goes to completion:

$$Cl_2 + H_2O \rightleftharpoons HCl + HOCl$$

In the sunlight, hypochlorous acid gradually decomposes according to the equation

$$2HOCl \rightarrow 2HCl + O_2 \uparrow$$

As the hypochlorous acid decomposes, more of the chlorine is converted to

Tank Cars Are Used for the Large-scale Transportation of Chlorine. (Courtesy, The Mathieson Alkali Works, Inc.)

HCl and HOCl, until, ultimately, all of the chlorine has reacted with the water to produce a solution of HCl with the evolution of oxygen.

6. Hydrogen Chloride

Sodium chloride and hydrogen chloride are the two most important compounds of chlorine from the standpoint of quantities used.

A. PHYSICAL PROPERTIES. At about 20° C., hydrogen chloride is a colorless gas of a pungent, irritating odor. It is so extremely soluble in water (503 ml. of the gas at S.T.P. dissolves in 1 ml. of water at 0° C.) that it dissolves in the moisture of the air, forming droplets of a mist or fog. The aqueous solution of hydrogen chloride is known as hydrochloric acid. The gas is more dense than air (36.5:29) and has a critical temperature of 52° C., so that it is fairly easily liquefied. Its boiling point at standard pressure is −85° C., and its melting point is −114° C. The fact that liquid hydrogen chloride is not an electrolyte is taken to be proof of the statement that the H and Cl atoms are held together by covalence.

B. PREPARATION. In addition to combining violently in ultraviolet light, chlorine and hydrogen will also combine violently when heated to 250° C. in the dark. When the first few molecules of chlorine have absorbed enough energy to react, sufficient energy is evolved by their union with the hydrogen to excite the remainder of the elementary molecules, thus making them capable of reaction. The method usually employed in the laboratory for the preparation of this compound is the action of concentrated sulfuric acid upon salt, according to the equation

$$NaCl + H_2SO_4 \rightarrow NaHSO_4 + HCl \uparrow$$

The by-product is sodium hydrogen sulfate, which is also known as sodium bisulfate. The gas is dried by passing it through a wash bottle of concentrated sulfuric acid, and is caught either by upward displacement of air or by dissolution in water. The same process is used commercially; however, by heating the reacting mixture to red heat, two molecules of salt may be converted to HCl by the same quantity of sulfuric acid as was used in the above reaction:

$$2NaCl + H_2SO_4 \xrightarrow[\text{heat}]{\text{red}} Na_2SO_4 + 2HCl \uparrow$$

The by-product in this case is sodium sulfate, which is known industrially as *salt cake*. It usually contains some unreacted sodium chloride and some sodium hydrogen sulfate.

Any soluble metallic chloride will react with sulfuric acid to produce HCl. Other acids might conceivably be used instead of sulfuric, but since it is cheap, nonvolatile, and nonreactive with the product, it is the one commonly used.

The chlorides of some nonmetals react with water to produce HCl. The phosphorus chlorides furnish good examples of such action:

$$PCl_3 + 3H_2O \rightarrow H_3PO_3 + 3HCl;$$
$$PCl_5 + 4H_2O \rightarrow H_3PO_4 + 5HCl$$

C. Chemical Properties. Anhydrous hydrogen chloride gas and the anhydrous liquid are not very reactive. (Anhydrous means *without water*, that is, *dry*.) This lack of activity is a consequence of its covalent nature. The gas will react with ammonia gas to form a white smoke of very fine solid particles which

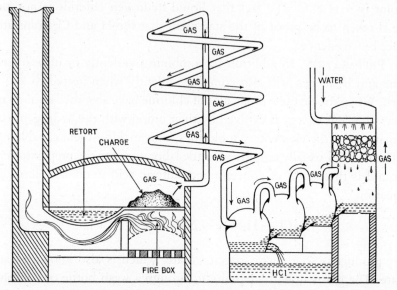

Diagram of a Plant for the Manufacture of Hydrochloric Acid. A mixture of salt and sulfuric acid is heated in the retort. The sodium hydrogen sulfate thus prepared is raked onto the hearth above the fire box where the temperature is sufficiently high to bring about the second step of the process, the conversion of the acid salt to HCl and sodium sulfate. The hydrogen chloride gas evolved is dissolved in the water descending through the washing tower and contained in the pots. Strong acid passes from the lowest of the pots to storage.

ultimately settle out, causing the film often seen on laboratory reagent bottles and equipment:

$$HCl + NH_3 \rightarrow NH_4Cl$$

Hydrogen chloride, when bubbled into nitric acid, is oxidized to free chlorine:

$$HNO_3 + 3HCl \rightarrow NOCl + 2H_2O + Cl_2 \uparrow$$

The compound NOCl is nitrosyl chloride. Because of its inactivity, anhydrous hydrogen chloride has few uses.

7. Hydrochloric Acid—Acids

In the HCl molecule, the nucleus of the chlorine atom bears a much stronger positive charge than does the hydrogen nucleus; because of this disparity of nuclear charges, the pair of electrons which the hydrogen and chlorine atoms share are drawn more closely to the chlorine nucleus than they are to the hydrogen nucleus, thus,

$$H : \overset{..}{\underset{..}{Cl}} :$$

The portion of the molecule containing the chlorine is, therefore, more negative than is the portion containing the hydrogen. When these molecules are placed in water, the water dipoles (cf. section 5, Chapter 5) exert such an attraction on the parts of the dipolar HCl molecules that they are pulled apart with the chlorine nucleus retaining the pair of shared electrons.

$$(+H_2O-) \; (+HCl-) \; (+H_2O-) \; \rightarrow \; (+H_2O-)H^+ + Cl^- \; (+H_2O-)$$

Thus, hydrogen and chloride ions are formed, making the solution of hydrogen chloride an electrolyte. Because the aqueous solution of hydrogen chloride has properties which are those of an electrolyte rather than of a covalent compound, it is known by a different name: *hydrochloric acid*. Crude commercial hydrochloric acid is sometimes known as *muriatic acid*.

Hydrochloric acid has certain properties in common with a large number of other compounds. It tastes sour, turns blue litmus red, will rot clothing, and will burn skin. Compounds which have these properties in any degree whatever are known as *acids*. By investigating these compounds, it has been found that all of them when dissolved in water, like hydrochloric acid, yield hydrogen ions:

$$HCl_{(pure)} \rightarrow H^+ + Cl^-_{(in sol.)}$$

It will be remembered that hydrogen ions are protons; therefore, *any substance which is capable of furnishing protons in aqueous solution is an acid.* Some substances are capable of providing a large number of available protons, while others are capable of providing only a few; the former are called strong acids, the latter weak acids. Naturally, there are also acids of intermediate strength. Acids as a class will be discussed more fully in a subsequent chapter.

Hydrochloric acid is a strong electrolyte, and consequently very active chemically and in much demand industrially because of this activity. The concentrated "chemically pure" acid of commerce has a density of 1.2 g./ml. and contains 37 per cent HCl by weight, with water making up the remainder of the weight. A liter of such a solution would contain $1000 \times 1.2 \times 0.37$ or 444.0 g. of hydrogen chloride.

Hydrogen chloride and water form a *constant boiling* or *azeotropic* mixture; that is, if one starts with either a solution containing much water and little HCl or much HCl and little water, and boils the solution, the component present in greatest quantity will boil away (evaporate) in greatest quantity until the composition of the solution is 20.24 per cent HCl and 79.76 per cent water.

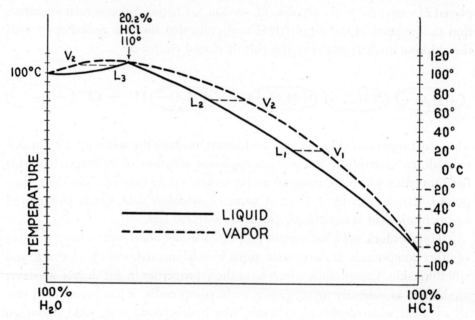

TEMPERATURE-COMPOSITION CURVE FOR HYDROCHLORIC ACID AND ITS VAPOR. At points L_1 and L_2 the vapor is richer in HCl than is the liquid. At point L_3 the vapor is richer in water than is the liquid. Thus, from either side of the constant boiling point, the liquid and vapor approach the same composition.

During the time the concentration of the solution is changing, the boiling point of the solution is also changing, but, when the above-mentioned concentration is attained, the boiling point of the solution becomes constant at a temperature of $110°$ C. at 760 mm., and continued boiling produces a vapor whose composition is identical with that of the solution. The constancy of the boiling point at this composition does not indicate the formation of a true compound, for a change in pressure causes a change in composition and a change in boiling point. Many azeotropic mixtures are known. A more complete discussion of such mixtures will be found in Chapter 12.

8. Salts—Neutralization

In section 13 of Chapter 7, it was stated that sodium hydroxide is a base, and several properties of bases were mentioned. Bases are the chemical opposites of acids, for, when a base is added to an acid, each loses its distinguishing characteristics or properties. If the two have been added in chemically equivalent quantities, the solution is neither sour nor soapy in taste, nor does it affect either red or blue litmus, nor yet does it burn the skin or rot clothing.

$$Na^+OH^- + H^+Cl^- \rightarrow H_2O + Na^+ + Cl^-$$

The hydroxyl ion of the base combines with the hydrogen ion of the acid to form the covalent, and therefore slightly ionized, water, and thus the distinguishing properties of acid and base disappear. The few hydrogen and hydroxyl ions which arise from the slight ionization of water are found in equal numbers so that neither variety is in excess. In effect, a solution of sodium chloride now exists, and, if the water is removed by evaporation, crystals of sodium chloride will form. If acids are proton-donors, *bases are proton-acceptors*. The OH^- ion is a strong proton-acceptor, as is shown by the above equation, and therefore compounds which furnish many OH^- ions are strong bases, but there are many other compounds which are capable in varying degrees of accepting protons, hence they, too, are bases. After the proton-donor and proton-acceptor have reacted, there are left ions which, upon removal of the water or other solvent, unite to form a compound. Compounds so formed are known collectively as *salts*, usually defined as *ionic compounds which in water solution yield a positive ion other than hydrogen and a negative ion other than hydroxyl. The process by which an acid and a base unite to form water and a salt is termed neutralization*. The term neutralization is used since each removes, or neutralizes, the characteristic properties of the other. It will be noted that neutralization is a metathetical reaction, and that it goes to completion because the covalent, slightly ionized water permits no reverse reaction. More general definitions for acids, bases, salts, and neutralization, and a more thorough discussion of their behaviors and relationships, will be given later.

9. The Chemical Properties of Hydrochloric Acid

The chemical behavior of this acid is based upon several considerations. In the first place, it is a *strong acid*, furnishing a high concentration of ions in solutions; in the second place, like all acids in aqueous solution, it furnishes hydrogen ions; and in the third place, it furnishes chloride ions, which property distinguishes it from all other acids.

With the hydroxides of the metals—even with those which are weak bases —it reacts to form metallic chlorides and water.

$$Ca(OH)_2 + 2HCl \rightarrow CaCl_2 + 2HOH$$
$$Al(OH)_3 + 3HCl \rightarrow AlCl_3 + 3HOH$$

It will be noted that these metathetical reactions are neutralizations.

With carbonates, bicarbonates, sulfites, and oxides of the metals, the acid also reacts to form chlorides and other products characteristic of each reaction:

$$CaCO_3 + 2HCl \rightarrow CaCl_2 + H_2CO_3$$

The carbonic acid usually decomposes thus:

$$H_2CO_3 \rightarrow H_2O + CO_2 \uparrow$$

so that the above equation might better be written

$$CaCO_3 + 2HCl \rightarrow CaCl_2 + H_2O + CO_2 \uparrow$$

Equations for the other three reactions are:

$$NaHCO_3 + HCl \rightarrow NaCl + H_2O + CO_2 \uparrow$$
$$Na_2SO_3 + 2HCl \rightarrow 2NaCl + H_2O + SO_2 \uparrow$$
$$MgO + 2HCl \rightarrow MgCl_2 + H_2O$$

Metals which are more active than hydrogen (i.e., above it in the activity series, q.v.) will displace that element from hydrochloric acid with the formation of metallic chlorides:

$$Zn + 2HCl \rightarrow ZnCl_2 + H_2 \uparrow$$

This reaction is often used in the laboratory to prepare small quantities of hydrogen. In fact, this acid finds wide application as a laboratory reagent.

All of the above methods may be employed to prepare metallic chlorides, and are so used both in the laboratory and in industry. Because of its action upon metallic oxides, hydrochloric acid is used commercially in large quantities for the removal of these oxides, or rusts, from metals, and because of its action upon carbonates it is sometimes used for opening oil-bearing limestone ($CaCO_3$) strata.

Three volumes of concentrated hydrochloric acid added to one volume of concentrated nitric yield a mixture known commonly as *aqua regia*, which is an oxidizing agent strong enough to attack even gold and platinum. It is termed *royal water* because of this action upon the noble, or royal, metals. Its activity is due mainly to the chlorine which is liberated according to the equation given at the end of section 6.

In a normal year, the United States produces sufficient hydrochloric acid to yield upwards of 125,000 tons of anhydrous hydrogen chloride.

10. Important Compounds of Chlorine

Among the binary compounds of chlorine, sodium chloride and hydrochloric acid are preëminent in importance. Other important chlorides are those of aluminum, magnesium, zinc, calcium, silver, carbon, phosphorus, sulfur, silicon, and titanium.

11. The Uses of Chlorine and Its Binary Compounds

Chlorine is an excellent oxidizing agent, and, because of this action, it is capable of destroying the color of many natural and synthetic coloring matters and of killing many varieties of germs. Great quantities of chlorine are used in the bleaching of wood pulp, paper, and cloth (especially cotton cloth) and in the purification of the drinking water of nearly all towns and cities which have central water systems. As a result of its use in the purification of water, deaths from typhoid fever have been greatly reduced. Sewage-disposal plants also use chlorine as a germ destroyer. A number of chlorides, including those of antimony, aluminum, zinc, titanium, arsenic, phosphorus, carbon, silicon, and sulfur, are made directly from chlorine, and one process for the recovery of tin from scrap tin-plate involves the conversion of the tin to stannic chloride, $SnCl_4$, by the action of free chlorine. Chlorine is also used in the preparation of dyes, drugs, explosives, and chemicals, and in the refining of sugar and petroleum.

Besides being a source of chlorine, hydrogen, sodium hydroxide, and hydrochloric acid, sodium chloride is used as a preservative and seasoning for food, in the brines of refrigerating plants, in the preparation of dyes, in the manufacture of ceramics, and for countless other purposes. The uses of hydrochloric acid were discussed in connection with its properties. The anhydrous chlorides of magnesium and calcium are the compounds from which the respective free metals are prepared. Anhydrous calcium chloride is used both in the laboratory and commercially as a drying agent, while anhydrous zinc and aluminum chlorides are used both industrially and in the laboratory as catalysts. (*A catalyst is a substance which alters the speed of a reaction without undergoing permanent change itself.* Such substances are very important and will be discussed at some length in Chap. 16.) Aluminum chloride is also used in the removal of sludge from motor oil, and zinc chloride is used in the preservation of wood. Silver chloride is used in the preparation of photographic films, plates, and papers. Carbon tetrachloride is an excellent solvent often used in dry cleaning; it is used in fire-extinguishers of the Pyrene type; it is used also in the treatment of hookworm disease and as a reagent. The tetrachlorides of silicon and titanium are used with ammonia to produce smoke screens. In the presence of the moisture always present in the air, they react to form dense white clouds of finely divided particles of ammonium chloride and the hydroxide of the element in question:

$$TiCl_4 + 4NH_3 + 4HOH \rightarrow Ti(OH)_4 + 4NH_4Cl$$

The chlorides of phosphorus find wide use in the laboratory and in chemical industry, as do also the chlorides of sulfur.

12. Analytical Tests for Chlorine and for Chlorides

Chlorine, when present in fair concentration in the air, may be identified by both its characteristic color and its odor. When present even in fairly small quantities, it may still be identified by its odor. Quantities too small to be detected by odor will displace iodine from a solution of potassium iodide, and even minute amounts of iodine will cause starch to turn blue. The easiest way to make this test is to wave in the air a piece of filter paper which has been moistened with starch paste containing potassium iodide in solution. Unfortunately, this test is not specific for chlorine, since ozone, nitrous oxide, bromine, and other gases will also liberate iodine under similar conditions. Chlorine may also be tested for by passing the gas into water and then testing the resulting solution for the chloride ion.

Hydrochloric acid, solutions of the majority of the metallic chlorides, and solutions of the nonmetallic chlorides which decompose in water, contain chloride ions which are tested for by the addition of a solution which contains the ions of silver, lead, or mercurous mercury. In any of these three cases, a white precipitate will form. The silver ion is most frequently used, since silver chloride is the least soluble of the three chlorides and has a curdy form which helps to distinguish it from other colorless, slightly soluble, silver compounds. This precipitate is further distinguished by the fact that it dissolves readily in concentrated ammonium hydroxide:

$$Ag^+ + Cl^- \rightarrow \underline{AgCl}$$
$$\underline{AgCl} + 2NH_4OH \rightarrow Ag(NH_3)_2^+ + Cl^- + 2H_2O$$

13. *The Balancing of Oxidation-reduction Equations*

The three equations given in section 4 are good examples of oxidation-reduction equations. Before one may balance such equations, he must first have the formulas for all the reagents and products in the proper member of the expression. Students often ask, "How can we tell what the products will be even when we know what the reagents are?" The ability to know what the products in such reactions will be comes from a knowledge of the behavior of the various elements in their various compounds, and is acquired as one continues his study of the elements. At the outset of an elementary chemistry course, the student is not expected to know all such answers, but, by the end of the course, he should be able to predict the products of a great many such reactions. A generalization which helps predict at least some of the products is: usually all of the metals present will be converted to salts of the acid used, and the hydrogen contained in the acid and any other reagents used will usually be converted to water by the oxidizing agent.

Once the formulas for all substances participating in a reaction have been written in their proper places, it is very easy to balance the equation. In section 7 of Chapter 5, it was shown how the oxidation numbers of elements may be calculated by use of the zero valence rule, and it was pointed out that, whenever an oxidation-reduction reaction occurs, the total gain in oxidation number of the substance oxidized must equal exactly the total decrease in oxidation number of the substance reduced. (That section should be reviewed at this time.) Consider the first method given for the laboratory production of chlorine. The reagents and products are:

$$MnO_2 + HCl \rightarrow MnCl_2 + Cl_2 + H_2O$$

By application of the zero valence rule, it is seen that the oxidation number of manganese in MnO_2 is $+4$ while in $MnCl_2$ it is $+2$; each manganese atom is, therefore, undergoing in this particular reaction a decrease of two units in its oxidation number. In HCl, the oxidation number of the chlorine is -1, as is the case with it in $MnCl_2$; from this, it is apparent that two molecules of hydrochloric acid will be required to convert each manganese atom into $MnCl_2$. The oxidation number of chlorine in the free state is zero, hence each chlorine atom which goes from -1 to 0 is increasing its oxidation number by 1. Each manganese atom loses two units in oxidation number while each chlorine which is oxidized gains one unit in oxidation number; thus two chlorine atoms must change for each manganese atom which changes. Each of these chlorine atoms must come from an HCl molecule, hence each manganese atom will require a total of four molecules of HCl—two molecules to offset its change and two molecules to convert it to manganous chloride. The numbers thus derived are set down in the equation, and all other coefficients are derived from them.

$$MnO_2 + 4HCl \rightarrow MnCl_2 + Cl_2 + H_2O$$

In each member there are now one Mn atom and four Cl atoms, but in the left member there are two oxygen atoms and four hydrogen atoms; therefore, in the right member there should be $2H_2O$, and the equation is balanced:

$$MnO_2 + 4HCl \rightarrow MnCl_2 + Cl_2 + 2H_2O$$

In the second method given for the preparation of chlorine, each manganese atom changes its oxidation number from $+7$ to $+2$, a loss of five units, while again the chlorine which enters into reduction changes from -1 to 0, a gain in oxidation number of one unit; hence for each Mn atom five Cl atoms must be supplied. From the equation, however, it is apparent that the Cl atoms must be paired to form Cl_2; five Cl atoms do not form pairs evenly, hence $2KMnO_4$ and $10HCl$ must be taken. The formulas used in the equation show that the 2K and 2Mn atoms supplied by $2KMnO_4$ will require together six Cl atoms, which must of necessity come from $6HCl$. For $2KMnO_4$, then, a total of $16HCl$ are required:

$$2KMnO_4 + 16HCl \rightarrow KCl + MnCl_2 + Cl_2 + H_2O$$

Continuing with the balancing, $2KMnO_4$ will produce $2KCl$ and $2MnCl_2$, leaving $10Cl$ which will form $5Cl_2$, and finally in the right member there are $8O$ and $16H$ which will produce $8H_2O$. The balanced equation is then

$$2KMnO_4 + 16HCl \rightarrow 2KCl + 2MnCl_2 + 5Cl_2 + 8H_2O$$

In the above equations, the hydrochloric acid served both as acid and as reducing agent. Such is not the case in an equation of the type

$$K_2CrO_4 + FeCl_2 + HCl \rightarrow KCl + CrCl_3 + FeCl_3 + H_2O$$

In this reaction, the oxidation number of the chromium (Cr) changes from $+6$ to $+3$, a loss of three units, while the oxidation number of iron (Fe) changes from $+2$ to $+3$, a gain of one unit; thus three molecules of $FeCl_2$ will be required for each molecule of K_2CrO_4. These two numbers show that the products will include $2KCl$, $1CrCl_3$, and $3FeCl_3$, which in turn will require $2 + 3 + 9$ or

14 chlorine atoms; six of these atoms will be furnished by the $3FeCl_2$, so $14 - 6$ or $8HCl$ must be used, and $8H$ and $4O$ will permit the formation of $4H_2O$. The balanced equation is then:

$$K_2CrO_4 + 3FeCl_2 + 8HCl \rightarrow 2KCl + CrCl_3 + 3FeCl_3 + 4H_2O$$

With a little practice, one soon becomes proficient in the balancing of such equations.

(*See Appendix for Exercises*)

COLLATERAL READINGS

Badger and Baker: *Inorganic Chemical Technology*, New York, McGraw-Hill Book Co., 1941.

Baldwin: Uses of chlorine, *J. Chem. Education*, **4,** 454 (1927).

Berry: *Stuff*, New York, D. Appleton-Century Co., 1936.

Brallier: A survey of products that afford industrial outlets for chlorine, *Chem. & Met. Eng.*, **30,** 624 (1924).

Killefer: Abundant chlorine, *Sci. American*, **17,** 202, Nov. (1944).

Latimer and Hildebrand: *Reference Book of Inorganic Chemistry*, New York, The Macmillan Co., 1941.

Mantell: Modern chlorine practice, *Chem. & Met. Eng.*, **47,** 166 (1940).

Martin: *Chlorine and Chlorine Products*, New York, D. Appleton & Co., 1915.

Payne: Modern practice in electrolytic chlorine caustic production, *Chem. & Met. Eng.*, **31,** 334 (1924).

Riegel: *Industrial Chemistry*, New York, Reinhold Publishing Corp., 1937.

Sadtler: *Chemistry of Familiar Things*, Philadelphia, J. B. Lippincott Co., 1937.

Weeks: *Discovery of the Elements*, 5th ed., Mack Printing Co., 1945.

WILHELM OSTWALD

(1853–1932, Russian [by birth])

Ostwald was a man of great energy and great versatility who is sometimes referred to as the father of physical chemistry. Certainly he, Arrhenius, and van't Hoff were the founding fathers of that branch of chemical science. In 1887 he was appointed professor of physical chemistry at the German University of Leipzig. Students came to him in numbers, and many of the world's outstanding physical chemists were trained in his classroom and laboratory. His contributions to physical chemistry have been both numerous and varied, and his numerous writings include works on philosophy, biography, and painting, in addition to many volumes devoted to scientific subjects. In 1887 he and van't Hoff founded the important *Zeitschrift für physikalische Chemie*, which he edited for many years. In 1909 he was awarded the Nobel Prize.

11

The States of Matter

II. LIQUIDS

1. Introduction

The liquid state occupies an intermediate position between the gaseous and solid states. The molecules of a liquid possess sufficient kinetic energy to prevent their gravitational attraction locking them into a rigid form, but they do not have sufficient energy of motion to permit them to separate completely; hence a given mass of a liquid has a definite volume but no definite shape. Like a gas, a liquid takes the shape of any vessel in which it is put, but, in contrast to a gas, a definite quantity of liquid is required to fill the vessel. It is not possible for a liquid to be compressed nearly so much as a gas because its molecules are already close together; large pressures produce only small changes in volume. An increase in temperature increases the kinetic energy of all molecules, permitting them to offer more opposition to gravitational attraction, hence a liquid expands when heated, but there are no general laws relating to the volume, pressure, and temperature of liquids. Since the change of a liquid into the gaseous or solid states is dependent upon the kinetic energy of the molecules, which in turn is dependent upon the temperature, there are definite temperatures characteristic for most liquids at which these changes occur; they are known as *transition temperatures*.

By placing one liquid layer carefully on top of a layer of a more dense liquid in which it is soluble, and setting the vessel where it will not be disturbed, it is found that the two liquids gradually mix until a homogeneous solution results. This experiment illustrates that the molecules of a liquid diffuse, though much more slowly than do those of a gas. This, of course, is to be expected, since the retarding action of gravitational attraction is so much stronger proportionally than it is in a gas. The molecules of a liquid are much closer together than they are in a gas, because of this greater relative strength of attraction, and consequently the density of liquids is much greater. Naturally, since the volume of a liquid varies with temperature, its density will also vary with temperature, but in an inverse fashion. The closeness of the molecules also

171

indicates that their mean free flight will be greatly reduced from that of the gaseous state.

2. Viscosity and Fluidity

The ability to flow is one of the properties of liquids. Everyday observation shows that all liquids do not flow with the same ease. Water, alcohol, and gasoline flow easily, while molasses, heavy motor oil, and glycerin flow very slowly. When a liquid flows, layers of molecules are rubbing over each other much as marbles rub and roll over each other when a box of them is tilted. Friction is generated by this rubbing of layers of particles, and the greater the friction the slower the flow. A liquid which resists flowing, or resists the action of any other deforming force upon it, is said to be *viscous*. Units for expressing viscosity have been defined, and measuring devices are available for its measurement. The opposite of *viscosity* is *fluidity*, which is defined mathematically as the reciprocal of the viscosity. Viscosity diminishes and fluidity increases with temperature. The viscosity of molasses in the winter month of January is proverbial.

3. Surface Tension

A molecule in a liquid well below the surface is completely surrounded by like molecules, so that the forces acting upon it are the same in all directions.

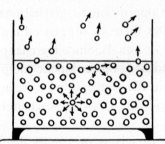

SURFACE TENSION. The forces acting on a particle in the liquid surface are unbalanced and there is a tendency for the particle to be drawn inward from the surface.

A molecule in a liquid surface, however, has no like molecules above it, hence it is more strongly attracted by the molecules below it and tends to be drawn down into the liquid. When molecules are withdrawn from the surface, the latter naturally shrinks, and work would therefore have to be done to extend the surface against this spontaneous contraction. For convenience in calculating, the surface of a liquid is considered as having a tension acting in it in all directions in its plane. This tension is measured in terms of the force in dynes acting on a unit length of the surface. (Consult a textbook of physics for the definition of a dyne.) It is surface tension which causes falling drops of liquid to assume a spherical shape, since a sphere is the shape which has the least surface for a given volume. Surface tension also causes liquids to rise in tubes made of materials which they wet. Surfaces of containing vessels are wet by a liquid when the attraction between their molecules and those of the liquid is greater than the attraction of the liquid molecules for each other; in the latter case, the surface is not wet by the liquid. If the liquid contains a dissolved substance, its surface tension will be altered, as will be the tension of a surface in contact with another liquid which is not soluble in the first.

4. The Refractive Index

Light traveling obliquely from a medium of lesser density to a medium of greater density has its velocity reduced and its direction of propagation altered, a phenomenon known as *refraction*. The ratio of the velocity of light in air to its velocity in another medium is known as the *index of refraction* of the medium. The index of refraction of a liquid is a property often useful in identifying it, especially when used in conjunction with others of its properties. The refractive indices of a great many liquids are rather easily measured with the instrument known as a refractometer.

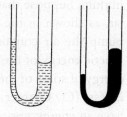

WETTING AND NONWETTING LIQUIDS IN TUBES OF UNEQUAL AREA OF CROSS SECTION.

5. Equilibrium

One encounters many examples of equilibrium in the study of the various physical sciences. *Equilibrium is a state of balance between two opposing forces.* It is a dynamic rather than a static state, for the operation of two opposing forces implies the operation of two opposing processes brought about by those forces. Equilibrium is attained when the opposing processes attain equal speeds. Since the speed of most processes is dependent upon the conditions under which they operate, equilibria may be shifted by a change in conditions. For example, a tank into which water runs from above has a valve in its bottom. With the valve closed, the tank is half filled, then the valve is opened sufficiently to permit water to escape at the same rate at which it is entering; the tank remains half full, but two opposing tendencies are in operation and the water is constantly changing though the level remains fixed. A state of equilibrium exists. Increasing the rate of flow of water into the tank raises the water level in the tank, but, as the level rises, the pressure is increased and the rate of flow from the drain valve increases, until presently the rate of flow from the tank is again equal to the new rate of influx. Thus equilibrium is reëstablished, but at a different point, for now the water level stands fixed at a higher mark on the tank wall. It is absolutely necessary for the student to have clearly in mind the conditions necessary for the existence of a state of equilibrium.

6. *Evaporation vs. Condensation*

The evaporation and condensation of liquids also offer an example of two opposing forces which, under proper conditions, may establish a state of equilibrium. Suppose that a small evaporating dish of ether is placed beneath a bell jar, as shown in the accompanying diagram, and that by means of a vacuum pump the air contained in this closed system is removed. Now the average kinetic energy of the ether molecules contained in the dish is the same, but the energy of some of the molecules is greater than this average, while that of others is less. (Cf. Chapter 9, the kinetic-molecular theory.) Those molecules which have an energy greater than the average have a tendency to leave their fellows, and as they reach the surface of the liquid they do leave, passing into the space above. This process is known as *evaporation*, and it is always in operation to a greater or lesser degree at a liquid surface. The evaporated molecules are now in the gaseous state, and are moving about striking each other and the confining walls and rebounding from these contacts. The paths followed by some of these molecules lead them again to the liquid surface, where, upon striking, they are likely to remain, at least temporarily. This return of molecules from the gaseous state to the liquid state is known as *condensation*. At first, when there are relatively few molecules in the gaseous state above the liquid contained in the dish, the chance that any of these few molecules will strike the liquid surface is small, but, as their number is increased by continued evaporation, the chance of their returning to the surface is increased. If the temperature remains constant, a time is ultimately reached when the number of molecules leaving the liquid surface per second is just equaled by the number rebounding into it; a state of equilibrium then exists.

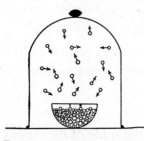

EVAPORATION VS. CONDENSATION. At equilibrium, the number of particles leaving the dish each second is equaled by the number of particles returning to the dish in the same time.

If the liquid in the dish is warmed, the average kinetic energy of the molecules of the liquid is increased and the number of molecules with an energy great enough to overcome the gravitational attraction of adjacent molecules is increased. As a result, the number of molecules leaving the dish each second is increased; this, in turn, increases the number of them in the gaseous state, and, therefore, their chance of colliding with the liquid surface. Presently, when the number in the gaseous state has increased sufficiently, the number returning to the liquid in a second will again be equal to the number leaving in that time, and a state of equilibrium will again be established but at a new point.

The gaseous molecules derived from a liquid by evaporation are referred to as the vapor of that substance, and at equilibrium the space above the liquid is said to be saturated with the vapor.

7. *Vapor Pressure*

The kinetic-molecular theory (Chapter 9) holds the pressure of a gas to be due to the bombardment of gas molecules against the walls of the containing vessel. When equilibrium exists between a liquid and its vapor, the number of molecules contained in a unit volume of the vapor is constant (since the number of particles returning to the liquid per second is equal to the number leaving it), and hence the pressure exerted by a vapor at equilibrium is constant for the substance in question under the specified conditions. *The pressure exerted by a vapor in equilibrium with its liquid is known as the vapor pressure of that liquid.*

The greater the number of gas molecules in a specified space, and the greater their average speed (kinetic energy), the greater will be the pressure they exert. According to section 6, as the temperature of a liquid in contact with its vapor is increased, the larger will become the number of particles in the space above the liquid before a new point of equilibrium is established, and the greater will be their speed. Thus, at a higher temperature, the vapor pressure of a liquid is greater than it is at a lower temperature, and for every liquid the temperature at which the vapor pressure was measured must be specified along with the value of the pressure.

WATER   ETHER

THE VAPOR PRESSURE OF LIQUIDS. At a given temperature, the vapor pressure of ether is much greater than that of water, hence the mercury in the second tube is depressed much more than in the first tube into which water was introduced.

Vapor pressures have to be determined experimentally, and the data for the vapor pressure of water at various temperatures contained in the Appendix and referred to in section 11 of Chapter 9 were so obtained. A rather simple method of determining vapor pressures consists of setting up a barometer tube and noting the height of the mercury contained in it. Then a small quantity of the liquid to be tested is introduced at the bottom of this tube by means of a medicine dropper with a curved tip. The liquid, being less dense than mercury, rises to the top of the mercury column, where it evaporates into the empty space of the closed tube. The pressure of the vapor above the mercury column causes it to be depressed. By reading the height of the column and subtracting it from the original height, the vapor pressure is obtained at the existing temperature. Since, according to Dalton's law, gases in a mixture exert their pressures independently, the very small amount of mercury vapor present in the empty space

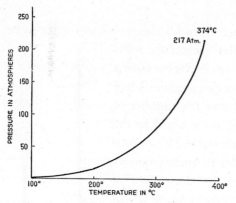

both before and during the determination in no wise affects its validity.

The dissolution of substances in a liquid alters its vapor pressure. This matter will be discussed in the next chapter.

8. Boiling and the Boiling Point

As the temperature of a liquid is raised, its vapor pressure is also increased. If one continues to raise the temperature, ultimately then a point should be reached at which the vapor pressure of the liquid is just equal to the pressure of the atmosphere upon the surface of the liquid. On adding more heat to the liquid, there is no further increase in pressure nor does the temperature of the liquid increase, but the rate at which evaporation takes place is accelerated. This phenomenon of the rapid passage of a liquid into the gaseous state against the external pressure exerted upon its surface is known as *boiling*, and *the temperature at which the vapor pressure of the liquid is equal to the external pressure is known as the boiling point*. The *normal boiling point* of a liquid is that temperature at which its vapor pressure is equal to the pressure exerted by 760 mm. of mercury.

At pressures of less than one atmosphere, a lower temperature is required to cause a liquid to boil than is required at standard pressure. Since it is heat that cooks food rather than the boiling, it is difficult to cook foods by boiling them in the open air at high altitudes where the pressure of the atmosphere is greatly reduced. Pressure cookers are used to obviate this difficulty. Essentially, these are tightly closed metal drums. Water placed in one of these boils first at the temperature characteristic of the atmospheric pressure of the locality. As the pressure of the water vapor above the water increases, the boiling point of the liquid gradually rises in an effort to equal this applied pressure. Most pressure cookers are equipped with a safety valve which is set for a maximum pressure

TEMPERATURE-VAPOR PRESSURE CURVE FOR WATER.

within the vessel of 16 to 18 lb. in excess of the current atmospheric pressure. Food cooks rapidly at the increased boiling point.

The addition of a solute to a liquid has a marked effect upon its boiling point, as will be seen in the next chapter.

9. *Heat of Vaporization*

At the boiling point, the application of more heat produces no rise in temperature, so one may well ask: What becomes of the absorbed heat? This heat is expended by the molecules in the performance of the work necessary to tear themselves away from the gravitational forces which attract them and their fellows to each other. The number of calories required to convert 1 g. of a substance from a liquid at its normal boiling point to a gas at the same temperature is known as the *heat of vaporization* of the substance. The heat of vaporization for water is 540 cal. per gram.

10. *The Boiling Points of Associated and Unassociated Liquids*

Boiling consists of the absorption by molecules in the liquid state of sufficient heat to afford them sufficient kinetic energy to tear themselves completely away from each other. In nonpolar liquids (cf. Chapter 5), the molecules will separate when they have acquired sufficient kinetic energy to overcome the gravitational forces attracting them to each other. Such liquids are said to be *unassociated*.

Molecules of polar liquids are held together not only by the usual gravitational forces, but also by the electrical forces which are brought into play by the separation of the charges in such polar, or dipolar, molecules. These dipolar molecules behave toward each other much as would a number of small bar magnets, their ends of unlike charges attracting each other. Closely associated groups of molecules are thus formed. Such liquids are known as *associated liquids*. To break up this added mutual attraction, more heat is required, and the boiling points of such liquids are much higher than those of comparable substances which are unassociated.

The molecular weight of methane, CH_4, is 16; that of carbon monoxide, CO, is 28; that of nitric oxide, NO, is 30; that of carbon dioxide, CO_2, is 44; that of phosphine, PH_3, is 34; and that of hydrogen sulfide, H_2S, is 34. All of these substances are gases at room temperature, but water, whose molecular weight is 18, is a liquid at room temperature and does not boil until its temperature is raised to 100° C. This abnormally high boiling point for water, as compared with those of substances of comparable molecular weight, is due to its high degree of association. Were water not abnormal in this respect, animal and plant life as we know it could not exist on the earth.

11. Critical Temperature and Pressure

The critical temperature and pressure have already been discussed from the standpoint of the gaseous state in section 20 of Chapter 9, but a few words concerning their relationship to the liquid state are appropriate at this time. It has already been mentioned that, when a liquid is heated in a closed container, the vapor pressure continues to rise as heat is applied. Ultimately, however, a temperature will be reached beyond which there will be no equilibrium between the liquid and vapor phases because the liquid phase has ceased to exist. The temperature at which the liquid phase ceases to exist under such circumstances is specific for each liquid, and is known as the *critical temperature*. It is the temperature at which the kinetic energy of the molecules just exceeds their gravitational attraction for each other. The pressure exerted by the vapor at this temperature is known as the *critical pressure* of the substance under investigation. The critical temperature of water is 374° C., and its critical pressure is 217.72 atmospheres. Carbon dioxide is a gas at room temperature, but it is so easily liquefied and has such a low critical pressure that a quantity of it sealed in a strong glass tube serves well for a visual demonstration of the behavior of a substance as it approaches, reaches, and passes its critical temperature.

12. The Liquefaction of Gases

The foregoing discussions assert that for every temperature below the critical temperature there is a definite vapor pressure characteristic of each substance. If at the critical temperature, or at any temperature below it, an external pressure in excess of the vapor pressure of the chosen substance acts upon the vapor, its molecules will be forced closer together, thus increasing their mutual gravitational attraction to the point that some of the less energetic molecules are reconverted to the liquid state. The volume of the gas is reduced by some of it returning to the liquid state, and, as a consequence, the pressure is reduced and equilibrium is reëstablished at a new point. Obviously, if the gas is cooled first to remove some of its kinetic energy, less pressure will be required to force its molecules close enough together for the force of gravity to begin to exceed the energy of motion of at least a few of the molecules. The gas may be liquefied without the application of external pressure if this cooling is carried sufficiently far. A gas, then, may be liquefied by cooling, by compressing (if it is at or below its critical temperature), or by a combination of cooling and compressing. Gases which are easily liquefied are usually converted to the liquid state at room temperature by pressure alone, while others are both cooled and compressed. Those gases which have low critical temperatures must of necessity be cooled first to this temperature, and are often still further cooled so that less pressure will be required.

Anyone who has ever used an automobile tire pump knows that when a gas is compressed its temperature rises. The explanation of this heating is that increased gravitational attraction caused by pushing the molecules closer together causes their motions to become more violent. More numerous and more violent collisions occur, liberating more heat. In other words, they have gained more energy so they try to give more energy to their surroundings, much as a hot stove tries to give energy to a cold room.

When a gas is condensed to a liquid, the amount of heat evolved per gram is equal to the heat absorbed per gram by the liquid when it changes to a gas—that is, it is equal to the heat of vaporization. Conversely, when a compressed gas is allowed to expand, the molecules do work in tearing themselves away from the gravitational attraction of their fellows. When work is done, energy is consumed, and, since these molecules take the energy to do this work from their own supply of kinetic energy,

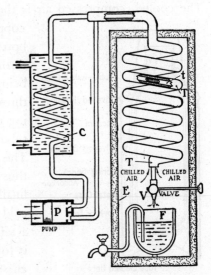

APPARATUS FOR THE LIQUEFACTION OF AIR. Air is compressed by the pump P, is cooled by water in coil C, enters the liquefier through pipe t, expands through valve V, escapes through the outer pipe T, and returns to the pump for recycling. Ultimately the entering air becomes cold enough to liquefy upon expansion and is caught in reservoir F. (Courtesy, Foley, A. L.: "College Physics," 3d ed., Philadelphia, The Blakiston Company.)

they emerge from the process less energetic, or cooler; hence, when a gas expands, it becomes cooler. Even on a hot day, the air escaping from an inflated tire from which the value stem has been removed feels cool. The higher the pressure of the escaping gas and the lower its initial temperature, the more pronounced will be the cooling effect when it expands, because the greater the attractive force among the molecules was beforehand, the greater the amount of energy required to overcome this attraction. The cooling of a gas which occurs when it expands without doing external work is known as the *Joule-Thompson effect*.

Use is made of the Joule-Thompson effect in the liquefying of a number of gases of low critical temperature. An excellent example of its use is in the liquefaction of air, which is today a large industry. Dust is filtered and water vapor and carbon dioxide are removed from the air which is to be liquefied, then it is subjected to a pressure of approximately 200 atmospheres and cooled by a flow of water over the pipes containing it to remove the heat of compression. The cooled, compressed air is then led through the inner of two concentric copper tubes in a well-insulated container. At the bottom of this coil the air expands suddenly through a needle valve to atmospheric pressure, being cooled during the expansion. It rises then through the outer of the concentric tubes, cooling the air flowing downward through the inner tube so that when it expands it is still colder. The upward-flowing air becomes ever colder, thus making the incoming air colder too, until finally the expanding air becomes sufficiently cold to liquefy. Liquid air is used scientifically as a refrigerant, but commercially its principal use is for separation, by methods which will be discussed in the next chapter, into oxygen, nitrogen, argon, and neon. Many interesting demonstrations can be performed with liquid air as a refrigerant.

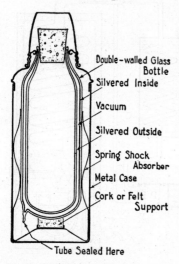

Double-walled Glass Bottle
Silvered Inside
Vacuum
Silvered Outside
Spring Shock Absorber
Metal Case
Cork or Felt Support
Tube Sealed Here

A Dewar Flask. This flask shown in the diagram is equipped with a protective metal case and a stopper. (Courtesy, Foley, A. L.: "College Physics," 3d ed., Philadelphia, The Blakiston Company.)

Hydrogen and helium have molecules of very small masses and in consequence the gravitational attraction between their respective molecules is very small at ordinary temperatures. Both gases therefore have to be pre-cooled to a considerable extent before the magnitude of the Joule-Thompson effect is sufficient to bring about their liquefaction.

Liquid air and other liquefied gases of low critical temperature are kept in containers known as Dewar flasks, which are of the type of the well-known vacuum bottle. These flasks are made of glass, and have double walls whose inner surfaces are silvered. The silver reflects any heat which might try to enter, as well as any heat which might try to leave the flask, and further to prevent the transfer of heat in either direction the space between the walls is evacuated. Any substance placed in such a container tends to retain its initial temperature, cooling or warming very slowly.

13. *The Use of Liquids and Gases in Refrigeration*

Commercial and home refrigerating machines both make use of the Joule-Thompson effect. In both instances, a gas is compressed to a liquid, the liquid is cooled and allowed to expand through a needle valve, turning again to a gas; heat is absorbed by the expanding liquid and gas from cold storage chambers

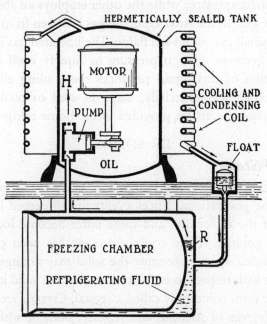

A Compression Refrigeration Machine. This diagram is greatly simplified but it shows the essential parts of a small home-type mechanical refrigerator. At the present time, it is common practice to place the motor and compressor below the food cabinet and the cooling coil in a flat arrangement on the back of the refrigerator. (Courtesy, Foley, A. L.: "College Physics," 3d ed., Philadelphia, The Blakiston Company.)

or from vats of brine whose freezing point is low enough to prevent its freezing. Cans of fresh water immersed in the brine tanks will form ice, however.

A gas to be used successfully in such a refrigeration plant must have a high critical temperature, a critical pressure which is not too high to be held satisfactorily by the normal industrial materials, a high heat of vaporization, and freezing and boiling points which will be satisfactory in relation to the operating temperature of the compressor and the low temperature compartment. In commercial refrigeration, ammonia, NH_3, is usually the gas chosen, but for home use it is not satisfactory because its rather high critical pressure requires equipment which is too bulky. Sulfur dioxide and difluorodichloromethane, CF_2Cl_2, commonly called *freon*, are the most common home refrigerants.

The ammonia is liquefied by means of a mechanical compressor in commercial refrigeration; home refrigerators are of two types. One type uses a small electrically driven compressor, while the other employs an absorbent to reduce the volume of the gas. In the latter type, the gas is driven from the absorbent by heating it with a small gas- or oil-fed flame. The liberated gas is evolved in such quantities as to generate enough pressure to liquefy itself after it has been cooled. Evaporation of this liquid produces the cooling effect, and the gas formed is reabsorbed. Commercially, water is used to cool the compressed liquid, while air-cooled coils are provided in the home refrigerators.

III. SOLIDS

14. *The Solid State*

As a liquid is cooled, its molecules lose energy. Cooling continued far enough causes the gravitational forces eventually to exceed in magnitude the kinetic energy of the molecules, and these latter become locked into a rigid form of definite volume. If the cooling process has been conducted slowly enough, the particles which constitute the solid may arrange themselves into definite positions with respect to each other so that the solid itself will exist in a regular geometric form commonly called a crystal. Crystals are of various forms and of varying degrees of strength and rigidity, both of which properties are dependent upon the substance of which they are composed.

The particles of which crystals are composed have not lost entirely their kinetic energy; they do this only at the absolute zero. This residual kinetic energy, which has merely decreased until the attraction between the particles exceeds it, manifests itself in a continued motion of the particles; but, since the particles are now fixed in space with reference to each other, this motion is manifest only as a vibration through a fixed point. Further cooling reduces the amplitude of this vibration, and presumably at the absolute zero it should cease altogether. A gas, then, and a very cold solid, offer the extremes in the physical states of matter. The properties of matter in the gaseous state are determined largely by the motion of the particles, while in the solid state they are determined largely by the rigidity of the structure formed and by the positions which the particles occupy with respect to each other in the structure; these latter are, in turn, dependent upon the magnitude of the forces of attraction and upon the size of the constituent particles.

The outstanding properties of solids are a definite rigid shape, a definite volume, a considerable resistance to distorting forces, and an abrupt change to the liquid state at a definite temperature for a fixed pressure.

15. *The Crystal Lattice*

All true solids exist as crystals. *A crystal is a three-dimensional figure which is bounded by plane surfaces which intersect at definite angles.* A company of soldiers whose members are wandering about at random presents no regular appearance, but the same company presents a very regular appearance when each of its members is occupying one of a series of points geometrically arranged with respect to each other. It has been shown that crystals are of a definite form because the particles which compose them are, like the soldiers, occupying definite points arranged geometrically in space. Such an imaginary system of points is referred to as a *space lattice* or a *crystal lattice*. The points of intersection of the steel girders which form the framework of a large building might be thought of as the space lattice which determines the very regular shape of the building.

The smallest portion of the lattice which represents the relative position of all the different particles which may be contained in it is known as the *unit cell*. Different numbers of these unit cells make up the different-sized crystals of the substance.

16. *Crystal Systems*

By the application of geometric principles, it can be shown that 32 types of three-dimensional figures bounded by plane surfaces are possible. In practice, 32 different crystal forms have been found in nature—no more, no less. All true solids exist in some one of these 32 possible forms. These forms may, in turn, be grouped into six major systems. This further simplification is made possible by consideration of the relative lengths and angles of inclination of a number of imaginary lines (usually three or four in number) called *axes*, which intersect at a point within the crystal. These systems are:

A. THE CUBIC SYSTEM: three axes of equal length intersect at right angles to each other.

B. THE TETRAGONAL SYSTEM: three axes of which two are of equal length intersect at right angles to each other.

C. THE RHOMBIC SYSTEM: three axes of unequal length intersect at right angles to each other.

D. THE MONOCLINIC SYSTEM: three unequal axes intersect so that one is at right angles to the other two which intersect obliquely.

E. THE TRICLINIC SYSTEM: three unequal axes intersect at oblique angles.

F. THE HEXAGONAL SYSTEM: three equal axes in the same plane intersect at angles of 60 degrees while a fourth axis of unequal length intersects their plane at right angles.

These characterizations indicate that the cubic system is the simplest. Both cubes and octahedra belong to it; these forms do not look at all alike, but their faces may be referred to the same system of axes. The external form of a crystal is determined by the development of certain of the possible faces which may be referred to a given set of axes to the exclusion of other possible faces. Cubic crystals further may be of three different space lattices. The simple cubic lattice contains one of the constituent particles at each corner of the unit cell; the face-centered lattice contains one particle at each corner of the cell and one in the center of each face of the unit cell; the body-centered lattice contains one particle at each corner and one in the center of the unit cell. Of these, the face-centered variety has been shown by x-ray examination to be the

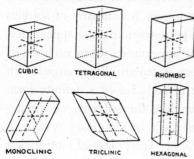

THE SIX MAJOR SYSTEMS OF CRYSTALS.

THE THREE TYPES OF CUBIC LATTICES.

most common; all of the metals which are the best conductors of heat and electricity form that type of cube.

17. The Determination of Space Lattices

The geometric form of a crystal may usually be determined by examining it with the naked eye, though occasionally a hand lens or microscope is necessary. The relative positions of the particles which form the space lattice of a crystal may not, however, be determined by an optical device which employs ordinary visible light. The particles of which crystal lattices are composed are of diameters which are shorter than the wavelength of ordinary light, hence they may not be seen, since to be visible an object must be larger than the wavelength of the radiation employed. X-rays, discovered by Roentgen in 1895, are similar in nature to ordinary light waves, but are of a much shorter wavelength. Because of their shortness, they are affected by the tiny particles of crystals. Photographs are made by permitting the emergent rays obtained by passing a beam of x-rays through the various planes of a crystal to fall on a photographic film or plate; and by calculations based upon the careful measurements made of the distance between the spots on the film caused by the emergent rays, it is possible to ascertain the geometric configuration of the particles and the distance between them. This method, whose details are beyond the scope of this

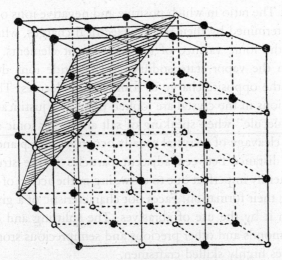

THE CRYSTAL LATTICE OF SODIUM CHLORIDE. The alternating dots and circles represent alternating ions of sodium and chlorine. (Courtesy, Hackh-Grant: "Chemical Dictionary," Philadelphia, The Blakiston Company.)

text, was developed by the Swiss scientist, Laue, and extended by the English scientists, W. H. Bragg and his son W. L. Bragg.

It has been found that the particles which occupy the points of a space lattice may be ions, atoms, or molecules. Nearly all salts and some acids and bases have structural units which are ions; since a given substance always contains both positively and negatively charged ions in equal numbers, these particles hold each other in place in the structure by means of their electrical attraction. Elementary metals such as sodium usually have atomic lattices, while a great many covalent compounds have molecular lattices. By the method mentioned above it has been shown that the crystals of salt are of the simple cubic type with ions of sodium and chlorine occupying alternate corners of the unit cell. The distance between the centers of any two consecutive ions in the structure has been calculated to be 2.81 Ångström units. By reference to the accompanying diagram of the space lattice of a sodium chloride crystal, it will be seen that an ion in the interior of the crystal is not especially associated with any other one ion of the opposite variety, but rather is surrounded by six of them; there are within the crystals, then, no sodium chloride molecules as such. Since each unit cell is made up of four sodium ions and four chloride ions, and since, regardless of the size of a salt crystal, it is made up of some finite number of unit cells, the sodium and chloride ions in any crystal of salt are always present in a ratio of 1:1. The ratio in which positive and negative ions occur in a crystal is, of course, determined by their relative electrical charges, which, in turn, are determined by the ionic valence of the constituent elements. There is some evidence that in the vapor state sodium and chloride ions do pair off with specific ions of the opposite charge to form true molecules. This fact and the 1:1 ratio of the ions in the crystal are looked upon as a justification for the use of the term "molecule" when speaking of salt and other ionic substances.

Fracture or cleavage of a crystal usually occurs along a plane at right angles to the greatest distance between adjacent particles in the structure. Natural crystals are frequently imperfect due to crowding or the action of other mechanical forces during their formation. Faces not characteristic of a given crystal may be ground upon it by the use of abrasives. The splitting and cutting of new planes upon diamonds and other precious and semiprecious stones is an industry which requires highly skilled craftsmen.

18. Freezing vs. Melting

If a liquid is cooled gradually, it presently reaches a temperature at which crystals of the solid form begin to appear. A thermometer placed in the mixture registers a certain temperature when these first crystals appear, and will continue to register the same temperature as long as crystals continue to form. When all of the liquid phase has disappeared, the temperature of the solid mass will go still lower if the cooling is continued. The constant temperature at which the solid phase formed is the *freezing point* of the liquid. Sometimes it is possible to cool a liquid a few degrees below its freezing point without having it solidify. Liquids in such a state are said to be *supercooled*, and are in a metastable (only apparently stable) state, for, if they are stirred or seeded with a small crystal of the same substance, or disturbed in other ways, solidification takes place at once with the temperature shooting up immediately to the normal freezing point. The heat to drive the temperature up is that given up by the particles themselves when they are locked into a rigid structure.

When a cool solid is heated, the particles of the crystal lattice absorb energy, increasing the amplitude of their vibrations until ultimately they have absorbed enough energy and increased the amplitude of their vibrations' sufficiently to tear themselves from the positions in which they have been locked. The temperature of the solid continues to rise until the structure begins to break down, with the formation of the liquid phase. Again, as long as liquid and solid both exist, there is no change in temperature even though heat is still being applied. This temperature is the *melting point* of the solid, and it is numerically equal to the freezing point. When the solid phase has entirely disappeared, a continued heating produces a rise in the temperature of the liquid.

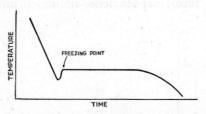

A TYPICAL TIME-TEMPERATURE FREEZING-POINT CURVE.

The melting point (or freezing point) may now be defined as that temperature at which the liquid and solid phases of a substance are in equilibrium under a pressure of one atmosphere. Each pure crystalline substance has a characteristic melting, or freezing, point. The freezing points of nonpolar substances are usually much lower than are those of either ionic or polar substances, because they do not have electrical forces to augment the attraction between their molecules.

19. Heat of Fusion

It was just stated that, once a substance has begun to melt, there is no further rise in temperature until all of the solid has turned to liquid. To tear down a house, or any other structure, energy must be expended. In the case of a solid, energy must be expended to tear down the crystal lattice by pulling the particles which compose it away from the attraction of each other. Until this structure is completely torn down, there is no energy available for increasing the motion and temperature of the particles which have already been torn from the structure. The quantity of heat necessary to tear down the structure of 1 g. of any crystalline solid is characteristic of each such substance, and is known as the *heat of fusion* of that substance. The heat of fusion of ice (that is, the quantity of heat necessary to turn 1 g. of ice at 0° C. to 1 g. of liquid water at 0° C.) is 80 cal. Naturally, the amount of heat given up by 1 g. of water at 0° C. in passing to ice at 0° C. is also 80 cal. It is usually fairly warm during a snowstorm because of the heat given off by the formation of the snowflakes from the moisture of the clouds.

20. The Vapor Pressure of Solids—Sublimation

The particles in the faces, edges, and corners of crystals are not surrounded on all sides by other particles, as are those inside the crystal, and they are consequently less tightly held. Some of these less firmly bound particles have more energy than others, and may make their escape from the structure into the surrounding space. Thus, solids are able to exert a vapor pressure. There are many solid substances which exert an appreciable vapor pressure at ordinary temperatures; naphthalene, of which mothballs are made, is one of these. As with liquids, the vapor pressure of solids increases with increasing temperature. Since the highest temperature at which a solid may exist is its melting point, then, naturally, the highest vapor pressure of a solid is that exhibited at its melting point. Conversely, since a liquid ceases to exist at the freezing point, it has its lowest vapor pressure at this temperature. The freezing point and melting point of a given substance being identical, then the vapor pressures at these points are identical, and these points may be defined further as *that temperature at which the solid and the liquid phase of a substance have the same vapor pressure under an external pressure of one atmosphere.* This latter specification is made for convenience of reference to compiled data.

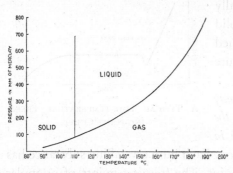

THE VAPOR-PRESSURE CURVE OF IODINE.

Many solids have melting points which are so much above 20° C. that at this temperature they do not retain sufficient energy to exert an appreciable vapor pressure; others, however, have melting points that are near enough to 20° C. to enable them to exert vapor pressures large enough to permit their complete evaporation without first melting. This phenomenon of a substance passing directly from the solid to the gaseous state is known as *sublimation.* Naphthalene, iodine, and carbon dioxide snow (dry ice) are examples of substances which sublime. When the vapors of such solids are cooled, they condense again directly to the solid state. Substances which have high vapor pressures at temperatures considerably below those at which they would be expected to melt have no true melting points at a pressure of one atmosphere. They may be forced to melt at higher pressures, and their gases may be forced to condense.

21. *Amorphous Solids*

Sometimes, if a substance normally crystalline in the solid state is melted, then cooled very rapidly, it will become rigid but will not have its characteristic form. Examination shows that it has no crystalline form whatever, but upon standing it gradually forms a mass of small crystals of its characteristic variety. On the other hand, there are a number of materials which, though possessing a fair degree of both strength and rigidity, never assume any crystalline form. Such substances which possess no definite form are described as *amorphous* (without form). Many substances once described as amorphous are really crystalline, but their crystals were so tiny that it was some time before investigators discovered that the small powdery particles did possess a definite form. There are, however, many amorphous substances; notable among these are the glasses and tars. Such substances have a random arrangement of their particles, presumably because their attractive forces are directed equally in all directions. They are characterized by a lack of definite melting and boiling points and specific heats of fusion, as well as by a lack of form. Often their melting and freezing points are not identical. Since x-ray patterns for them are similar to those of fluid liquids, they are looked upon as liquids which have extremely high viscosities, and are often referred to as *supercooled liquids*—that is, as liquids which have been cooled below their freezing points but which have not frozen, or set, to a true solid.

22. *Polymorphism and Allotropy*

It is often possible to produce crystals of two, or more, varieties by varying the conditions under which a given substance crystallizes. Not all substances are capable of such behavior, but there are many which are; these latter are said to be *polymorphic* (many forms). The terms dimorphic, trimorphic, tetramorphic, etc., are used to indicate the exact number of forms which may exist. For a given set of conditions, a given substance always crystallizes in the same form. It is stable, if it can exist indefinitely under those conditions, but, if it soon changes to another form, even though there is no change of conditions, it is only metastable. Some polymorphic forms are mutually interconvertible, and are described as enantiotropic. In other instances, only one form may change into the other regardless of conditions; such substances and such uni-directional changes are described as *monotropic*. For enantiotropic changes such as the interconversion of the two crystalline varieties of sulfur, there is a definite temperature at which the change occurs. Such temperatures are known as *transition temperatures*, and for the sulfur change it is 96° C. Definite transition temperatures imply the association of definite quantities of energy with the different forms. Generally, then, as a gas or liquid cools, the solid form containing the greater amount of energy tends to form first, but, as the cooling continues, this form will become unstable and pass with an evolution of energy into the more stable form, or it will exist for a time in a metastable condition at the lower temperature, then pass into the more stable form.

The existence of more than one distinct solid modification of elementary substances is known as *allotropy*. This term is used much more loosely than is polymorphism, for it applies to crystalline forms, amorphous varieties, and varieties of the element which are not homogeneous but are mixtures of other modifications. Allotropes result from either the arrangement of the same units into different crystal lattices or from the combination of different numbers of atoms to form different molecules. As in the cases discussed above, conditions as related to energy considerations determine the allotrope which will exist under specified conditions. Many examples of allotropy and polymorphism will be encountered in subsequent descriptive chapters.

23. Isomorphism

There are, of necessity, many substances whose crystals have the same form, since only 32 crystalline forms are possible. Such substances are said to be *isomorphic* (of same, or equal, form). Usually, such compounds have essentially similar chemical constitutions so that a structual unit of one such compound may replace a similar unit in the building up of a crystal of the other. As a result of this ability, mixed crystals of the two substances may be formed. The two substances may be crystallized simultaneously, giving a crystal of homogeneous appearance, or one isomorphic substance may be crystallized on a nucleus of a crystal of another isomorph. Strikingly beautiful crystals of the second type may be made by crystallizing colorless potassium aluminum alum on a crystal of the violet-colored potassium chromium alum. Crystals of the first type may have their percentage constitution varied widely by varying the relative proportions of the substances in the mixture from which they were crystallized. This wide range of variability indicates that no compound is formed by the components, and such crystals are known as *solid solutions*. In the past, considerable use was made of the knowledge that isomorphic substances frequently have similar chemical constitutions, in order to assist in the determination of valences and formulas.

(See Appendix for Exercises)

COLLATERAL READINGS

Eddington: *The Nature of the Physical World*, New York, The Macmillan Co., 1928.

Findlay: *The Spirit of Chemistry*, New York, Longmans, Green & Co., 1934.

Getman and Daniels: *Outlines of Physical Chemistry*, New York, John Wiley & Sons, Inc., 1943.

Hildebrand: *Principles of Chemistry*, New York, The Macmillan Co., 1941.

Kraus: *Gems and Gem Materials*, New York, McGraw-Hill Book Co., 1931.

Pigman: *A Story of Water*, New York, D. Appleton-Century Co., 1938.

Any standard textbook of physical chemistry.

COLLATERAL READINGS

Edgington, The States of Matter, New York, The McGraw Hill Co., 1958.

Bradley, The structure...

Getman and Daniels...   ...iley & Sons, Inc.,
    1943.

Hildebrand, Principles...

Kraus, Gases and Gas...

Pigman, A Text of...   ...1931.

Any standard textb...

JOSEPH CHRISTIE WHITNEY FRAZER
(1875–1944, American)

The work of Frazer and Morse upon the measurement of osmotic pressure is regarded as a classic of its kind. Other contributions of Frazer were the exact measurement of the vapor pressures of aqueous solutions of nonvolatile solutes, the development (with Bray of California) of a catalyst for the low-temperature oxidation of carbon monoxide, and a series of valuable papers on problems in the baffling field of heterogeneous catalysis. Frazer took his graduate training at Johns Hopkins University, where he studied with Ira Remsen and Harmon Northrop Morse. Upon receiving his degree, he worked four years for the U.S. Bureau of Mines, then returned in 1911 to Johns Hopkins to serve on its Faculty of Philosophy until his death. For many years he was chairman of the department of chemistry. He was a quiet man of great wisdom and wide knowledge who was held in more than ordinary esteem by his own students and those of the department in general.

12

Solutions

1. Introduction

A majority of the reactions of inorganic chemistry with which the student comes in contact take place in solution—especially in aqueous solution. Because of this fact, the student should add to his knowledge an understanding of the properties of solutions and the laws which govern their behavior. Solutions are homogeneous mixtures of two or more substances (cf. section 9, Chapter 2). Since the particles of the substances which are mixed are too small to be seen with the finest optical device, they are taken to be of molecular dimensions, and the nature and behavior of solutions is best understood from a consideration of these particles. The solutions most frequently encountered are of a solid in a liquid or of a liquid in a liquid, but there are examples of the whole variety of solutions which may result from dissolving material in any one state in a material of any other state. Air is a solution of gases in a gas; carbonated water affords an example of a gas dissolved in a liquid; and the mixed crystals discussed in connection with isomorphism in the preceding chapter are solid solutions; these examples serve to illustrate a few of the possibilities. Solutions result from physical rather than chemical change, as is shown by the facts that the composition of solutions can be varied over rather wide ranges and that by proper physical processes the components of solutions may be separated. Solutions are usually classified by the final phase in which they exist. Because of the importance of aqueous and other liquid solutions, the primary emphasis of this chapter shall be upon them.

2. Dissolution vs. Crystallization

Consider the case of a crystal of sucrose (table sugar) placed in a small beaker of water. Remember that particles in the surface of a crystal are less firmly held in the structure than are the interior particles. Between these surface particles and the particles which make up the liquid water, there exists an attraction strong enough to pull the surface particles from the crystal structure into the liquid phase where they are free to move among the particles of the liquid. The passing of these particles into the liquid phase is known as *dissolution*, and the process is in many respects analogous to the evaporation of a liquid. As more of the sugar molecules pass into solution, the probability of some of them striking against the undissolved portion of the crystal increases, until ultimately the number of sugar molecules returning to the crystal in a unit of time has become equal to the number leaving the crystal in that time, and a state of equilibrium exists under the existing conditions. The return of particles from the liquid phase to points in the crystal lattice is known as *crystallization*.

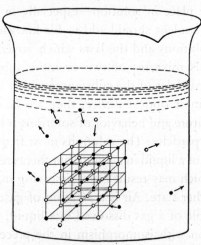

DISSOLUTION VS. CRYSTALLIZATION.

3. *Saturated and Unsaturated Solutions*

   A solution in which a state of equilibrium has been established between the undissolved solute and the solution is said to be saturated, and there is no further change in the concentration of the solution under the specified conditions, although dissolution and crystallization are still in progress. A solution which has not yet reached such a state of equilibrium and in which dissolution of the solute may still take place is described as *unsaturated*.

4. *The Dissolution of Liquids and Gases in Liquids*

   There are pairs of liquids, such as alcohol and water, which will form solutions in any proportions in which they may be mixed. Such pairs are said to be *miscible in all proportions*, and in such cases no saturated solutions are possible. Other pairs of liquids are only moderately soluble in each other, and still other pairs are only very slightly miscible. Liquids of this latter type, after being shaken together, separate into two layers when the shaking ceases. At the interface between the two liquid layers molecules from each layer pass into the other layer, until eventually the number of molecules of variety A passing back from layer B into layer A is just equal to the number of A molecules leaving A to pass into B, and a similar situation exists with B molecules passing from layer B into A and back into B. A double equilibrium is thus established, and each layer is saturated with respect to molecules of the other variety.

Some gases have a great solubility, others a moderate solubility, and still others a very limited solubility in a given liquid. Solutions of gases in liquids are usually prepared by shaking the two together, bubbling the gas through the liquid, or by leaving the gas under pressure in contact with the liquid. Again, as more and more gas passes into the liquid, there is a tendency for more and more gas to leave it, and there is finally established an equilibrium at which these two rates are equal with a saturated solution resulting.

5. *Factors Which Affect Solubility*

A. THE NATURE OF THE SOLUTE AND SOLVENT. The extent to which a given solute is soluble in a given solvent depends upon the nature of both. In general, the old household rule that "likes dissolve in likes" is scientifically sound. Particles which are similar in general character, as might be expected, are much more likely to mix than are dissimilar ones. Nonpolar liquids and solids are much more soluble in nonpolar liquids than they are in polar solvents, while polar solids dissolve most readily in polar liquids. Since the ions which make up the structure of ionic crystals are electrically charged, such solids are much more soluble in polar liquids, such as water or ammonia, than they are in nonpolar solvents. Unfortunately, at present there is no generally applicable theory to account for the wide differences of solubility which exist.

B. THE EFFECT OF TEMPERATURE. It has been shown that a change of state is accompanied by a change in the energy content of the particles of the substance in question. A liquid in dissolving a solid must do work to tear down the crystal lattice of the solid. It does this work at the expense of its own energy supply; the change is consequently endothermic. Often, though, there are other accompanying changes so that the net change may be either endo- or exothermic, depending on the nature of the other processes and the magnitude of the energy changes involved in them. Since the tearing down of the lattice is endothermic, raising the temperature of the solvent would increase the quantity of available energy and consequently the quantity of solute which could be dissolved by the specified quantity of solvent. Because of the accompanying changes mentioned above, and their influence upon the overall process, there are a number of solids whose solubility is less in hot water than in cold. Calcium butyrate is an example of this relatively small class of substances. There is no change of state when a liquid dissolves in a liquid, hence no general prediction can be made as to the effect of a change of temperature in such cases, but experimentation has shown that the solubility of most partially miscible liquids in each other is increased with a rise in temperature. When a gas dissolves in a liquid it is passing from a more energetic to a less energetic state, and hence should give up energy. Such a process is exothermic, and therefore should be favored by cooling to remove this evolved heat. A lower temperature would favor dissolution in this case, as is shown by the fact that the evolved heat would tend to be reabsorbed with a resulting evaporation of the gas if cooling were not provided.

C. THE EFFECT OF PRESSURE. Pressure has very little effect upon the solubility of liquids and solids in liquids, since there are only very slight changes of volume between these states. The solubility of a gas in a liquid is, however, in accord with Henry's law, as discussed in section 21, Chapter 9. A gas dissolved in a liquid may be removed by bubbling a second, insoluble gas through the solution. The atmosphere above the solution will now contain both gases, and, according to Dalton's law, the pressure of the original gas will now be only a fraction of the whole; and according to Henry's law the solubility of the first gas must now decrease because its pressure above the solution is less. Heating will, of course, assist the process.

D. THE EFFECT OF PARTICLE SIZE. Dissolution takes place at the crystal surface, therefore increasing the surface by pulverizing (that is, using many small crystals instead of one large one) greatly increases the rate at which dissolution occurs. Calculation shows that if a cube 1 cm. on an edge having a surface area of 6 sq. cm. is broken up into particles whose edges are 0.01 cm., the surface area exposed will be 600 sq. cm. If both small and large crystals are present, the rate of dissolution is greater from the former than from the latter, but the return rate is the same per unit of area, hence the small crystals grow smaller and the big ones become bigger, provided there is a sufficient quantity of the smaller crystals to saturate the solution.

6. Supersaturated Solutions

A saturated solution of one of the numerous solids which are more soluble at higher temperatures than at lower ones should, upon being cooled, deposit crystals of the solute until equilibrium is established at the lower temperature. If, however, the saturated solution at the higher temperature contains no undissolved solute and no particles of foreign matter, and if it is allowed to cool without being disturbed in any way, it is often possible to cool it without crystallization of the excess solute occurring. A solution which has been so cooled naturally contains more solute than can normally be dissolved in the given quantity of solvent at the existing temperature, and is therefore in a metastable condition; such solutions are said to be *supersaturated*. If such solutions are disturbed by the addition of a tiny crystal of the solute, by scratching the inside of the container with a glass rod, by the introduction of a particle of dust, by shaking, or by a number of other means, crystallization of the excess solute usually takes place rapidly until a stable state of equilibrium is established between deposited solute and the solution at the new temperature.

Table 9

VARIATION OF SOLUBILITY WITH TEMPERATURE
(IN GRAMS PER 100 G. OF WATER)

Salt	10°	20°	30°	40°	50°	80°
KBr	59.5	65.2	70.6	75.5	80.2	95.0
K_2SO_4	9.22	11.11	12.97	14.76	16.50	21.4
NaCl	35.8	36.0	36.3	36.6	37.	38.4
$NaNO_3$	80.	88.	96.	104.0	114.	148.

Supersaturation is very easily demonstrated by the use of a solution saturated with sodium sulfate at 30° C. Below this temperature, the solubility of a hydrated form of this salt falls off rapidly so that a supersaturated solution is easily prepared by observing the above-mentioned precautions while cooling the solution to 15°. Introduction of a small crystal of the hydrated salt produces immediate crystallization of the excess solute.

7. *Solubility*

The quantity of solute required to saturate a specified quantity of solvent at a given temperature is known as the *solubility* of the solute in that solvent at the established temperature. The solubility of solids and liquids is usually expressed in terms of the number of grams that will dissolve in 100 g. of the solvent, while the solubility of gases is frequently expressed as the number of volumes of the gas which will dissolve in one or one hundred volumes of the solvent at the specified temperature.

Since solubility varies with temperature, a very convenient method of pre-

senting solubility data is to plot solubilities as ordinates against their temperatures as abscissas. Usually, smooth curves may be passed through the plotted
points so that temperature-solubility relationships may be read for all combinations. Such curves are known as *solubility curves.* Sharp breaks such as the one
noted in the solubility curve of sodium sulfate are known as transition points,

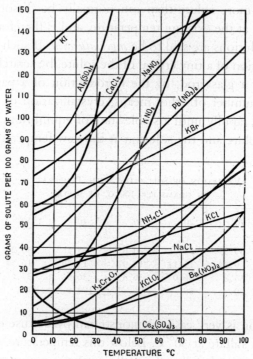

TEMPERATURE-SOLUBILITY CURVES OF VARIOUS SALTS
IN WATER.

and indicate a change in the composition of the solid phase in contact with the
solution. In this case, above 32.4° C. the solid phase consists of anhydrous
(without water) sodium sulfate, while below that temperature the solid phase
is sodium sulfate decahydrate, $Na_2SO_4.10H_2O$. At the transition temperature,
both solid phases may exist in equilibrium with the solution.

There is no such thing as a totally insoluble substance, but the solubility
of some substances is so extremely small that for all practical purposes they
may be considered insoluble and are frequently so referred to.

8. Concentration

Chemistry is an exact science, so it is usually essential for the chemist to
know the concentration—i.e., the quantity of solute contained in a unit volume

—of the solution with which he is working. There are a number of methods of expressing the concentration of solutions, each of which has its own peculiar advantages.

A. WEIGHT PER CENT SOLUTIONS. The number of grams of solute contained in 100 g. of the solution is an index of the strength of the solution. Thus 12 g. of any solute dissolved in 88 g. of solvent to prepare 100 g. of solution is a 12 per cent solution. Percentage concentration may always be found by dividing the weight of solute by total weight of solution, and then multiplying by 100. Such solutions are more frequently used in industrial chemical work, or in physical work than in chemical laboratory work.

B. MOLAR SOLUTIONS. Chemical equations are based upon molecular formulas which, in turn, are indicative of gram-molecular weights, or moles, therefore it is often convenient to employ solutions which contain a specified number of moles per unit of volume. *A molar solution is one which contains one gram-molecular weight of solute per liter of solution.* A two- or five-molar solution naturally would be one which contains 2 or 5 moles of solute, respectively, per liter of so-

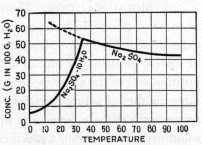

THE SOLUBILITY CURVE OF SODIUM SULFATE. The break in the curve indicates a transition point at which a change in the composition of the solid phase occurs. The transition temperature for sodium sulfate is 32.4° C. Above that temperature the anhydrous salt constitutes the solid phase in equilibrium with the saturated solution, while below that temperature the decahydrate constitutes the solid phase.

lution. One milliliter of a one-molar (1 M) solution would contain 1 millimole of solute. Calculations involving volumes of molar solutions are very simple. For instance, in the reaction

$$Pb(NO_3)_2 + 2HCl \rightarrow \underline{PbCl_2} + 2HNO_3$$

it is apparent that 2 moles of hydrochloric acid are required for each mole of lead nitrate; hence, if both solutions were 1 M in concentration, then the volume of the hydrochloric acid solution required would always be twice that of the lead nitrate solution. Equal volumes of a 1 M lead nitrate solution and a 2 M hydrochloric acid solution might be used, and so on.

C. NORMAL SOLUTIONS. Even more convenient for use in chemical reactions than molar solutions are normal solutions. *A normal solution is one which contains one gram-equivalent weight of solute per liter of solution.* A half normal (N/2) solution is, of course, one which contains a half gram-equivalent weight per liter of solution, while a three normal ($3N$) solution contains three gram-equivalent weights in the specified volume. Since equivalent weights are capable of performing like amounts of chemical work, solutions of the same normality react volume for volume, and the reacting volumes of solutions of unlike normality bear an inverse relationship to their normalities. Methods of calculating equivalent weights for both metathetical and oxidation-reduction reactions have already been given (cf. section 16, Chapter 8).

D. MOLAL SOLUTIONS. There are certain physical properties of solutions, as shown below, which depend not upon the variety or the nature of the particles present in solution, but only upon their number as related to the number of solvent particles per unit of volume. Solutions of the same percentage composition and of the same molarity and normality do not necessarily contain the same number of solute particles per unit of volume; hence, for comparisons of properties which are dependent upon the relative numbers of particles present, solutions which contain a specified number of moles per 1000 g. of solvent are employed. Naturally, if the molecules of solute in such a solution become divided into fragments, then the total number of solute particles will become increased by a multiple whose value is determined by the number of fragments formed by each molecule. Solutions so prepared are known as *molal solutions*.

E. MOLE PER CENT SOLUTIONS. In physical chemical work, it is occasionally necessary that the concentration of a solution be known in terms of the relationship of the number of moles of solute present to the number of moles of solvent present. Thus, if a solution contains 2 moles of solute in 8 moles of solvent, the mole percentage strength of the solution is

$$\frac{2}{(8+2)} \times 100 = 20 \text{ mole per cent}$$

9. Standard Solutions

Any solution whose concentration is known accurately is said to be a *standard solution*. Standard solutions may be prepared by the careful weighing and measuring of the requisite components, or the concentration of an unknown solution may be determined by the use of a suitable analytical method. Any such process by which concentration is determined is known as *standardization*. Molar and normal solutions are most conveniently prepared by the use of volumetric flasks (cf. section 11, Chapter 3). Preparation of solutions of the other types mentioned in the preceding section require the use of accurate weighing and measuring devices.

10. Extraction and the Partition Principle

Many solutes are soluble in liquids which are soluble in each other to only a very slight degree. For instance, at 25° C. iodine is 675 times more soluble in carbon disulfide than it is in water, and water and carbon disulfide are virtually insoluble in each other. Consequently, if a solution of iodine in water is shaken with a small volume of the disulfide, most of the iodine passes into it, and when the shaking is stopped the liquids separate into two layers which may be separated by means of a separatory funnel. *This process of removing a solute from a solvent in which it is less soluble into one in which it is more soluble is known as extraction.*

Although the iodine is very much more soluble in the carbon disulfide than it is in the water, it does not leave the water completely, for each liquid tends to extract the solute from the other and a state of equilibrium is established. *The solute thus becomes divided between the two liquids so that its concentration in each is in the same ratio as its solubility in each.* This statement is known as the *partition principle* or *distribution law.* In the example chosen, the equilibrium may be represented

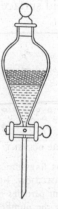

$$I_2 \text{ (in } H_2O) \rightleftarrows I_2 \text{ (in } CS_2)$$

and the expression for calculating the quantity of iodine in each solvent is

$$\frac{\text{Grams } I_2 \text{ in } CS_2}{\text{Volume } CS_2} \bigg/ \frac{\text{Grams } I_2 \text{ in } H_2O}{\text{Volume } H_2O} = 675$$

A SEPARATORY FUN-
NEL. By the use of this device, immiscible liquids may be separated from each other.

To make this expression general, let m_1 and m_2 represent the mass of solute in each liquid; let v_1 and v_2 represent the volumes of the two solvents; and let K equal the distribution constant; whence one has

$$\frac{m_1}{v_1} \bigg/ \frac{m_2}{v_2} = K$$

K will be specific for each combination of two solvents and one solute, and, because solubility varies with temperature, K will vary with temperature also.

Extraction has many uses in the laboratory, especially in the recovery and refining of organic compounds, as well as numerous industrial applications.

11. *The Effect of a Solute upon the Escaping Tendency of a Solvent*

It has been stated that molecules in the surface of a pure liquid tend to leave it to pass into the gaseous state. When a solute is dissolved in a pure liquid, the molecules of the two varieties become so intimately mixed that in the liquid surface the two varieties of particles are present in the ratio of the mole percentages of the components. The number of particles of solvent now in the liquid surface is considerably decreased as compared with the number of particles in a surface of equal area of the pure solvent. The lowered concentration of solvent molecules decreases the rate of evaporation of solvent from the liquid surface, and therefore the concentration of its vapor required to establish equilibrium will be decreased. Experimentation has shown that in every instance the escaping tendency of a substance is lowered by the presence in it of a solute. *Raoult's law*, which is based upon experimental observations, deals especially with the effect of a solute upon the vapor pressure of a liquid, and states that the vapor pressure of a liquid solvent is proportional to its mole fraction in the solution. Thus, if 4 moles of water and 1 mole of any solute which may dissolve in that quantity of water are mixed, the vapor pressure of the water in the solution should be only four-fifths as great as would be the vapor pressure of pure water at the same temperature. Raoult's law, however, applies strictly only to *ideal solutions*. These are defined as solutions which, when prepared from matter in the same state, exhibit no energy changes, or which, when prepared from matter in different states, have only energy changes which are equal to the energy of the change of state. In practice, most dilute solutions of non-ionic substances conform very well to the law as stated above.

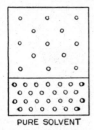 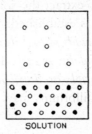

PURE SOLVENT   SOLUTION

VAPOR PRESSURES OF A PURE SOLVENT AND OF ITS SOLUTION. In the solution, the number of solvent particles in the liquid surface is smaller hence the number of solvent particles leaving this surface in a unit of time is smaller than the number leaving the surface of the pure solvent.

12. *Deliquescence*

It is apparent that the more concentrated a solution is, the lower is its vapor pressure. Highly concentrated aqueous solutions have vapor pressures which often are considerably lower than is the pressure of the water vapor present in the air. Such a system will tend to establish equilibrium by absorbing moisture from the air; this, in turn, tends to lower the vapor pressure of the atmospheric moisture while at the same time it dilutes the solution, thereby raising its vapor pressure so that the two pressures approach more nearly to each other in value. This phenomenon can be demonstrated very nicely by placing in a closed vessel a small beaker half filled with a concentrated solution of sulfuric acid and a second small beaker filled to a noted level with water. In even a few hours it may be noted that the level of the pure water has been lowered while the level of the liquid in the beaker containing the acid has been raised. The explanation is, that as the acid withdraws water vapor from the enclosed space to establish equilibrium, the pure water keeps evaporating to maintain the vapor pressure which is characteristic of it at the temperature of the vessel. *This phenomenon of a substance drawing to itself moisture from the air is known as deliquescence.*

13. Drying Agents and Dehydrating Agents

Substances which possess the property of deliquescence to a high degree are useful in the laboratory for absorbing moisture, and when so used are called *drying agents*. There are a number of such substances which will absorb water readily because the vapor pressure which they maintain is so low. The reasons for the maintenance by various drying agents of such low vapor pressures are

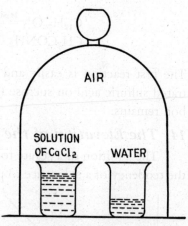

A DEMONSTRATION OF DELIQUESCENCE. As time passes, the liquid level in the beaker of water becomes lower while the liquid level in the beaker containing the calcium chloride solution rises.

several. Substances like sodium hydroxide are so extremely soluble that they form solutions of such high concentration that only low vapor pressures may be maintained. Substances like phosphorus pentoxide and calcium oxide maintain low pressures because they react with the absorbed water to form new compounds: phosphoric acid in the first instance and calcium hydroxide in the second. Anhydrous calcium chloride, anhydrous copper sulfate, and sulfuric acid utilize the absorbed water to form hydrated compounds. (Hydrated compounds are those which have water dipoles closely associated with their ions.) A fourth class of drying agents includes those like the specially prepared form of silica known as silica gel, which has a very porous structure into whose many fine capillary tubes water and other liquids and gases are drawn by the action of their own surface tension.

Dehydrating agents have little to do with deliquescence, but since some drying agents act also as dehydrating agents, they are conveniently defined at this juncture. *A dehydrating agent is a substance which has such a pronounced affinity for water that it will tear down a molecule containing both hydrogen and oxygen atoms in the ratio of two to one, cause these atoms to combine into water, and then either absorb or combine with the water formed.* Sulfuric acid and phosphorus pentoxide are both excellent dehydrating agents as well as drying agents. Examples of their action are:

$$C_{12}H_{22}O_{11} \xrightarrow{H_2SO_4} 12C + 11H_2O$$
$$CH_3CONH_2 + P_2O_5 \rightarrow CH_3CN + 2HPO_3$$

The first reaction is easily and strikingly demonstrated by dropping concentrated sulfuric acid on sucrose (table sugar); soon only a black pile of wet carbon remains.

14. *The Elevation of the Boiling Point*

The addition of a solute to a liquid lowers its escaping tendency, therefore the tendency of a substance to pass from the liquid state to the gaseous state as a result of boiling should be diminished. As a consequence of this diminution, more heat should have to be applied to the liquid to make it boil; that is, the boiling point of a solution should be higher at a specified external pressure than is that of the pure solvent. Observation shows this to be the case. The explanation is simple: The boiling point of a liquid is that point at which its vapor pressure is equal to the external pressure, and a solute lowers the vapor pressure of the solution below that of the pure solvent; therefore, to increase the vapor pressure to a value equal to that of the external pressure, heat must be applied, and, as a consequence, the temperature at which boiling occurs is raised. According to Raoult's law, the vapor pressure lowering is proportional to the mole fraction of the solute in the solution; and since the boiling point elevation is

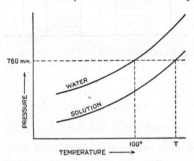

TEMPERATURE-VAPOR PRESSURE CURVE FOR WATER AND FOR AN AQUEOUS SOLUTION. This graph shows the effect of a solute upon the vapor pressure and the boiling point of water.

proportional to the vapor pressure depression, therefore *the elevation of the boiling point is proportional also to the mole fraction of solute contained in the solution.* Abnormal effects are noted for solutes whose molecules break into fragments in solution. These will be discussed in a later chapter. Practical application of boiling point elevation is made by motorists in Death Valley, who use solutions whose boiling points are above those of water; in this fashion, the loss of radiator fluid by boiling is diminished in this region of extremely high summer temperatures.

15. *Distillation*

Solid solutes of low vapor pressures and of a considerable stability to heat may be removed from solution by boiling away the liquid solvent. The boiling points of such solutions are, as has been shown, above the boiling point of the pure solvent, and, as evaporation of the solvent continues, the boiling point rises as the solution becomes more concentrated. If the evaporation is conducted so that the vapor of the solvent may be condensed to a liquid and collected, the process is known as *distillation* and the equipment used is known as a still. Distillation is important both in the laboratory and in industry for the recovery of either solute, solvent, or both. Naturally, if the solute has any appreciable vapor pressure at the boiling point of the solvent, some of it too will pass over with the distillate, or if the solute is decomposed by heat some of the decomposition products may be volatile and pass over with the distillate. Fresh water is readily obtained from salt water by distillation, and nearly all very pure water for scientific work is prepared by this process.

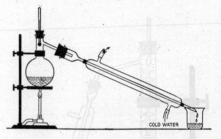

APPARATUS USED FOR LABORATORY DISTILLATIONS.

16. *Fractional Distillation*

When one liquid is dissolved in another, each is a solute dissolved in the other as a solvent, and as a consequence each usually has its vapor pressure lowered. The extent of this lowering of vapor pressure is dependent upon the concentration of the liquids in each other—that is, upon the amount of each present in the solution—and to some extent upon the specific natures of the liquids. Usually, the vapor pressure of such a liquid mixture is intermediate between those of the pure components, but sometimes it is lower than that of either component, while in other cases it is higher than that of either. Consider first the behavior of a mixture of the usual type.

When such a solution is heated, each liquid establishes a vapor pressure dependent upon the temperature and the concentration of the other liquid dissolved in it. The mixture will boil when the sum of the vapor pressures (cf. Dalton's law) is equal to the external pressure. The vapor above the boiling mixture contains both substances. The more volatile of the two substances will furnish the greater vapor pressure, and will be present in the vapor in greater quantity than the less volatile component. It will also be present in greater proportion than it was in the liquid mixture. As the boiling is continued, the liquid in the boiling vessel becomes poorer in the more volatile and richer in the less volatile liquid, so that to maintain boiling the temperature must be steadily increased. The boiling point continues to rise, until virtually all of the more volatile component has escaped, and then becomes constant at the boiling point of the less volatile component. Further heating produces only an evaporation of this component.

A suitable condensing device arranged to reconvert the vapors to the liquid state may obviously then be used to separate liquid mixtures. This process is known as *fractional distillation*. If the temperature range between the boiling points of the two pure liquids is divided into several arbitrary divisions, or fractions, each of several degrees, and a clean receiving vessel provided for each fraction, the first fraction will be richer in the more volatile (lower boiling) liquid, the last fraction will be richer in the less volatile (higher boiling) liquid, and the middle fractions will contain varying

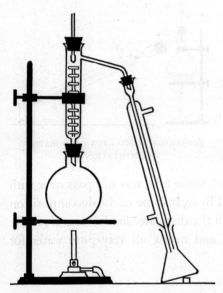

APPARATUS FOR FRACTIONAL DISTILLATION ON A LABORATORY SCALE.

mixtures of the two. By repeatedly refractionating these original fractions, one may ultimately secure an almost complete separation of the two components.

Repeated fractionation as described above would be much too tedious for practical application. In practice, both in the laboratory and in industry, frac-

INDUSTRIAL FRACTIONATING COLUMNS OF THE TYPE USED IN THE PETROLEUM INDUSTRY.
(Courtesy, Standard Oil Co. of New Jersey.)

tionating columns are used. In essence, these columns, be they large or small, are simply towers filled with material which does not prevent the upward flow of vapor but does offer a large area of condensing surface. The liquid which condenses in the lower part of this tower is richer in the more volatile component than is the liquid in the boiler. The rising hot gases from the boiler cause a portion of this first condensate to be revolatilized, and the vapor which this time passes on upward is still richer in the more volatile component. This process of condensation and revolatilization is repeated on up the length of the tower so that the vapor which ultimately arrives at the top and passes into the condenser is almost entirely the vapor of the more volatile liquid. This rising vapor has been even further purified in the column by the return flow of condensed liquid drawn downward by gravity. As this downward-flowing liquid meets the rising vapors, it condenses the less volatile and some of the more volatile liquid, allowing only a very pure portion of the latter to pass on up and into the condenser. There is thus a tendency for the liquid and the vapor to establish equilibrium, but, since heat is being continuously applied to the boiler, a state of equilibrium is never reached and the separation continues.

Fractional distillation is widely used in industry. The petroleum industry makes an important use of it in the separation of the components of natural petroleum and in the separation of the products prepared from petroleum. The separation of the components of liquid air is also effected by this means. The taller the tower used and the greater the condensing surface offered, the more effective is the separation. Fractionating columns vary in length from a few inches to a few feet for laboratory work and upward to many feet for the great steel columns of industry. Towers of any considerable length require auxiliary heaters along their walls to prevent total condensation of the ascending gases. Liquids which form constant boiling mixtures cannot be separated by fractionation, and those which have boiling points separated by only a few degrees are not easily separated by this method.

17. Constant Boiling Mixtures

The preceding discussion emphasizes that when one liquid is dissolved in another, the vapor pressure of the solution is usually intermediate between the vapor pressures of the two pure liquids. There are, however, many pairs of liquids which dissolve in each other to form solutions whose vapor pressures are either higher or lower than that of either component taken separately. A given pair of liquids capable of forming solutions whose pressures are in excess of that of either pure component will form, at a given external pressure, one particular solution of the two whose vapor pressure will exceed that of all other possible mixtures of the two. This solution of maximum vapor pressure will, of necessity, have a minimum boiling point. Similarly, two liquids capable of forming solutions whose vapor pressures are lower than that of either pure component will form one particular mixture of the two, under existing conditions, whose vapor pressure will be lower than that of any other possible mixture of them, and this particular solution of minimum vapor pressure will have a maximum boiling point.

Distilling, at a given external pressure, a mixture of two liquids capable of forming a solution of maximum boiling point, but which are present in pro-

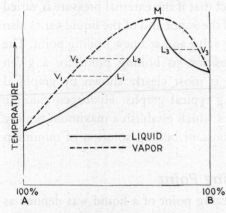

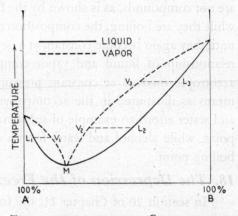

TEMPERATURE-COMPOSITION CURVE FOR AN AZEOTROPIC MIXTURE OF MAXIMUM BOILING POINT.

TEMPERATURE-COMPOSITION CURVE FOR AN AZEOTROPIC MIXTURE OF MINIMUM BOILING POINT.

portions other than those of that particular solution, causes the distillation always to proceed so as to decrease the vapor pressure of the residual solution until the maximum boiling point is reached. In other words, of the two liquids present, the one which is present in excess of the concentration required for the establishment of the maximum boiling point will evaporate in greater quantity until the relative concentrations of the two are correct for the establishment of that boiling point. When this concentration has been established, the vapor of the boiling mixture will have the same relative concentration of the two components as does the boiling liquid, and the boiling point will remain constant until all of the liquid has evaporated.

When one distills a mixture of two liquids which are capable of forming a solution of minimum boiling point but which are not present in the proper quantities to form that particular mixture, the distillate gradually approaches the composition of the most volatile mixture, i.e., that of the maximum vapor pressure and of the minimum boiling point. The composition of the residual liquid in the still meanwhile approaches that of one or the other of the pure components, depending upon which at the outset was in excess of the proportions required for the establishment of the mixture of minimum boiling point.

Because the boiling points of liquid mixtures which have either a maximum or a minimum boiling point remain unchanged throughout their distillation, they are often referred to as *constant boiling mixtures*. They are also known as *azeotropic mixtures*. These mixtures of maximum and minimum boiling points are not compounds, as is shown by the fact that if the external pressure is varied while they are boiling, the composition of the vapor and of the liquid varies also until they again become constant at a new value and at a new boiling point. The relationship of liquid and vapor composition to boiling point for a given azeotropic mixture at constant pressure is most clearly shown by graphical means as illustrated in the accompanying typical graphs. Hydrogen chloride and water afford an example of substances which establish a maximum boiling point, while alcohol and water form a constant boiling solution of minimum boiling point.

18. *The Depression of the Freezing Point*

In section 20 of Chapter 11, the freezing point of a liquid was defined as the temperature at which the liquid and solid states of the substance in question have equal vapor pressures. It has been shown in this chapter that the presence of a solute in a liquid lowers the vapor pressure of the latter. At zero degrees the vapor pressure of a solution of sugar in water will be less than the vapor pressure of either water or ice at that temperature, and, as a consequence, a state of equilibrium between the solution and the solid form of the solvent (ice) could not be established. If ice were added to the solution at zero degrees, it would melt to pass into the solution, since, as a liquid in the solution, it

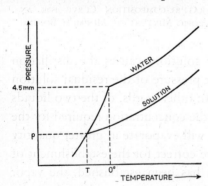

THE EFFECT OF A SOLUTE UPON THE VAPOR PRESSURE AND FREEZING POINT OF WATER.

would exert a lower vapor pressure. For ice and the sugar-water solution to exist in equilibrium (that is, for the freezing point of the solution to be reached), the temperature would have to be lowered until the vapor pressure of ice was equal in value to the vapor pressure of the solution. This is further evidence that a solute decreases, or lowers, the escaping tendency of its solvent. This knowledge is put to good use in the addition of salt to the ice-water mixture used in the freezing of ice cream, in the addition of a solute to the radiator water of automobiles in the winter to prevent freezing, and in the addition of salt to the water in the freezing vats of ice plants (cf. section 13, Chapter 11).

Lowering the freezing point of a liquid by the addition of a solute is a consequence of the lowering of its vapor pressure which in turn is proportional, according to Raoult's law, to the mole fraction of the solute contained in the solution. It follows, then, that *the depression of the freezing point is proportional also to the mole fraction of the solute contained in the solution, and is approximately proportional to the number of moles of solute contained in 1000 g. of solvent.* Abnormal effects, which will be discussed later, are noted for solutes whose molecules break into fragments in solution, as in the case of boiling point elevation.

19. Osmosis

A number of materials exist which, when used to separate a volume of a pure liquid from a solution prepared from the liquid and a solute, will permit the molecules of the solvent to pass freely in both directions while restraining the molecules of the solute. Such materials are known as *semipermeable membranes*. For laboratory use, a very satisfactory semipermeable membrane is prepared by precipitating cupric ferrocyanide in the pores of an unglazed porcelain cup, or thimble.

$$2CuSO_4 + K_4Fe(CN)_6 \rightarrow 2K_2SO_4 + \underline{Cu_2Fe(CN)_6}$$

If an aqueous solution of table sugar is placed in the prepared cup, and the cup securely closed with a rubber stopper carrying a length of glass tubing and then submerged in a vessel of distilled water, the level of the water in the attached tube will gradually rise to a height of several feet. Water is passing from the vessel through the semipermeable membrane generated in the pores of the cup into the solution contained in the cup. This phenomenon is known as *osmosis*, which may be defined as *the selective flow through a semipermeable membrane of a solvent from a solution in which it has greater concentration to one in which it has less concentration.* Of course, in conventional terms of the concentration of the solute in the solution, the reverse is true—that is, the flow of liquid is from the less concentrated to the more concentrated solution.

If a sufficiently long tube is attached to the cup, and if sufficient distilled water is provided in the experiment described above, water will rise to a con-

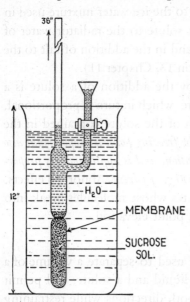

APPARATUS FOR THE DEMONSTRATION OF OSMOSIS. Water passes through the semipermeable membrane, causing the liquid level to rise in the tube. (Courtesy, Davies: "Fundamentals of Physical Chemistry," Philadelphia, The Blakiston Company.)

siderable height in the tube, but ultimately will cease to rise. At this point, the weight of the column of liquid in the tube must be just sufficient to exert a pressure equal to the pressure exerted by the osmosing liquid. Observation has shown that, for a given solute and solvent at a specified temperature, the height to which liquid in the tube attached to the cell will rise is dependent upon the concentration of the solution employed. Since the membrane will permit the passage of solvent molecules, it seems logical to suppose that they will pass through in both directions, but since the number of solvent molecules in contact with a unit area of the membrane surface is greater in the pure solvent than in the solution, it also seems logical that the number of solvent molecules passing into the solution would be greater than the number passing out of it. A second factor favoring a greater flow of solvent into the solution than out of it is that the attraction between solvent and solute molecules in the solution is greater than the attraction of the solvent molecules for each other in the pure solvent. There should then be an increase in the percentage of solvent molecules in the solution contained in the cell, and liquid should rise in the attached tube. As more solvent enters the solution, the concentration of the latter decreases progressively until the rate of passage of solvent molecules from it back into the solvent approaches the rate of their passage in the opposite direction; furthermore, as the solution becomes more dilute, the hydrostatic pressure of the liquid in the attached tube also increases the rate of passage of solvent molecules from the solution back through the membrane into the solvent. Thus there is established ultimately a state of equilibrium in which the rate of passage of solvent molecules through the membrane is the same in both directions. *Osmotic pressure* may be defined, then, as *the difference in pressure necessary to establish equilibrium between a solution and its pure solvent at a semipermeable membrane.*

The principal consideration involved in the foregoing is the relative numbers of solute and solvent particles in the solution. As in the case of the lowering of freezing points and the raising of boiling points, the nature of these particles has little to do with the matter just so long as there is no chemical interaction between them. As in boiling point and freezing point work, the concentration of solutions used in the measurement of osmotic pressures is usually expressed in terms of the number of moles of solute contained in 1000 g. of solvent. Osmotic pressure is directly proportional to the concentration for solutions which contain 1 mole, or less, of solute per 1000 g. of solvent. The osmotic pressures of concentrated solutions are so high that they are difficult to measure; a solution which contains only 1 mole of solute per 1000 g. of solvent (a one-molal solution) has a pressure of about 25 atmospheres at 0° C. Like vapor pressure, osmotic pressure varies directly with the absolute temperature. The most accurate measurements of osmotic pressures are those made by Morse and Frazer at the Johns Hopkins University and by the Earl of Berkeley in England.

Many examples of osmosis exist. The cell walls of plant and animal tissues are semipermeable membranes. Thus, a blood cell placed in distilled water absorbs enough liquid to burst, while one placed in a strong salt solution shrivels; a flower placed in water receives water into its cells and appears refreshed, while one placed in a strong sugar solution loses moisture from its cells, quickly becoming wilted in appearance. It is apparent that osmosis plays an important role in the life processes of both plants and animals.

An interesting demonstration of osmotic pressure is available in the so-called "chemical flower garden," which is prepared by placing various brightly colored soluble salts in the bottom of a beaker of moderately dilute sodium silicate, "water glass." Near the surface of the crystals, where some solution has taken place, semipermeable membranes of a metallic silicate are formed. Water passes inside these membranes until they burst, permitting the formation of new membranes which in turn burst until queer, colored formations cover the bottom of the beaker, extending upward like the growths in a tropical submarine garden.

Solutes whose molecules break into fragments in solution naturally cause abnormalities in the osmotic pressures of their solutions. The behavior of such substances will be discussed in a later chapter. Solutions whose osmotic pressures are identical under similar conditions are said to be *isotonic*.

20. *The Determination of Molecular Weights of Soluble Substances*

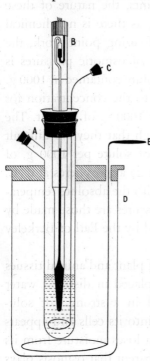

APPARATUS FOR THE DE-TERMINATION OF MOLECULAR WEIGHT BY THE FREEZING-POINT DEPRESSION METHOD. The solution of known concentration is introduced into tube A which contains a differential thermometer B and a stirrer C. A freezing mixture is placed in vessel D and agitated with stirrer E. From the freezing points of the solution and the pure solvent, the molecular weight of the solute may be calculated.

Properties of a solution which are dependent only upon the molecular composition of the solution are known as *colligative*, or *molecular*, *properties*. The lowering of the vapor pressure, the raising of the boiling point, the lowering of the freezing point, and the increasing of the osmotic pressure of a solvent by the addition of a solute are dependent only upon the relative numbers of the two varieties of particles present, and, therefore, the vapor pressure, boiling point, freezing point, and osmotic pressure of a solution are colligative properties. Careful measurement of the changes wrought in these properties by the addition of carefully measured quantities of solute to carefully measured quantities of solvent affords a means of determining the molecular weight of many substances. The method is not applicable to substances which are insoluble, which interact with the solvent, or which disperse in the solvent into particles other than molecules. Since changes in vapor pressure and in osmotic pressure are both much more difficult to measure than are changes in temperature, measurements of boiling point elevation and freezing point depression are much more commonly employed in laboratory determinations of the molecular weights of soluble substances.

One must have pure samples of both solute and solvent and he must know the molal freezing point constant of the solvent in question in order to determine the molecular weight of a solute by the freezing point method. *The molal freezing point constant is the number of degrees the freezing point of a pure solvent should be lowered by the addition of a mole of solute to 1000 g. of solvent.* Because concentrated solutions show deviations from the theoretical behavior, the effects of small fractions of a mole upon the properties of 1000 g. of solvent are noted, and by multiplication the theoretical effect which should be produced by a mole of solute is calculated. The freezing point constant of the solvent to be employed must be determined by measurements made with a solute of known molecular weight, or its value must be found in some reference work. The molal freezing point constants for several common liquids are given in the following table.

Table 10

MOLAL FREEZING POINT CONSTANTS

Acetic acid	3.90° C.	Nitrobenzene	7.00° C.
Benzene	4.90	Phenol	7.40
Formic acid	2.77	Water	1.86
Naphthalene	6.80 to 6.90		

The actual determination of the lowering of the freezing point is made by dissolving a known weight of solute in a known weight of solvent, and then placing the solution in the inner chamber of the apparatus illustrated herewith. The apparatus is placed in a freezing mixture and the solution is stirred to insure uniform cooling until a solid phase begins to form. The temperature at which the solution and the solid phase are in equilibrium is read as the freezing point.

Suppose that it was found that 0.09 g. of a certain sugar when dissolved in 20 g. of water produces a solution whose freezing point is $-0.046°$ C. Since the freezing point constant for water is given in terms of the quantity of solute dissolved in 1000 g. of water, the given data must be recalculated to similar terms

$$0.09 \text{ g.} / 20 \text{ g.} = x / 1000 \text{ g.}$$
$$x = 4.5 \text{ g. per 1000 g. of water}$$

1 mole produces a lowering of 1.86° C., hence the fraction of a mole which would produce a lowering of 0.046° C. would be

$$1 / 1.86 = y / 0.046$$
$$y = 0.0244 \text{ mole}$$

Therefore, 4.5 g. = 0.02444 mole and 1 mole = 184.4 g.

This method, like that involving gas densities given in Chapter 11, is not precise, but, from the closely approximate molecular weight obtained, one may decide which multiple of the simplest, or empirical, formula is correct, and obtain the exact molecular weight from the correct formula.

In a similar manner, close approximations of the molecular weight of various solutes may be determined by observation of the raising of the boiling point of a solvent by the addition of the solute. At the outset, one must know or determine for the solvent its molal boiling point constant, which is defined as the number of degrees by which the boiling point of the solvent should be raised by the addition of a mole of solute to 1000 g. of it. Again, because concentrated solutions show marked deviations from Raoult's law, the effect of small fractions of a mole of solute upon 1000 g. of the solvent are noted and the proportional effect of a whole mole calculated from these observations. The molal boiling point constants for several common solvents are noted in the following table.

Table 11

MOLAL BOILING POINT CONSTANTS

Acetic acid	3.07° C.	Chloroform	3.63° C.
Acetone	1.71	Ethyl alcohol	1.22
Aniline	3.52	Ethyl ether	2.02
Benzene	2.53	Methyl alcohol	0.83
Carbon disulfide	2.34	Toluene	3.33
Carbon tetrachloride	5.03	Water	0.512

In laboratory practice, the effect upon the freezing point caused by adding a small mass of solute to a small mass of solvent is noted, the proportionate mass of solute which would have to be in 1000 g. of solvent to yield a solution of the same concentration is calculated, the fraction of a mole required to produce such a lowering is calculated, and from these last two pieces of information the molecular weight of the solute is calculated.

(*See Appendix for Exercises*)

COLLATERAL READINGS

Cartledge: *Introductory Theoretical Chemistry*, Boston, Ginn & Co., 1929.
Chapin and Steiner: *Second Year College Chemistry*, 5th ed., revised, New York, John Wiley & Sons, Inc., 1943.
Findlay: *The Spirit of Chemistry*, New York, Longmans, Green & Co., 1934.

Getman and Daniels: *Outlines of Physical Chemistry*, New York, John Wiley & Sons, Inc., 1943.

Hildebrand: *Solubility of Non-Electrolytes*, New York, Reinhold Publishing Corp., 1936.

Lincoln and Banks: *General Chemistry*, New York, Prentice-Hall, Inc., 1928.

Taylor and Taylor: *Elementary Physical Chemistry*, 2d ed., New York, D. Van Nostrand Co., 1937.

Any standard textbook of physical chemistry.

HENRI LOUIS LE CHATELIER
(*1850–1936, French*)

Le Chatelier is best known for the establishment of the principle which bears his name, but he made notable contributions to our knowledge of metallurgy, metallography, chemical mechanics, the combustion of gases, microscopy, chemical equilibrium, and the chemistry of solutions. He was also prominent as a teacher, writer, and editor. In 1908 he succeeded Moissan as professor of general chemistry at the Sorbonne in Paris, and from then until his retirement in 1922 he taught and counseled many students. One of his principal tenets was that the pure and applied forms of a science must of necessity aid and supplement each other. In 1904 he founded the *Revue de métallurgie*, whose editor he was until 1914. (Courtesy, *Journal of Chemical Education*.)

13

Magnesium and Its Compounds

1. Introduction

Magnesium is the second element of the third period. Like its predecessor, sodium, it is a metal, and, like all of the other members of the third period, it is both theoretically and economically important. Its atomic number is 12, whence the distribution of its planetary electrons is 2, 8, 2. This distribution shows that the magnesium atom need lose only the two electrons of its outermost energy level to attain an electronic distribution similar to that of the atom of the inert gas, neon. These considerations indicate why magnesium shows only a valence of $+2$ in all of its compounds.

A. THE IONIZING POTENTIAL. The two electrons which the magnesium atom must lose in its quest for stability are possessed of approximately the same energy as is the one electron which sodium loses when it reacts, since all three normally exist in the 3_0 level. As shown by their respective atomic numbers, however, the magnesium atom possesses a larger nuclear charge than does the sodium atom. This larger nuclear charge permits the magnesium atom to attract its 3_0 electrons more strongly than does the sodium atom; hence, to remove one of the 3_0 electrons from a magnesium atom in the gaseous state requires a higher voltage than is the case for the removal of the 3_0 electrons of the gaseous sodium atom. Where 5.12 v. is required for the latter, 7.61 v. is required for the former.

After one of the 3_0 electrons of the magnesium atom has been removed, the 11 remaining electrons are held by the same nucleus, with its $+12$ charge, which formerly held the 12 original electrons. This means, then, that the remaining 11 electrons are pulled in more closely and are held more tightly than were the original 12. To remove the second of the two 3_0 electrons should, therefore, require more energy than was required for the removal of the first one. This is found to be the case, for to remove the second 3_0 electron from the gaseous ion a potential of 14.97 v. is required across the terminals of the discharge tube.

When both of the 3_0 electrons have been removed, the nucleus with its charge of $+12$ then has to hold only 10 electrons, which are pulled in still more closely and held still more tightly. These considerations explain why any positively charged ion is smaller than its parent atom, and point to the fact that as the number of electrons lost increases the resulting ion becomes increasingly smaller, provided, of course, that the resulting ions all have the same inert gas structure.

B. THE ELECTRODE POTENTIAL. As ionizing potentials tend to go in one direction, electrode potentials tend to go in the other (cf. section 9, Chapter 7). From this, it may be inferred that, since the ionizing potential of magnesium is higher than that of sodium, the electrode potential of the magnesium ion will be less than that of the sodium ion; this is the case. The electrode potential of the magnesium ion is 2.34 v. as compared with 2.71 v. for the sodium ion. Relating these figures to the activity series indicates that magnesium should be less active chemically than sodium; experimentation confirms this expectation.

2. Physical Properties

Magnesium is a light, silvery-white metal which is both moderately tough and moderately rigid. Its silvery luster is not always apparent since it has a tendency to tarnish slightly upon continued exposure to air. The density of the metal is 1.74 g. / ml.; its melting point is 651° C., and its boiling point is 1110° C. While the density of this metal is greater than that of water, it is considerably lower than the density of most rigid metals. The combination of fair rigidity with low density has created a high demand for magnesium in the present era of light-weight trains and light, metal-covered airplanes. The metal may be drawn into wires and hammered into sheets—in other words, it is both malleable and ductile.

3. Occurrence

Because of its activity as an electron-loser, magnesium is always found in nature in combination with other elements, never in the free state. Ores containing it were first discovered in the district of Magnesia in Thessaly, which is part of modern Greece, hence the name magnesium. Compounds of magnesium have been found to be widely distributed in nature, but, since a majority of the simpler compounds are soluble, large deposits of them are seldom found save in arid regions. The notable exception to the foregoing statement is the Stassfurt salt beds of Germany, where huge deposits of *kainite* ($KCl.MgSO_4.3H_2O$), *carnallite* ($KCl.MgCl_2.6H_2O$), and other salts of magnesium and potassium are to be found. Once these soluble salts were dissolved in the waters of an inland sea which dried up, leaving the salt deposits. The solubility of the simple salts of magnesium makes the ocean the greatest reservoir of magnesium. Although the percentage of these dissolved salts in sea water is small, it is estimated that each cubic mile of this water contains 5,700,000 tons of magnesium, principally as the chloride and sulfate. In the states which border the Great Lakes, there are salt wells and natural springs whose waters contain considerable quantities of magnesium salts. The waters of the famous French Lick Springs of Indiana owe their bitter taste and medicinal action largely to dissolved magnesium sulfate (Epsom salts), and the waters of Michigan salt wells are used as a source of raw material for the recovery of metallic magnesium.

ASBESTOS AS IT OCCURS IN NATURE. (Courtesy, Research Laboratory, Johns Manville Corp.)

The least soluble salts of magnesium which occur naturally in any quantity are the carbonate and the various silicates. Large deposits of magnesium carbonate (known to the mineralogist as *magnesite*) are found in many parts of the world, including the states of Nevada and California. A mixed carbonate of magnesium and calcium, $MgCO_3.CaCO_3$, which is known as *dolomite* from its wide occurrence in the Dolomitic Alps of northern Italy, occurs in many parts of the world, including the western part of the United States. Both of these minerals are used as ores for the production of metallic magnesium.

Other naturally occurring minerals of magnesium are *talc* or *soapstone* $(Mg_3H_2(SiO_3)_4)$, *asbestos* $(CaMg_3(SiO_3)_4)$, and *meerschaum* $(Mg_2Si_3O_8.2H_2O)$. These minerals all have important uses but are not treated as ores for the recovery of magnesium.

4. Preparation

Magnesium was first recognized by Black in 1755, first prepared in an impure form by Sir Humphry Davy in 1808, and first prepared in an essentially pure form by Bussy in 1831. The method of this latter investigator was the displacement of magnesium from its chloride by the use of the more active potassium metal. Because of the tediousness and expensiveness of this method, little magnesium was available for many years.

With the development of cheap electric power, the metal became more available, but it remained both relatively scarce and relatively expensive until the growing demand for rigid metals of low density made feasible its production on a large scale. Prior to World War II, nearly all of the magnesium of commerce was prepared by the electrolysis of the molten, anhydrous chloride. Sodium and calcium chlorides were usually added to the magnesium chloride

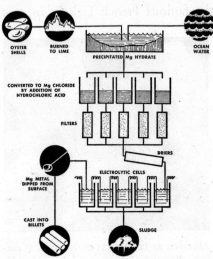

to lower its melting temperature. During this time, magnesium ores were converted to the chloride which was then electrolyzed. The process and the equipment used are both very similar to the process and equipment described in Chapter 7 for the production of sodium from molten sodium chloride.

With the advent of World War II, the necessity of building thousands of metal-sheathed airplanes with light mechanisms greatly increased the demand for magnesium. During this time much magnesium, especially that from sea water and salt wells, continued to be produced by electrolysis of the chloride,

THE PRODUCTION OF MAGNESIUM FROM SEA WATER. (Courtesy, The Dow Chemical Co.)

but other processes have also been put into operation. In one of these, magnesite is roasted to magnesium oxide,

$$MgCO_3 \xrightarrow{\Delta} MgO + CO_2 \uparrow$$

which is then reduced with carbon to yield the free metal:

$$MgO + C \xrightarrow{\Delta} Mg + CO \uparrow$$

For the second step, a temperature attainable only by the electric furnace is required. At such a temperature, the magnesium produced is volatilized and is recovered by being thrown down as a powder by a blast of cold hydrogen gas. If the hot vapor were to come in contact with oxygen, it would of course burn to the oxide again immediately. In another of these newer processes, dolomite is calcined to yield a mixture of magnesium and calcium oxides, thus

$$MgCO_3.CaCO_3 \xrightarrow{\Delta} MgO.CaO + 2CO_2 \uparrow$$

The mixed oxides are then heated in an electric furnace with ferrosilicon. The iron of the ferrosilicon does not enter into the reaction.

$$2(MgO.CaO) + Si \xrightarrow{\Delta} 2Mg + Ca_2SiO_4$$

At the temperature of the reaction the magnesium is volatilized so that the vapor may be drawn off by the use of vacuum pumps and condensed.

Another of the later processes involves the electrolysis of molten magnesium oxide, whose melting point has been lowered by the admixture of magnesium fluoride.

A MODERN MAGNESIUM PLANT, showing cast ingots being dipped.
(Courtesy, The Dow Chemical Co.)

The price of magnesium has declined through the years as the demand for the metal and its production have increased. The first of the metal produced in this country sold for $10.00 per pound. In 1915 the price was $5.00 per pound; in 1933, 30 cents per pound; and the current price is in the neighborhood of 25 cents per pound. It is estimated that the peak production in the United States during World War II was 600,000,000 pounds annually.

5. Chemical Properties

Although magnesium is somewhat less active than sodium as an electron-loser, it is still classed among the elements which are most active in this respect. As a consequence of this activity, magnesium will react with a wide variety of substances which are capable of accepting electrons and will enter into both combination and displacement reactions.

A. COMBINATION REACTIONS. At about 20° C. and below, even powdered magnesium is perfectly stable with respect to the oxygen of the surrounding air, but, if the temperature of the powdered metal is raised to any marked extent, it reacts violently to form the white, powdery oxide whose production is accompanied by the emission of intense white light.

$$2Mg + O_2 \rightarrow 2MgO + 292,000 \text{ cal.}$$

As a result of the large quantity of energy liberated by this reaction, some of the available metal will also combine with the nitrogen present in the air to form the equally white nitride,

$$3Mg + N_2 \rightarrow Mg_3N_2$$

One of the earliest uses of magnesium involved the two reactions mentioned above; the powdered metal mixed with a dry oxidizing agent was sold as *flashlight powder* and used as a source of light for the taking of indoor photographs. At the present time, use is made of these reactions to remove the last remaining traces of air from radio vacuum tubes. The molten metal must be handled with the greatest of care to prevent its burning to the oxide, though the heated massive metal may be forged without this danger.

It should also be noted here that magnesium nitride reacts readily with water to yield ammonia and the metallic hydroxide:

$$Mg_3N_2 + 6HOH \rightarrow 3Mg(OH)_2 + 2NH_3 \uparrow$$

A heated piece of the metal, when introduced into a container of either fluorine or chlorine gas, burns brightly to form the corresponding anhydrous halide:

$$Mg + F_2 \rightarrow MgF_2$$
$$Mg + Cl_2 \rightarrow MgCl_2$$

With bromine it forms the corresponding bromide, and when heated with iodine or with sulfur it forms the iodide and sulfide respectively:

$$Mg + I_2 \xrightarrow{\Delta} MgI_2$$
$$Mg + S \xrightarrow{\Delta} MgS$$

Magnesium will also react when heated with silicon or phosphorus to form the silicide or phosphide respectively:

$$2Mg + Si \xrightarrow{\Delta} Mg_2Si$$

$$3Mg + 2P \xrightarrow{\Delta} Mg_3P_2$$

So far as is known, magnesium forms no hydride. This is presumed to be due to the fact that this metal, unlike sodium, is not a strong enough electron-loser to force hydrogen, which ordinarily is also an electron-loser, to turn electron-acceptor. In other words, the electrode potential of magnesium is not high enough for it to undergo such a reaction.

B. DISPLACEMENT REACTIONS. Magnesium will displace from their compounds elements which stand lower in the electromotive series, but conditions under which such reactions are possible must obtain before the various replacements will take place. For instance, in the activity table the position of magnesium is superior to that of zinc, iron, and a number of other metals, but these metals are displaced from their salts only when the magnesium is added to a solution of the salts or to the salts when they are in the molten condition. Replacement reactions, as shown by the following equation, involve ions, hence they may occur only when the ions are freed from the forces which "lock" them into the crystal structure.

$$\underline{Mg} + FeCl_2 \rightarrow MgCl_2 + \underline{Fe}$$

or

$$\underline{Mg} + Fe^{++} + 2Cl^- \rightarrow Mg^{++} + 2Cl^- + \underline{Fe}$$

Similarly, from the position of this metal in the electromotive series, one might expect it to displace hydrogen from cold water, but the reaction does not take place according to expectation. The reaction fails to take place because, as soon as the reaction between the water and the metal begins, a thin protective coating of magnesium hydroxide forms, preventing further contact between the water and the metal. If ammonium chloride, or some other substance which will dissolve the hydroxide, is added to the water, the metal continues to displace hydrogen from the water and ultimately disappears. If the water is heated to steam, the reaction between the metal and the water proceeds readily:

$$Mg + H_2O \rightarrow MgO + H_2 \uparrow + energy$$

Even with hot water the reaction goes very well.

The slight tarnishing which the metal undergoes in air is thought to be due to the action of the moisture in the air in which traces of carbon dioxide have dissolved. The gray adhering film would thus be a mixed hydroxide and carbonate.

In the case of acids, the hydrogen is ionized so that it is in a condition which makes it much more susceptible of replacement, and, furthermore, any hydroxide which might tend to form would be immediately removed by its neutralization by the hydrogen ions. The metal reacts readily with all acids to liberate hydrogen and to form salts characteristic of each of the various acids employed.

6. *Magnesium Oxide and Hydroxide*

In the preceding paragraph, it was seen that magnesium oxide may be prepared by burning the metal in oxygen. This method is much too expensive, however, for commercial application, and in quantity the oxide is produced by heating the carbonate obtained from the mineral *magnesite*.

$$MgCO_3 \xrightarrow{\Delta} MgO + CO_2 \uparrow$$

The process of heating a metallic carbonate to obtain the corresponding metallic oxide is known as *calcining*. This term comes from the early practice of chemistry and alchemy, as does the practice of calling metallic oxides by a name formed by deleting the final *-um* or *-ium* of the name of the metal and adding *-a*. By this older terminology, magnesium oxide is *magnesia*. So much heat is liberated in the formation of the oxide by union of the elements that it is difficult to add enough heat to the oxide to drive the reaction in the opposite direction, thus causing its decomposition. The oxide is said, therefore, to be very stable to heat, and because of this stability, as well as a high melting point and low ability to conduct heat, it is used as a heat insulator both alone and mixed with other insulating substances such as asbestos. Bricks for lining furnaces are often made of compressed magnesium oxide or contain it as an ingredient. Materials which will withstand high temperatures are said to be refractory. A very fluffy form of the oxide prepared by calcining the carbonate at temperatures in the neighborhood of 700° C. is used in medicine as an antacid and in the preparation of cosmetics.

The oxide of magnesium is not nearly so soluble as is that of sodium. The small amount of it which does dissolve reacts with the water to form the hydroxide whose solutions turn red litmus blue; hence, the oxide is a basic anhydride, but since the hydroxide is itself only sparingly soluble, strong concentrated solutions of magnesium hydroxide comparable to the strong solutions of sodium hydroxide are unknown. Magnesium hydroxide is also a weaker base than is sodium hydroxide. The relative strengths of various hydroxides will be discussed in a later chapter.

Because of its slight solubility, magnesium hydroxide is readily prepared by the addition of a soluble hydroxide to solutions of magnesium salts thus:

$$2NaOH + MgSO_4 \rightarrow \underline{Mg(OH)_2} + Na_2SO_4(2Na^+ + SO_4^{--})$$

If ammonium ions are added to the solution of the magnesium salt before the soluble hydroxide is added, no precipitate of magnesium hydroxide forms. The reason is, ammonium hydroxide is such a weak (slightly ionized) substance that the moment NH_4^+ and OH^- ions come into the presence of each other they unite to form NH_4OH molecules, thus leaving insufficient OH^- ions to bring about the precipitation of the Mg^{++} ions as $Mg(OH)_2$. Solid magnesium hydroxide is easily decomposed by heat, according to the equation

$$\underline{Mg(OH)_2} \xrightarrow{\Delta} H_2O \uparrow + \underline{MgO}$$

The hydroxide is sufficiently strong as a base to neutralize acids, thus forming salts characteristic of the acid used. With sulfuric acid the salt would thus be the sulfate,

$$Mg(OH)_2 + H_2SO_4 \rightarrow MgSO_4 + 2H_2O$$

In commercial practice, the various salts required in quantity are usually prepared by the metathetical reactions which occur between the oxide or the carbonate and the proper acid. For the preparation of the nitrate, the reactions would be, respectively:

$$MgO + 2HNO_3 \rightarrow Mg(NO_3)_2 + H_2O$$

and

$$MgCO_3 + 2HNO_3 \rightarrow Mg(NO_3)_2 + H_2O + CO_2 \uparrow$$

A suspension of finely divided magnesium hydroxide in water is known as *milk of magnesia*, and is used in medicine in large quantities as a laxative and as an antacid.

7. Important Compounds and Their Uses

A. MAGNESIUM OXIDE. The production and use of this important substance have already been discussed in preceding sections.

B. MAGNESIUM CARBONATE. The carbonate ranks high in importance as a source of the free metal as well as of the oxide and the salts of magnesium. It occurs naturally in our Western states in a high degree of purity. In the laboratory, the pure carbonate cannot be precipitated from solution by the addition of a soluble carbonate to a magnesium salt. Reasons for this statement will be adduced in a later chapter. The product which precipitates under these circum-

MAGNESIA INSULATING MATERIAL INSTALLED ON PIPES, TANK, AND HEATER.
(Courtesy, Keasby & Mattison Co.)

stances has the formula $3MgCO_3.Mg(OH)_2.3H_2O$. This substance, when dried, is sold under the name of *magnesia alba*, and is used in toothpowders and -pastes, in cosmetics, and in metal polishes. A crude, fibrous form of it is used as a heat-insulating material. Strong heating of the substance causes its decomposition into magnesium oxide.

C. MAGNESIUM CHLORIDE. This compound is of importance because of its use in the electrolytic production of its parent metal. When it is crystallized from solution, it has the formula $MgCl_2.6H_2O$, but only the anhydrous salt can be employed for use in the production of the metal; otherwise hydrogen, which has a lower electrode potential than magnesium, would be liberated at the cathode. Unfortunately, the anhydrous chloride cannot be prepared by heating the hydrated variety in an open vessel. When this is tried, the product obtained is the oxide:

$$MgCl_2.6H_2O \xrightarrow{\Delta} MgO + 2HCl \uparrow + 5H_2O \uparrow$$

The anhydrous chloride may be obtained by heating the hydrated variety in an atmosphere of hydrogen chloride, thus reversing the reaction above, or it may be obtained by heating the double salt $MgCl_2.NH_4Cl.6H_2O$. This salt loses its water upon gentle heating, then, upon more pronounced heating, the NH_4Cl portion of the salt decomposes thus:

$$NH_4Cl \xrightarrow{\Delta} NH_3 \uparrow + HCl \uparrow$$

In this way, the ammonium chloride serves as the source of the atmosphere of HCl gas specified in the previous process. When left exposed to an atmosphere in which the vapor pressure is even moderately high, both the hydrated and anhydrous chloride readily deliquesce. If left exposed long enough, the salt will attract enough moisture in which to dissolve completely.

The hydrated salt is used as a filler for woolen and cotton goods, and when mixed properly with the oxide it sets to a hard mass known as magnesia cement or Sorel cement. This material may be used alone or with a filler, and is employed in plastering walls, in stuccoing exteriors, and in doing other construction jobs.

D. MAGNESIUM SULFATE. The sulfate of magnesium occurs in the Stassfurt salt deposits and in various salt wells and natural springs. Deposits are also found in the drier portions of some of our Western states. When crystallized from solutions whose temperatures lie between 1.8° and 48° C., the salt has the formula $MgSO_4.7H_2O$ and is known as Epsom salts. Crystals formed from solutions whose temperature is below 1.8° C. have the formula $MgSO_4.12H_2O$. Above 48° C., hydrates of lower water content than the heptahydrate are formed, and above 200° C. all of the hydrated crystals lose their water of hydration. This compound is used as a medicine both externally and internally, and is also used as a filler for cotton cloth and in dyeing and tanning.

E. MAGNESIUM NITRATE. Magnesium nitrate is usually prepared by the action of nitric acid on the carbonate. It crystallizes from solutions as colorless monoclinic crystals of the formula $Mg(NO_3)_2.6H_2O$, and is a common source of the magnesium ion in laboratory work.

F. MAGNESIUM PERCHLORATE. When prepared in the anhydrous form, this salt has the formula $Mg(ClO_4)_2$, and is an excellent drying agent capable of taking up water vapor to the extent of 30 per cent of its own weight. It is prepared commercially for this purpose.

G. ASBESTOS. This substance is a compound of magnesium, silicon, and oxygen, and as such is best discussed with the silicates.

8. *Magnesium, Its Alloys, and Their Uses*

The magnesium produced by most of the commercial processes is already in a high state of purity, but it may be further refined by subliming the metal in a vacuum at a temperature just below its melting point. The crystal mass which forms when the drawn-off gas is cooled is of almost complete purity. The uses of pure or nearly pure magnesium are nearly all chemical. It is used as a laboratory reagent in both inorganic and organic chemistry, and it also finds use in the manufacture of flashlight powders, flashbulbs, fireworks, and signal flares, and in the removal of air from high vacuum tubes and equipment. Magnesium ribbon is sometimes used as a high temperature fuse for starting other reactions.

By far the greater portion of the present-day production of magnesium is used, however, in mixtures with other metals. As long ago as the beginning of the Bronze Age of antiquity, man discovered that by mixing molten metals and allowing them to harden he obtained a product whose properties differed in many respects from those of the parent metals. While these metallic mixtures may vary greatly as to their components and properties and somewhat even as to the relation of the components in them, they are generically known as alloys. Often alloys have properties which are superior to those of any of the constituent metals; such is the case with the wide variety of alloys of magnesium and aluminum which are used in modern construction where a light, strong metal is needed.

Notable among the alloys of magnesium are those known collectively as the *Dow metals*. These contain from 88 to 98 per cent of magnesium, with the remaining percentage aluminum, save for small fractions of a per cent of manganese and of zinc, which also vary from one alloy to another. The manganese greatly increases the resistance of the magnesium to attack by water, especially water containing dissolved substances. Besides being light, these alloys possess a high tensile strength and may be drawn, forged, cast, rolled, and machined. During World War II, the major portion of these alloys was diverted to the production of military airplanes, but with the conclusion of the war they have found an increasing use in the construction of other machines. Also of importance are the *magnalium alloys*, which contain from 10 to 30 per cent of magnesium, with the remainder of the composition consisting of aluminum.

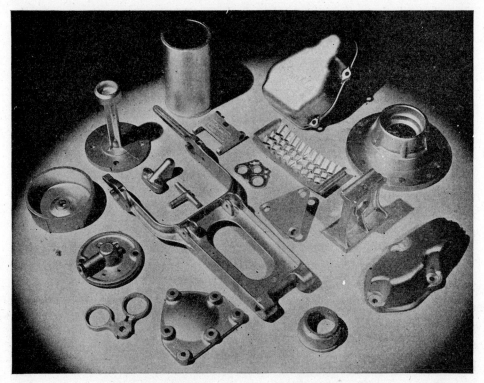

CASTINGS OF DOWMETAL. (Courtesy, The Dow Chemical Co.)

The use of these metals is similar to that of the Dow metals. Certain of the magnesium alloys may even be hardened and tempered.

The surfaces of articles made of these light metal alloys are protected from the action of the weather, water, and other agents by treating objects made of them either electrolytically in certain oxidizing solutions or under pressure with sodium hydroxide. In both cases, a thick and adherent protective film is formed.

9. Analytical Tests

Magnesium compounds impart no characteristic color to the flame, hence purely chemical tests must be relied on. The majority of the compounds of this element are readily soluble in water and are also colorless, unless the negative ion be colored, which renders testing by chemical means difficult to a degree. As pointed out in section 6, the hydroxide may be precipitated provided ammonium ions are absent, but since there are a number of colorless, insoluble hydroxides, this constitutes no proof of the presence of magnesium ions. It was shown in section 7 that a basic carbonate may be precipitated by the addition of a solution containing carbonate ions. This reaction is frequently employed in analytical procedures, but here again, if an excess of ammonium ions is present, no precipitate will form because the ammonium ion will react with the carbonate ion to form the bicarbonate ion and ammonia,

$$NH_4^+ + CO_3^{--} \rightleftarrows NH_3 \uparrow + HCO_3^-$$

thus leaving an insufficient concentration of the carbonate ions to bring about the precipitation of the basic magnesium carbonate.

The traditional method of confirming the presence of magnesium ions is to add to the solution, from which interfering ions have been removed, a solution of any soluble orthophosphate and solutions of ammonium hydroxide and any ammonium salt. A colorless, finely crystalline precipitate of magnesium ammonium phosphate will form within a short time:

$$Mg^{++} + PO_4^{---} + NH_4^+ + 6H_2O \rightarrow \underline{MgNH_4PO_4.6H_2O}$$

The purpose of the ammonium salt added is to prevent the precipitation of magnesium hydroxide by the ammonium hydroxide (cf. section 6). The manganous ion, if present, will undergo the same reaction and yield a precipitate of similar appearance, though in any quantity the manganous ammonium phosphate has a slightly pinkish coloration.

$$Mn^{++} + PO_4^{---} + NH_4^+ + 6H_2O \rightarrow \underline{MnNH_4PO_4.6H_2O}$$

In quantitative analysis, magnesium is determined by precipitating it as $MgNH_4PO_4.6H_2O$, which is then heated until it decomposes into magnesium pyrophosphate:

$$2(\underline{MgNH_4PO_4.6H_2O}) \overset{\Delta}{\rightarrow} Mg_2P_2O_7 + 2NH_3 \uparrow + 13H_2O \uparrow$$

This substance is then weighed, and from the known percentage of magnesium which it contains may be calculated the weight of this element in the chosen sample of the unknown.

A more modern qualitative test, and one which is entirely specific, though it may illustrate less of the chemical behavior of the ion, is the S. and O. test, which consists of adding to a slightly acidic solution of magnesium ions a few drops of S. and O. reagent (a dilute, slightly basic solution of paranitrobenzene-azoresorcinol). The mixture should be yellowish in color. Upon the addition of sodium hydroxide until the solution is basic, a sky-blue, gelatinous precipitate will form. A purplish solution is significant since the S. and O.

reagent always turns this color when made basic. The gelatinous precipitate is magnesium hydroxide which has absorbed the colored organic reagent to become blue. A precipitate which absorbs a colored substance to become colored itself is known as a *lake*. The presence of ammonium ions prevents the precipitation of the hydroxide in the usual manner and thus interferes with the test. This test takes its name from its Japanese discoverers, the chemists Sutsu and Okuma.

Another test involving the use of an organic reagent consists of making the solution to be tested alkaline with ammonium hydroxide, then adding a few milliliters of a 2 per cent alcoholic solution of orthohydroxyquinoline. A greenish-yellow precipitate of magnesium hydroxyquinolate, $Mg(C_9H_6ON)_2.12H_2O$, should form. Calcium, barium, and other ions interfere with this test.

In general, the S. and O. test is the quickest and most reliable.

(See Appendix for Exercises)

COLLATERAL READINGS

Alico: *Introduction to Magnesium and Its Alloys*, New York, Ziff-Davis Publishing Co., 1945.

Bagley: *Chem. & Eng. News*, **22**, No. 11, 921 (1944).

Creighton and Koehler: *Electrochemistry*, New York, Vol. II, John Wiley & Sons, Inc., 1944.

Franke: *Chem. & Met. Eng.*, **48,** No. 3, 75 (1941).

Furnas: *Roger's Industrial Chemistry*, Vol. II, New York, D. Van Nostrand Co., 1943.

Holmes: *Out of the Test Tube*, New York, Emerson Books, Inc., 1937.

Hopkins: *General Chemistry for Colleges*, revised, Boston, D. C. Heath & Co., 1937.

Latimer and Hildebrand: *Reference Book of Inorganic Chemistry*, New York, The Macmillan Co., 1941.

Pannell: *Magnesium: Its Production and Use*, New York, Pitman Publishing Corp., 1944.

Weeks: *Discovery of the Elements*, 5th ed., Mack Printing Co., 1945.

SVANTE ARRHENIUS
(1859–1927, Swedish)

The name of Arrhenius is associated with the theory of electrolytic dissociation which he presented in his doctoral dissertation at the University of Upsala in 1884 and in a short paper which he published in 1887. During his lifetime he held various professorships in Sweden and wrote a number of books on physical chemistry. In 1903 he was the recipient of the Nobel Prize, and in 1905 he was awarded the Davy Medal.

PETER JOSEPH WILHELM DEBYE
(1884–   , Dutch [by birth])

Debye is another physicist who has done work of value to theoretical chemistry. To chemists he is best known for the theory of electrolytic solutions which he and Erich Hückel developed and according to which all electrolytes are completely ionized in solution. He was educated at Aachen and Munich and held professorships at Zurich, Utrecht, Göttingen, and Leipzig, and in 1935 was appointed director of the Kaiser Wilhelm Institute for Physics at Berlin-Dahlem. He is also noted for his work on the electrical moments of molecules, atomic and molecular structures, and x-ray diffraction. In 1936 he was awarded the Nobel Prize in chemistry. He is at present serving as head of the department of chemistry at Cornell University, Ithaca, N. Y. (Courtesy, *The Catalyst*.)

14

Electrolytes and Electrolytic Solutions

1. Introduction

In the early 1800's it was discovered that solutions of certain substances are capable of conducting an electric current while solutions of many other substances do not have this ability. Later in the century it was discovered that the same solutions which are capable of carrying the electric current have colligative properties which are abnormal as compared with the same properties of nonconducting solutions of equal concentration. For example, the vapor-pressure lowering, the freezing-point depression, the boiling-point elevation, and the increase in osmotic pressure for a 0.1 molal solution of salt are about twice those for a 0.1 molal solution of sugar. This would indicate that more particles were dissolved in the 0.1 molal salt solution than in the 0.1 molal sugar solution. Today we believe that substances which impart these properties to solutions do so because they yield electrically charged fragments of molecules (ions) in solution rather than atoms or whole molecules.

2. Electrolytes

The first man to study thoroughly the electrolytic properties of solutions was Michael Faraday, who fathered the majority of the terms which are used in connection with work of this kind. To those solutes capable of yielding a solution which would conduct the current, he gave the name *electrolyte* (cf. section 6, Chapter 7). Members of this family are the classes of substances known as acids, bases, and salts (cf. definitions). The ability of these three classes of compounds to act as electrolytes lies in the fact that some of the compounds already contain ions in their structures while the others exist as molecules which may be broken into ions by the action of the solvent to which they are added. A few points concerning each of these three types of electrolytes should be considered briefly.

3. Salts

In previous chapters, it was seen that, when metals react with nonmetals, there is usually a transfer of electrons from the atoms of the metal to the atoms of the nonmetal, and that the compound resulting from such a reaction usually forms crystals the points of whose space lattices are occupied alternately by the two varieties of oppositely charged ions. When such a crystal is put into water, each of the ions in its various surfaces immediately attracts and is attracted by the oppositely charged end of a number of water dipoles (cf. section 5, Chapter 5). If this attraction of the dipoles for a given ion in the crystal surface becomes greater than the attraction of the other ions in the crystal, then the ion is torn from the crystal, becoming

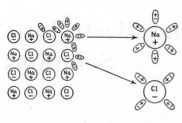

DISSOLUTION OF A SALT CRYSTAL IN WATER.

a "free ion" surrounded by a cloud of solvent dipoles. This reaction may be represented by an equation thus:

$$NaCl_{(s)} \rightarrow Na^+ + Cl^-_{(in\ sol.)}$$

though to indicate that even in the solid state salt consists of ions one should perhaps write

$$Na^+Cl^- \rightarrow Na^+ + Cl^-$$

These equations indicate that one gram-molecule, or mole, of salt is capable of producing one gram-ion of sodium ion and one gram-ion of chloride ion. Ordinarily, a gram-ion is also referred to as a *mole*.

If the attraction of the water dipoles for an ion in the surface of a crystal does not exceed the attraction of the other ions in the crystal for it, then the surface ion remains in place and such crystals are only very slightly soluble in that solvent. There are a number of salts whose solubility in water is slight, but the portion which dissolves is usually highly ionized.

4. Acids

In section 7 of Chapter 10, it was pointed out that acids have a number of properties in common and that they owe these common properties to the hydrogen ions which all of them furnish in varying degrees in aqueous solution. In this same section, it also was pointed out that, since hydrogen ions are protons, an acid may be defined as a substance which when dissolved in water is capable of furnishing protons. A more modern concept of *acids* is that they *are substances which under any circumstances are capable of giving up protons to a second substance.* It must be remembered, however, that the protons will not be given up until there is an acceptor to receive them. In brief, then, acids may be said to be proton-donors.

The foregoing definitions of acids are satisfactory for most purposes, but those who continue the study of chemistry will find that none of them is entirely adequate. A more general view of acids is that they are substances which yield in solution the same positive ion as the weakly ionized solvent in which they are dissolved. Space limitations will not permit discussion of this and other ideas pertaining to acids; however, since most of the solutions encountered in the average inorganic chemistry laboratory are prepared with water as the solvent, the definitions of the preceding paragraph will be adequate for students who use this textbook.

The commoner mineral acids when pure and at room temperature do not exist as crystals. Examination of these substances further reveals that they exist as molecules rather than in the ionic condition, but that the molecules are of the polar variety. It is a well-known fact that these molecular substances when dissolved in water yield solutions which conduct electricity, which affect abnormally the colligative properties of the solution, and which show all the properties of the hydrogen ion; hence the molecules must have been broken into charged fragments by the solvent. The case of the ionization of hydrogen chloride (cf. section 7, Chapter 10) has already been discussed. It is assumed similarly for other acids that the oppositely charged ends of their dipolar molecules attract the oppositely charged ends of water dipoles. The forces within the acid molecule are weakened as a result of this outside attraction, and ultimately the molecule is pulled apart, with the electrically charged fragments (ions) thus formed going their separate ways accompanied by one or more of the attendant water dipoles. Such compounds, then, in the strictest sense, are not electrolytes, but they yield electrolytic solutions when dissolved in polar solvents.

5. Bases

Bases are the exact antithesis of acids; hence, a base may be defined as any substance capable of uniting with hydrogen ions or protons—a proton-acceptor. These definitions also suffer from limitations similar to those pointed out in the preceding paragraph for acids; however, for reasons analogous to those set forth above, they will suffice for the present study. Since the most notable proton-acceptors to be encountered when water is used as a solvent are metallic hydroxides, we shall here confine our remarks to them. Hydroxides of the active metals at room temperature are crystalline solids whose structures are made up of ions. Their dissolution to furnish free ions in solution is, of course, entirely analogous to the dissolution of the majority of the salts. The majority of the hydroxides of the less active metals are only slightly soluble in water, and a few of these, along with a few other substances which act as bases, have abilities to produce ions which are largely due to the influence of the solvent, as in the case of the acids mentioned in the preceding section.

6. The Abnormalities in the Colligative Properties of Electrolytic Solutions

In Chapter 12, it was shown that the lowering of the escaping tendency of a pure solvent, as manifest in its changing vapor pressure, boiling point, freezing point, and osmotic pressure, by the addition of a solute, depends only upon the relative numbers of solute and solvent particles present. When, of two solutions of equal concentration, the electrolytic one produces an alteration of these properties which is very nearly an integral multiple of the alteration produced by the nonelectrolytic one, the only conclusion to be drawn is that the former is contributing more particles to the mixture than is the latter. A tenth of a mole of sugar dissolved in a given volume of water should provide $\frac{1}{10}$ of 6.023×10^{23} molecules to be distributed among the solvent molecules, but when a tenth mole of salt is dissolved, the crystal should not break into $\frac{1}{10}$ of 6.023×10^{23} molecules of salt. Rather, it should break into twice that number of ions, for from the equation,

$$Na^+Cl^- \rightarrow Na^+ + Cl^-$$

it is seen that each theoretical salt molecule should give rise to two ions. As a consequence, salt solutions have almost twice the effect upon these properties that sugar solutions of equal concentration do.

The dissolving of a $\frac{1}{10}$ mole of magnesium chloride in the same volume of water used above would produce an effect nearly three times as great as that produced by the tenth mole of sugar, for to constitute the theoretical molecules of magnesium chloride three ions are necessary:

$$Mg^{++}Cl_2^{--} \rightarrow Mg^{++} + 2Cl^-$$

Observations are in agreement here with the theory.

7. The Ionization of Electrolytes

It was said above that electrolytic solutions produce an alteration that is *very nearly an integral multiple* of the effect produced by a nonelectrolytic one of like molar concentration. This naturally raises the question: Why, since each molecule gives an integral number of ions, is not the effect produced an *exact* integral multiple? Two possible explanations immediately present themselves. The first is that not all of the molecules break up into free ions. The second is that the anticipated number of ions is formed but that because of their concentration and their electrical charges they somehow interfere with each other so that some are not able to act as free and totally independent particles. These possible explanations are worthy of consideration.

At the outset, in the case of the ionic, crystalline solid, the ions are already formed and are not paired off in any definite way, and there appears to be no logical reason why all of the ions in such a crystal should not be set free upon its dissolution. Here the first explanation apparently fails, but in the case of molecules, such as those of the acids, which must be broken apart by the solvent before ions may be formed, it seems highly likely that a certain percentage of them might not be disrupted. A state of equilibrium would then exist between the undisrupted molecules and the ions formed from the disrupted ones. This situation may be represented by the equation:

$$HA \rightleftarrows H^+ + A^-$$

where A stands for the acid radical. Further support is offered by the fact that solutions of the same concentration of different acids differ widely in their effect upon the colligative properties of the solvent and in their ability to carry the electric current.

When concentrated solutions of substances which exist as ionic crystals are diluted, the degree of ionization appears to increase, approaching 100 per cent at extreme dilution. A logical explanation for this behavior is to suppose that a crystal which contains nothing but ions would, upon complete dissolution, be completely ionized. If these ions of two varieties bearing unlike charges are crowded into a relatively small volume of solvent, it may be presumed that they are still near enough to each other to exert a dragging or hindering effect upon each other, and there may even be cases of two ions of unlike charge colliding and thus setting up a momentary union which is broken up shortly by further collisions or by the action of the solvent dipoles. As the dilution is increased by the addition of more solvent, the distance between the ions is increased so that their attraction for each other is decreased, as is the chance of their colliding. As a result, each ion acts more independently of the others and the apparent degree of ionization increases until it approaches the 100 per cent mark at extreme dilution. This idea is generally referred to as the *interionic attraction theory*.

8. The Strength of Electrolytes

Some substances evidently already contain ions before they are added to a polar solvent and hence are already electrolytes, while others exist in the molecular form until the action of a polar solvent disrupts some of the molecules into ions. Strictly speaking, then, these latter substances are not electrolytes themselves, though they do yield electrolytic solutions when dissolved in polar solvents. It is common practice to refer to substances of both classes as electrolytes, but the above distinction should be firmly fixed in the minds of all who use the term. Note, also, that as a result of the existence of these two groups not all electrolytes are of the same *strength*. Those which are true electrolytes and are held to be completely ionized in solution are termed "strong" electrolytes. Practically all salts save a few of mercury, cadmium, and lead are strong electolytes. The soluble bases of the very active metals are "strong" bases, while the less soluble bases of the heavier metals do not produce many ions because of their relative insolubility, yet the portion which does dissolve seems to be well ionized. The strength of the molecular compounds as electrolytes varies all the way from weak to strong. Acids like acetic, whose molecules strongly resist the destructive action of the solvent dipoles, are classed as "weak," while those like hydrogen chloride, whose molecules are easily disrupted, are classed as "strong." In between these extremes are many "moderately strong" electrolytes. The strong electrolytes, being highly ionized, naturally conduct the electric current much more readily than do moderately strong or weak ones, and, for the same reason, their solutions exhibit colligative properties which are much more abnormal than are those of the less highly ionized substances.

9. Heat of Hydration and Heat of Solution

The tearing down of any crystal structure requires energy, and hence is an endothermic process. It has also been shown that if the particles which occupy the points of the crystal lattice are ions, these ions attract to themselves a number of water dipoles. When ions become thus hydrated, energy is always evolved; that is, the process being spontaneous is always an exothermic one. A given quantity of a specific variety of ion upon hydration will always yield, under the same conditions, the same quantity of heat energy. The heat liberated by a mole of any ion as a result of hydration is known as the *heat of hydration* of that ion, or, more specifically, as its *molar heat of hydration*. Since the two heat effects involved in the dissolution of such crystals are of opposite sign, it is apparent that the net heat effect will be determined by the algebraic sum of the two. If the heat evolved by hydration is in excess of the heat absorbed in the destruction of the lattice, then the temperature of the solution will rise; conversely, if the heat of hydration is less than the heat absorbed in the destruction of the lattice, then the temperature of the solution will drop. This net heat effect expressed in calories per mole of solute is known as the *heat of solution*, or, more specifically, as the *molar heat of solution*. When solutions are prepared in

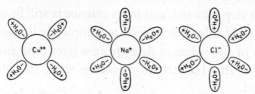

HYDRATED IONS. Water dipoles attach themselves to the electrically charged ions.

calibrated glassware, it is advisable to allow the temperature to return to room value before adding solvent to the desired level.

10. Hydrates

Some ions become so firmly attached to water dipoles during the process of hydration that, when the concentration of the solution becomes great enough for crystallization to occur, they carry with them into the crystal structure a characteristic number of the water molecules. For instance, when copper sulfate crystallizes from solution, five molecules of water are carried into the structure by every pair of copper and sulfate ions. The water molecules seem to be attached to the ions by coördinate covalence. The formula for the crystalline substance is, therefore, $CuSO_4.5H_2O$, and its full name would be copper sulfate pentahydrate. Aluminum sulfate, when crystallized from solution, has the formula $Al_2(SO_4)_3.18H_2O$, a substance whose full name would be aluminum sulfate octadecahydrate. The number of water molecules in such formulas is indicated by the proper prefix derived from Greek numerals. X-ray examinations of the structures of such hydrated crystals indicate that the water is present as molecular particles which are held in combination by the other units. In the copper sulfate crystal it is found that the copper ion holds four of the water molecules while the sulfate ion holds the fifth one.

When water is driven out of such hydrated substances, the crystals naturally collapse to a powder. A brick house would also collapse if 5 bricks out of every 7, or 18 out of every 23, were removed. Substances which have never contained water of hydration (or water of crystallization, as it is often called), or which have been forced to give up all of their water of hydration, are described as *anhydrous*. The stability of hydrates will be discussed in a later chapter.

11. *Theories of Ionization*

The first theory which attempted to correlate and explain the ability of electrolytes to conduct electricity and to affect abnormally the colligative properties of solutions was that proposed by the Swedish chemist, Svante Arrhenius, in the year 1887. This theory, though it was not too readily accepted at the time, represented a great step forward, and in its essence is still in use today. The idea that ionic crystals yield solutions which are completely ionized regardless of the degree of dilution of the solution dates from a later time and is due largely to the work of Debye and Hückel, from whose work the interionic attraction theory also stems.

12. *The Activity of Electrolytic Solutions*

Many molecular substances are not completely ionized in solution and many of the ionic substances which are completely ionized, as a result of interionic attraction, act as if they were not, and for all practical purposes might as well not be. In practical laboratory and industrial work, it is the extent to which a solution appears to be ionized as determined by its effect, rather than its absolute degree of ionization, which is important. This extent to which a solute appears to be ionized, as determined from its effect in the solution, is known as its *apparent degree of ionization.*

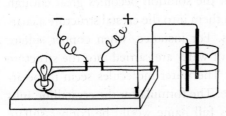

APPARATUS FOR TESTING QUALITATIVELY THE RELATIVE CONDUCTIVITIES OF SOLUTIONS. The greater the conductivity of the solution being tested, the more brilliantly the lamp glows.

The apparent degree of ionization depends first upon the nature of the solute itself. For strong electrolytes, like the majority of the salts, it has been found that those which yield ions of the same charge have approximately the same apparent degree of ionization if all other conditions are identical. As the electrovalence of the ions increases, the apparent degree of ionization decreases. This could be predicted, for, according to Coulomb's law, electrically charged particles have an attraction for each other which varies directly as the product of their charges and inversely as the square of the distance which separates them. Hence, even if the number of ions were not increased, their greater charges would cause a greater interionic attraction, thus decreasing their effective concentration. The extent to which a molecular substance ionizes depends upon the forces within the molecule if all other factors remain constant.

Secondly, the apparent degree of ionization of a solute is dependent upon the nature of the solvent in which it is dissolved. The tearing down of an ionic crystal lattice is dependent upon the attraction of the solvent dipoles for the individual ions, and the disruption of molecules into ions depends not only upon the magnitude of the forces within the molecule but also upon the magnitude of the forces of the dipoles. This latter force depends upon the degree of separation of the positive and negative charges within the dipole and is measured by the dielectric constant (cf. section 5, Chapter 5); hence, the solvent with the highest dielectric constant, all other things remaining equal, is likely to be the solvent in which a given solute will have the highest apparent degree of ionization. Among the best polar solvents are water, methyl alcohol, and ammonia.

Table 12

DIELECTRIC CONSTANTS OF COMMON SOLVENTS AT 18° C.

Acetic acid	9.7	Chloroform	5.2
Ammonia	22.	Ethyl alcohol	26.
Aniline	7.3	Methyl alcohol	33.
Benzene	2.3	Water	81.07

In the third place, as shown above, the apparent degree of ionization increases with increasing dilution. Further, with dilution, the distance between ions increases, and, in accord with Coulomb's law, the interionic attraction should decrease, leaving each ion much freer to act independently.

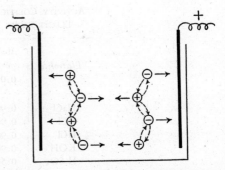

Lastly, the apparent degree of ionization of electrolytes is affected by the presence of other ions. The most notable effects of this type are obtained when one adds to a solution of a weak electrolyte, or to a solution of a strong electrolyte of slight solubility, a second electrolyte which has one ion in common with the first. In the first case, there is a decrease in the ionization of the first electrolyte, while in the second case, there is a decrease in solubility of the first electrolyte. This matter will be discussed more fully in the chapter on equilibrium. In general, the effect of a second solute upon dilute solutions of strong electrolytes is small.

THE MUTUAL ATTRACTION OF IONS SLOWS THEIR RATE OF MIGRATION UNDER THE INFLUENCE OF THE ELECTRIC CURRENT. This phenomenon is sometimes referred to as the "drag effect."

At this juncture it is convenient to introduce the concept of *activity*, which may be considered to be an *effective concentration*, i.e., the actual concentration after a correction has been applied for the retarding influence of interionic or other attraction between particles in the solution. From the considerations set forth in the preceding paragraphs, it is evident that the apparent degree of ionization of most electrolytes will be less than 100 per cent and that to arrive at the activity, or effective concentration, of the ions in a given solution one must multiply the molal concentration of the solute in the solution by a factor of the proper value. Such factors are known as *activity coefficients*, and may be thought of as representing the fraction of the solute which appears to be ionized.

$$\text{activity} = \text{molality} \times \text{activity coefficient}$$

Activity coefficients have been measured experimentally for a great many compounds at various temperatures and in various concentrations. In Table 13 there are listed activity coefficients for some of the more important compounds at several concentrations.

Table 13

ACTIVITY COEFFICIENTS OF SOME STRONG
ELECTROLYTES IN WATER AT 25° C.

Electrolyte	Molal Concentration of Solution		
	0.01	0.1	1.0
NaCl	0.903	0.778	0.656
KCl	0.902	0.770	0.607
HCl	0.906	0.798	0.811
KOH	0.901	0.772	0.743
H_2SO_4	0.545	0.266	0.131

13. *The Hydronium Ion: Radicals*

The ionization of molecular acids always yields both positive and negative ions, as do the true electrolytes. In this case, however, the positive ion is always the hydrogen ion. Elsewhere it has been shown that the hydrogen ion is the simple positively charged proton which is an extremely small entity. Because of its extreme smallness as compared with its electrical charge, many physical chemists doubt whether the hydrogen ion ever has a chance to exist alone in solution. Remembering, also, that the proton is pulled out of its molecule by the action of water dipoles, it seems all the more logical to presume that the proton stays attached to at least one dipolar water molecule thus:

$$H\overset{..}{\underset{\overset{.}{\circ}}{O}}: + H^+ \rightarrow H\overset{..}{\underset{\overset{.}{\circ}}{O}}:H^+$$
$$H \qquad\qquad H$$

The H_3O^+ ion is known as the hydronium ion, and is, in all likelihood, the ion which gives all aqueous solutions of acids their characteristic behavior. Despite a knowledge of the hydronium ion, many chemists in their speech and writing still refer to *hydrogen ions* in aqueous solutions; this is due both to force of habit and to the knowledge that when the hydronium ion reacts, the proton enters into the reaction while the water dipole to which it is attached is generally once more set free.

Ions, such as the hydronium ion, which are made up of several atoms held together by covalence, yet bear collectively an electrical charge, are known as *radicals*. Thus one refers to the nitrate ion, NO_3^-, the sulfate ion, SO_4^{--}, the phosphate ion, PO_4^{---}, etc. as the nitrate, sulfate, and phosphate radicals, respectively.

14. The Migration of Ions

Reference to electrolysis in section 9 of Chapter 7 reveals that the ions contained in the solution of an electrolytic cell will travel, when the current is turned on, to the pole of unlike charge. That ions do migrate to the pole of unlike charge can be shown by the following simple experiment. Agar jelly prepared with a solution of potassium chloride is allowed to set in the lower portion of a U-tube as shown in the accompanying diagram. In the right arm of the tube is placed a solution of some cupric salt, while a solution of potassium chloride is placed in the left arm. A small platinum cathode is placed in the colorless solution of potassium salt and a small platinum anode is placed in the blue cupric solution. The current is then turned on. The blue color of the cupric solu-

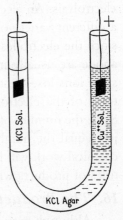

APPARATUS FOR THE DEMONSTRATION OF THE MIGRATION OF IONS. Under the influence of the electric current, the blue cupric ions migrate into the colorless agar jelly.

tion is due to the hydrated cupric ion, $[Cu(H_2O)_4]^{++}$. These ions travel toward the cathode as shown by the agar jelly becoming tinted with blue from right to left. As time passes, the blue color extends farther into the jelly, and ultimately a blue coloration may be noted in the bottom of the potassium chloride solution. That the colorless chloride ions are traveling in the opposite direction could be shown in other ways.

It is characteristic of the positively charged ions of the metals and the positively charged hydronium ion that they travel toward the cathode. The hydroxide ion, the simple ions of the nonmetals, and compound ions of the nonmetals and oxygen, all of which bear negative charges, travel toward the anode.

The speed of ionic migrations is not so great as might be expected because of the numerous collisions which the ions make with solvent particles and with other ions.

15. Reactions at the Electrodes

When the migrating ions arrive at the electrode which attracts them, the electrical transfers occur which account for the ability of electrolytic solutions to conduct the electric current. Chemical reactions accompany these electrical transfers, which, together with the ionic migration, constitute the process of electrolysis. An electrolytic cell contains two electrodes, each of which attracts a different variety of ion, hence there are always two electrode reactions; and, since the electrodes are well separated in the cell, the products formed at the anode are usually independent of those formed at the cathode. Furthermore, since ions lose electrons at the anode and gain them at the cathode, the reactions of the electrolytic cell are of the nature of oxidations and reductions. Since the number of electrons gained at one electrode during the process must just equal the number lost at the other, it is apparent that equal amounts of chemical work will be performed at each and that chemically equivalent quantities of products will be produced at each.

16. The Products of Electrolysis

Although water is an extremely weak electrolyte, nevertheless aqueous solutions of electrolytes contain not only the ions of the solute but also very small concentrations of hydronium and hydroxyl ions. There are present, therefore, two varieties of cations and two varieties of anions. If the solute is a metallic salt, one might expect hydrogen rather than the metal to be discharged at the cathode, and this will be the case if the salt is a compound of one of the active metals which is capable of displacing hydrogen from water; if, on the other hand, the salt is a compound of a metal which will not displace hydrogen from water under ordinary conditions, the metal will be displaced from the solution of its ions and will be deposited on the cathode. Simple nonmetallic anions are set free at the anode as the nonmetal unless such ions are less readily acted upon than are the hydroxyl ions from the water. Oxygen is liberated at the anode when hydroxyl ions are so acted upon, and water is left in the solution as a result of their oxidation:

$$4OH^- - 4\epsilon \rightarrow 2H_2O + O_2 \uparrow$$

The electrolysis of a solution of sodium chloride as discussed in section 14 of Chapter 7 well illustrates the fact that the cations of metals of high activity are more stable than is the hydronium ion, and are consequently less readily discharged than are hydronium ions. This stability determines that the electrolysis of solutions of such ions always produces hydrogen at the cathode:

$$2H_3O^+ + 2\epsilon \rightarrow 2H_2O + H_2 \uparrow$$

It is also because of this stability that such metals may be prepared electrolytically only by use of their molten salts.

A majority of the oxygen-containing, compound anions of the nonmetals are less readily discharged at the anode than are hydroxyl ions; this is also true of a few simple nonmetallic ions which are derived from the most active nonmetals. The fluoride ion is a good example of the latter type. It is reasonable to expect that, if the nonmetal is extremely active in securing extra electrons to become an ion, the ion will not readily return to the atomic or molecular state, thus reversing the original spontaneous process. In cases of this kind, the hydroxyl ion of the water will be oxidized, as shown above with the liberation of oxygen at the anode. For instance, the electrolysis of a solution of zinc sulfate ($ZnSO_4$) should yield

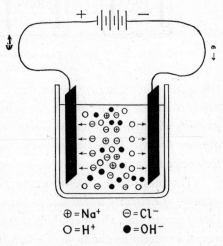

$\oplus = Na^+ \quad \ominus = Cl^-$
$O = H^+ \quad \bullet = OH^-$

THE ELECTROLYSIS OF BRINE.

zinc at the cathode and oxygen at the anode while the electrolysis of a solution of potassium nitrate (KNO_3) should yield hydrogen at the cathode and oxygen at the anode. In this latter case, the solvent would be undergoing decomposition rather than the solute.

The products obtained during an electrolysis by the direct discharge of ions at the electrodes are known as *primary products*. Products which may be obtained as a result of the action of the primary products upon each other, or upon the electrodes, or upon the solvent, or upon other substances produced during the process, are known as *secondary products*. There will be occasion in later chapters to refer to some secondary electrolytic products and the processes which produce them.

17. The Quantitative Aspects of Electrolysis—Faraday's Laws

During his famous study of electrolytic processes, Michael Faraday discovered the relationship which exists between the quantity of electricity passed and the quantity of electrolyte decomposed as a result of its passage. These findings, which were set forth in 1833, are known as Faraday's laws. His first

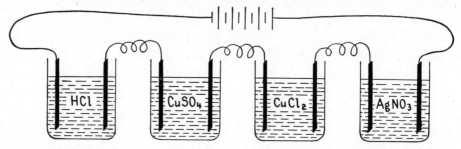

CELLS CONNECTED IN SERIES. Chemically equivalent quantities of various substances will be liberated at each of the eight electrodes.

law states that *the mass of the products liberated at each pole is proportional to the quantity of electricity passed through the solution*. His second law states that *if the same quantity of electricity is passed through several different solutions, the quantities of the different products formed at the several electrodes will stand to each other in the ratio of their respective equivalent weights*.

The unit of measure of quantity of electricity is the *coulomb*, defined as *the quantity of electricity which will be delivered in one second by a current flowing at the rate of one ampere*. Thus, coulombs may be calculated by multiplying the amperage of a current by the time in seconds during which it acts. A current of 8 amp. acting for 20 seconds would deliver 8×20 or 160 coulombs of electricity.

Faraday found that 96,500 coulombs were required to liberate 1.008 g. of hydrogen. While this quantity of hydrogen is being liberated at the cathode, a proportional quantity of some other product will be liberated at the anode. Since 1.008 g. of hydrogen is the equivalent weight of that substance, it follows that an equivalent weight of the anodic product will also be formed, and that the same current passed through other electrolytic solutions would also produce an equivalent weight of product at *each* electrode. This is readily demonstrated by putting a different electrolytic solution in each of several cells connected in series, as shown in the accompanying illustration. Since the cells are so connected, the same quantity of electricity must pass through each. By passing 96,500 coulombs through the system and weighing the products formed, it is found that an equivalent weight of some product is produced at every electrode.

The reason for this relationship becomes evident when one considers the changes which take place at the electrodes. When one equivalent weight of hydrogen is produced, each hydrogen ion is being supplied with the one electron required to convert it once more into a hydrogen atom. In 1.008 g. of hydrogen, there are 6.023×10^{23} atoms, hence 6.023×10^{23} electrons have been supplied (cf. section 10, Chapter 8). These electrons which were supplied to the hydrogen ions were stripped from negative ions at the anode and sent around through the metallic external circuit to them at the cathode surface. A like amount of change must also have taken place at the anode.

To convert a zinc ion, Zn^{++}, to a zinc atom would require two electrons per ion, or per atom, hence only half of 6.023×10^{23} atoms or half of an atomic weight of zinc could be liberated by the passage of 96,500 coulombs. This half atomic weight of zinc is its equivalent weight, $E = A/V$, the quantity which would do the same amount of chemical work as 1.008 g. of hydrogen.

In recognition of Faraday's brilliant work in this field, 96,500 coulombs have been designated as 1 Faraday.

Calculating the quantity of product yielded at an electrode during an electrolytic reaction necessitates knowing only the equivalent weight of the product and the number of Faradays of electricity passed. As an example to illustrate such a calculation, consider the following: What weight of copper and what weight of chlorine would be produced in 1 hr., 20 min. by the action of a current of 2 amp. on a solution of cupric chloride?

Solution:

$$1 \text{ hr., } 20 \text{ min.} = 60 + 20 \text{ min.}$$
$$= 80 \times 60 \text{ seconds}$$
$$4800 \times 2 = 9600 \text{ coulombs}$$
$$(\text{no. of Faradays passed}) = 9600 / 96,500$$
$$\text{equiv. wt. of cupric ion} = 63.57 / 2$$
$$\text{quantity of copper deposited} = (9600 / 96,500) \times (63.57 / 2)$$
$$= 3.16 \text{ g.}$$
$$\text{equiv. wt. of chlorine} = 35.456 / 1$$

$$\text{quantity of chlorine liberated} = (9600 \big/ 96,500) \times 35.456$$
$$= 3.53 \text{ g.}$$

If one chooses, he may use ratio and proportion:

$$9600 : 96,500 = x : 63.57/2$$

whence

$$96,500 \, x = 9600 \times 63.57/2$$
$$x = 3.16 \text{ g. of copper}$$

18. The Chemical Properties of Electrolytes

Thus far, our discussion of electrolytes has included only their physical behavior and their chemical behavior as induced by the effects of the electric current. Most of the reactions of inorganic chemistry are those which occur between solutions of electrolytes, so it is highly important that the chemical behavior of such solutions be considered. Because of the equilibria encountered in such reactions, however, discussion of them will not be undertaken until the chapter on chemical equilibrium is reached.

(*See Appendix for Exercises*)

COLLATERAL READINGS

Arrhenius: Electrolytic dissociation, *J. Am. Chem. Soc.*, **34,** 353 (1912).
Cartledge: *Introductory Theoretical Chemistry*, Boston, Ginn & Co., 1929.
Chapin and Steiner: *Second Year College Chemistry*, 5th ed., revised, New York, John Wiley & Sons, Inc., 1943.
Creighton and Koehler: *Electrochemistry*, Vol. I, 4th ed., New York, John Wiley & Sons, Inc., 1943.
Davidson: Solutions of electrolytes, *J. Chem. Education*, **12,** 24 (1935).
Hall, *et al.: Acids and Bases*, Mack Printing Co., 1941.
Hildebrand: *Principles of Chemistry*, New York, The Macmillan Co., 1941.
Hogness and Johnson: *Qualitative Analysis and Chemical Equilibrium*, New York, Henry Holt & Co., Inc., 1940.
Walden: *Salts, Acids, and Bases*, New York, McGraw-Hill Book Co., 1929.
Any standard textbook of physical chemistry.

15

Aluminum and Its Compounds

1. Introduction

Aluminum is the third element of the third period and the most abundant of the metals to be found in the earth's crust. Its importance in present-day civilization is well known. Also of importance are a number of its compounds. Its relative atomic weight is 26.97 at. wt. units.

The atomic number of the aluminum atom is 13, whence the distribution of the 13 planetary electrons among the first three main energy levels is 2, 8, 3. This electronic distribution leads one to expect the atom to lose three electrons in an effort to attain a neonlike structure thus showing a valence of $+3$. Aluminum does this in many of its compounds. In a few of its compounds, however, it appears to form covalent linkages by the sharing of its three valence electrons.

A. THE IONIZING POTENTIAL. The three valence electrons of aluminum are not all in the same sub-level; two are in the 3_0 level and one is in the 3_1 level. Because of this slight difference, the 3_1 electron is removed from the atom a bit more easily than are the 3_0 electrons of either the sodium or magnesium atom. When this one electron has been removed, however, the two remaining 3_0 electrons are removed with even more difficulty than are the 3_0 electrons of the preceding two elements, for the nucleus of the aluminum atom is heavier and bears a larger positive charge than they do. Further, as in the case of the magnesium atom, when the first of the 3_0 electrons is removed the remaining one is removed with still greater difficulty. A comparison of the difficulty encountered in removing the valence electrons of the first three atoms of the third period is afforded by the ionizing potentials given in the following table.

Table 14

IONIZING POTENTIAL (VOLTS)

Element	First Stage	Second Stage	Third Stage
Sodium...........................	5.12	..	..
Magnesium.......................	7.61	14.96	..
Aluminum........................	5.96	18.74	28.31

B. THE ELECTRODE POTENTIAL. The Al^{+3} ion is formed with more difficulty than is the Mg^{+2} ion, hence it is to be expected that the Al^{+3} ion will be more easily reconverted to its atomic condition than is the Mg^{+2} ion. This is the case as shown by an electrode potential of 1.67 v. for aluminum as compared with one of 2.34 v. for magnesium.

C. THE SIZE OF THE ION AND ITS HEAT OF HYDRATION. As one progresses from left to right across any period of the periodic chart (cf. section 11, Chapter 6), the positive ions become smaller in size as the magnitude of the charge becomes larger. As might be expected, these smaller, more highly charged ions have a greater attraction for the oppositely charged ends of water dipoles. A quantitative measure of this attraction is afforded by the heat of hydration of the ions, for, the greater the attraction is, the greater also will be the *heat of hydration*. This quantity is defined as the number of calories of heat which would be evolved if a mole of gaseous ions could be completely hydrated in solution. Measurements show that the heat of hydration does increase from sodium to magnesium to aluminum.

2. *Physical Properties*

Aluminum is a light metal which exhibits a silvery luster tinged with a faint bluish cast. When left exposed to the air, its luster gradually gives place to a dull whitish-gray appearance which is the result of the formation of a thin coating of the oxide. The density of the metal is 2.7 g./ml.; its melting point is 669.7° C.; and its boiling point is 1800° C. The density of aluminum is considerably larger than that of water and slightly in excess of that of magnesium, but it is so much less than that of iron, copper, and the other widely used metals that it is classed as a light metal. At about 20° C., the pure metal is rather soft, as a consequence of which it is both malleable and ductile. At 100° to 150° C., it is even more easily worked, but just below its melting point it becomes so brittle that it easily may be ground to a powder.

If the ability to conduct electricity of a copper wire and of an aluminum wire of the same length and cross-section be compared, the aluminum is found to be only about two-thirds as effective as the copper, but, if the conductive ability of equal masses of copper and aluminum is compared, the aluminum is found to be about twice as effective as the copper. Because of this ability to conduct the current, and because of its high tensile strength, aluminum is frequently the material chosen for the cables of high-tension power lines. The metal is also a good conductor of heat.

Aluminum sheet and foil are used as reflectors in heat insulation because their surface will take a high polish, and reflector mirrors for reflecting telescopes are frequently coated with aluminum rather than silver. Aluminum is preferred to silver for this latter use because it reflects ultraviolet rays more readily than does silver, and mirrors so prepared last better than do silvered ones.

3. Occurrence

Though less active than either sodium or magnesium, aluminum is still sufficiently active never to be found free in nature. It is the most plentiful of the metals and is widely distributed in nature, being present in the earth's crust in quantities inferior only to those of oxygen and silicon. All rocks save those of a limestone or sandstone nature contain aluminum compounds, and, hence, most soils contain aluminum compounds. The distribution of the element in the earth's crust is estimated as slightly in the neighborhood of 8 per cent. The most common naturally occurring compounds are the silicates. These include the feldspars, such as $KAlSi_3O_8$; the micas, such as $H_2KAl_3(SiO_4)_3$; and the clays, such as the pure white *kaolin* $H_2Al_2(SiO_4)_2.H_2O$, all of which are to be found all over the world. The commercially important minerals are the various ones which contain the oxide. *Corundum* is an anhydrous form of the oxide which is inferior in hardness only to diamond and silicon carbide, and is in much demand as an abrasive. *Emery* is the anhydrous oxide discolored by the presence of iron oxide. The gem stones known as *rubies* and *sapphires* are also composed of the oxide. The former stone owes its red color to the presence of traces of chromium oxide, while the latter owes its blue color to the presence of the oxides of iron and titanium. None of these forms of the anhydrous oxide are used as ores for the refining of the metal, but there exist large deposits of the hydrated oxides which are so used. The principal ore of aluminum is *bauxite*, which is a mixture of $Al_2O_3.H_2O$ and $Al_2O_3.3H_2O$. Other hydrated oxides which occur in large quantities are *diaspore*, $Al_2O_3.H_2O$, and *gibbsite*, $Al_2O_3.3H_2O$. Because it is used in the refining of the oxide ores, the rather rare mineral *cryolite*, Na_3AlF_6, is of considerable importance. Also worthy of mention are *alunite*, $K_2SO_4.Al_2(SO_4)_3. Al_2O_3.6H_2O$, and the gem stone *turquoise*, $Al_2(OH)_3PO_4.H_2O$, which owes its blue color to traces of copper phosphate and which is so dear to the hearts of the Indians of the Southwestern states.

The world's most famous rubies come from Burma, while the best sapphires are reputedly those found in Montana. The largest deposits of the hydrated oxide ores in the United States are found in central Arkansas, whence, in 1939, came 96 per cent of the national output of the free metal. Deposits of these oxides are also found in Tennessee, Alabama, Georgia, and the Pacific

Northwest, and in France, Yugoslavia, Brazil, and British and Dutch Guiana. Alunite is found in some of the very dry Western states, and turquoise is found in New Mexico, Arizona, and Nevada as well as in Iran and other countries. Cryolite is obtained principally on the island of Greenland, though, as an outgrowth of World War II, synthetic cryolite is now prepared domestically on an industrial scale.

An Arkansas Aluminum Ore Mine. (Courtesy, Aluminum Company of America.)

4. Preparation

Although the clays and rocks which contain the aluminum silicates are much more plentiful than are the deposits of the hydrated oxides, the latter serve at the present time as the source of the free metal. In the first place, being even more stable than the oxides, the silicates are more difficult to decompose, and the percentage of aluminum in the oxide ores runs much higher. The present process used in the refining of these ores is that which was developed by Charles Martin Hall, who became interested in the problem while he was a student in Oberlin College in Ohio and who found its solution in 1886 just a few months after his graduation. The same process was discovered independently a few months later by the French scientist, Heroult.

The Hall process is carried on in a coke-lined iron cell. The lining of the cell is the cathode, and dipping into the material contained in it are a series of carbon rods which are the anodes. The container is charged with a quantity of purified aluminum oxide which has been mixed with cryolite. The heat generated by the resistance of this charge to the passage of the electric current serves to melt the charge. The chief function of the cryolite is to lower the temperature at which the charge will melt. The surface of the molten mixture is covered with

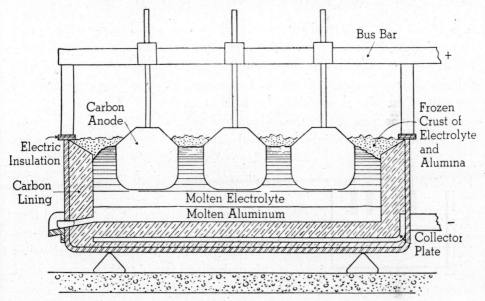

CELL FOR THE PRODUCTION OF ALUMINUM BY ELECTROLYSIS OF THE MOLTEN OXIDE. (Courtesy, Aluminum Company of America.)

coke to decrease radiation. Aluminum collects in the bottom of the cell and at the high temperature maintained remains liquid. At regular intervals, the molten metal is drawn from the cell and cast in molds.

For many years, there was no successful method of purifying the metal obtained by the Hall process, hence to obtain a pure product it was necessary to purify the bauxitic ores to be used. The principal contaminants of the Arkansas ores are salts of iron and titanium. To remove these, the ore is digested with a strong solution of sodium hydroxide. The aluminum oxide is converted to soluble sodium aluminate, $NaAlO_2$, while the iron and titanium are precipitated as their respective hydroxides and are removed by filtration. Upon dilution of the filtrate with water, a hydrated form of the aluminum oxide is reprecipitated, and this is collected and heated. The heat drives off the water of hydration, leaving the pure Al_2O_3 ready for the cells.

There are other processes for purifying the aluminum oxide to be used in the electrolytic cells. For instance, in France the Serpek process once found wide application. This procedure consists of heating the ore with carbon and nitrogen to bring about the formation of the nitride, AlN. This compound, upon treatment with water, yields a pure hydrated oxide and ammonia, which is a valuable by-product.

$$2AlN + 6H_2O \rightarrow 2NH_3 \uparrow + \underline{Al_2O_3.3H_2O}$$

In Italy, the Fink-de Marchi process is used, by which method the ore is heated strongly with sulfur. The iron, which is present in rather large quantities in the Italian ores, is converted to iron sulfide. This mixture is then treated with chlorine at a temperature of 920° C. It is reported that at this temperature 94 per cent of the iron is removed as volatile ferric chloride. The remaining impurities may be removed by the sodium hydroxide method.

Within relatively recent years, a method of purifying metallic aluminum has

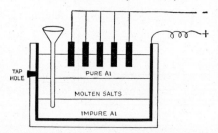

HOOPES CELL FOR THE ELECTROLYTIC
REFINING OF ALUMINUM.

been developed. Known as the Hoopes process, this method consists of electrolyzing an alloy of aluminum, copper, and silicon. The electrolyte is a molten mixture of aluminum salts. At the temperature at which the cell operates, the alloy is molten and settles to the bottom, where it is connected to the source of current and made to serve as the anode. Above this layer is the molten layer of salts, and floating on this is a layer of the pure metal which serves as the cathode. As the cell operates, the cathodic layer increases, and molten metal is drawn from it from time to time. A metal whose purity is reported as 99.85 per cent is produced by this method.

Aluminum was first isolated by Oersted of Denmark in 1825. From shortly after its discovery until 1854, all of the free metal to be had was prepared by its displacement from its anhydrous chloride by potassium metal,

$$AlCl_3 + 3K \xrightarrow{\Delta} 3KCl + Al$$

The cost of the metal during this period averaged about $160 per pound, and the small bits available were to be found only in laboratories, or museums, or in jewelry. This latter use was based on its cost rather than on its beauty. In 1854 the use of sodium metal was substituted for that of potassium, and the use of the double chloride of sodium and aluminum was substituted for that of the straight aluminum chloride. This brought the price down to $27 per pound in 1858, and still lower in succeeding years. With the development in the United States of a cheaper process for the preparation of sodium, the price of aluminum dropped as low as $4 per pound. The industrial application of the Hall process brought the price down so low that kitchen utensils of aluminum became standard articles in the dime stores of the nation. The 1946 price of 98 to 99.5 per cent aluminum was 15 cents per pound.

5. *Chemical Properties*

Aluminum is a less active loser of electrons than either sodium or magnesium, but it is much more active in this respect than are many of the heavier metals and is consequently classed as an active metal. Like the two metals which precede it in the third period, aluminum will enter into both combination and displacement reactions, reacting with a wide variety of substances which are capable of accepting electrons.

A. COMBINATION REACTIONS. Like powdered magnesium, powdered aluminum is perfectly stable at room temperatures. Because of its stability and cheapness, the powdered metal is often suspended in a vehicle of varnish or bronzing fluid for use as a paint. It has good covering qualities and gives a surface of great reflecting power. When heated to red heat in the open air or in an atmosphere of oxygen, the finely divided metal burns with the emission of an intense white light. For this reason, photographic flash bulbs often contain aluminum turnings, foil, or gauze in an atmosphere of oxygen. The product is the white powdery oxide, when only oxygen is present,

$$4Al + 3O_2 \rightarrow 2Al_2O_3$$

but in air the product is a mixture of the oxide and the equally white nitride,

$$2Al + N_2 \rightarrow 2AlN$$

Because of its ability to combine with both oxygen and nitrogen, the metal is often used to remove air bubbles from molten metals and to remove air from various vessels and containers. Like magnesium nitride, aluminum nitride is easily decomposed by the action of water, as shown in the preceding section.

Aluminum forms the anhydrous chloride when heated in pure chlorine. The reaction is exothermic when once begun and at the high temperature developed the product sublimes to collect as a fine, slightly yellowish powder in the cool end of the reaction vessel. The metal combines with the other halogens when heated with them, and it will also combine with carbon and with sulfur when heated with these elements:

$$4Al + 3C \rightarrow Al_4C_3$$
$$2Al + 3S \rightarrow Al_2S_3$$

Like the nitride, these binary compounds are also susceptible to hydrolysis:

$$AlCl_3 + 3H_2O \rightarrow Al(OH)_3 + 3HCl$$
$$Al_4C_3 + 12H_2O \rightarrow 4Al(OH)_3 + 3CH_4 \uparrow$$
$$Al_2S_3 + 6H_2O \rightarrow 2Al(OH)_3 + 3H_2S \uparrow$$

In each case, one product is the gelatinous aluminum "hydroxide"; the second products in the equations given above are, in order, hydrogen chloride, methane, and hydrogen sulfide. A discussion of hydrolysis will be presented in Chapter 17.

Aluminum is not sufficiently active as an electron-loser to form a binary compound with hydrogen, neither does it form a binary compound with silicon. The phosphide, AlP, may be prepared by heating phosphorus and aluminum together in the absence of air, but the product is so difficult to obtain in pure form that it was not isolated and characterized until 1944.

B. DISPLACEMENT REACTIONS. Aluminum will not displace hydrogen from cold water. This behavior presumably is explained by the formation of a very thin but adherent coat of the oxide which prevents further contact between the metallic surface and the water. If hydrochloric acid, sodium hydroxide, or another substance which will react with the oxide to remove it is added, the liberation of hydrogen proceeds apace. The metal readily displaces hydrogen from steam.

The hydrogen of acids is much less firmly held than is the hydrogen of water, so one should expect aluminum to displace hydrogen readily from these former compounds. This expectation is realized with hydrochloric and other nonoxidizing acids, but little hydrogen is evolved with sulfuric and nitric acids. The action with nitric acid is so slight that tank cars lined with aluminum are usually used to transport it in industrial quantities. Here, again, the lack of activity is explained presumably by the formation of an adhering coat of oxide. The tendency of the hydrogen ions present to remove the film is offset by the strong oxidizing nature of these acids.

Aluminum, unlike sodium and magnesium, reacts readily with strong bases to form a ternary salt of the metal and to liberate hydrogen:

$$2Al + 2NaOH + 2H_2O \rightarrow 2NaAlO_2 + 3H_2 \uparrow$$

The salt formed in the given example is sodium aluminate. This unusual behavior of aluminum will be discussed in section 7 of this chapter.

Because of its ability to combine with oxygen at high temperatures, powdered aluminum is often used in high-temperature, dry displacements which involve the oxides of less active elements. The powdered metal in such reactions is mixed intimately with the powdered oxide and the charge is placed in a well-insulated refractory crucible. A piece of magnesium ribbon at whose base is a small quantity of a strong oxidizing agent serves as the fuse. Once begun, the reaction is strongly exothermic, so that the reaction spreads through the whole charge. At the temperature of the reaction, the displaced element is melted and collects in the bottom of the crucible. Molten iron for welding fractures is sometimes prepared in this way, and elements which are difficult to obtain from their oxides by other methods are often prepared in this way.

$$Fe_2O_3 + 2Al \rightarrow 2Fe + Al_2O_3$$

The process goes by three names: (1) The *Goldschmidt process*, after its discoverer; (2) the *thermite process*, after the name given to the powdered mixture of aluminum and oxide; and (3) *aluminothermy*, from the use of aluminum and heat. Future reference will be made to the process.

6. Aluminum Oxide and Hydroxide

Aluminum oxide, as already pointed out, occurs in quantity in nature in both the anhydrous and hydrated forms. Water is driven off when the hydrated forms are heated at temperatures between 200° and 300° C., leaving a white powdery mass which is similar to the white powder obtained when the metal is burned in oxygen. If this form of the oxide is now heated to 2050° C., it will fuse to a dense mass which, upon cooling, is extremely hard. This fused, or sintered, aluminum oxide has properties in common with the natural *corundum*, and is sold under the trade name of *alundum*. It is used in both the massive and the powdered form as an abrasive, and is also used to make porous laboratory ware and laboratory and industrial ware which must withstand high temperatures.

Synthetic rubies and sapphires of excellent quality are produced by fusing the oxide with the proper coloring material and allowing crystallization to occur under proper conditions. Production of these gem stones is now a well-established industry.

The oxide is very insoluble, and the fused form is relatively unreactive. It is not attacked readily by acids, but it can be converted to the sulfate by fusion with either sodium or potassium bisulfate:

$$Al_2O_3 + 6NaHSO_4 \xrightarrow{\Delta} Al_2(SO_4)_3 + 3Na_2SO_4 + 3H_2O \uparrow$$

The unfused oxide will react with hydrochloric acid and other strong acids.

The material commonly referred to as aluminum hydroxide is obtained by adding a soluble hydroxide to solutions which contain aluminum ions. If the

ARC TYPE ELECTRIC FURNACES FOR THE PRODUCTION OF SINTERED ALUMINUM OXIDE. In these furnaces bauxite mixed with portions of coke and mill scrap is subjected to a temperature of about 3000° F. (Courtesy, The Carborundum Co.)

soluble hydroxide is a weak one, or if the hydroxide, whether weak or strong, is not added in excess of the theoretical quantity required, a colorless, gelatinous precipitate will form. X-ray examinations of this freshly formed precipitate show that it has no crystalline structure. Upon standing, the precipitate gradually loses water in no definite quantities, and in very dry atmospheres will lose water until only a powdery mass of aluminum oxide remains. For these reasons, it appears that there is no true aluminum hydroxide, and the material which is precipitated as described above is a gelatinous, hydrated form of the oxide. The formula for this substance should, therefore, be written $Al_2O_3.3H_2O$ rather than $Al(OH)_3$; by custom and for convenience, however, chemists write the formula $Al(OH)_3$ and speak of aluminum hydroxide.

If the gelatinous precipitate is made to lose its water at a temperature below 315° C., the mass which remains is very porous and will absorb both water vapor and gases. This is known as activated alumina. When the mass has absorbed all it will hold, it may be reactivated by heating to drive out the absorbed gases and water.

The "hydroxide" will react with strong and moderately strong acids to form the corresponding salts and water:

$$Al(OH)_3 + 3HCl \rightarrow AlCl_3 + 3H_2O$$
$$2Al(OH)_3 + 3H_2SO_4 \rightarrow Al_2(SO_4)_3 + 6H_2O$$

The $Al(OH)_3$ is apparently acting as a base in such reactions. Strangely enough, it will also react with strong and moderately strong bases to form salts and water:

$$Al(OH)_3 + NaOH \rightarrow NaAlO_2 + 2H_2O$$

Evidently, if too much of a strong base is used in precipitating the "hydroxide," it will redissolve to form the aluminate of the strong base. In this case, the $Al(OH)_3$ apparently is neutralizing the basic NaOH to form a salt and water, hence it must be acting as an acid. Compounds which partake of two natures are described as being *amphoteric*. Since $Al(OH)_3$ may act, under proper conditions, as either a base or an acid, it is said to be amphoteric. An explanation of this behavior will be presented in the next section.

Neither weak acids nor weak bases will react with aluminum "hydroxide" to produce salts. The carbonates and sulfides of many metals are readily precipitated from solution by the action of $H_2CO_3(H_2O + CO_2)$ and H_2S, respectively, but these acids are far too weak to act similarly in the present case. Even the aluminum sulfide which is prepared by direct fusion of the component elements is decomposed as was pointed out in section 5, as soon as it comes in contact with water. Ammonium hydroxide is not sufficiently ionized as a base to form an aluminate salt. From this it may be inferred that the "hydroxide" is itself very weak both as an acid and as a base.

A crystalline form of the "hydroxide," which is less soluble than the gelatinous form, may be precipitated by passing carbon dioxide gas into a solution of sodium aluminate

$$2NaAlO_2 + CO_2 + 3H_2O \rightarrow Na_2CO_3 + \underline{2Al(OH)_3}$$

7. The Ionization of Hydroxides

A review of the properties of the hydroxides of the elements of the third period thus far studied reveals that, as one passes through these elements from left to right, the strength of their hydroxides as bases decreases. The hydroxide of sodium is a strong base, that of magnesium is found to be weaker, and that of aluminum may act either as a very weak base or as an extremely weak acid. Such observations naturally require an explanation.

Consider the hydroxide $Z(OH)_x$, in which Z may represent any element of the third period and x may be any number from 1 to 7 in correspondence to the oxidation number of Z. Oxygen is generally thought of as having a negative oxidation number, hence both Z and H which are combined with it must have positive oxidation numbers. Both the positive Z and the positive H will attract the negative oxygen and will in turn be attracted by it, but, both being positive, will repel each other. According to Coulomb's law, the attraction between charged particles varies directly as the product of their charges, and inversely as the square of the distance between them. If Z stands for sodium, the attraction between the oxygen and the sodium particles and between the oxygen and the hydrogen particles, as determined by the product of their charges, is the same because both sodium and hydrogen have a characteristic charge of one. The hydrogen atom, having its valence electrons in the first level, is smaller in diameter than is the sodium atom, whose valence electron is in the third level; hence, the hydrogen and oxygen atoms approach each other more closely than do the sodium and oxygen atoms, and thus the attraction between the hydrogen and oxygen is greater than the attraction between the sodium and oxygen. Consequently, when the system containing these competing particles is placed under any strain such as that created by the addition of heat energy, or that created by the influence of solvent dipoles, the break occurs between the sodium and the oxygen rather than between the oxygen and the hydrogen. Furthermore, since the sodium has a much greater tendency than does hydrogen to lose its one valence electron, it is to be expected that an ionic hydroxide of sodium would be formed:

$$NaOH_{(s)} \rightarrow Na^+ + OH^-$$

If Z stands for magnesium, there is again a competition between it and the hydrogen for the oxygen. In this case, however, the oxidation number of the magnesium is $+2$ to a $+1$ for the hydrogen. Again (section 1, Chapter 13), the diameter of the bivalent magnesium ion is less than that of the monovalent sodium ion. As a result of both its larger charge and its smaller radius, the magnesium particle is much more strongly attracted by the oxygen than was the sodium. Furthermore, the repulsion between the $+2$ magnesium and the $+1$

hydrogen is greater than was the repulsion between the $+1$ sodium and the $+1$ hydrogen. The result of these conditions, and of the increased tendency of the magnesium atom to retain its valence electrons, is that magnesium hydroxide should be less ionic in nature than sodium hydroxide and should be less highly ionized in solution than the sodium compound, and in consequence a weaker base.

When Z represents the aluminum atom, its charge has become sufficiently large $(+3)$ and its size sufficiently small that the attraction between the aluminum and the oxygen atoms has increased considerably while the union between the oxygen and the hydrogen atoms has been weakened as a result of the increasing repulsion between the hydrogen and the other increasingly positive particle. In this particular compound, the attraction of the oxygen for the two positive particles is so nearly equal that it exhibits no strong tendency to ionize in either way. However, when in contact with a strong acid it will act as a weak base, and when mixed with a strong base it will act as an even weaker acid. In other words, aluminum "hydroxide" enters into a double equilibrium, thus:

$$H^+ + AlO_2^- + H_2O \rightleftharpoons Al(OH)_3 \rightleftharpoons Al^{+3} + 3OH^-$$

If a base is added to remove H^+ ions, further ionization of the $Al(OH)_3$ occurs to replace the ions removed, and the compound thus continues to act as an acid, but if an acid is added, OH^- ions are removed, whereupon the $Al(OH)_3$ ionizes farther in that direction to replace the removed ions and thus continues to act as a base. Amphoteric substances are often referred to as *ampholytes* and amphoteric hydroxides like aluminum "hydroxide" are known as *ampholytic hydroxides*.

As the charge on Z increases still more, and as the accompanying decrease in radius takes place, the attraction between Z and O increases while the attraction between O and H decreases, as a result of increasing repulsion between Z and H. Such hydroxides tend to be ruptured between the O and the H thus:

$$Z(OH)_x \rightarrow xH^+ + ZO_x^{-x}$$

When this occurs, the hydroxides are furnishing protons and hence are acting as acids. As the positive oxidation number of Z increases, the strength of the compound as an acid increases. As one passes across the third period, then the hydroxides of the elements in their highest states of oxidation change from strong bases through amphoteric substances to strong acids at the other extreme of the period.

The foregoing discussion indicates that the manner in which a hydroxide ionizes is largely a function of the charge and size of the ions of the element with which the hydroxyl group is combined. In section 12 of Chapter 6, *q.v.*, a quantity derived from the ionic charge (valence) and the ionic size (radius) was defined. This quantity, the ionic potential, is usually represented by the symbol ϕ, which is generally employed in the form of its square root and is useful in describing the manner in which the hydroxide of a given element will ionize. It may now be said that, if the value of $\sqrt{\phi}$ for a cation is less than 2.2, the hydroxide will be a base, and the smaller the value of $\sqrt{\phi}$ the stronger will be the base; if the value of $\sqrt{\phi}$ for a cation lies between 2.2 and 3.2, the hydroxide will be amphoteric; and if the value of $\sqrt{\phi}$ is in excess of 3.2, the hydroxide will ionize as an acid and the larger the number the stronger will be the acid.

8. Aluminum "Hydroxide" as an Acid

The equilibrium equation for the ionization of aluminum "hydroxide" given in the preceding section connotes that when the "hydroxide" acts as an acid it yields only one hydrogen ion, the remainder of the hydrogen being evolved as water:

$$Al(OH)_3 \rightarrow H^+ + AlO_2^- + H_2O$$

It has also been noted that this compound readily loses water.

Increasing the positive charge on an ion increases its ability to hold a greater number of negative hydroxyl ions; at the same time, however, its size is decreasing, leaving less room for the greater number of attracted hydroxyl ions to occupy. The result of this anomalous situation is that a water molecule often forms from two hydroxyl groups, leaving one divalent oxygen to offset the two positive charges on the cation which two monovalent hydroxyl ions should have offset had there been room enough for them around the cation.

$$\begin{array}{c} OH \\ \diagup \\ Al{-}OH \rightarrow Al{=}O + H_2O \\ \diagdown \qquad\quad \diagdown \\ OH \qquad\quad OH \end{array}$$

The lines in these diagrams are to be thought of only as representing a union rather than as representing any true picture of molecular structure.

Since aluminum "hydroxide" does at times have enough hydrogen in it to permit the use of the formula $Al(OH)_3$, or H_3AlO_3, this formula is conceived of as representing its highest state of hydration. The most highly hydrated form of an oxide which acts as an acid when so hydrated is referred to as the *ortho* form of the acid, hence H_3AlO_3 may be called orthoaluminic acid. The form of the acid obtained by the expulsion of one molecule of water from the ortho acid is known as the *meta* acid, hence $HAlO_2$ is metaaluminic acid. Oxygen-bearing acids whose names end in *-ic* form salts whose names end in *-ate*, thus $NaAlO_2$ is properly called sodium metaaluminate.

9. *Important Compounds and Their Uses*

A. ALUMINUM OXIDE. The importance of the oxide as a source of the free metal, as a material for the manufacture of laboratory ware, as an abrasive, and as gem stones when properly colored with impurities has already been dealt with.

B. ALUMINUM CHLORIDE. This compound exists in two forms: the color-less, crystalline hexahydrate, $AlCl_3.6H_2O$, and the slightly yellowish, powdery anhydrous variety, $AlCl_3$. The hydrated variety may be prepared by the action of hydrochloric acid on either the free metal or the gelatinous hydrated oxide. It may also be prepared by the addition of the anhydrous variety to water. The hydration is highly exothermic, and is accompanied by some hydrolysis with its attendant evolution of HCl gas. The hydrated salt is so very soluble that in the solid form it deliquesces readily. Because of its solubility, it is difficult to obtain from solution. By saturating the solution with gaseous HCl, however, the crystals of the hydrated salt separate much more readily than otherwise.

The anhydrous chloride cannot be prepared by heating the hydrated form to remove water. Since aluminum "hydroxide" is even weaker than magnesium hydroxide, the salts of aluminum are even more susceptible to hydrolysis than are those of magnesium. When the hydrated chloride is heated strongly, the final product is the oxide:

$$2(AlCl_3.6H_2O) \xrightarrow{\Delta} \underline{Al_2O_3} + 6HCl \uparrow + 9H_2O \uparrow$$

Some years ago, it was discovered that anhydrous aluminum chloride added to motor oil which was already apparently refined caused a sediment of dark sludgy material to form. Large quantities of motor oil are now treated in this way. The process is sometimes referred to as *alclor refining*. At the time this dis-covery was made, practically all of the commercial anhydrous chloride was made by the direct union of the elements and the price was about $1.25 per pound. This price naturally prohibited its use in large quantities in oil refining, so the research staff of the oil company set to work to develop a cheaper process of manufacture. As a result of this research, the chloride is now prepared by heating the oxide ores with carbon and chlorine:

$$Al_2O_3 + 3C + 3Cl_2 \rightarrow 2AlCl_3 + 3CO \uparrow$$

Prior to World War II, the price had fallen to five cents per pound, and in 1946 it was eight cents per pound. The compound may be purified by subliming it at

178° C. Below 350° C., the vapor has the formula Al_2Cl_6. The solid melts if heated under pressure to 194° C.

This ability of the anhydrous chloride to sublime further points to the fundamental difference between it and the chlorides of sodium and magnesium. The melting points of these anhydrous salts are high, their vapor pressures low, and their solubilities negligible save in polar liquids such as water. Anhydrous aluminum chloride will dissolve in water to yield an ionic solution too, but it will also dissolve in a wide variety of organic liquids of low polarity. These behaviors suggest that this compound has linkages which are much less ionic than are those of the

ARTICLES MADE OF ALUMINUM. (Courtesy, Aluminum Company of America.)

other two chlorides already studied. Its ability to ionize in aqueous solution is probably conferred by the action of the water dipoles as was the case with hydrogen chloride.

This compound finds wide use in organic chemistry as a catalytic agent. *A catalyst is a substance which alters the speed of a reaction without itself being consumed in the reaction.* Catalysis will be discussed in section 7 of Chapter 16.

c. ALUMINUM SULFATE. This salt is used in large quantities industrially and is prepared by heating either the oxide ores or clay with sulfuric acid. The silicon present in both the ores and clay is at first converted to silicic acid, then to silicon dioxide as the reaction mixture is heated strongly. The insoluble dioxide may then be removed by filtration. Since the ores and clays usually contain iron, ferric sulfate will also be present in the filtrate. Aluminum and ferric sulfates cannot be readily separated by crystallization, so the iron salt is reduced to ferrous sulfate, from which the aluminum salt can be separated by fractional crystallization. The crystals which form have the formula $Al_2(SO_4)_3.18H_2O$.

$$H_2Al_2(SiO_4)_2.H_2O + 3H_2SO_4 \rightarrow Al_2(SO_4)_3 + \underline{2SiO_2} + 5H_2O$$

Like all soluble aluminum salts, the sulfate is readily hydrolyzed, yielding both aluminum "hydroxide" and a solution which is acidic. The wide use of the salt depends upon this property. It yields an acidic solution when moistened, making it useful in baking powders and fire extinguishers. In both instances, the acidic solution acts upon sodium bicarbonate to yield carbon dioxide. In the first instance, this gas makes the dough porous, or causes it to "rise," while in the second, it furnishes pressure to spray water and also helps to blanket the fire, thus smothering it. The other product of hydrolysis is also utilized in the clarification of water and in mordant dyeing. The gelatinous precipitate of the "hydroxide" when formed in a water reservoir gradually settles, carrying down with it a large portion of the suspended matter which may be present. Many dyes will not adhere directly to some varieties of cloth—notably cotton. By soaking the cloth first in a strong solution of aluminum sulfate, then in a dilute solution of sodium carbonate, or other mild base, aluminum "hydroxide" is precipitated in the fibers of the cloth. When the cloth is then dipped in the dye bath the precipitate absorbs the coloring matter, forming a lake. A substance thus used is known as a *mordant*, a word derived from the French word *mordre*, to bite.

D. ALUMS. If equimolecular quantities of aluminum sulfate and a sulfate of some monovalent cation are mixed in a solution which is then concentrated until crystallization will take place, there will form colorless octahedra of the formula $M^+Al(SO_4)_2.12H_2O$, where M^+ stands for the monovalent cation. Such a salt is known as an *alum*. It has been found that other trivalent ions, such as the ferric and chromic ions, may be substituted for the aluminum ion. Thus, the general formula for an alum is $M^+M^{+3}(SO_4)_2.12H_2O$. All of these salts crystallize in octahedra, that is, they are isomorphous. Of the monovalent alkali sulfates, that of lithium alone shows little tendency to form alums. The tendency of the ions of the alkali metals to form such double salts increases with their increasing atomic weights, and, as this tendency increases, the solubility of the double salts formed decreases. The most important alums of aluminum are potassium aluminum sulfate and ammonium aluminum sulfate. Both of these are less soluble than aluminum sulfate, hence may be purified more readily by crystallization. These alums are used like the plain sulfate in baking

CHARLES MARTIN HALL

(*1863–1914, American*)

The fame of Hall rests principally upon his development of the first successful electrolytic process for the winning of aluminum from its ores. His interest in the problem was aroused by lectures delivered at Oberlin College by Prof. F. F. Jewett who had studied in Germany with Wöhler, who is generally, though apparently erroneously, credited with discovery of the element. Shortly after his graduation from Oberlin, Hall succeeded in developing the process which has made possible the cheap production of aluminum and its widespread use. A few short weeks after Hall announced his discovery, the young French scientist Héroult made the same discovery independently. By coincidence, both men were born in the same year and died in the same year. Hall was prominent as a chemist, metallurgist, inventor, and philanthropist.

powders, in fire extinguishers, and as mordants; they are also used as astringents, in the making of pickles, in the sizing of paper, in fireproofing cloth, and in the processing of photographic films and papers.

E. ALUMINUM ACETATE. This salt and the *nitrate* are frequently used in the laboratory as sources of aluminum ions. Both are very soluble in water. The acetate is often used as a mordant and is in general used for the same purposes as is the sulfate.

F. ULTRAMARINE. The mineral *lapis lazuli* is a complex sodium aluminum silicate and sulfide. The blue pigment *ultramarine* is this mineral ground to a powder. At the present time, this blue material is prepared synthetically by heating together a mixture of clay, carbon, and sodium sulfate. It is used as a blue pigment in laundering, in preparing water colors, and in the whitening of paper, cloth, sugar, and other materials which have a slight yellowish cast. Ultramarine is stable to bases, but decomposes to yield hydrogen sulfide when treated with acids.

10. Aluminum, Its Alloys, and Their Uses

A few of the uses of aluminum have already been referred to, and the common use of this metal in a relatively pure state for the manufacture of cooking utensils

THE HANDSOME CAST ALUMINUM DOORS OF THE PITTSBURGH OFFICES OF THE ALUMINUM COMPANY OF AMERICA. (Courtesy, Aluminum Company of America.)

and other household articles is well known. Aluminum alloy pistons have been used in some automobile engines for a number of years, and other parts of automobiles are made of the metal or of its alloys. During World War II, great quantities of aluminum alloys were used in the manufacture of both the engines and fuselages of airplanes. For the most part, these alloys are those of magnesium also, hence the student is referred to the discussion of the Dow metals and magnalium in section 8 of Chapter 13. Other important alloys are *duralumin*, which contains approximately 95 per cent aluminum and 5 per cent of various mixtures of copper, magnesium, and manganese. *Alclad* is an alloy of essentially the same composition, coated with the purest aluminum obtainable. Alloys so protected are less susceptible to deterioration resulting from exposure to the weather. The *Lynite* alloys, of which there are several, contain from 87 to 95 per cent of aluminum with the difference made up largely of copper, though small amounts of various other metals, such as zinc, iron, and magnesium, are also present. Aluminum bronze is a bright, golden-yellow metal

A Light-weight, Streamlined Train Containing Much Aluminum. (Courtesy, Aluminum Company of America.)

which contains about 90 per cent of copper to about 10 per cent of the aluminum. In general, the alloys of this light metal have a greater tensile strength than does the free metal; in addition, they may be machined readily while the free metal sticks to the cutting tools when one attempts to turn it on a lathe.

With the expansion of the domestic production of this metal during World War II, its postwar use should be far in excess of anything seen in the past.

11. Analytical Tests

Like the compounds of magnesium, those of aluminum impart no characteristic color to the gas flame. A further similarity exists in the general lack of color in their common compounds. Both sodium and ammonium hydroxides, as noted, will precipitate the hydroxide from solutions of aluminum salts, and in excess of sodium hydroxide this precipitate is soluble while in excess of ammonium hydroxide no dissolution occurs. Since there are, however, many colorless hydroxides, this behavior does not furnish incontrovertible proof of the presence of aluminum.

In the older manuals of qualitative analysis, the confirmatory test most frequently given requires that the hydroxide precipitate obtained by the use of ammonium hydroxide be collected, moistened with a few drops of a moderately strong solution of cobalt nitrate, and heated to red heat. The presence of aluminum is confirmed by the formation of a blue mass of cobalt aluminate, commonly referred to in such tests as *Thenard's blue*. The use of too much cobalt salt or the presence of sodium and potassium ions will interfere materially with this test.

The more recent manuals direct that the hydroxide precipitate be filtered out, washed, and redissolved in hot hydrochloric acid. The acidity of this solution is reduced by the addition of a solution of ammonium acetate, whereupon a few drops of a solution of *aluminon* (the ammonium salt of aurin tricarboxylic acid; an organic dyelike compound), are introduced and ammonium hydroxide is added until the mixture becomes basic. Aluminum hydroxide is reprecipitated and absorbs the dye, which in basic solution is red. A red lake is thus formed. This test is specific in the absence of iron.

Quantitatively, aluminum is precipitated as the hydroxide. The precipitate is collected and heated until it is converted to the anhydrous oxide. This substance is weighed, and from its weight the quantity of aluminum present in the original sample is calculated.

(*See Appendix for Exercises*)

COLLATERAL READINGS

Creighton and Koehler: *Electrochemistry*, Vol. II, New York, John Wiley & Sons, Inc., 1944.

Furnas: *Roger's Industrial Chemistry*, Vol. II, New York, D. Van Nostrand Co., 1943.

Holmes: The story of aluminum, *J. Chem. Education*, **7**, 233 (1930).

Hopkins: *General Chemistry for Colleges*, revised, Boston, D. C. Heath & Co., 1937.

Latimer and Hildebrand: *Reference Book of Inorganic Chemistry*, New York, The Macmillan Co., 1941.

Rose: Thermite branches out, *Sci. American*, **171**, 199, Nov. (1944).

Wade: Man-made gems, *J. Chem. Education*, **8**, 1015 (1931).

Weeks: *Discovery of the Elements*, 5th ed., Mack Printing Co., 1945.

Aluminum, *Fortune*, **10**, No. 3, 46 (1934).

THEODORE WILLIAM RICHARDS

(1868–1928, American)

An analytical chemist of unusual ability, Richards was recognized as an outstanding authority on atomic weights and atomic-weight determination. In the period 1886–1888, he received the A.B., A.M., and Ph.D. degrees at Harvard University, then after a period of study in Europe he returned to his alma mater to serve on its faculty until his death in 1928. He was the first American chemist to receive the Nobel Prize (1914), and was the recipient of many medals and honors both at home and abroad. He was decorated with the cross of the Legion of Honor by the French government, and was the recipient of more than a dozen honorary degrees from both domestic and foreign universities.

Chemical Equilibrium

1. Introduction

Reference already made (cf. section 5 of Chapter 11) shows that, when two opposing processes oppose each other at the same rate, a state of equilibrium exists. A number of physical equilibria have been discussed, and, by reference to reversible reactions, which may be represented in equation form by the use of the double arrow, the suggestion has been made that chemical equilibria also exist. Attention is now directed to these chemical equilibria and the factors which affect them.

2. Chemical Equilibrium and the Point of Equilibrium

The requisites for chemical equilibrium are, in essence, the same as those for any other example of the phenomenon: First, there must be two processes, in this case two chemical reactions, which must be the opposite of each other; and secondly, at the point of equilibrium the products of one of the reactions must be entering into the reverse reaction at the same rate at which they are being produced. Consider the reaction which occurs between acetic acid and ethyl alcohol. Only these two substances are present at the outset, but, as time passes, more and more of the products of their reaction, ethyl acetate and water, are formed:

$$HC_2H_3O_2 + C_2H_5OH \rightleftarrows C_2H_5C_2H_3O_2 + HOH$$

As the initial substances are used up, the speed of their concomitant reaction decreases. The quantity of the products is increasing at the same time and hence the speed of their reaction with each other to reform the initial substances is also increasing. As a result of one reaction decreasing in velocity while the other is increasing, a point presently is reached at which the two reactions are proceeding at the same rate and the products of each reaction are being used up at the same rate at which they are formed. When this state of affairs obtains, there will be, of course, no further increase in yield under the existing conditions, and apparently the reaction has come to a halt; actually, however, the system is still active and therefore *dynamic*.

If such a reaction is carried out so that all of the various substances involved remain in contact with each other, they collectively constitute what is generally referred to as a *closed system*. The equilibrium is described as *homogeneous* if all of the substances involved are in a single phase and are uniformly mixed; if, on the other hand, two or more distinct phases are present, the equilibrium is described as *heterogeneous*.

Describing the point at which chemical equilibrium is established is largely a matter of convenience. In the case of systems which involve only a single liquid phase, it is usually most convenient to describe the point of equilibrium by saying that it is reached when some one of the involved substances has a certain concentration in moles per liter; or, one may say that it is reached when a certain percentage of one of the original substances has been converted. In the case of systems having a single gaseous phase, as well as in the case of systems in which the partial pressures of the gaseous constituents are directly proportional to the various substances present, the point of equilibrium may be described in terms of the partial pressures of the gases present. Usually, the quantity which is both characteristic of the equilibrium and most easily measured is chosen. Finally, the conditions under which the state of balance was achieved must be stated, for, as will be shown hereafter, the point of equilibrium may shift with a change of conditions.

3. Equilibrium and the Velocity of Reactions

Some chemical reactions are irreversible and are hence completed. Others go so nearly to completion under ordinary conditions that they are considered as being completed. Still other reactions are reversed under ordinary conditions to such an extent that they are far from complete, and a fourth group of reactions is composed of those which are easily reversed to a marked extent by changes in the existing conditions. The practical concern of chemical equilibrium is with the extent to which reversible reactions will take place. To understand this matter thoroughly, one must have first a knowledge of reaction velocities and the factors which influence them.

At the outset, *the velocity of a reaction is the rate at which the concentration of the reactants is decreased*. The prime factor controlling the velocity of any reaction is the specific nature of the reactants involved. Very unstable molecules are much more inclined to react than are moderately stable, or very stable, ones. Since the specific natures of reacting substances vary so widely, however, no quantitative rules can be laid down for general use.

Other factors which influence reaction velocity are, in the main, those which somehow serve to increase the likelihood of the reacting particles coming in contact with each other. Before two particles may react, they must come in contact with each other, that is, they must collide; hence, any factor which will increase the likelihood of collision should increase the velocity of reaction. But every collision does not produce a reaction—only a certain fraction of the collisions is energetic enough, but, even though this fraction should remain the same, if the total number of contacts be increased the quantity of material undergoing change during a specified time will be increased. Factors which influence the contact of the particles and hence the rate of reaction are (1) concentration, (2) temperature, (3) pressure (largely in the case of reactions involving gases), and (4) the presence of a catalyst.

4. The Effect of Concentration on Velocity of Reaction

Two substances, designated A and B for convenience, react by one molecule of A combining with one molecule of B to form a new molecule of a third substance, C,

$$A + B \rightarrow C$$

Suppose, now, that A and B are present in equimolecular quantities. Before a molecule of A can possibly combine with a molecule of B, the two, as pointed

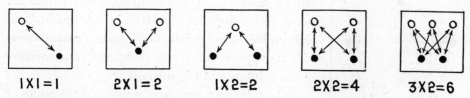

THE EFFECT OF CONCENTRATION UPON THE RATE OF REACTION. As the number of particles is increased, the possibility of collision, and hence the possibility of reaction, is increased.

out above, must first come in contact. If, now, the quantity of substance A is doubled, the chance of an A-B collision occurring is doubled, and hence the rate of reaction is doubled. Or, if the quantity of A were held at its original value and the quantity of B doubled, the chance of an A-B collision occurring would be doubled and the rate of reaction also doubled. If both the original quantities of A and B are now doubled, the chance of an A-B collision occurring is now four times (2 × 2) as great as it was originally, and the rate of reaction is also four times as great. Therefore, it is at once apparent that, if all other factors remain constant, the rate of reaction is proportional to the concentration of the reactants. Mathematically, this may be expressed thus: [A] × [B] is proportional to rate of reaction. By convention, brackets placed around a formula or a symbol are usually used to indicate the molar concentration of the substance so enclosed; they usually imply the concentration is expressed in moles per liter. Any proportionality may be converted to an equality by multiplying one member of the proportion by a suitable constant. For instance, if one writes $3 \propto 6$ he may also write $3 \times 2 = 6$ or $3 = \frac{1}{2} \times 6$. In the case stated above, the following equation may be written:

$$[A] [B]k = \text{rate of reaction}$$

where k stands for a constant of the proper numerical value and is known as the *velocity constant* of the reaction in question.

If reactants A and B are both in the gaseous state, under the conditions of the reaction instead of writing

$$[A] [B]k = \text{rate of reaction}$$

one may write if he prefers

$$p_A \times p_B \times k_p = \text{rate of reaction}$$

which is read: "the partial pressure of gas A times the partial pressure of gas B times a special pressure constant (k_p) is equal to the rate of reaction." This substitution is possible because, according to the laws of Avogadro and Dalton, the partial pressure of a gas in a gaseous mixture is proportional to the molecular concentration of the substance in the mixture.

Consider the reaction in which two molecules of substance C react with one molecule of substance D to produce one molecule of substance E, thus:

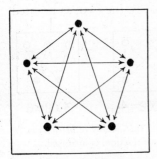

$$4 + 3 + 2 + 1 = 10$$
$$\frac{5(5-1)}{2} = 10$$
$$\frac{N(N-1)}{2} = T$$

THE CHANCE OF TWO LIKE PARTICLES COLLIDING IS $\frac{n(n-1)}{2}$.

$$2C + D \rightarrow E$$

For this reaction to occur, for the sake of convenience one may assume that two molecules of substance C must collide with each other, then with a molecule of D, before reaction may occur. If n molecules of C are present in the reaction chamber, the chance of two of them colliding will be given, as can be shown mathematically, by the formula $n(n-1)/2$. A particle of matter even as large as a pinhead contains billions of molecules. It is therefore apparent n will be such a large number that for all practical purposes n and $n-1$ will be of essentially the same value and for $n(n-1)/2$ one may write $n^2/2$. Thus the chance of two C molecules colliding is proportional to n^2, or, since the number of molecules is proportional to the concentration (n is proportional to the concentration of C in the above equation), one may say that the chance of two C molecules colliding is proportional to the concentration of C squared, $[C]^2$. The chance of a pair of these collided C molecules further colliding with a D molecule as shown in the first example will be the product of the concentrations of the respective particles involved in the collisions, whence

$$[C]^2[D] \propto \text{ rate of reaction,}$$

and

$$[C]^2[D]k = \text{ rate of reaction}$$

or, if C and D are gases,

$$p_C^2 \times p_D \times k_p = \text{ rate of reaction}$$

5. The Effect of Temperature on Velocity of Reaction

According to the kinetic-molecular theory, the adding of heat energy to molecules increases their rate of movement. As the speed of a molecule increases, the number of collisions which it should make in a specified time should increase proportionately, and, of course, as the total number of collisions increases, the number of them which will be effective will increase also. The rate of reaction, however, is often increased by an amount in excess of that which might be attributed to an increased number of collisions. The suggested explanation here is that, as a result of the increased energy of the molecules, there are not only more abundant collisions, but there are also now more collisions whose energy is sufficiently great to permit reaction—that is, there are more fruitful collisions. No exact rule may be stated to cover the relationship between increase in temperature and increase in the rate of reaction, but, on the average, a rise in temperature of 10° C. will approximately double the rate of reaction.

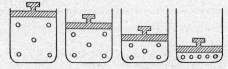

6. The Effect of Pressure on Velocity of Reaction

Pressure exerts a considerable influence upon the velocity of reactions

THE EFFECT OF PRESSURE UPON THE RATE OF REACTION OF GASES. Under greater pressure the molecules are closer to each other and, hence, the chance of their colliding is greater.

which take place in the gaseous phase. In a gaseous mixture, the molecules are relatively far apart. By exerting pressure upon such a mixture, the molecules are forced to occupy a smaller volume, and hence the likelihood of their colliding with each other is increased. Solids and liquids undergo very little compression as a result of the application of pressure, consequently the velocity of reactions which involve only these phases is affected very little by the application of pressure.

7. The Effect of Catalysts on Velocity of Reaction

A catalyst, as already defined, is a substance which influences the velocity of a given reaction without itself being permanently changed as a result of the reaction. Some catalysts increase the speed of reaction and are known as *positive catalysts*, while others decrease the speed of a given reaction and are known as *negative catalysts*, or *inhibitors*. Positive catalysts usually fall into two classes: (a) *contact catalysts*, which are not changed during the course of the reaction; and (b) substances which during the course of the reaction form an intermediate compound which is then decomposed to yield the original catalyst and other products. Catalytic substances of the first type are described as being heterogeneous, while those of the second type are said to be homogeneous because there is no boundary surface between the reagents and the catalysts. The heterogeneous group is at present far larger than the homogeneous.

Contact catalysts are able to increase the speed of a reaction because they have the ability to attach to their surfaces a layer of the molecules of one or more of the reacting substances which is only one molecule thick. They are generally described as being able to *adsorb* (adhere + absorb) a monomolecular layer. The adsorption of a molecule so alters its energy and field of force that the collision with it of a molecule from outside is much more apt to be productive of a reaction than would be the case if it were not first adsorbed. Such increased activity occurs only on the surface of the catalyst, therefore it should be in either a finely divided or spongy condition so that a maximum of surface for the mass present will be afforded. Catalysts are highly selective, so one which serves well for hastening one process may have no effect on another. However, catalysis does not always follow adsorption. In such cases, the introduction of small quantities of foreign substances will sometimes cause the adsorbing surface to become catalytic. Substances so used are called *promoters*. Also, small quantities of foreign substances will sometimes cause a contact catalyst to lose its activity. Substances which have this effect are called *catalytic poisons*, and behave as they do usually as a result of their having reacted with the surface molecules of the catalyst to change their composition.

An example of a catalyst of the second type is nitric oxide as used in the reaction between sulfur dioxide and oxygen. At even relatively high temperatures, the rate of reaction between these latter substances is negligible, but, when a small quantity of nitric oxide is introduced, the reaction proceeds readily. The nitric oxide reacts easily with the oxygen to form nitrogen dioxide, and this in turn reacts with the sulfur dioxide to form sulfur trioxide and nitric

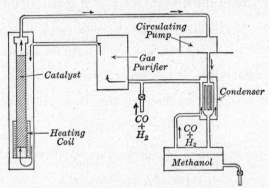

· DIAGRAM OF APPARATUS USED FOR THE CATALYTIC PRODUCTION OF METHANOL. (From Conant, James B.: "Chemistry of Organic Compounds." By permission of The Macmillan Company, publishers.)

oxide once more. Thus, the nitric oxide is used over and over and is left free when all of the reactants have combined.

$$2NO + O_2 \rightarrow 2NO_2$$

and

$$SO_2 + NO_2 \rightarrow SO_3 + NO$$

Catalysts of both varieties are thus seen to be highly specialized in their use. There are many reactions which would be of high commercial value if a catalyst could be found which would enable them to be conducted at a practical velocity. It is not strange, therefore, that there is much research in progress in the field of catalysis.

8. The Law of Chemical Equilibrium

The law of chemical equilibrium is a statement which permits the chemist to establish a quantitative relationship between the velocity of a reaction and the concentration of the reactants. A mathematical statement of the law may be arrived at in the following way. In section 4, it has been shown that the rate of a reaction is equal to the product of the concentrations of the reactants raised to their proper powers times a properly chosen velocity constant. In cases of chemical equilibrium, there are two reactions which proceed simultaneously, hence the rate of each reaction is given by a statement of the type just mentioned. Consider, for example, the equation

$$aA + bB \rightleftarrows cC + dD$$

which indicates that a molecules of substance A react with b molecules of substance B, etc. The rate of the forward reaction is given by the expression

$$[A]^a[B]^b k_1 = \text{rate of forward reaction}$$

while the rate of the backward reaction is given by the expression

$$[C]^c[D]^d k_2 = \text{rate of backward reaction}$$

At equilibrium the two rates must of necessity be equal, whence

$$[A]^a[B]^b k_1 = [C]^c[D]^d k_2$$

By application of the principles of algebra, this equation may be restated thus:

$$[C]^c[D]^d / [A]^a[B]^b = k_1 / k_2$$

Since a constant divided by a constant is a constant, the quotient of the two velocity constants may be replaced by a single new constant K, which is known as the *equilibrium constant*, and the equation thus becomes

$$[C]^c[D]^d / [A]^a[B]^b = K$$

It is customary in writing such an equilibrium expression to place the concentrations of the substances appearing in the right member of the chemical equation in the numerator.

In words, the equilibrium law might be stated thus: *At the point of equilibrium of a given reversible chemical process, the product of the concentrations of the substances produced by the forward reaction when divided by the product of the concentrations of the reactants in the forward reaction, each concentration being raised to the proper power as indicated by its coefficient in the chemical equation representing the process, is equal to a constant characteristic of that process.* This law was originally formulated in 1864 by Guldberg and Waage, and was named by them the law of mass action. However, since its operation is dependent on the molecular concentrations of the substances present rather than on their total mass, the original name appears to have been poorly chosen.

9. The Determination of the Equilibrium Constant

The values of the equilibrium constant K for many reversible reactions are given in various reference books. In each case, the numerical value given represents hours of work spent in the laboratory. As an example of the manner in which these constants are determined, consider again the reaction between ethyl alcohol and acetic acid. These two substances are mixed in the equimolar quantities required by the equation

$$C_2H_5OH + HC_2H_3O_2 \rightleftharpoons C_2H_5C_2H_3O_2 + H_2O$$

and are left in contact until equilibrium has been established. At that time, by the application of the proper quantitative analytical procedures, the quantity of each of the four substances present in the mixture is determined. The analysis reveals the presence of two-thirds mole each of the products and of one-third mole each of the two initial reactants; and, since the concentration of each substance is raised to the same power the volume terms cancel and quantities in moles may be used instead of the conventional concentration units of moles per liter. By substituting these values in the equilibrium expression for the reaction.

$$\frac{[C_2H_5C_2H_3O_2][H_2O]}{[C_2H_5OH][HC_2H_3O_2]} = K$$

one has

$$\frac{(2/3)(2/3)}{(1/3)(1/3)} = K$$

whence

$$\frac{4/9}{1/9} = K$$

and

$$K = 4$$

To say that the equilibrium constant for this reaction is 4 means that in any equilibrium mixture of the four substances involved in the reaction, under the same conditions of temperature, the product of the concentration of ethyl acetate and of water will always be four times as great as the product of the concentration of alcohol and of acetic acid. If the convention is followed in setting up the equilibrium equation, then a large equilibrium constant will indicate a preponderance of products while a constant smaller than one will signify the reverse.

10. The Principle of Le Chatelier and the Displacement of Equilibrium

In the example of a physical equilibrium discussed in section 5 of Chapter 11, q.v., it was pointed out that if the original equilibrium was disturbed the system would do its very best to reëstablish equilibrium under the new conditions. This is a property of all systems in equilibrium, whether physical, chemical, economic, political, or what not, and this general behavior is described in the theorem known as the *Principle of Le Chatelier*, which states that *if some condition of a system in equilibrium is altered, the system will react, if possible, in such a manner as to endeavor to undo the effect of the imposed change.* In the example given, as more water ran into the tank, more water began to run out, and equilibrium was reëstablished at a new and higher water level. The application of this rule to a system in a state of chemical equilibrium should now be considered.

A. CHANGES OF CONCENTRATION. Consider again the equilibrium mixture of alcohol, acetic acid, and their products. If a second mole of alcohol is added to this mixture, the number of collisions between alcohol and acid molecules will increase and the speed of the forward reaction will be increased. As a result of these collisions, however, a portion of the added alcohol will be used up; this is in accord with Le Chatelier's principle. Not all of the alcohol is necessarily used, but the system does go in a direction to undo the effect of the change made. More of the products are formed as the forward reaction gains in velocity, and, as their concentrations increase, the speed of the back reaction increases until presently both reactions have again attained the same speed and a new point of equilibrium has been established.

If, instead of adding alcohol to the equilibrium mixture, one had removed the water from it, the back reaction would be stopped while the forward one continued unabated, forming water to replace that which was removed, thus undoing the effect of the imposed change. If water were continuously removed, ultimately all of the reactants would be used up and only ethyl acetate would be left and a state of equilibrium would never have been reëstablished, but the reaction would have been driven to completion. This points to a practical application of this principle.

The chemical equation for this reaction states that from one mole of each of the reactants may be produced as a maximum a mole of each of the products, but one may add amounts in excess of the theoretical value and if an equilibrium mixture is produced the yields will not be in accord with the amounts stated in the chemical equation.

It is well to consider a practical use of the equilibrium law while considering the effect of concentration. In producing ethyl acetate by the establishment of this equilibrium, how much more ethyl acetate would be obtained if, instead of using the reactants mole for mole, two moles of the cheaper (the alcohol) were used for each mole of the more expensive (the acid)? It is seen from the chemical equation that the molar quantities of the products will always be the same, in this case an unknown quantity x. Also, the number of moles of reactants used up will be the same as the number of moles of products obtained, hence the quantity of unreacted alcohol at equilibrium will be $2 - x$ while the quantity of unreacted acid will be $1 - x$. Now

$$\frac{[C_2H_5C_2H_3O_2][H_2O]}{[C_2H_5OH][HC_2H_3O_2]} = 4$$

so

$$\frac{(x)(x)}{(2 - x)(1 - x)} = 4$$

and

$$x^2 = 8 - 12x + 4x^2$$

By solving this quadratic equation, it is found that the value of x is 0.85 mole. Like all quadratic algebraic equations, this one yields a second value for x, but the second value is readily recognized as an impractical solution of the problem. The yield of ethyl acetate in the mixture has thus been increased from 0.666 mole to 0.85 mole by doubling the concentration of one of the reactants. In such a case, the equilibrium is said to be shifted to the right. Had water been added to the mixture, more alcohol and acid would have been formed and the equilibrium would then be said to have been shifted to the left.

B. CHANGES OF PRESSURE. The reaction for the synthetic production of methyl alcohol, usually known as the Patart synthesis, involves the union of carbon monoxide and hydrogen gases in the presence of a catalyst:

$$2H_2 + CO \overset{\Delta}{\rightleftarrows} CH_3OH$$

The chemical equation shows that, when this reaction occurs, two gram-molecular volumes of hydrogen and one of carbon monoxide are required to produce only one of the methyl alcohol, which at the temperature of the reaction is also in the gaseous state. A shrinkage of volume thus takes place from left to right. When pressure is put on this mixture, the equilibrium is shifted to the right in accordance with Le Chatelier's principle, for, by going in that direction, the volume shrinks from 3 to 1 and the added pressure is reduced proportionately.

In the reaction

$$N_2 + O_2 \overset{\Delta}{\rightleftarrows} 2NO$$

two gram-molecular volumes of the reactants produce two of the products, hence a total increase in pressure causes no shift of the equilibrium and there is no undoing of the changed condition. Because the change cannot always be undone, the phrase "if possible" is employed in the statement of Le Chatelier's principle.

C. CHANGES OF TEMPERATURE. The equation for the Patart synthesis is more properly written,

$$2H_2 + CO \rightleftharpoons CH_3OH + \text{heat}$$

for a considerable quantity of heat is produced along with each mole of methyl alcohol; or one may think of heat and the alcohol as reacting to produce hydro-

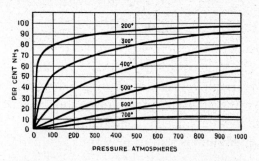

THE EFFECT OF CHANGES IN TEMPERATURE AND PRESSURE ON THE YIELD OF AMMONIA BY DIRECT UNION OF THE ELEMENTS.

gen and carbon monoxide. If heat from an external source is applied to the equilibrium mixture of these three substances, the equilibrium will be shifted to the left in accordance with the overall principle, for by going in that direction the added heat is used up.

Very little heat is liberated in the reaction between alcohol and acetic acid, hence an increase in temperature shifts that equilibrium very little. Since heat generally increases the speed of reactions, both the forward and back reaction will proceed more rapidly, and equilibrium will be established more quickly than would have been the case otherwise.

There are a number of reactions of commercial value which, like the Patart reaction, are driven in the less desirable direction by the application of heat. These reactions reach equilibrium so slowly, however, when not heated, that from a practical standpoint it is more advantageous to heat them moderately, thus obtaining smaller yields more frequently, than it is to obtain one larger yield in a much longer period of time. In actual practice, the Patart process operates at pressures as high as 200 atmospheres, and at temperatures which vary from 1000° C. to 400° C.

D. ADDITION OF A CATALYST. It is a peculiarity of catalysts that they have exactly the same effect on the velocity of a back reaction as they do upon the velocity of the forward reaction which produced the substances that take part in the back reaction. It has been demonstrated experimentally many times that this is so, and it can be shown by theoretical considerations which involve the principles of thermodynamics that this would have to be the case. Since the effect on the speed of both reactions is identical, there can be no shift of equilibrium as a result of adding a catalyst.

11. The Value of the Equilibrium Constant Varies with the Absolute Temperature

That concentration, pressure, and temperature changes cause a shift in the point of equilibrium has just been shown in the preceding section. The effect of these changes upon the value of the equilibrium constant must be considered. When the concentration of one of the substances present in an equilibrium mixture is increased, reaction proceeds more rapidly in the direction which uses up the added substance so that more of the substances in the other member of the equation are produced. As the quantity of these latter substances increases, the rate of the reverse reaction increases until the two rates again become equal; since the changes produced are equal, no change in the value of the constant occurs. Pressure exerted upon a gaseous system is exerted equally upon the substances represented in both members of the chemical equation, hence there is no change in the value of the equilibrium constant as a result of the application of pressure. For those instances in which the concentrations, or other conditions, are such that the gas laws do not apply, then a change in pressure may cause a change in value of the constant.

The situation is somewhat different with a change in temperature. An increase in temperature (section 5) usually causes an increase in the velocity of reaction, but the effect of a given temperature increase is not the same upon all reactions. Since the forward and back reactions of a given system are distinct and individual reactions, it follows that in most cases their velocities will not be affected equally, and hence the concentrations of the substances in the equilibrium mixture will be changed, causing the value of the constant to change also. It has been shown that every chemical change is accompanied by a definite energy change. It can be shown also that, when the energy change for a given reaction and its reverse are small, the variation of the value of the equilibrium constant with temperature is also small. The energy liberated by the alcohol and acetic acid reaction discussed above is small, hence the value of the equilibrium constant varies only slightly as the temperature at which the reaction occurs is altered.

By surveying the values of the equilibrium constant for a specified reaction at different temperatures, one may chose the conditions which are best suited to the production of the results desired.

12. *Heterogeneous Equilibrium*

The law of chemical equilibrium applies strictly only to homogeneous systems; however, if a heterogeneous system is of such a nature that it may be considered homogeneous, changes may be made in the equilibrium equation so that it may be used in its modified form. Under the conditions of the reaction which takes place when limestone is heated to produce lime, both calcium carbonate and calcium oxide are solids while carbon dioxide is a gas

$$CaCO_3 \overset{\Delta}{\rightleftharpoons} CaO + CO_2 \uparrow$$

Here the equilibrium law and expression in their usual forms are not applicable. If the two solids are assumed to be vaporized before they react and the reaction is assumed to occur in a homogeneous, gaseous mixture, one might write

$$\frac{(p_{CaO} \times p_{CO_2})}{p_{CaCO_3}} = K_p'$$

Still assuming that the two solids are first vaporized, it will be readily seen that the pressure of the CO_2 will be very large as compared with the pressures of their gases, and as long as any of the solid phase of these two substances remains they will be able to maintain at a constant value the small pressures of their respective gases. For all practical purposes, then, p_{CaCO_3} and p_{CaO} are constants and may be included with the constant K_p'. By algebra,

$$p_{CO_2} = K_p' \cdot \frac{p_{CaCO_3}}{p_{CaO}}$$

Constants when multiplied and divided by other constants yield results which are constant, hence,

$$K_p' \cdot \frac{p_{CaCO_3}}{p_{CaO}} = K_p$$

and

$$p_{CO_2} = K_p$$

Similar adaptations may be made for other cases of heterogeneous equilibrium.

13. The Stability of Hydrates

Several references have been made to crystalline substances which contain water molecules in their structures. In a sense, such substances are addition compounds of water and the substance whose ions became hydrated and whose name the crystals bear. Hydrates furnish an interesting example of equilibrium which is in a sense physical, but is also chemical if one considers them to be chemical compounds which undergo a change in composition as water is gained or lost.

Many ions will withdraw water from solution into the crystal structure which is being built up; however, when the crystals are removed from the solution, unless the forces of attraction between the individual ions and their water dipoles are large, water will tend to pass from the crystals into the surrounding air. The higher the temperature, the greater will be this tendency. Every hydrated substance thus maintains at a specific temperature a vapor pressure which is characteristic of it. Those which are very stable will of necessity maintain a low vapor pressure, while less stable ones will maintain pressures of a higher value. A crystal in a closed container will establish a state of equilibrium between the water which it still contains and that in the space around it, thus affording another example of heterogeneous equilibrium.

Water vapor is always present in the atmosphere so that a fraction of the total atmospheric pressure is that accounted for by the fraction of water vapor present. If a hydrated crystal which maintains a fairly high vapor pressure is surrounded with air in which the partial pressure due to water vapor is rather low, water will pass from the crystal into the air. This tends to restore equilibrium by raising the pressure of water vapor in the air to a point equal to the pressure characteristic of the crystal at the existing temperature. Such spontaneous loss of water of hydration is known as *efflorescence*. If the surrounding atmosphere is very dry, efflorescence may continue until the crystal becomes completely dehydrated, crumbling to a powder.

A crystal which has lost water of hydration until it is incapable of maintaining its characteristic equilibrium pressure, when placed in an atmosphere whose vapor pressure is higher than the current vapor pressure of the crystal, absorbs water with the consequent partial or total regeneration of the original hydrate. This is an example of *deliquescence*. Anhydrous substances which absorb water in this manner to form hydrates which at ordinary temperatures maintain low vapor pressures may be used as drying agents.

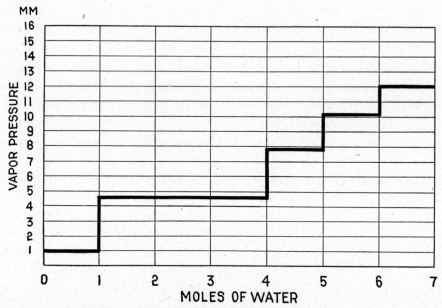

THE VAPOR PRESSURE OF HYDRATES OF MAGNESIUM SULFATE AT 25° C.

The equilibrium reaction involved in the above changes may be represented thus for magnesium sulfate heptahydrate:

$$MgSO_4.7H_2O \rightleftarrows MgSO_4 + 7H_2O$$

Such an equilibrium can be described in terms of the vapor pressure of the water whence

$$K_p = P_{H_2O}^7$$

Some substances are capable of forming more than one hydrate. Each of these is stable at a fixed temperature when in contact with concentrations of water vapor which may vary only within definitely fixed limits characteristic of each. If two such hydrates are in contact with each other at a specified temperature, then there is only one definite pressure at which the two may so exist in equilibrium (see illustration). At all other pressures for that temperature, one hydrate will begin to change into the other, moving to reëstablish equilibrium within the limits in which the substance being formed is stable. When a given substance forms several different hydrates, each has its own characteristic form, its own characteristic solubility, and other properties which distinguish it from its sister hydrates.

(See Appendix for Exercises)

COLLATERAL READINGS

Cartledge: *Introductory Theoretical Chemistry*, Boston, Ginn & Co., 1929.

Chapin and Steiner: *Second Year College Chemistry*, 5th ed. revised, New York, John Wiley & Sons, Inc., 1943.

Findlay: *The Spirit of Chemistry*, New York, Longmans, Green & Co., 1934.

Getman and Daniels: *Outlines of Physical Chemistry*, New York, John Wiley & Sons, Inc., 1943.

Hildebrand: *Principles of Chemistry*, New York, The Macmillan Co., 1941.

Hogness and Johnson: *Qualitative Analysis and Chemical Equilibrium*, New York, Henry Holt & Co., Inc., 1940.

Lohse: *Catalytic Chemistry*, New York, Chemical Publishing Co., 1945.

Any standard textbook of physical chemistry.

MICHAEL FARADAY
(*1791–1867, English*)

It has been remarked that Sir Humphry Davy's greatest discovery was Michael Faraday, whom he appointed his assistant in the laboratory of the Royal Institution in 1813. In 1825 Faraday succeeded Davy to the professorship of the Institution, and in 1833 he was made Fullerian professor, a position which he held until his death. His contributions to both physics and chemistry were numerous. His studies upon the relationship of magnetism and electricity laid the foundation for modern electrical engineering; to him we owe much of our fundamental knowledge of electrochemistry as well as its terminology; he did much work upon the liquefaction of gases; he discovered magnetic optical rotation; and lastly he discovered the important compound which we know as benzene.

17

Equilibria Involving Electrolytes

1. Introduction

Because ionization may be a reversible process and because many of the reactions between electrolytes are reversible, it is essential that the student have an understanding of chemical equilibrium as applied to these reversible processes which involve electrolytes.

2. Equilibria in Metathetical Reactions

Very nearly all salts are highly or even completely ionized; hence, when aqueous solutions of sodium chloride and potassium nitrate are mixed, the resulting solution contains ions of four varieties, Na^+, Cl^-, K^+, and NO_3^-. If these ions were to swap partners thus,

$$NaCl + KNO_3 \rightarrow KCl + NaNO_3$$

potassium chloride and sodium nitrate would be the products, but they too are salts and highly ionized. So long as the solvent is there, then, the solution contains only four species of ions paired off in no particular way. If the solvent is evaporated, a mixture containing all four solid salts is obtained. In section 10 of Chapter 16, it was shown that a metathetical reaction which might otherwise establish an equilibrium can be driven to completion if one of the products is removed from the mixture. This is also the case with metatheses involving electrolytes; if certain of the ions involved are removed from solution, then the reaction may go to completion using up the original reactants.

3. Complete Metathetical Reactions

There are four ways in which ions may be removed from solutions of electrolytes so that a metathesis may go to completion.

A. A PRECIPITATE MAY BE FORMED. Chloride ions may be tested for by adding a solution containing silver ion to the solution containing the chloride ion; a white precipitate forms.

$$Ag^+ + Cl^- \rightarrow \underline{AgCl}$$

These two varieties of ions withdraw each other from solution to form the very slightly soluble silver chloride, which appears as a solid precipitate. Since silver chloride is a salt, the part of it which dissolves is highly ionized, but so little dissolves that very few silver and chloride ions are furnished to the solution. If the original solution containing silver ions was one of the nitrate of silver, and if the solution containing the chloride ion was one of sodium chloride, then left in the mixed solutions after the precipitation of the silver chloride are sodium and nitrate ions. Sodium nitrate is quite soluble, hence no precipitate of it forms, but if the silver chloride is removed by filtration and the filtrate evaporated to dryness, crystals of sodium nitrate will be obtained and none of the original reactants will remain:

$$AgNO_3 + NaCl \rightarrow \underline{AgCl} + NaNO_3$$

More properly, this equation should be

$$Ag^+ + NO_3^- + Na^+ + Cl^- \rightarrow \underline{AgCl} + Na^+ + NO_3^-$$

It is apparent, then, that whenever a precipitate is formed, a metathesis involving electrolytes will go to completion, or nearly so.

B. A GASEOUS SUBSTANCE MAY BE FORMED. When sodium sulfide is dissolved in water, it ionizes thus:

$$Na_2S_{(s)} \rightarrow 2Na^+_{(in\ sol.)} + S^{--}_{(in\ sol.)}$$

while hydrochloric acid may be represented to ionize thus:

$$HCl \rightarrow H^+ + Cl^-$$

When solutions of these two substances are mixed, the reaction is

$$Na_2S + 2HCl \rightarrow H_2S \uparrow + 2Na^+ + 2Cl^-$$

At about 20° C., hydrogen sulfide is a gas which gradually escapes from the reaction mixture. When it has gone, there can be no reversal of the reaction. Evaporation of the remaining solution yields crystals of sodium chloride. It is further apparent, then, that a metathesis involving electrolytes also goes to completion when one of the products is a gas which is allowed to escape.

C. A SLIGHTLY IONIZED SUBSTANCE MAY BE FORMED. The example has already been given of the reaction of a base and an acid to form a salt and water:

$$Na^+ + OH^- + H^+ + Cl^- \rightarrow HOH + Na^+ + Cl^-$$

Water formed from hydrogen and hydroxyl ions is so slightly ionized that it supplies an insufficient number of its parent ions to permit a reversal of the reaction. Evaporation of the solvent forces the remaining sodium and chloride ions together so that salt crystals result, but the original reactants have been completely converted. A metathesis involving electrolytes goes to completion when a slightly ionized product is formed.

D. A COMPLEX ION MAY BE FORMED. A complex ion is formed by the union of two or more simple ions or by the union of simple ions with molecules. If an excess of ammonia is added to a solution of a cupric salt, the following reaction occurs:

$$Cu^{++} + SO_4^{--} + 4NH_3 \rightarrow Cu(NH_3)_4^{++} + SO_4^{--}$$

In this case there can be no reversal of the reaction because ammonia molecules have been withdrawn to form the rather stable complex ion, $Cu(NH_3)_4^{++}$. Complex ions will be discussed more fully in a future chapter. Here it is sufficient to say that metathetical reactions in which they are formed go to completion.

4. The Solubility Product

The solubility of slightly soluble substances, such as silver chloride, provides still another case of equilibrium. If a quantity of silver chloride is placed in a quantity of water, silver and chloride ions begin to leave the surface of the solid in small numbers. Soon, however, the number of these ions returning to the surface in a unit of time is equal to the number leaving in the same time; a state of equilibrium then exists and the solution is said to be saturated with respect to the silver chloride. The process may be represented by the equation

$$AgCl_{(s)} \rightleftharpoons Ag^+_{(in\ sol.)} + Cl^-_{(in\ sol.)}$$

whence the equilibrium equation would be

$$[Ag^+][Cl^-] / [AgCl_{(s)}] = K'$$

Here again the equilibrium is two phase and hence heterogeneous, therefore alterations must be made to adapt the use of the expression. Since the concentration of an undissolved solid depends only upon its density, which remains practically constant under ordinary conditions, it follows that for all practical purposes its concentration will remain virtually constant. In this case, then, the concentration of the solid silver chloride may be considered a constant and the term $[AgCl_{(s)}]$ so used, whence

$$[Ag^+][Cl^-] = K'[AgCl_{(s)}] = K_{s.p.}$$

Again, the brackets signify concentration in gram-ions or moles per liter.

The solubility of silver chloride at 25° C. is given as 1.87×10^{-4} g. per 100 g. of water. A liter of water would dissolve 10 times this quantity, or 1.87×10^{-3} g. The gram-molecular weight of silver chloride is approximately 143.4 g. $(107.9 + 35.5)$, hence dissolved in the liter of water are $(1.87 \times 10^{-3} \text{ g.}) / 143.4$ g., or 1.3×10^{-5} moles of that salt. Since for each mole of AgCl dissolved a gram-ion (also called mole) of each of its ions is formed, and

$$[Ag^+] = [Cl^-] = 1.3 \times 10^{-5}$$

then

$$[Ag^+][Cl^-] = (1.3 \times 10^{-5})^2 = 1.69 \times 10^{-10}$$

The figure 1.69×10^{-10} is the solubility product constant for silver chloride at 25° C. Its significance is that in any solution in which the product of the concentrations of silver and chloride ions at 25° C. exceeds the solubility product, precipitation of the solid salt should occur. For instance, if to a solution which is $M/5$ in silver ions there is added an equal volume of a solution which is $M/5$ in chloride ions, the product of these two concentrations would be 0.1×0.1 or 0.01, a value which is far in excess of 1.69×10^{-10}. Precipitation would occur until the concentrations of the ions in solution had been reduced to such a point that the product of their concentrations would not exceed 1.69×10^{-10}. It becomes apparent, then, from this discussion that solid, strong electrolytes of low solubility may always be precipitated by mixing solutions which will supply their constituent ions in such concentrations that the product of these ionic concentrations when raised to their proper powers will exceed in value the solubility product constant of the particular substance in question. The formation of precipitates is of value not only in driving metatheses to completion, but also in qualitative and quantitative analysis where their formation is of value in identifying ions, in separating ions from each other, and in determining their concentration.

A second example will illustrate further the calculation of solubility product constants. The solubility of silver chromate is 0.0431 g. per liter. The gram-molecular weight of silver chromate is 331.8 g., hence the solubility of this salt in moles per liter is $0.0431 / 331.8$ or 1.3×10^{-4}. According to the ionization equation,

$$Ag_2CrO_{4(s)} \rightleftarrows 2Ag^+ + CrO_4^{--}{}_{(in\ sol.)}$$

each mole of the salt gives rise to 2 moles of silver ion, but to only 1 mole of chromate ion, whence

$$[Ag^+] = 2(1.3 \times 10^{-4}) = 2.6 \times 10^{-4}$$

and

$$[CrO_4^{--}] = 1.3 \times 10^{-4}$$

The mathematical expression for this equilibrium according to the usual conventions is

$$[Ag^+]^2[CrO_4^{--}] = K_{S.P.}$$

By substituting the numerical values of the ionic concentrations

$$(2.6 \times 10^{-4})^2 \, (1.3 \times 10^{-4}) = K_{S.P.}$$
$$(6.76 \times 10^{-8}) \, (1.3 \times 10^{-4}) = K_{S.P.}$$

and

$$K_{S.P.} = 8.8 \times 10^{-12}$$

Solubility product constants vary with temperature, usually increasing as the temperature increases, and they vary also with the nature of the solvent. Such constants are accurate only for dilute, saturated solutions of substances of slight solubility; nevertheless, they serve as a guide for the interpretation of the behavior of saturated solutions of other solutes whose solubility is not large.

5. The Common-ion Effect

In the preceding section, it was stated that precipitation will occur whenever the product of the concentrations of the ions of a slightly soluble substance exceeds the solubility product constant of that substance at the experimental temperature. Suppose, now, that to 1 l. of a solution which is saturated with silver chloride at 25° C. there is added 0.001 mole of sodium chloride. Since sodium chloride is completely ionized into sodium and chloride ions, and since the solution is relatively dilute, it may be assumed that the salt furnishes 0.001 mole of Cl^-. If no change occurred in the solution, the total concentration of chloride ion is in the solution would now be the sum of that furnished by the two metallic chlorides present, $1.3 \times 10^{-5} + 10^{-3}$. When one adds these figures, it is readily seen that 0.000013 is negligible in comparison with 0.001, hence the chloride-ion concentration of the solution may be taken as 0.001. In this same solution, the concentration of the silver ion would be 1.3×10^{-5}. The product of these concentrations would be given by the equation

$$[Ag^+][Cl^-] = 1.3 \times 10^{-5} \times 10^{-3} = 1.3 \times 10^{-8}$$

and is a number which is considerably larger than 1.69×10^{-10}, the solubility product constant of silver chloride. As a result of 1.3×10^{-8} exceeding the constant, precipitation will occur. When precipitation occurs, both silver and chloride ions will be withdrawn to form the solid silver chloride and the concentration of both silver and chloride ions will be reduced. Since the concentration of the silver ions was very small to start with, it will be seen that after the addition of the sodium chloride the silver-ion concentration will have been reduced almost to the vanishing place:

$$[Ag^+][Cl^-] \text{ cannot exceed } 1.69 \times 10^{-10}$$
$$\therefore [Ag^+](10^{-3}) = 1.69 \times 10^{-10}$$

and

$$[Ag^+] = 1.69 \times 10^{-10} / 10^{-3} = 1.69 \times 10^{-7}, \text{ or } 0.000000169 \text{ mole/liter}$$

This behavior is general for all strong, slightly soluble electrolytes, hence it may be stated that the solubility of such a salt is decreased by the addition to its solution of a second electrolyte which has one ion in common with it.

Complete precipitation is often insured by use of the common ion effect. For example, if silver ion is being removed from a solution by precipitation as a chloride, the addition of a few extra milliliters of hydrochloric acid will raise the chloride-ion concentration so high that the silver-ion concentration will become negligibly small.

6. *The Solution of Precipitates*

Often it is necessary to dissolve a precipitate, or substance of slight solubility. Here the usual means of displacing equilibrium may be involved as with silver chloride, for which

$$[Ag^+][Cl^+] \text{ may not exceed } 1.69 \times 10^{-10}$$

If water is added to a saturated solution containing a precipitate of this substance, the concentration of silver and chloride ions in moles per liter becomes momentarily smaller due to the dilution, and to undo this effect, in accord with the principle of Le Chatelier, more of the precipitate will dissolve, restoring the equilibrium concentration:

$$AgCl_{(s)} \rightleftharpoons AgCl_{(sol.)} \rightarrow Ag^+ + Cl^-$$

Also, if no extra water is added, but if the temperature of the existing equilibrium mixture is raised, the solubility of most substances will increase. In this instance, if the solubility of the precipitate is small, large quantities of water or a large increase in temperature respectively would be necessary to account for the dissolution of any appreciable quantity of the solid.

The third and most common method of dissolving precipitates is their chemical conversion into soluble products. To effect such a change, it is necessary to add to the precipitate a reagent which will combine with one of the ions to remove it from solution. Consider, for example, the silver chloride equilibrium written above. If something reacts with either the silver or chloride ions to remove them, then more of the solid salt will go into ionic solution to restore the decreased ion concentration and the state of equilibrium; again in conformity with the principle of Le Chatelier.

As a more specific example, consider the case of bismuth sulfide, which is readily precipitated from solutions of bismuth ions. If one adds HCl to the sulfide and heats the mixture, the precipitate dissolves. The hydrogen ions of the acid unite with the sulfide ions of the sulfide to form volatile hydrogen sulfide, which goes off as a gas. Sulfide ions are continually removed from the equilibrium by this means while more and more of the sulfide dissolves in an effort to restore their concentration to its normal value. Ultimately, all of the sulfide will dissolve:

$$Bi_2S_3 + 6HCl \rightarrow 2BiCl_3 + 3H_2S \uparrow$$

7. The Equilibrium of Weak Electrolytes

It has been said (cf. section 7, Chapter 14) that the ionization of weak electrolytes is a reversible process. Therefore, an equilibrium between the un-ionized molecules and the ions of the dissociated ones will exist. Acetic acid furnishes an excellent example of a weak acid:

$$HC_2H_3O_2 \rightleftharpoons H^+ + C_2H_3O_2^-$$

The equilibrium equation for this process is

$$[H^+][C_2H_3O_2^-] / [HC_2H_3O_2] = K_i$$

where the subscript i is used to indicate that the constant is one for an ionization process. By actual measurement in the laboratory, it is found that a 0.1 M solution of acetic acid is 1.36 per cent ionized at 25° C. The concentration of both hydrogen and acetate ions in this solution will be, therefore,

$$0.1 \times 0.0136 \text{ or } 0.00136 \text{ mole/liter}$$

and the concentration of the un-ionized molecules will be

$$0.1 \times 0.9864 \text{ or } 0.09864 \text{ mole/liter}$$

and the value of K_i will be given by substituting these values in the above equation.

$$K_i = \frac{(0.00136)(0.00136)}{(0.09864)}$$

$$K_i = 0.0000185, \text{ or } 1.85 \times 10^{-5}$$

Practically, this means that in any aqueous solution containing hydrogen ions, acetate ions, and molecules of acetic acid, the respective concentrations of these particles will have to be such that

$$[H^+][C_2H_3O_2^-]\big/[HC_2H_3O_2] = 1.85 \times 10^{-5}$$

From this equation, it may be seen that when K_i is small, ionization is slight, and that as K_i becomes bigger, it does so as a result of increased ionization.

Other weakly ionized, soluble substances establish equilibria in the same way as does acetic acid, and equilibrium constants of the K_i type may be established for them.

8. Buffer Solutions

The common-ion effect may be applied to weak electrolytes too, but with different results. In a 0.1 M solution of acetic acid at 25° C, as shown above, the concentration of both H^+ and $C_2H_3O_2^-$ ions in solution is 0.00136 mole per liter. If there is now added to this solution sufficient sodium acetate to make the solution 0.01 M with respect to this salt, the acetate-ion concentration of the solution becomes increased (if an activity coefficient of 1 is assumed for the salt) by 0.01 M. According to the principle of Le Chatelier, the equilibrium will shift in such a direction as to tend to undo the imposed change; thus, $HC_2H_3O_2$ molecules will be formed, and the small concentration of H^+ ions which originally existed will be made even smaller. The exact quantitative value of the hydrogen-ion concentration after equilibrium has been reëstablished may be calculated by the use of the ionization constant and the equilibrium equation. If, now, there is added to this solution any reagent which uses up hydrogen ions, some of the un-ionized acetic acid molecules will ionize to offset this displacement of equilibrium. Because such a solution has a small *momentary acidity* while maintaining a *reserve acidity* which is large by comparison, it is capable of maintaining a small but steady acidity over a considerable period of time.

Solutions of weak bases will behave in an analogous manner when a salt of the base is added. For example, if one adds ammonium chloride or ammonium nitrate to a solution of ammonium hydroxide, the total concentration of ammonium ions is made large because these salts are both very soluble and highly ionized. As the concentration of ammonium ions becomes larger, the equilibrium is maintained only by the concentration of the hydroxyl ion decreasing to produce a consequent increase in the concentration of the un-ionized molecules of NH_4OH. Such a solution has, therefore, a large reserve of un-ionized hydroxyl groups but a very small momentary concentration of hydroxyl ions, which it is capable of maintaining over a considerable period.

Solutions which are thus prepared from a weak acid and a salt of that acid or from a weak base and a salt of that base are known as buffer solutions. They are used to maintain a small but constant concentration of either H^+ or OH^- ions, and they are useful in industry, in the laboratory, and in the life processes of plants and animals. The blood is a buffered solution.

9. The Ionization of Polybasic Acids

A polybasic acid is an acid one molecule of which in solution is able to furnish two or more hydrogen ions. An example of such an acid is orthophosphoric acid, H_3PO_4. When this molecule has furnished one hydrogen ion,

$$H_3PO_4 \rightleftharpoons H^+ + H_2PO_4^-$$

the two remaining hydrogen ions are now held to the phosphate radical by a force which is capable of holding three such atoms; hence, they are held more tightly than they were originally, and further ionization is more difficult. If, now, the outside forces acting on the $H_2PO_4^-$ ion are made strong enough, it will further ionize thus:

$$H_2PO_4^- \rightleftharpoons H^+ + HPO_4^{--}$$

The one remaining hydrogen atom is now separated from the PO_4 radical with even greater difficulty:

$$HPO_4^{--} \rightleftharpoons H^+ + PO_4^{---}$$

That ionization does become more difficult is shown by the decrease in the value of the successive ionization constants for the three processes represented by the above equations:

$$K_{i_1} = 1.1 \times 10^{-2}; \quad K_{i_2} = 2 \times 10^{-7}; \quad \text{and} \quad K_{i_3} = 3.6 \times 10^{-13}$$

This behavior is true of all polybasic acids, though in varying degrees. Such a compound, which may have a strong first degree of ionization, will have a much weaker second degree, and so on. Because these successive stages of ionization become weaker and weaker, stronger and stronger bases are required to bring them about. Very weak acids, therefore, form salts only with strong bases, while weak bases for similar reasons form salts only with strong acids.

There are also polyacid bases. The stronger members of this class are substances one molecule of which is capable of furnishing two or more hydroxyl ions. Here each successive hydroxyl ion is removed with more difficulty than was the preceding one, and successively stronger acids are required to bring about their removal.

10. *Types of Salts*

Polybasic acids are classified more specifically by the total number of hydrogen ions which they are capable of providing per molecule of acid. Those with two ionizable hydrogens such as sulfuric acid, H_2SO_4, are *dibasic acids*, while those with three are *tribasic acids*. In similar fashion, acids which can furnish only one H^+ ion per molecule are *monobasic acids*. The preceding section has shown that polybasic acids may have their hydrogens replaced one at a time as well as collectively. For example, one gram-molecule of sulfuric acid may react with either 1 or 2 moles of sodium hydroxide:

$$H_2SO_4 + NaOH \rightarrow NaHSO_4 + HOH$$
$$H_2SO_4 + 2NaOH \rightarrow Na_2SO_4 + 2HOH$$

The first product which contains both sodium and replaceable hydrogen is an example of an *acid salt*, while the second product, Na_2SO_4, is an example of a *normal salt*. Orthophosphoric acid, with sodium hydroxide, yields the acid salts NaH_2PO_4 and Na_2HPO_4, and the normal salt Na_3PO_4.

Basic salts result when polyacid bases are not completely neutralized. Thus, from the diacid base, lead hydroxide, one may obtain either basic lead nitrate or the normal salt:

$$Pb(OH)_2 + HNO_3 \rightarrow Pb(OH)NO_3 + H_2O$$
$$Pb(OH)_2 + 2HNO_3 \rightarrow Pb(NO_3)_2 + 2H_2O$$

Normal salts, then, contain neither replaceable hydrogen nor hydroxyl radicals, while an acid salt contains the former radical and a basic salt contains the latter. These names do not indicate anything whatsoever about the manner in which their solutions will react to litmus. This matter will be discussed in a succeeding section.

Since polybasic acids and polyacid bases may be neutralized in stages, it is possible to carry out successive steps with different reagents so that *mixed salts* may be produced. Salts which yield more than one variety of positive ion or more than one variety of negative ion are called mixed salts. Examples of such compounds are $NaNH_4HPO_4$, $NaKCO_3$, and $CaCl(OCl)$.

Hydrated salts have been discussed in section 10 of Chapter 14.

11. The Ionization of Water

Before discussing further the reactions between acids and bases and the behavior of aqueous solutions of weak electrolytes, it will be necessary to consider briefly the ionization of water. Water is a very weakly ionized substance. Careful measurements have revealed that in 1 l. of water at 20° C. there are about 10^{-7} mole of hydrogen ions present. Water might possibly be considered a polybasic acid as a consequence of having two hydrogen atoms in its molecule. Actually, however, its primary stage of ionization is so extremely small, the second stage would be so tiny as to be considered nonexistent. For all practical purposes, then, the ionization may be considered to be

$$HOH \rightleftharpoons H^+ + OH^-$$

In section 13 of Chapter 14, it was shown that hydrogen ions become hydrated to form the hydronium ion, H_3O^+, but, since the concentrations of H^+ and H_3O^+ ions are identical, the simpler notation will be used here. It is seen from the equation representing the ionization that H^+ and OH^- ions are produced mole for mole. In pure water, then, the OH^- ion concentration will also be 10^{-7} mole/liter. These concentrations are so small in comparison with the quantity of un-ionized water present that this latter value is, for all practical purposes, a constant, whence the equilibrium expression for the ionization would be

$$[H^+][OH^-] = K_i[H_2O] = K_w$$

where the subscript w is used to signify the constant for water. The value for this constant at 20° C. is calculated:

$$K_w = 10^{-7} \times 10^{-7} = 10^{-14}$$

The value of the constant increases somewhat at higher temperatures and varies somewhat with the presence of various solutes.

Water is a *neutral solution* (that is, it is neither acid nor basic); hence, *a neutral solution is one in which the concentration of H^+ ions is exactly equal to the concentration of OH^- ions.* From the value calculated above for the value of K_w, it is also apparent that, in any solution which contains both H^+ and OH^- ions, the product of their respective concentrations may not exceed 10^{-14}. Any time this value is exceeded, H^+ and OH^- will combine to produce molecules of water, thus reducing their respective concentrations in the solution. Also in accordance with this equilibrium expression, no matter how acidic a solution may become there will always be a minute concentration of OH^- ions, and conversely, no matter how strongly basic a solution may become, there will always be a very low concentration of H^+ ions present. For example, an acid which is 0.1 molar with respect to hydrogen ion will have a concentration of OH^- ion of 10^{-13} mole per liter:

$$[H^+][OH^-] = (0.1)[OH^-] = 10^{-14}$$

whence

$$[OH^-] = 10^{-14}\Big/10^{-1} = 10^{-13}$$

12. The pH Scale

There are several instances in the preceding chapters of new scales of measurement having been evolved so that values which are very small in absolute units may be expressed in numbers that are more conveniently employed. The value of the hydrogen-ion concentration in pure water at 20° C., 10^{-7} mole per liter, is so small numerically as to have little in common with our ordinary conception of numbers. Partly for the reason that these small numbers might be replaced with larger ones which permit also a more compact scale, in 1909 Sörensen proposed that the hydrogen-ion concentration of a solution be given in terms of the logarithm to the base 10 of the reciprocal of the concentration, rather than in terms of the concentration itself. The scale thus developed is known as the *pH scale* where *pH* is derived from *potential of hydrogen*. The pH of pure water is 7:

$$pH = \log 1\Big/[H^+] = \log 1\Big/10^{-7}$$
$$= \log 10^7 = 7$$

Any neutral solution, therefore, will have a pH of 7, save as changes of temperature and the addition of certain solutes cause variations.

In the acid solution mentioned at the close of the preceding section, the hydrogen-ion concentration was 0.1 mole per liter; the pH of this solution would be 1:

$$pH = \log 1\Big/10^{-1} = \log 10 = 1$$

A solution which is acidic will thus have a pH whose value is less than 7, and the smaller the pH value the more acidic the solution; conversely, a solution which is basic will have a pH whose value is greater than 7, and the larger this number the more basic the solution.

13. Calculations Involving pH

Often it is necessary to calculate the pH value of a solution whose H^+ or OH^- ion concentration is known. Examples of these calculations follow.

a. What is the pH value of a solution whose hydrogen-ion concentration is 2.5×10^{-3} gram-ion (mole) per liter?

Solution:

$$
\begin{aligned}
pH &= \log 1 / [H^+] \\
&= \log 1 / (2.5 \times 10^{-3}) \\
&= \log (0.4 \times 10^3) \\
&= \log (4 \times 10^2) \\
&= \log 4 + \log 10^2 \\
&= 0.60 + 2 \\
&= 2.60
\end{aligned}
$$

b. What is the pH of a solution whose hydroxyl-ion concentration is 0.0325 gram-ion (mole) per liter?

Solution:

$$
\begin{aligned}
[H^+][OH^-] &= 10^{-14} \\
[H^+] &= 10^{-14} / [OH^-] \\
&= 10^{-14} / 0.0325
\end{aligned}
$$

$$
\begin{aligned}
pH &= \log 1 / [H^+] \\
&= \log 1 / (10^{-14} / 0.0325) \\
&= \log (0.0325 / 10^{-14}) \\
&= \log (3.25 \times 10^{12}) \\
&= \log 3.25 + \log 10^{12} \\
&= 0.51 + 12 \\
&= 12.51
\end{aligned}
$$

The reverse of these calculations is also necessary. An example of such a calculation will serve to illustrate the process.

c. What is the hydrogen-ion concentration of a solution whose pH is 5.36?

Solution:

$$pH = \log 1 \big/ [H^+]$$

and

$$- \log [H^+] = pH$$
$$= 5.36$$

$$\log [H^+] = -5.36$$
$$= -6 + 0.64$$
$$= \log 10^{-6} + \log 4.37$$
$$= \log (4.37 \times 10^{-6})$$

$$[H^+] = 4.37 \times 10^{-6} \text{ mole/liter}$$

14. Neutralization

Reference has already been made to the fact that metathetical reactions between acids and bases are known as neutralizations, and also to the fact that such reactions go virtually to completion because weakly ionized water is one of the products. At this juncture, the process is deserving of further scrutiny.

In previous chapters, it has been pointed out that acids and bases, unlike most salts, are of widely varying degrees of strength, as electrolytes. Consider the case of the addition of chemically equivalent quantities of a strong base and a strong acid. For the sake of illustration, it may be assumed that 10 ml. of 0.5 N sodium hydroxide is added to 10 ml. of 0.5 N hydrochloric acid. The reaction will be

$$H^+ + Cl^- + Na^+ + OH^- \rightarrow HOH + Na^+ + Cl^-$$

so that there remains a solution of Na^+ and Cl^- ions in water. Also present will be the small concentration of H^+ and OH^- ions which water characteristically furnishes. Because HCl and NaOH are both highly ionized in solution, there will be little tendency either for Na^+ and OH^- to reunite to form NaOH molecules or for H^+ and Cl^- ions to reunite to form un-ionized HCl molecules. Consequently, solutions which contain chemically equivalent quantities of a strong base and a strong acid contain the normal concentrations of H^+ and OH^- ions furnished by water and are therefore practically neutral.

To illustrate the case of the reaction between a strong base and a weak acid, imagine that 10 ml. of 0.5 N sodium hydroxide is mixed with 10 ml. of 0.5 N acetic acid. Again, chemically equivalent quantities of the two reagents are present, and, according to the equation, the products of the reaction should be water containing sodium and acetate ions:

$$Na^+ + OH^- + HC_2H_3O_2 \rightleftarrows HOH + Na^+ + C_2H_3O_2^-$$

Here, as in the former case, water will be furnishing its small concentration of H^+ and OH^- ions, but at this point the similarity ceases. As a result of the reaction, the concentration of acetate ions is now large, and it has been shown (cf. section 7) that, any time $[H^+][C_2H_3O_2^-] \big/ [HC_2H_3O_2]$ exceeds 1.85×10^{-5} in value, un-ionized acetic acid molecules will begin to form and continue to form until equilibrium is restored. Hence, at the point of chemical equivalency in this reaction, there will be some unreacted acid molecules present in the solution. Also present in the solution will be an excess of hydroxyl ions. Water normally furnishes H^+ and OH^- ions in equal numbers, but when H^+ ions are withdrawn to form $HC_2H_3O_2$ molecules, an excess of OH^- ions is left in solution. From this discussion, then, it is seen that, when chemically equivalent quantities of a strong base and a weak acid are added, the resulting solution is not neutral but is slightly basic. The weaker the acid with respect to the base the more basic will be the solution at the point of equivalence.

The situation in regard to the mixing of chemically equivalent quantities of a weak base and a strong acid are very similar. Imagine, for this case, that chemically equivalent quantities of ammonium hydroxide and hydrochloric acid are mixed. The reaction will be

$$NH_4OH + H^+ + Cl^- \rightleftarrows HOH + NH_4^+ + Cl^-$$

There is no tendency here for Cl^- and H^+ ions to withdraw each other from solution by uniting, because HCl is a strong acid, but the large NH_4^+ ion concentration which has been generated by the reaction will cause a union of NH_4^+ and OH^- ions to restore the equilibrium between un-ionized ammonium hydroxide and its ions, and an excess of H^+ ions from the water will remain in the solution, giving it an acidic reaction. A solution which contains chemically equivalent quantities of a strong acid and a weak base will react acid, and the greater the difference in electrolytic strength between the two reagents the more acidic the solution will be.

When weak acids are added to weak bases in chemically equivalent quantities, the solution may be either acidic or basic in its reaction. In a manner analogous to that employed in discussing the two preceding examples, it may be shown that the reaction will be basic if the base is the stronger of the two reagents, and acidic if the acid is the stronger.

From this discussion, it will be seen that only chemically equivalent quantities of strong bases and strong acids exactly neutralize each other. In its essence, then, neutralization is the union of hydrogen, or hydronium, ions with hydroxyl ions to form water. This view is supported by the fact that in all cases in which a strong base reacts with a strong acid, save those instances in which the anion of the acid and the cation of the base also combine, the quantity of heat evolved per mole of water formed is identical. *This quantity of heat evolved when a mole of water is formed by neutralization is known as the heat of neutralization, and is equal to about 13,000 cal.* Naturally, if either or both of the substances used in the neutralization are weak electrolytes, and therefore only partially ionized at the end-point, the heat evolved will deviate from the value given.

The fact that the heat of neutralization for strong acids and bases is constant was one of the reasons cited originally in support of the ionization theory.

EQUIPMENT FOR TITRATION. (Courtesy, Mallinckrodt Chemical Works.)

15. The Titration of Acids and Bases

One of the most common methods of determining the concentration of a solution of unknown value is that of *titration. This method consists of measuring carefully the volume of a solution of known concentration which is required to react with an equally carefully measured volume of a solution of unknown concentration.* The instruments commonly used for making such careful measurements of volume are burets, which are usually read to the nearest 0.01 ml. This method and these instruments may be used to determine the concentration of solutions of acids and bases. When the strength of an acid solution is sought, the process is frequently referred to as *acidimetry*, while when the strength of a basic solution is sought, the process is known as *alkalimetry*.

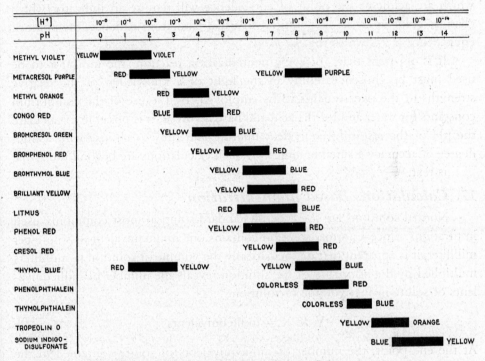

THE pH RANGE OF A NUMBER OF COMMON INDICATORS.

16. Indicators

Since reactions between bases and acids usually produce only colorless solutions, a means of determining when the point of chemical equivalence is reached in such a reaction had to be devised. Fortunately, there are a number of substances whose color undergoes changes with varying concentrations of the hydrogen, or hydronium, ion. Some of these substances occur naturally, and some are synthetic. Fortunately different members of the group change color at different hydrogen-, or hydronium-ion concentrations. They are known collectively as *indicators*.

Sec. 14 has shown that a solution containing chemically equivalent quantities of a strong base and a strong acid is approximately neutral, and therefore has a pH of approximately 7. For a titration involving two such substances, an indicator whose color changes at a pH of 7 would be required. When a strong base and a weak acid are mixed in equivalent quantities, the resulting solution is basic in nature; for such a reaction, an indicator which changes color in a slightly basic solution will be required to indicate the point of equivalence. Solutions which are acidic at the point of equivalence will require an indicator which changes color in an acidic solution. In usual laboratory parlance, the point of equivalence is known as the *end-point*.

It is apparent that, for every neutralization reaction, the indicator to be used must be chosen carefully in the light of a knowledge of the relative strengths of the two reagents to be employed. By the use of the equilibrium constants for water and for the acid and base involved, it is possible to calculate the pH of the resulting equivalent mixture and thus to choose with a high degree of accuracy a suitable indicator. Such calculations are beyond the scope of this text.

17. Calculations Based upon Titration

Normal solutions are the type of standard solution most commonly used in titrations. Since a normal solution contains one milliequivalent of solute per milliliter, it is apparent that mathematically the volume of solution in milliliters multiplied by the normality of the solution reveals the number of milliequivalents of solute in that volume of solution:

$$V \times N = \text{milliequivalents}$$

At the end-point, the number of milliequivalents of solute contained in the known volume of the solution of unknown concentration must be equal to the number of milliequivalents in the known volume of standard solution; hence, at end-point

$$V_1 \times N_1 = V_2 \times N_2$$

A problem will indicate such a calculation: What is the normality of a solution of sodium hydroxide, 40 ml. of which reacts exactly with 30 ml. of 2 N hydrochloric acid solution?

Solution:

$$40 \times N = 30 \times 2$$
$$40N = 60$$
$$N = 60/40$$
$$= 1.5$$

What volume of 3 N acetic acid should be required to react with 10 ml. of 2.5 N sodium hydroxide?

Solution:

$$V \times 3 = 10 \times 2.5$$
$$3V = 25$$
$$V = 25/3$$
$$= 8.3 \text{ ml.}$$

Sometimes pure, dry solids are weighed, dissolved in an unknown volume of water, and titrated. To illustrate the calculations involved in this type of procedure, the following problem may be considered: What will be the normality of a solution of sulfuric acid, 48.80 ml. of which is required to react with 1.293 g. of pure sodium carbonate?

Solution:

$$\text{Mol. wt. } Na_2CO_3 = 106.00$$
$$\text{Equiv. wt. } Na_2CO_3 = 106.00/2$$
$$= 53.00$$
$$\text{Milliequiv. wt. } Na_2CO_3 = 0.053 \text{ g.}$$
$$\text{Milliequivalents of } Na_2CO_3 \text{ used} = 1.293/0.053$$
$$= 24.40$$

Milliequivalents of H_2SO_4 which
must be used to react with 24.40
milliequivalents of Na_2CO_3 $= 24.40$
Let N $=$ normality of H_2SO_4 required
Then $N \times 48.80$ $= 24.40$
and N $= 24.40/48.80$
$= 0.5$

In other processes, one of the reaction products may be collected and weighed. In such a case, the number of milliequivalents of each product is equal to the number of milliequivalents of each reagent involved in the reaction, and hence a similar calculation may be made.

18. Hydrolysis

In the reactions

$$Na^+ + OH^- + HC_2H_3O_2 \rightleftarrows HOH + Na^+ + C_2H_3O_2^-$$

and

$$H^+ + Cl^- + NH_4OH \rightleftarrows HOH + NH_4^+ + Cl^-$$

it has been noted already that the ions formed by the forward reaction tend to react with the few ions formed by water to set up a backward reaction, which is also a metathesis. In general, then, *any metathetical reaction in which water is one of the reactants is referred to as hydrolysis.* In the particular hydrolyses cited above, it is seen that hydrolysis is the opposite of neutralization; that is, it is a process by which a salt and water react to produce an acid and a base.

Hydrolysis offers an explanation of the observed facts that, in solution, all normal salts are not neutral; all acid salts do not react acidic; all basic salts do not react basic; and some acid salts even react basic. Consider the dissolution of the normal salt, sodium chloride; sodium ions and chloride ions are formed, but there is no tendency for these to withdraw either the H^+ or OH^- ions of the water, since in each case a strong electrolyte would be formed by such withdrawals. In the case of a solution of potassium acetate, ionization would be strong, but, since acetic acid is a weak electrolyte, acetate ions and H^+ ions from the water would immediately combine, leaving an excess of OH^- ions in the solution. Sodium acid carbonate (sodium bicarbonate) in water yields sodium ions and bicarbonate ions:

$$Na^+HCO_3^- \rightarrow Na^+ + HCO_3^-$$

Carbonic acid (H_2CO_3) is such an extremely weak acid, however, that bicarbonate ions immediately begin to withdraw H^+ ions to form H_2CO_3; the remaining solution, therefore, contains largely Na^+ and OH^- ions, as a consequence of which it reacts basic. The H_2CO_3 molecules are unstable and soon break down to yield carbon dioxide gas which is evolved.

$$Na^+HCO_3^- + HOH \rightarrow H_2CO_3 + Na^+ + OH^-$$
$$\rightarrow Na^+ + OH^- + H_2O + CO_2 \uparrow$$

In summation, it may be said that the great majority of salts ionize strongly, and that all of these salts, save those whose parent acids and bases are both strong, will have a reaction in solution which is characteristic of the stronger of the two parent substances.

From the examples given, it will be noted that hydrolytic reactions are metatheses, and as such they are subject to the general behavior characteristic of all metatheses. Some such reactions will, therefore, be reversible, while others will not be. The first two examples given above are of reversible hydrolysis, while the second is irreversible because the H_2CO_3 is decomposed into a substance which is removed from the mixture. Hydrolyses are also irreversible if both products are of the same chemical nature, or if one of the products is unreactive. The hydrolysis of phosphorus trichloride to produce two acids is an example of the first instance, and the hydrolysis of aluminum carbide is an example of the second:

$$PCl_3 + 3HOH \rightarrow 3HCl + H_3PO_3 \text{ (two acids)}$$
$$Al_4C_3 + 12HOH \rightarrow 4Al(OH)_3 + 3CH_4 \uparrow$$

In general, then, hydrolysis of ionic compounds is reversible while the hydrolysis of molecular substances is usually irreversible and therefore complete.

The equilibrium constants for hydrolyses, which are the reverse of neutralizations, are, of course, the reciprocals of the equilibrium constants for the corresponding neutralizations. It can also be shown that the hydrolysis constant (K_H) for a salt of a strong base and a weak acid is equal to K_W/K_A, where K_A is the ionization constant of the acid in question. For salts of a strong acid and a weak base, $K_H = K_W/K_B$, and for salts of two weak parent substances, $K_H = K_W/(K_A \times K_B)$, where K_B is the ionization constant for the weak base. As in other equilibria, a large value for K_H indicates extensive reaction, and hence a relatively large degree of hydrolysis; a small value for K_H indicates a small degree of hydrolysis. Since K_W is very small (10^{-14}), it becomes apparent, then, that K_W/K_A or K_W/K_B, and hence K_H becomes larger as the values for K_A and K_B become smaller—that is, as the degree of ionization of these compounds decreases. In the case of a salt both of whose parents are weak, the product $K_A \times K_B$ will be very small, making $K_W/(K_A \times K_B)$ and K_H large. The hydrolysis of such a salt will be extensive.

(See Appendix for Exercises)

COLLATERAL READINGS

Bjerrum: Acids, salts, and bases, *Chem. Rev.*, **16**, 287 (1935).

Chapin and Steiner: *Second Year College Chemistry*, 5th ed. revised, New York, John Wiley & Sons, Inc., 1943.

Creighton and Koehler, *Electrochemistry*, 4th ed., Vol. I, New York, John Wiley & Sons, Inc., 1943.

Foster: Hydrolysis and its relation to ionic charge and radius, *J. Chem. Education*, **17**, 509 (1940).

Getman and Daniels: *Outlines of Physical Chemistry*, New York, John Wiley & Sons, Inc., 1943.

Hall, *et al.: Acids and Bases*, Mack Printing Co., 1941.

Hammett: *Solutions of Electrolytes*, New York, McGraw-Hill Book Co., 1936.

Hildebrand: *Principles of Chemistry*, New York, The Macmillan Co., 1941.

Hogness and Johnson: *Qualitative Analysis and Chemical Equilibrium*, New York, Henry Holt & Co., Inc., 1940.

Taylor and Taylor: *Elementary Physical Chemistry*, 2d ed., New York, D. Van Nostrand Co., 1937.

18

Silicon and Its Compounds

1. Introduction

Silicon is the fourth element of the third period and is second only to oxygen in abundance in the earth's crust. Its compounds are both numerous and useful. Its relative atomic weight is 28.06 at. wt. units.

The atomic number of silicon is 14, and the electronic distribution among the first three energy levels of the atom is 2,8,4. Having four electrons in its outer level with eight electrons in the next lower level, the atom apparently might attain stability by either losing four electrons or gaining four electrons. Because the nucleus of this atom is heavier and more positively charged than its predecessors, planetary electrons are drawn in more closely, making the atom smaller and causing each electron to be held more tightly. There is, therefore, little likelihood of the four outermost electrons being lost, and the likelihood of four electrons being gained is also slight. The great majority of silicon compounds are thus formed as the result of a sharing of electrons, and are hence covalent.

The silicon atom, being only slightly heavier than the aluminum atom and a bit smaller in radius, is also very active. Since it lies midway in the period between the most active electron-loser and the most active electron-taker, we may expect its activity to represent about an average for the elements of the period.

2. Physical Properties

In the chapter on aluminum it was shown that, as one passes through the first three elements of the third period, their chemical properties become progressively less metallic, although their physical properties remain distinctly those of metals. It may be anticipated that silicon will be even less metallic in its properties. This is true not only of the chemical properties of the element, but also of its physical properties. The element exists in two readily recognizable modifications: *crystalline silicon*, which exists as dark grayish crystals which have some luster, but are otherwise distinctly nonmetallic in appearance, and *amorphous silicon*, which is a brown powder. In this instance, the word amorphous is incorrectly applied, since microscopical examination of the substance shows it to be made of tiny crystals and fragments of crystals which are of the same variety as those found in the more patently crystalline variety.

Crystalline silicon has a density of 2.48 g./ml. as compared with 2.35 g./ml. for the powdered variety. The melting point of the element is 1420° C., and its boiling point is 2620° C. A comparison of these figures with similar figures for the other elements of the third period shows that silicon has the highest melting and boiling points of any element in the period. This observation indicates that the smaller silicon atoms are much more firmly bound together in the crystal structure than are the atoms of the three preceding elements of the period.

The crystalline variety of the element will conduct electricity poorly, while the so-called amorphous variety will not conduct.

When the specific heat of silicon is measured at room temperature and its atomic heat calculated, there is found to be a wide deviation from the constant of the law of Dulong and Petit. When the specific heat determination is made at elevated temperatures, this deviation becomes negligible.

3. Occurrence

Silicon is present in the earth's crust to the extent of about 25.8 per cent, but, because of its activity, it is never found in the free state. It occurs principally as the oxide SiO_2, and as metallic salts of this oxide which were formed by the fusion of metallic oxides with SiO_2 in the days when the earth was very hot. Compounds containing both oxygen and silicon make up about 87 per cent of the earth's crust, and hence most of the sand, rocks, clay, and just plain dirt which abound.

The best source of silicon is its dioxide, which is found in many mountainous regions as quartz crystals and nearly everywhere in the form of sand which is largely quartz that has been broken by the action of wind and water.

Important metallic compounds of silicon and oxygen are: the *feldspars*, a typical one of which is *orthoclase*, whose formula is $KAlSi_3O_8$; the *micas*, such as *muscovite*, whose formula is $KAl_3H_2(SiO_4)_3$; the *zeolites*, such as *analcite*, whose formula is $NaAl(SiO_3)_2.H_2O$; the *asbestos* group of compounds, which includes several magnesium silicates such as $CaMg_3(SiO_3)_4$; *kaolin*, or pottery clay, $H_2Al_2(SiO_4)_2.H_2O$; *talc*, or *soapstone*, $H_2Mg_3(SiO_3)_4$; *meerschaum*, $H_4Mg_2Si_3O_{10}$; and a host of others, many of which when containing colored ions are used as semiprecious gem stones.

It is well to note here that granite, which makes up such a large portion of most mountain masses, is an *igneous*, or fire-formed, variety of rock whose heterogeneity is accounted for by the presence of readily distinguishable particles of mica, quartz, and the feldspars.

GRANITE. (Courtesy, American Museum of Natural History.)

Silicon compounds, then, constitute the most prevalent feature of any landscape, and are even incorporated by some plants into their structures.

4. Preparation

Free silicon was first prepared in 1823 by Berzelius, and was named silicon from *silex*, the Latin name for flint rock, which, in the days before the invention of matches, was an especially important silicon compound. The usual method of preparation consists of reducing the finely powdered dioxide, SiO_2. In the laboratory, the customary reducing agents are powdered aluminum and powdered magnesium. When the latter metal is used, care must be taken to see that it is not in excess, since it will enter into a reaction with the silicon formed in the primary process, forming magnesium silicide:

$$2Mg + SiO_2 \xrightarrow{\Delta} 2MgO + Si$$
$$2Mg + Si \xrightarrow{\Delta} Mg_2Si$$

When the reaction mixture has cooled, it is treated with hydrochloric acid which decomposes the magnesium oxide and any silicide which may be present, leaving the brown amorphous silicon.

When aluminum is used as the reducing agent, it may be used in excess since it does not form a silicide:

$$4Al + 3SiO_2 \xrightarrow{\Delta} 2Al_2O_3 + 3Si$$

The silicon so produced is dissolved in the excess of molten metal so that the mixture, when cooled, crystallizes as a whole. The solid mass is then treated with hydrochloric acid, which reacts with the metal to leave crystals of the free silicon.

The amorphous silicon may be converted to the crystalline variety by dissolving it in molten aluminum or zinc, allowing the mass to cool, and consuming the metal with acid.

On an industrial scale, free silicon is usually prepared by reducing the dioxide with coke in an electric furnace:

$$SiO_2 + 2C \xrightarrow{\Delta} 2CO \uparrow + Si$$

Here, too, an excess of the reducing agent must be avoided, since silicon and carbon react at the temperature of the electric furnace to form silicon carbide. At the present time, there are relatively few uses for the free element, though there is an increasing use of it in the preparation of alloys of aluminum and other metals.

If iron oxide is made a component of the reaction mixture with which the electric furnace is charged, the product obtained is an impure mass containing both silicon and iron and known as *ferrosilicon*. This material is used in large quantities in the preparation of silicon-bearing steels, which are valuable for their resistance to the action of acids and for their high magnetic permeability.

5. *Chemical Properties*

Silicon is an active sharer of electrons, and as such enters into a wide variety of combination reactions with both metals and nonmetals. Since its position is midway in the period between active metals and active nonmetals, it is to be anticipated that it would combine with elements of both varieties. Having little tendency either to gain or to lose electrons, it enters into few displacement reactions. Its reaction with acids is so slow as to be negligible, but with sodium hydroxide solution it reacts readily, forming the very stable silicate ion and displacing hydrogen:

$$Si + 2NaOH + HOH \rightarrow Na_2SiO_3 + 2H_2 \uparrow$$

A mixture of ferrosilicon and dry sodium hydroxide, which when moistened undergoes the above reaction, is sold under the trade name of *hydrogenite*, and is used for generating hydrogen gas.

With superheated steam, silicon reacts slowly to form SiO_2 and H_2, and, when fused with an alkali carbonate, it will displace the nonmetal carbon:

$$Na_2CO_3 + Si \rightarrow Na_2SiO_3 + C$$

Neither of these reactions is of practical importance.

6. *Silicides*

It has been noted above that silicon will dissolve in some metals and will react with others. With a number of metals in which it dissolves it simply forms solutions as it does with aluminum, but with many others it forms definite metallic binary compounds, called silicides, as it does with magnesium. Notable in this latter group of metals are lithium, calcium, iron, cobalt, nickel, platinum, manganese, and magnesium.

Calcium silicide is a powerful reducing agent, and as such is used as a deoxidant in the manufacture of steel and is incorporated into certain industrial explosives to prevent their premature oxidation. This compound is usually prepared by simultaneous reduction of the oxides of the requisite elements, which primary reactions are followed by the combination of the elements:

$$CaO + 2SiO_2 + 5C \rightarrow CaSi_2 + 5CO \uparrow$$

Metallic silicides characteristically enter into metathesis with solutions of strong acids to produce hydrides of silicon:

$$Mg_2Si + 4HCl \rightarrow 2MgCl_2 + SiH_4 \uparrow$$

It may be mentioned here that, at high temperatures, silicon unites with both sulfur and nitrogen to form the corresponding sulfide and nitride, neither of which is of practical importance.

7. *Halides*

All of the halogens will unite directly with silicon, forming compounds of the type SiX_4, where X stands for any of the four halogens. Amorphous silicon and fluorine unite spontaneously at about 20° C. to form the gaseous tetrafluoride. As the weight of the halogens increases, the tendency toward reactivity decreases; in fact, *it is a general rule in chemistry that, as the weight of the members of a given family increases, reactivity decreases.* The reaction between silicon and chlorine takes place at about 430° C., while the combination with iodine occurs only at red heat. The tetrachloride and tetrabromide are liquids at about 20° C., while the tetraiodide is a solid. Considerable quantities of the tetrachloride are prepared for the laying of military smoke screens and for aerial sky-writing. Where such large quantities of this substance are needed, the preparation is usually

$$SiC + 2Cl_2 \xrightarrow{\Delta} SiCl_4 + C$$

or

$$SiO_2 + 2C + 2Cl_2 \xrightarrow{\Delta} SiCl_4 + 2CO \uparrow$$

For preparing the smoke screens, a mixture of the tetrachloride and ammonia are atomized into the air, where they react with water vapor,

$$SiCl_4 + 3H_2O + 4NH_3 \rightarrow \underline{H_2SiO_3} + \underline{4NH_4Cl}$$

to produce fine particles of solid silicic acid and solid ammonium chloride, which appear as a dense white smoke.

It is a characteristic of all the halides save the tetrafluoride that they are very nearly completely hydrolyzed:

$$SiCl_4 + 3H_2O \rightarrow \underline{H_2SiO_3} + 4HCl \uparrow$$

The tetrafluoride reacts with water to yield two acids of silicon:

$$3SiF_4 + 3H_2O \rightarrow \underline{H_2SiO_3} + 2H_2SiF_6$$

8. Properties of Halides

A review of the properties of the chlorides of sodium, magnesium, and aluminum reveals that all three of these substances are solids. The first two are crystalline, ionic, and of high melting point. The third, when in the anhydrous condition, is a solid, but is apparently covalent and sublimes at ordinary pressures. Silicon tetrachloride is found to be a liquid, and conductivity tests establish that it is a nonconductor and, therefore, presumably covalent. Sodium chloride undergoes no hydrolysis; magnesium chloride hydrolyzes to some extent in the cold and markedly when heated; aluminum chloride is extensively hydrolyzed, especially when heated; and silicon tetrachloride is almost completely hydrolyzed by cold water.

Apparently, then, as one passes from left to right across a given period of the periodic chart, the chlorides change from high melting, crystalline solids of an ionic nature, and with little tendency to hydrolyze, to low melting compounds which are already liquids or gases at room temperature, which are covalent in nature, and which show a marked tendency toward hydrolysis. These statements also apply to the other halides, although, because of the high atomic weight of iodine, the covalent iodides may be, and usually are, solids. *In general, as the weight of a given type of compound increases, the state at about 20° C. tends to pass from gas to liquid to solid.*

As was the case with hydroxides, the varying properties of halides may be related to $\sqrt{\phi}$, which is a function of the ionic radius and the valence. In general, elements for which $\sqrt{\phi}$ is less than 2.2 form ionic halides of high melting point and slight tendency to hydrolyze, while elements for which $\sqrt{\phi}$ is greater than 2.2 form halides which are covalent, poor conductors in the liquid state, and at about 20° C. are either gases, liquids, or low-melting solids which show a pronounced tendency toward hydrolysis.

9. Hydrides

Silicon and hydrogen do not combine directly, but by indirect means several hydrides of the element may be prepared. These compounds are of little practical value, but, because they illustrate well one of the chemical characteristics of the element, they are worthy of brief consideration here. Ability to form binary compounds with hydrogen is a characteristic of nonmetallic elements which becomes more pronounced as nonmetallic properties increase; chlorine at the end of the period has been shown to combine directly with hydrogen, the reaction proceeding with explosive violence in the presence of ultraviolet light. Other differences which may be noted are: that very active nonmetals yield only one hydride, while the less active nonmetals yield of these compounds a number which increases with decreasing activity; and that the hydrides of the less active nonmetals are far less stable than are those of the active ones.

In section 6, it was shown that magnesium silicide reacts with acid to produce SiH_4, a gas of unpleasant odor, which is known as silicane, as monosilane, and as silicomethane after the corresponding carbon compound, CH_4, methane. At the same time, smaller quantities of several other silicon hydrides are produced. All together, some seven or eight of these compounds are known. Their formulas correspond to the type formula Si_nH_{2n+2}, where n stands for the number of Si atoms present. Their individual formulas would be SiH_4, Si_2H_6, Si_3H_8, ... Si_8H_{18}. The existence of so many of these compounds is explained by the fact that the silicon atoms are able to share electrons with each other, thus:

$$\begin{array}{ccc} H & H & H \\ \cdot o & \cdot o & \cdot o \\ H \circ Si : Si : Si \circ H \\ o \cdot & o \cdot & o \cdot \\ H & H & H \end{array}$$

This ability is possessed to a strong degree only by the lighter elements of column IV of the periodic system. Carbon has the greatest ability for such sharing. The names of the silicon hydrides are:

SiH_4, monosilane, silicomethane
Si_2H_6, disilane, silicoethane
Si_3H_8, trisilane, silicopropane
Si_4H_{10}, tetrasilane, silicobutane
Si_5H_{12}, pentasilane, silicopentane, etc.

The first two of these compounds are gases at about 20° C.; the remainder through octasilane are liquids.

All of these compounds are so unstable with respect to oxygen that they inflame spontaneously upon coming in contact with air:

$$SiH_4 + 2O_2 \rightarrow SiO_2 + 2H_2O$$

Free from oxygen, they may be kept indefinitely, but, when warmed strongly, they decompose:

$$SiH_4 \rightarrow Si + 2H_2 \uparrow$$

These gases also decompose slowly when in contact with water, though their initial solubility is small:

$$SiH_4 + 3H_2O \rightarrow \underline{H_2SiO_3} + 4H_2 \uparrow$$

With solutions of strong bases, the decomposition is more rapid, and the by-product is a metallic silicate rather than silicic acid:

$$SiH_4 + 2NaOH + H_2O \rightarrow Na_2SiO_3 + 4H_2 \uparrow$$

Contrast these indications of instability with hydrogen chloride, and further contrast the behavior of these nonmetallic covalent hydrides with the solid, crystalline, ionic hydride of sodium (cf. section 8, Chapter 7).

10. Carbide

The carbide of silicon is manufactured in large quantities by a process developed by the American chemical engineer, Edward G. Acheson, and is sold

A Furnace for the Manufacture of Carborundum. (Courtesy, The Carborundum Co.)

under the trade name of *Carborundum*. It is made by heating together at about 3000° C. for 36 hours in an electric furnace a mixture of sand and coke, containing small quantities of sawdust and salt. The carbon packed as a core between the electrodes of the furnace offers sufficient resistance to the passage of the current to cause the necessary temperature to be reached. The gases formed by the charring of the sawdust keep the mass porous, while the salt helps to volatilize metallic impurities which may be present. Carborundum is manufactured at Niagara Falls, where a good supply of relatively cheap electricity is available.

$$SiO_2 + 3C \rightarrow SiC + 2CO \uparrow$$

Industrial silicon carbide is black in color, with a strong iridescence, and is one of the hardest substances known to man. With the hardness of diamond set at 10, the hardness of carborundum on the same scale is 9.15. The finished product is washed with sulfuric acid, sodium hydroxide, and water, and the particles are carefully sized. The smaller particles are used in preparing grinding and cutting pastes and dusts, and are cemented together with sodium silicate to form grinding wheels and burrs. Some of the powder is used as a source of both silicon and carbon in the manufacture of steel. In more massive form, the material is used as a refractory, and pieces of it are used to form the resistor element in various electrical devices. Large quantities of Carborundum are produced annually.

A more pure variety of silicon carbide can be produced as colorless or green transparent plates.

PHOTOGRAPH OF A DIORAMA REPRESENTING EDWARD G. ACHESON'S FIRST LABORATORY.
(Courtesy, The Carborundum Co.)

11. *Oxides*

Silicon is the first element of the third period to exhibit more than one valence in its oxides. Of the four valence electrons of this element, two are in the 3_0 level and two are in the 3_1 level; it is, therefore, possible for the two 3_1 electrons to be involved in reaction without the other two being involved. It is thus that the formation of the oxide, SiO, silicon monoxide, may be explained. This oxide, as might be predicted, is not stable at high temperatures, readily forming SiO_2, which is extremely stable. The yellowish-brown SiO is prepared by heating carbon with an excess of sand at about 2000° C. Unless the product is cooled rapidly to the solid state, it decomposes thus:

$$2SiO \rightarrow SiO_2 + Si$$

The monoxide is used both as a pigment and as an abrasive.

The dioxide of silicon in its various forms is plentiful. It is estimated, in fact, that at least 12 per cent of the earth's crust is composed of this substance, which is usually referred to generically as *silica*. Besides the numerous modifications of silica which are found in nature, there are three definite crystalline forms of the pure substance; in other words, it is trimorphic. These crystalline modifications are known as *quartz, tridymite,* and *cristobalite,* and each of these in turn has modifications all of which differ from each other slightly in form and in behavior toward light. There are definite transition temperatures (cf. section 22 of Chapter 11) at which changes between the various varieties occur; the changes and their characteristic temperatures are indicated in the following schematic representation.

$$
\begin{array}{ccccc}
575° & 870° & & 1470° & 1710° \\
\alpha\text{-quartz} \rightleftarrows & \beta\text{-quartz} \rightleftarrows & \beta_2\text{-tridymite} \rightleftarrows & \beta\text{-cristobalite} \rightleftarrows & \text{molten silica}
\end{array}
$$

$$\updownarrow 163° \qquad\qquad \updownarrow 225°$$

$$\beta_1\text{-tridymite} \qquad \alpha\text{-cristobalite}$$

$$\updownarrow 117°$$

$$\alpha\text{-tridymite}$$

CRYSTALS OF QUARTZ. (Courtesy, American Museum of Natural History.)

The only one of these modifications which should be stable at ordinary temperatures is seen from the diagram to be alpha-quartz; however, if any of the varieties which are stable at higher temperatures are cooled very rapidly, no time is allowed for the occurrence of the changes which should take place (indicated above), and consequently *metastable* crystals of these varieties are frequently found in nature—principally in volcanic rocks and lavas which presumably underwent a rapid cooling. All forms of silica melt at 1710° C., and this molten material may be cooled so rapidly that it has no time to assume any of the above forms. There results, then, an amorphous variety of silica known as *fused silica* or *silica glass*, which is especially valuable for use in sanatoria windows and as lenses for ultraviolet lamps because it transmits ultraviolet light to a much greater degree than does ordinary glass. Some laboratory ware is made of fused silica because this material has such a low coefficient of expansion that it may be heated to red heat and directly plunged into ice water without breaking.

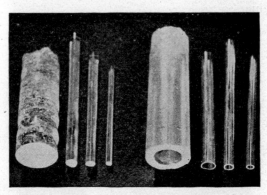

OBJECTS MADE OF FUSED QUARTZ. (Courtesy, General Electric Company.)

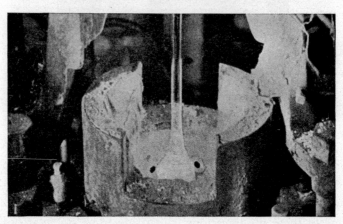

DRAWING A FUSED QUARTZ INGOT FOR THE MANUFACTURE OF HOLLOW TUBING. (Courtesy, General Electric Company.)

When pure, quartz, the most stable form of silica, is found as colorless transparent crystals which have six sides and ends which are hexagonal pyramids. These crystals may range in size from very tiny ones to others so large that a man can scarcely reach around them. They are found in many parts of the world; some of the best come from Brazil. Some of the best domestic quartz crystals come from the Ouachita Mountains near Hot Springs National

Park, Arkansas. Sections of such crystals are used to control the frequencies of radio broadcasting stations as well as in other electronic devices. It may be noted here that the density of quartz is 2.65 g./ml. and that helium will diffuse through cold quartz while hydrogen will diffuse through heated quartz.

Many quartz crystals have been discolored by traces of impurities; thus we have smoky quartz (containing charred organic matter), rose quartz, ame-

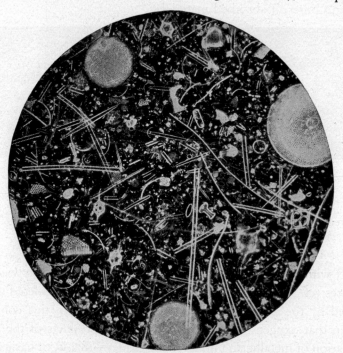

A PHOTOMICROGRAPH OF DIATOM SKELETONS. (Courtesy, Research Laboratory, Johns Manville Corp.)

thyst, chalcedony, jasper, agate, flint, etc. Opal is a hydrated form of silica, and sand is simply silica particles weathered from the various crystalline forms. White sand comes largely from pure quartz, while the ordinary brownish sand contains iron-bearing impurities. *Kieselguhr*, or diatomaceous earth, is silica which once constituted the skeletons of the tiny marine animals known as diatoms. This material is found in quantity along both our seaboards and is used as a filter, as an absorber for nitroglycerin in the manufacture of dynamite, in metal polishes, and for a number of other purposes.

Silica gel is an industrial variety of silica which is made by mixing sodium silicate and hydrochloric acid (cf. section 12), washing the precipitate of silicic acid to remove salts, and heating it until only about 5 per cent of the water remains. The product is an opaque mass of silica containing many minute capillary spaces which make it an excellent absorber of gases and dissolved substances. It is used in gas masks, in the motorless type of home refrigerators, in purifying gases and solutions, in air conditioning, in the refining of petroleum, and as a catalyst. Used silica gel is reactivated by heating it strongly to drive out and burn off absorbed materials.

SILICA GEL. (Courtesy, The Davison Chemical Corp.)

Silica reacts almost not at all with all acids save hydrofluoric, HF, which attacks it readily:

$$SiO_2 + 4HF \rightarrow SiF_4 \uparrow + 2H_2O$$

It will react with strong alkalies, especially when heated strongly with them, to form silicates (cf. section 13). Thus far, salts have been considered to be products formed by the interaction of an acid and a base. In this connection, it will be seen that oxygen-bearing salts are also the products of the interaction or combination of metallic and nonmetallic oxides—that is, of basic anhydrides and acid anhydrides.

$$Na_2O + SiO_2 \xrightarrow{\Delta} Na_2SiO_3$$

In a similar fashion, one might consider magnesium sulfate to be the combination product of magnesium oxide and sulfur trioxide:

$$MgO + SO_3 \xrightarrow{\Delta} MgSO_4$$

Many ores which are to be refined often contain considerable quantities of silica when they reach the refinery. As much of this silica as is possible is removed by mechanical means before the reduction of the ore is begun; remaining traces of it are then often removed by the addition of limestone

($CaCO_3$) which reacts at the temperature of the reduction process to form a glassy, molten calcium silicate which is removed while it is still molten and discarded or made into mineral wool, to be used in packing and in insulation:

$$CaCO_3 + SiO_2 \rightarrow CaSiO_3 + CO_2 \uparrow$$

Silicates so produced are called *slags*.

The pronounced stability of silica is to be expected when one considers the large quantity of heat which is evolved in its formation from the elements:

$$Si + O_2 \rightarrow SiO_2 + 200,000 \text{ cal.}$$

Here again is demonstrated the fact that, in general, the more heat that is lost in the formation of a compound, the more stable it is and the less likely it is to enter into further reactions. The formation of the fluoride from the oxide could be predicted on the grounds that SiF_4 is even more stable, since the heat of formation of 1 mole of it from the elements is 360,000 cal.

12. Hydroxides (*the Silicic Acids*)

Since silicon characteristically shows a valence of four, it would naturally be expected to form the hydroxide $Si(OH)_4$, but, since the Si atom is even smaller than the aluminum atom, there is not adequate room around it for four hydroxyl groups. Consequently, the compound $Si(OH)_4$, which has been isolated, readily loses water (cf. section 8, Chapter 15) to form the compound H_2SiO_3, in which the valence of the silicon is still four.

Both H_4SiO_4 and H_2SiO_3 ionize as weak acids. It will be recalled that the hydroxide of aluminum was amphoteric in nature. Since the silicon atom is even smaller than the aluminum atom, and is possessed of an even more highly charged nucleus, it is to be anticipated that ionization would tend to occur between the H and O particles rather than between the Si and O particles (cf. section 7, Chapter 15). The repulsion here between the Si and H particles has not yet become great enough to bring about a high degree of H^+ ion formation; however, in conformity with the discussion given in section 8 of Chapter 15, H_4SiO_4 is known as *orthosilicic acid* and H_2SiO_3 as *metasilicic acid*.

Silicon dioxide is a true anhydride of these acids, but, because of its extremely slight solubility in water, it does not react with it to produce the acids. Generally, the acids are prepared by dissolving SiO_2 in strong alkalies (cf. section 11) and then treating the product with a strong acid:

$$SiO_2 + 2NaOH \rightarrow Na_2SiO_3 + H_2O$$
$$Na_2SiO_3 + 2HCl \rightarrow H_2SiO_3 + 2NaCl$$

The second of these reactions is noteworthy in that if the acid is poured into the sodium silicate solution a gelatinous precipitate forms, while if the silicate solution is poured into the acid a *colloidal sol* results. A colloidal sol (cf. Chapter 19) differs from a true solution in that while the particles dispersed in the solvent are too small to be caught on the best filter paper, they are much bigger than molecules and are usually considered to be aggregates of many molecules. The precipitated acid very closely resembles the precipitate of hydrated aluminum oxide in appearance, and, like the aluminum oxide precipitate, this one gradually loses water to give the oxide:

$$H_2SiO_3 \rightarrow H_2O + SiO_2$$

Unlike gelatinous aluminum hydroxide, the gelatinous silicon hydroxide, or silicic acid, is capable of forming still more hydrated compounds. Some of these additional silicic acids have been prepared, while others are *hypothetical acids;* that is, their salts are known, but they themselves have never been isolated. The formulas and names of some of these other acids are given in the following table.

Table 15

SOME SILICIC ACIDS

orthodisilicic acid	$H_6Si_2O_7 = 2SiO_2.3H_2O$
metadisilicic acid	$H_2Si_2O_5 = 2SiO_2.H_2O$
orthotrisilicic acid	$H_8Si_3O_{10} = 3SiO_2.4H_2O$
orthotetrasilicic acid	$H_{10}Si_4O_{13} = 4SiO_2.5H_2O$

Because the silicic acids are extremely weak, they react only with strong bases to form salts, and these salts, being formed from parent acids and bases of unequal strength, are hydrolyzed to a considerable extent to yield basic solutions. Also, because these acids are both weak and unstable, they are of little value, although their salts, the silicates, are numerous and find a wide application. In general, the salts of acids which contain oxygen and whose names end in *-ic* are given names which correspond to those of the parent acid but which end in *-ate*.

13. Silicates

Impure sodium silicate is known as *waterglass* and is prepared in large quantities. While it may be prepared from sodium hydroxide and sand, as indicated in the preceding section, it is usually prepared industrially by fusing together sodium carbonate, sand, and carbon (charcoal):

$$Na_2CO_3 + SiO_2 + C \rightarrow \underline{Na_2SiO_3} + 2CO \uparrow$$

The reaction mass is heated in an autoclave (a pressure kettle) with water, which leaches the Na_2SiO_3 from the unreacted sand, and charcoal, yielding a colloidal sol which may be filtered and then concentrated to a syrupy consistency by evaporation. It should be mentioned here that the product is not pure Na_2SiO_3, since other silicates are also present. This liquid is used as a water softener; an egg preservative (the pores of the shells of eggs submerged in it are sealed); a glue for wood, porcelain, glass, and paper (corrugated pasteboard cartons are prepared with it); a fireproofing agent for cloth; a sizing agent for paper; etc.

Other silicates of sodium are sold in solid form as water softeners and cleaning agents. A wide variety of other silicates may be prepared by substituting other strongly basic substances for the sodium carbonate used above.

That many metallic silicates occur in nature has already been pointed out (cf. section 3). All such compounds are insoluble in water save those of the metals of the I A family. A few of these substances will react with acids, when heated strongly, to form a salt of the acid and a solid residue of partially dehydrated silicic acids; the majority of them react only with strong alkalies upon fusion and with hydrofluoric acid to form silicon tetrafluoride.

14. Fluosilicic Acid and Its Salts

The preparation of fluosilicic acid by the hydrolysis of the tetrafluoride was referred to in section 7. The compound may be prepared also by the combination of the tetrafluoride and hydrofluoric acid:

$$SiF_4 + 2HF \rightarrow H_2SiF_6$$

Industrially, the acid is usually obtained as a by-product in the preparation of superphosphate fertilizers by the action of sulfuric acid on phosphate rock. Usually present in the rock are considerable amounts of both silica and calcium fluoride, which account for the formation of the acid. Because it is obtained as a by-product, and because the quantity of it which could thus be prepared is far in excess of the demand, the acid and its salts are very cheap.

In contrast to silicic acid, fluosilicic acid is a strong acid in solution and will thus form a variety of salts when treated with bases:

$$H_2SiF_6 + Ca(OH)_2 \rightarrow \underline{CaSiF_6} + 2HOH$$

The sodium, potassium, calcium, and barium salts are so sparingly soluble in water that sometimes the first two of these ions are tested for by precipitating them as their fluosilicates. Magnesium fluosilicate is applied in solution to concrete to give it a hard nondusting surface, while the sodium salt is used as an antiseptic, a germicide, a deodorant, an antihemorrhagic, and as a dusting powder for fowls to rid them of mites and lice.

The free acid is stable only in solution. When kept in the pure state, or when its aqueous solutions are heated, it decomposes thus:

$$H_2SiF_6 \rightarrow 2HF \uparrow + SiF_4 \uparrow$$

15. Glass

Essentially, glass is a fused, amorphous mixture of various metallic silicates, prepared by heating together to high temperatures various mixtures of sand and metallic oxides or carbonates. Ordinary window glass, or soft glass, is prepared by heating together to about 1400° C. a mixture of approximately 15 parts of calcium carbonate (limestone), 30 parts of sodium carbonate, and 100 parts of silica (sand). The product is a mixture of various calcium and sodium silicates which assume no definite crystalline shape on solidifying, so that glass is often referred to as a supercooled liquid. It must be cooled slowly to prevent the cracking which would result from the outer layers cooling more rapidly than the inner ones; this process of slow cooling is known as *annealing*.

Bottles and most of the soft glass tubing used in the laboratory are made of such lime-soda glass. It is easily worked because of its relatively low softening temperature, but it is etched by strong alkalies which slowly dissolve it, and, like all silicate products, it is attacked by hydrofluoric acid which in time will completely dissolve a glass bottle:

$$CaSiO_3 + Na_2SiO_3 + 12HF \rightarrow 2SiF_4 \uparrow + CaF_2 + 2NaF + 6H_2O$$

Use is made of this reaction in the etching of designs on glass. Usually, the article to be so treated is coated with a protective layer of wax which is scraped away with a sharp tool to form the desired design. It is then immersed for about 10 minutes in a 60 per cent solution of the commercial acid, after which it is washed in boiling water. The etched area is rough and translucent, but a smooth "satin" finish such as that to be seen on the interior of frosted light bulbs may be obtained by the use of ammonium bifluoride (NH_4HF_2).

By altering the proportions of the ingredients mentioned above and by substituting these materials with other metallic and nonmetallic oxides, a great variety of glasses having characteristic properties may be prepared. Potash-lime glasses made by substituting potassium compounds for those of sodium in the above preparation are much harder than soda-lime glasses and are known to the trade as *Bohemian glass*. If lead oxide is substituted in part or completely for the

A FURNACE FOR THE MANUFACTURE OF GLASS. (Courtesy, Pittsburgh Plate Glass Co.)

calcium carbonate, a potash-lead glass known as *flint glass* is obtained; this glass has a greater density and a higher index of refraction so that it is suitable for optical use and for the manufacture of the incised decorative pieces of table and household ware known as cut glass. Pyrex laboratory ware and household oven and flame ware are prepared from sand, boron oxide (B_2O_3), and compounds of sodium and aluminum. Sand makes up about 80 per cent of the fusion mixture, and B_2O_3 12 to 15 per cent. By increasing the quantity of these ingredients, a glass which expands very little when heated and contracts very little when cooled is produced. Glasses so prepared are much more resistant to chemical action than are other glasses. A glass which is resistant to the action of hydrofluoric acid and the other fluorides was prepard in 1945 by Pincus. It is reported to be prepared by the substitution of phosphorus pentoxide (P_2O_5) for silicon dioxide in the melt.

If very pure ingredients are employed, colorless glasses are produced. Much sand contains appreciable quantities of iron salts which color glass prepared from it a pale bluish green. To purify the sand for making cheap glass would be unthinkable and well nigh impossible, so the greenish color is either allowed to persist or is overcome by adding to the melt some substance which will produce the complementary color in just the proper intensity. By introducing small amounts of either manganese dioxide (MnO_2) or a mixture of selenium and cobalt oxide, a faint lavenderish color is produced which causes the product to appear to be colorless. Glasses of pronounced color are produced by introduc-

THE FRAME BEARING THE HUGE GLASS FORM FROM WHICH THE 200-IN. MIRROR FOR THE MOUNT PALOMAR TELESCOPE IS BEING POLISHED.
(Courtesy, Corning Glass Co.)

ing into the melt quantities of the oxides of certain metals whose silicates are colored, or quantities of various elements which become colloidally suspended in the glass to give it color. Thus cobalt oxide yields a deep blue color, manganese dioxide purple to black, sodium dichromate green, antimony sulfide yellow, while colloidal selenium yields red glass and colloidal gold yields red, purple, or blue glass depending on the size of the dispersed particles. The colored glazes used on most pottery are but thin layers of fused-on colored glasses.

The manufacture of glass is one of the oldest of the chemical industries. Archeological findings show that the Egyptians were making it as long ago as 5,000 years before the time of Christ, and there is a likelihood that the industry goes farther back into antiquity. Much beautiful glass was manufactured in Europe during the Middle Ages, and the lovely colors of the stained glass of that day can now rarely be equaled. Research in the field of glass chemistry was negligible until the twentieth century, but considerable progress has already been made, and even greater advances may be anticipated. The heat-resistant borosilicate glasses of the Pyrex type are commercial products of this century, as are glass building blocks, glass fiber cloth, supercooled glass which is very resistant to strain and shock but metastable to scratching, invisible glass, one-way glass, and the more or less plastic glasses made from organic compounds and silicon. These latter compounds belong to the new class of organosilicon compounds known as the silicones, which find use as varnishes, plastics, and greases. Fluid silicones are also produced.

The manufacture of certain synthetic silicate gem stones follows very closely the procedures described for the colored glasses.

16. *Pottery, Porcelain, Brick, and Tile*

These products are all very similar in composition and method of manufacture, and, with glass, they constitute the most prominent members of the class of materials known as *ceramics*. Tile, brick, pottery, and porcelain are all made from varying mixtures of clay, silica, and feldspar. The first three of these products are usually prepared from natural clays which already contain silica and feldspar along with impurities—mostly iron—which gives the finished product a buff to red color. These natural clays are made into a workable mud with water, given the desired shape, and then fired in special ovens or kilns. As the temperature rises, water is first driven from the mixture, then various decomposition products are formed, and above 1250° C. the feldspar fuses to bind the other materials present. The firing converts the iron-bearing impurities present into ferric oxide (iron rust), which accounts for the buff to red color. Essentially, then, these products are all mixtures of silicates.

Porcelain is made from the fine white clay known as kaolin, whose occurrence in the world is not too abundant. To this are added very pure sands and feldspars in varying mixtures to give the fine white porcelains. Soft porcelain is obtained by adding calcium phosphate to the mud; the product is sometimes called *bone china* since the phosphate may be obtained from bone ash.

Cheap pottery is glazed with sodium chloride near the end of the firing period. The better grades are coated—often in designs—with various metallic oxide-silicate mixtures and then refired. Pure feldspar gives a clear transparent glaze.

CHEMICAL PORCELAIN WARE MADE FROM COLORADO CLAYS. (Courtesy, Coors Porcelain Co.)

The best laboratory porcelain ware is made in Colorado at the town of Golden, a few miles west of Denver.

17. Cement

Cement is, in essence, a mixture of the silicates and aluminates of calcium, and is one of the most important of the modern-day silicon-bearing products. Since its manufacture, however, is closely related to the manufacture of lime (CaO), further discussion of it will be postponed until the chapter on calcium and the other alkaline earth metals and their compounds is reached.

18. Analytical Tests

Throughout this chapter, attention has been called to the fact that the majority of the compounds of silicon, whether they be binary or otherwise, are not soluble to any appreciable degree in water. Because of this characteristic, the usual types of qualitative tests cannot be applied successfully to these compounds. The customary qualitative test for silicon is made by grinding the solid under observation to a powder, which is then placed in a lead dish and treated with hydrofluoric acid. Or the powder may be mixed intimately with calcium fluoride and the mixture treated in a lead dish with sulfuric acid so that the hydrofluoric acid is produced *in situ*. In either case, the principal reaction is the conversion of any silicon present in the compound to silicon tetrafluoride, which passes off as a gas. When this gas strikes a drop of water on a stirring rod or in a wire loop, the water will become cloudy due to the formation of silicic acid:

$$3SiF_4 + 3H_2O \rightarrow 2H_2SiF_6 + H_2SiO_3$$

Quantitatively, silicates are usually determined by first being decomposed to pure silica, which is collected, washed, dried, and weighed. The decomposition methods employed depend largely upon the composition of the compound under investigation.

(*See Appendix for Exercises*)

COLLATERAL READINGS

Furnas: *Roger's Industrial Chemistry*, Vols. I and II, New York, D. Van Nostrand Co., 1943.

Kraus: *Gems and Gem Materials*, New York, McGraw-Hill Book Co., 1931.

Latimer and Hildebrand: *Reference Book of Inorganic Chemistry*, New York, The Macmillan Co., 1941.

Parmalee: *Clays and Some Other Ceramic Materials*, Ann Arbor, Mich., Edwards Bros., 1937.

Phillips: *Glass, the Miracle Maker*, New York, Pitman Publishing Corp., 1941.

Riegel: *Industrial Chemistry*, New York, Reinhold Publishing Corp., 1937.

Sadtler: *Chemistry of Familiar Things*, Philadelphia, J. B. Lippincott Co., 1937.

Scholes: *Modern Glass Practice*, Chicago, Industrial Publications, 1935.

Slosson: *Creative Chemistry*, New York, Century Co., 1923.

Weeks: *Discovery of the Elements*, 5th ed., Mack Printing Co., 1945.

PAUL SABATIER
(1854–1941, French)

Pioneer work in the field of catalysis—especially upon catalytic hydrogenation—was the chief contribution of Sabatier, who for many years, despite more tempting offers, served as professor of chemistry at the University of Toulouse. His early work was done principally in the field of physical chemistry, but with the passing of the years his interest shifted largely to organic. For his work on catalysis, he received the Nobel Prize in 1912. His important treatise, entitled *Catalysis in Organic Chemistry*, was translated into English by Dr. E. Emmet Reid, who for many years was professor of organic chemistry at Johns Hopkins University.

19

The Colloidal Condition of Matter

1. Colloids and Colloidal Particles

If one shakes sand and water together in a closed vessel, he obtains a momentary suspension of the sand particles in the water. As soon as the agitation ceases, however, the sand particles begin to settle to the bottom of the vessel, where, in a very short time, nearly all of them collect, leaving a clear supernatant liquid above. If, on the other hand, one shakes sugar and water together, there is formed a homogeneous mixture from which none of the solute tends to settle so long as there is sufficient water present to maintain the mixture. The first of these systems is usually referred to as a *coarse suspension;* the second as a *solution.* Intermediate between systems of these two types is a third type of dispersion in which the size of the dispersed particles lies between the minute molecular dimensions of the solute particles in the true solution and the finite dimensions of the coarse particles momentarily suspended in a mechanical suspension. The particles of this middle class, when suspended, are too small to be seen with the aid of the best of optical microscopes; they are too small to be caught by the most fine-grained filter paper; and they do not settle to the bottom of the containing vessel. However, these particles when suspended in a liquid do not tend to diffuse into an adjoining layer of the pure dispersing liquid, nor do such suspensions show the vapor-pressure lowering and other alterations of the colligative properties of the dispersing liquid which are characteristic of true solutions.

Between the years 1861 and 1864, Thomas Graham made a careful study of such systems, and to substances which became thus dispersed he gave the name *colloid.* This name was chosen as a result of his observation that crystalline substances, which he dubbed *crystalloids*, usually gave true solutions, while glue, gelatin, and many other amorphous substances gave suspensions of the type discussed above. The term "colloid" he derived from *kolla*, the Greek word for "glue." In time, it came to be recognized that even crystalloids under proper conditions will form the colloidal type of suspension, hence today the term *colloid* and its adjective colloidal do not refer to definite categories of matter, but rather to particles of any variety of matter whose dimensions lie within a certain range.

The smallest particles in the average coarse suspension have a length of about 5×10^{-5} cm., while particles whose length, or diameter, is 1×10^{-7} cm., or less, have all the characteristic behaviors of the particles which constitute a true solution. Hence colloidal particles must have at least one dimension which lies between 1×10^{-7} cm. and 5×10^{-5} cm. This range, as will be seen immediately, is purely arbitrary, so that at one end of the scale there is no sharp line of demarcation between coarse mixtures and colloidal dispersions while at the other end the boundary between such dispersions and true solutions is equally lacking in sharpness. For example, a substance which had unusually large molecules would give in a solvent a mixture whose behavior would be more that of a colloidal dispersion than that of a true solution.

In seeking a suitable definition for colloid chemistry, Bancroft of Cornell University, who is a leading American authority in the field, has written, "Adopting the very flexible definition that a phase is called colloidal when it is sufficiently finely divided, colloid chemistry is the chemistry of bubbles, drops, grains, filaments, and films, because in each of these cases at least one dimension of the phase is very small." From this statement and from the foregoing discussion it will be seen that, in a sense, the colloidal condition of matter is more the concern of the physicist than of the chemist, but when one considers that colloidal phases are so ubiquitous in nature and that the surface offered by the particles of a substance has a great deal to do with its own chemical behavior and that of other substances with which it may come in contact, it is readily seen that the chemist also cannot fail to be concerned.

2. Some Terms Used in Colloid Chemistry and the Types of Colloidal Dispersions

A substance which is dispersed in particles of colloidal size throughout another is called the *dispersed* or *internal phase* of the mixture, while the second component is known as the *dispersion medium* or the *external phase*. When a solid is colloidally dispersed in a liquid, it is often referred to as a *suspensoid*, while a liquid colloidally dispersed in a second liquid is often referred to as an *emulsoid*. Since each of the three states of matter might be suspended colloidally in matter of each of the three states, it might be anticipated that there would be nine types of colloidal dispersions; actually there are only eight, for mixtures of gases, because of the relatively large distances between their molecules, form only true solutions. These eight types, their characteristic names, and examples of each are set forth in the following table.

Table 16

TYPES OF COLLOIDAL DISPERSIONS

Dispersed Phase	Dispersion Medium	Name	Examples
Liquid	Gas	Liquid aerosol	Fog, mist, liquid sprayed from an atomizer
Solid.	..	Solid aerosol	Any kind of dust or smoke
Gas.	Liquid	Foam	Soapsuds; meringues
Liquid.	..	Emulsion	Milk; mayonnaise
Solid.	..	Sol	Starch prepared for application to clothes; mucilage
Gas.	Solid	Solid foam	Pumice stone
Liquid	..	Solid emulsion	Certain types of minerals like opal; butter
Solid.	..	Solid sol	Red signal glasses; many alloys

A sol whose dispersion medium is water is a *hydrosol;* one whose dispersion medium is alcohol is an *alcosol;* etc. Some sols will gradually lose liquid to form jellylike semisolids which are called *gels. Hydrogels* are formed by hydrosols, *alcogels* by alcosols, *benzogels* by benzosols, etc. In a gel, the solid and liquid phase are continuous, but a gel may continue to lose liquid until only a solid residue is left; this residue also is usually known as a gel, e.g., silica gel. The losing of liquid by a gel is known as *syneresis,* while the absorbing of more liquid by a gel is known as *imbibition.* The imbibition of water is strongly influenced by the concentration of hydrogen ions present. Gels may be of two types. There are those gels which separate from an excess of the dispersion medium as *gelatinous precipitates* (cf. hydrous aluminum oxide, section 6, Chapter 15), and there are others such as dessert gelatins which set in such a way as to include all of both phases and which are known as *jellies.*

All colloidal systems of whatever type may be further divided into two general groups, membership in which is based upon the relative affinities between the materials of the internal and external phases. If this affinity is small, the dispersed phase is described as being *lyophobic.* In this case, also, the prefix may be substituted by one which denotes the exact nature of the dispersion medium: hydrophobic (meaning water-fearing), alcophobic, etc. Such substances are also known as *irreversible colloids,* since they are easily precipitated by electrolytes and if subsequently they are heated to dryness they may not again be dispersed. Colloidal substances which exhibit a marked affinity for the dispersion medium are said to be *lyophilic*, or, more specifically, *hydrophilic* (water-loving), alcophilic, benzophilic, etc. Lyophilic colloidal systems are affected very little by electrolytes, and if the dispersed substance is collected, dried, and remixed with the dispersion medium, the system is readily regenerated. This latter behavior accounts for lyophilic substances also being described as *reversible colloids*.

3. *Properties of Colloidal Dispersions*

Reference has already been made in section 1 to certain properties of colloidal dispersions, but it may be well to repeat those facts before proceeding

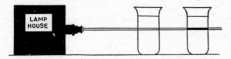

THE TYNDALL EFFECT. The path of the beam of light may be noted in the colloidal sol but not in the true solution.

to other properties. Colloidal particles are small enough to pass through a filter paper. They do not settle, though they may become more numerous in the lower portion of the containing vessel if the sol is more dense than the dispersing medium. They diffuse very slowly. They have very slight effects upon the freezing point and other colligative properties of the dispersing medium, and they cannot be seen with the best of optical microscopes.

A. THE TYNDALL EFFECT. If a beam of light is permitted to enter an otherwise dark room, one may, if he stands to one side, see its path sharply defined as a bright area traversing the gloom. Colloidal dust particles in the

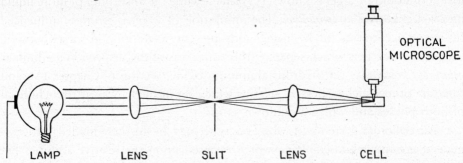

DIAGRAMMATIC REPRESENTATION OF THE ULTRAMICROSCOPE. The liquid system to be investigated is placed in the cell.

beam are acting as tiny mirrors to reflect some of the entering light to the eye of the beholder. Similarly, when a strong beam of light is passed through a sol, which may otherwise appear to be homogeneous, the path of the beam through the liquid appears quite turbid when viewed from one side. The turbidity is due to reflection of some of the incident light by the dispersed particles. In both cases, this phenomenon of the reflection of light by colloidal particles is known as the *Tyndall effect*. When a sol so illuminated is viewed through a microscope whose axis is at right angles to the direction of the beam, small flashes of light from the individual particles may be seen. Such an arrangement of microscope and optical apparatus for passing the strong beam of light through a sol is known as an *ultramicroscope*, and through it the particles appear as tiny, bright, moving stars in a dark field. Very fine particles of substances which have little ability to absorb light, when suspended in a transparent liquid or gas, scatter blue light more than they do red light. As a result of this behavior, such a system appears blue by reflected light and red by transmitted light. This explains why skimmed milk, wood smoke, and the sky appear blue (the atmosphere contains colloidal dust particles and water droplets) and why a rising or setting moon or sun appears unduly red (we are seeing them through many more miles of atmosphere with its attendant particles, and the light is transmitted, not reflected).

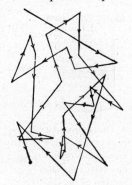

B. THE BROWNIAN MOVEMENT. When one views a sol by means of the ultramicroscope, he not only sees bright flashes of light reflected from the particles, but he also notes that each tiny point of light seems to be doing a wild, erratic dance. Similarly, everyone may note the erratic motion of the bright particles in a beam of sunlight penetrating a dark room. Robert Brown, a

DIAGRAMMATIC REP-RESENTATION OF THE BROWNIAN MOVEMENT OF A SINGLE MOLECULE. (Courtesy, Foley, A. L.: "College Physics," 3d ed., Philadelphia, The Blakiston Company.)

Scotch botanist, while studying a suspension of pollen dust in 1827, first noted this behavior, which has since been known as the *Brownian movement*. The explanation now accepted was the one proposed some 50 years later by the Belgian, Carbonelle. In essence, this explanation is that the molecules of the dispersion medium, being in constant motion in accord with the kinetic molecular theory, beat against the suspended particles, driving them hither and thither. Coarser particles are not so affected because their surfaces are so large that the average number of molecules striking any one side is about the same as the number striking every other side, with the result that their tendency to move in any one direction is offset by their tendency to move in the opposite one. Furthermore, the larger particles are sufficiently large for gravity to exert a downward attraction which is in excess of the impetus in any other direction afforded by molecular bombardment. The Brownian movement accounts in part for the ability of colloidal particles to remain suspended against the attraction of gravity.

c. DIALYSIS. Although the pores of filter papers are too large to retain colloidal particles, the pores of parchment paper, cellophane, and animal membranes are small enough to retain them, though large enough to pass particles of molecular dimensions. Such membranes are described as being semipermeable. Their property of semipermeability makes possible the process known as *dialysis*, which is used to remove dissolved substances from sols. Suppose that

one has a hydrosol of starch which contains dissolved sugar. This mixture may be poured into a glass tube across one of whose open ends has been stretched and secured a piece of wet parchment. This dialyzer is then suspended in a vessel of water through which a stream of fresh water continuously flows. In accordance with the principles of osmosis (cf. section 19, Chapter 12) water enters the cell and the sugar molecules gradually diffuse into the water and are washed away, leaving ultimately only starch particles and water in the dialyzer. This process is often of value in purifying both suspended and dissolved substances.

A DIALYZING APPARATUS. Note the membrane which constitutes the bottom of the dialyzing cell. (Courtesy, Hackh-Grant: "Chemical Dictionary," Philadelphia, The Blakiston Co.)

d. SURFACE EFFECTS. It has been noted in a previous chapter that, as the number of particles in which a given weight of material exists is increased, the total surface exposed by the material is increased. For example, it may be calculated that, if a cube whose edge is 1 cm. and whose area is 6 sq. cm. were divided into 10^{21} cubes each of those edges were 1×10^{-7} cm. (the dimension of the smallest of colloidal particles), the total surface exposed would become 6,000 sq. m., or about six-sevenths of an acre. It has also been noted elsewhere (cf. section 7, Chapter 16) that the forces about a particle in a solid surface are unbalanced as compared with the forces about an interior particle which is completely surrounded by other particles. As the amount of surface of a given quantity of material is increased, the magnitude of this unbalanced surface force is increased proportionately, thus colloidal particles have a set of properties related to this increased surface force which matter in other conditions does not have. In the section referred to above, attention was directed to the fact that adsorption and contact catalysis are dependent upon surface forces, hence matter in the colloidal state should be especially useful as contact catalysts. On the surfaces of colloidal particles both ions and molecules may be adsorbed, but in general, since the surface forces of a given variety of particle are dependent upon the chemical nature of the substance as well as upon the surface exposed and the surface tension, a given colloidal substance usually adsorbs well only one or more specific varieties of particles, and may not, therefore, be used indiscriminately for all types of adsorption and as a catalyst for all reactions. Silica gel (cf. section 11, Chapter 18) and activated charcoal (cf. section 2, Chapter 27) are two of the most widely used adsorbing agents, while finely divided platinum is used as a catalyst for a number of important reactions.

Surface effects are often to be noted in the physiological field. For example, if one swallows a dime or other small piece of massive silver, he notes little ill effect, but if he swallows a sol of silver he may die as a result. Similarly, sols of gold and sols of silver protein compounds are used in the treatment of disease because of their toxic effects upon organisms.

E. ELECTRICAL EFFECTS. Nearly all suspended colloidal particles are electrically charged, as is shown by the fact that they will travel toward one pole or the other of an electrolytic cell. It is a result of this behavior that rubber gloves may be built up on hand-shaped electrodes from colloidal suspensions of rubber, or latex, particles. The source of this charge has not been established definitely for all cases, but it is believed to be due in many instances, to the specific adsorption of certain varieties of ions, and in other instances to the formation of ions by unbalanced surface forces acting on surface molecules. Since all of the colloidal particles of a given substance in a given sol behave in like manner, they become charged alike, and this repulsion of like charges aids in keeping the particles separated and suspended. In this respect, the electrical effect is even more important than is the Brownian movement.

If two sols whose particles have unlike charges are mixed in equal proportions, mutual precipitation of the dispersed phases takes place; if, however, an excess of one of the sols is added, it may reverse the charge on the particles of the other, leaving them still mutually repellent and therefore unprecipitated. A solution of ions whose charge is opposite to that on the particles of a given sol may also be used to neutralize the charge on the particles. For instance, the colloidal soil particles of fresh-water streams are precipitated when the streams bearing them are discharged into the salt water of the ocean. The effectiveness of ions as precipitants depends upon the extent to which they are adsorbed and upon the charge upon the ions. As might be expected, if two ions are adsorbed to an equal extent, the one with the higher valence number is the more effective. It should not be inferred, however, that two ions whose charges are equal and of the same sign are equally effective as precipitants.

Colloidal particles of many substances have both the ability to adsorb hydrogen ions and the ability to give them up. Such particles are most readily coagulated when these two tendencies have become equal, and under such conditions the particles will travel toward neither pole of an electrolytic cell. The strength of these tendencies is determined by the hydrogen-ion concentration in the sol, and the hydrogen-ion concentration at which no migration will occur is known as the *isoelectric point* of that sol.

4. *Preparation of Colloidal Dispersions*

Notwithstanding the fact that milk, leather, starches, ores, and many other colloidal dispersions occur in nature, it is often desirable to prepare particles of various materials whose size falls within the established limits. Since the size of these particles lies between those of crude suspensions and of average molecules, it is at once apparent that two methods of preparation are available: the larger particles may be made smaller or the molecules may be grouped to form the larger colloidal aggregates. Methods which involve the former procedure are known collectively as *dispersion methods*, while those of the latter type are known as *condensation methods*.

5. *Dispersion Methods*

The most obvious solution of the problem of making smaller particles out of bigger ones is to grind coarser material. In preparing particles of colloidal dimensions, however, *grinding* is not always the simplest solution, for such tiny particles attract each other strongly and do not separate readily in the dispersing medium. Often other substances which aid in the separation of the particles are ground in the "colloid mills" with the substance to be dispersed; thus hydrosols of sulfur are prepared by grinding the sulfur with urea and adding the mixture to water in which the urea forms a true solution, leaving the sulfur suspended, and hydrosols of graphite are prepared by grinding this substance with tannin and adding the mixture to water. Zinc oxide paints are prepared by putting both the oxide and the oil in which it is to be suspended through a colloid mill, and various siliceous substances are reduced to particles of proper size in such a device.

In the process of digestion, the enzyme *pepsin* disperses albuminous proteins into colloidal particles; by analogy, any process in which colloidal dispersion is brought about by the action of a chemical is referred to as *peptization*. Some substances become peptized when placed in contact with certain liquids, because the forces exerted by the liquid are sufficient to cause disintegration to that extent. This behavior is comparable with that of the action of the solvent upon the solute in the formation of true solutions. More specifically, it may be due to the fact that the dispersed substance, while almost insoluble in the dispersion medium, is just soluble enough to lower the surface tension of the latter sufficiently to permit it to wet each particle about which there is formed a protective film, which, in turn, serves to decrease the tendency toward coagulation. The removal of dirt by soapy water is believed to be due to this type of action. In general, lyophilic substances are the ones most apt to be peptized by the action of the dispersion medium.

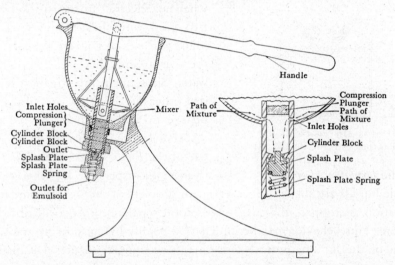

DIAGRAMMATIC REPRESENTATION OF A COLLOIDAL MILL. (Courtesy, International Emulsifiers, Inc., Dept. C, 2409, Surrey Court, Chicago.)

Other substances which are not peptized by the pure dispersion medium are peptized when the medium contains a small concentration of ions, especially when the ions present are the specific ions which can be readily adsorbed by the substance to be dispersed. The force exerted by these adsorbed ions acts to facilitate the disintegration of the solid into colloidal particles, and, since the particles so formed will have a like charge, they repel each other and are thus prevented from coagulating. Precipitates formed as the result of various chemical reactions often are difficult to filter because of peptization resulting from adsorbed ions. Other precipitates may be filtered easily enough from reaction mixtures but run through the filter when washed with distilled water. This behavior may be due to the removal of soluble ions to the extent that the small quantity of them remaining is sufficient to cause peptization, or, in other instances, it may be due to the removal by the wash water of adsorbed salts which gave stability to the precipitate. Substances which give stability in this manner, thereby preventing peptization, are known as *agglomerating agents*. Because of this action of salts, solutions of them are often used instead of pure water for washing precipitates. Many of the procedures of analytical chemistry require the removal of precipitates by filtration, hence a knowledge of the causes of peptization and of means of avoiding it is of value.

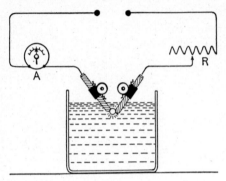

APPARATUS FOR THE PRODUCTION OF COL-
LOIDAL PARTICLES BY THE BREDIG METHOD.

It was discovered by Bredig that when an electric arc is struck between two gold wires held under water, colloidal particles of gold are separated from the wires and dispersed through the water. Subsequent investigation revealed that other metals of low chemical activity behave in a like manner. Such metallic dispersions are frequently prepared by use of the *Bredig* or *arc method*.

The *formation of emulsions* is also a variety of dispersion, for when two immiscible liquids are shaken together, small droplets of the two become mixed. If agitation is stopped, the two liquids soon separate into two distinct layers as before. This behavior may be understood readily by considering the surface tension of the liquids. Surface tension (cf. section 3, Chapter 11) manifests itself by acting to cause a liquid surface to reduce its area. When two liquid layers are broken up into droplets, the total surface of each is greatly increased; surface tension acts to reduce this increased surface. When two like droplets come together, they coalesce, since one larger drop has less surface than the two smaller ones. This drop in turn coalesces with others until the two original layers have been reformed. To prevent reformation of these layers it would therefore be necessary to decrease the surface tension of one, or of both, of the liquids. A substance which will have this behavior is called an *emulsifying agent*. Water and gasoline or water and kerosene will form an emulsion when soap is shaken with them; casein is the emulsifying agent which keeps the oily butterfat of milk and the watery component mixed; while egg yolk is the emulsifying agent which keeps watery vinegar and the oil of mayonnaise in intimate mixture.

Various explanations of the ability of emulsifying agents to act as they do have been given. The most generally acceptable is that such substances have molecules one end of which is soluble in one liquid while the other end is soluble in the second liquid; there is thus formed a link between unlike droplets. A second theory has it that the agent is adsorbed to form a protective coat around one variety of droplets so that they cannot coalesce, thus staying suspended; a third postulates that the agent forms a hydrate or other compound, which forms a protective film about one variety of droplets. All of these theories agree that the agent collects in the surface of one or both of the varieties of droplets with a consequent decrease in their surface tension and in their tendency to coalesce.

6. *Condensation Methods*

Ions and molecules are the smaller particles which must "condense" to form colloidal particles, therefore it is to be anticipated that condensation methods will have to be applied to solutions and that they will be related to reactions in which insoluble substances are formed. To insure the formation of particles whose dimensions fall within the established limits, conditions under which such reactions are performed must be carefully controlled. Special attention must be given to the concentrations of all solutions employed. This is necessary to insure that there will be present no concentrations of any ions, or other substances, sufficiently large to act as an agglomerating agent upon the particles formed by the reaction.

Salts of the inactive metals such as gold, silver, platinum, etc., are very easily *reduced* to the free metal by a wide variety of organic and inorganic reducing agents. If dilute solutions of these salts of low ionic concentrations are carefully reduced, preferably by nonionic reducing agents, colloidal suspensions of the free metals are formed. The colors of such sols depend upon the size of the particles formed; for example, sols of the smaller gold particles are red while those of the larger ones are blue, and mixtures of these particles, or particles of intermediate size, yield sols which are purplish. The particles of such metallic sols coalesce readily. The addition of a hydrophilic colloidal substance greatly reduce this tendency.

Sols may also be prepared by *oxidation*. The classic example of such a preparation is the addition of sulfur dioxide gas to a weak aqueous solution of hydrogen sulfide. The overall reaction is

$$2H_2S + SO_2 \rightarrow \underline{3S} + 2H_2O$$

but in actuality the process proceeds by several steps with some of the intermediate products serving to promote the formation of colloidal particles. Metallic sols of the type referred to in the preceding paragraph may be oxidized to sols of their respective halides by treatment with the free halogens. Sols prepared in this manner also remain stable much longer when lyophilic substances are added.

There are many inorganic reactions which yield one or more insoluble products. Ordinarily, such products form as particles which are easily removed as insoluble precipitates by filtration. In many such reactions, however, by carefully controlling the conditions under which the reaction occurs, the insoluble substance may be obtained as a colloidal suspension. For example, when either arsenous compounds such as $AsCl_3$ or a strongly acid solution of arsenous acid is treated with hydrogen sulfide, a massive precipitate of arsenous sulfide forms:

$$2AsCl_3 + 3H_2S \rightarrow \underline{As_2S_3} + 6HCl$$

but when a weak solution of arsenous acid to which no excess of mineral acid has been added is treated with hydrogen sulfide, a colloidal suspension of arsenous sulfide is formed:

$$2H_3AsO_3 + 3H_2S \rightarrow As_2S_3 + 6H_2O$$

When hydrogen sulfide passes into water, it ionizes slightly, forming hydrogen and hydrosulfide ions:

$$H_2S \rightleftharpoons H^+ + SH^-$$

Arsenous sulfide has a great tendency to adsorb the negative hydrosulfide ions, and when it does so, its particles all become negatively charged and are thus held apart by the repulsion of like charges. If an acid is formed, as in the reaction with $AsCl_3$, or if an excess of strong acid is present, the large hydrogen-ion concentration reduces the hydrosulfide-ion concentration of the H_2S in accordance with the principles of equilibrium so that few SH^- ions are left to be adsorbed by the arsenous sulfide particles, which, therefore, coalesce readily to form a precipitate. It is apparent from this discussion that, if one seeks to prepare an insoluble salt in a colloidal condition, he must carry out the reaction in a solution whose ionic concentration is low, except when the ions present are those specifically adsorbed by the insoluble substance formed.

Hydrous metallic oxides of the type of hydrous aluminum oxide, aluminum "hydroxide," discussed in section 6 of Chapter 15, may be prepared in the colloidal condition by *hydrolysis* of the salts of metals which form such oxides. A sol of hydrous ferric oxide is easily prepared by pouring a concentrated solution of ferric chloride into boiling water:

$$FeCl_3 + 3HOH \rightarrow Fe(OH)_3 + 3HCl$$

In accordance with the principles set forth above, if one would prevent coalescence he must remove the strongly ionized HCl which is also formed.

7. The Stabilization of Colloidal Dispersions

Attention has already been called to the facts that the charges which colloidal particles bear and the Brownian movement of the particles serve to prevent their coagulation. It has also been pointed out that the dissolution of various substances in the surface films of colloidal droplets helps to prevent their coalescence. Another method of stabilizing colloidal dispersion is the use of protective colloids. *A protective colloid is one which forms a film or coating about other suspended particles*, thus helping them to remain dispersed. In general, these protective substances are hydrophilic in nature. Gelatin, gums, and egg yolk all have this behavior. Commercial ice cream contains gelatin whose protective action prevents the coalescence of the sugar into coarse grains; mayonnaise contains egg yolk as a protective agent; and various lotions, candies, and other preparations contain vegetable gums to serve in the same capacity. Silver halides used in the preparation of photographic plates, films, and papers must be finely divided. To prevent the formation of precipitates when solutions of silver salts are added to solutions containing the proper halide ions, gelatin in the requisite quantity is added to both solutions before they are mixed. The resulting silver halide is formed as a colloidal dispersion each of whose particles is protected by a sheath of gelatin. The use of such protective substances is a common practice in the laboratory, in industry, and in nature.

8. Foams

Foams are usually prepared by agitating a liquid with a gas. Gas bubbles surrounded by a film of liquid are formed in great numbers, and, if the surface forces of the liquid are of the proper magnitude, the foam will persist. The bubbles so formed are, on the whole, much larger than the limits established for the colloidal condition, but the thickness of the encasing films falls easily within that range. Many foams are of short duration, but those of viscous liquids persist. Short-lived foams may be stabilized by the addition of finely divided solids which will collect in the liquid-gas interface. Again, lyophilic substances serve as the best stabilizing agents. Soap foams are of use in cleaning and in wetting, while foams of carbon dioxide and water stabilized with aluminum "hydroxide" are used for smothering fires; the blanket of CO_2-filled bubbles excludes the oxygen necessary for combustion.

Foams are of especial importance in the concentration of certain ores, especially those which contain metallic sulfides. The finely ground ores are passed through a trough, where they are stirred with water which contains pine oil and an emulsifying and stabilizing agent known as *xanthate*. The particles

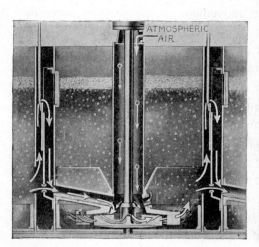

DIAGRAM SHOWING THE OPERATION OF A STANDARD FROTH-FLOTATION CELL. (Courtesy, Denver Equipment Co.)

A FROTH-FLOTATION CELL IN OPERATION. (Courtesy, Denver Equipment Co.)

of the ground ore which contain the desirable metallic compounds are wet by the oil, while the particles of siliceous material are wet only by the water. As a result of the agitation, air bubbles surrounded by films of the ore-bearing oil are formed. These bubbles rise to the top and are skimmed off. The collected foam is given a heat treatment which drives off both oil and water, to leave a valuable "concentrate" of the mineral. This so-called "froth-flotation process" has been of great value since it permits the working of low-grade ores whose concentration by older methods would have cost more than their worth. The story is that this process was developed as the result of the observation of a woman who was washing a miner's overalls. She noticed that dust particles which showed the glint of values collected in the soapsuds while the siliceous particles sank to the bottom of the tub. The value of close observation followed by interpretation and application is again underscored.

While foams often have value, they are even more often a nuisance to be overcome. The foaming of boiler water is an example of the latter case; dissolved salts foster the foaming and colloidal particles present stabilize the bubbles formed. Just as emulsions may be broken by adding some substance which will destroy or weaken the droplet surfaces, so foams may be destroyed by adding some substance which will destroy the liquid films by reacting with them, or which will weaken the films in some manner. A blast of cold air helps to prevent foaming by shrinking the gas bubbles and causing them to collapse.

9. Aerosols

Aerosols in the form of smokes, dusts, mists, and fogs are of considerable importance in the life of all of us. In the thinking of the average man, their value is perhaps more negative than positive, yet they all do have their valuable uses. Strictly speaking, there is little difference between dusts and smokes, though it is customary to think of particles suspended in the air as the result of combustion or other direct chemical action as constituting a smoke while particles which become suspended as the result of grinding, pounding, exploding, or other physical processes are thought of as a dust. Smoke in many cities becomes a nuisance from many standpoints, while dust, in addition to being a nuisance, can be a danger to health, and a fire hazard if it is combustible. Many cities are now engaged in smoke-eradication campaigns. Grain elevators, planing mills, flour mills, cotton gins, etc., find it necessary to keep dust at a minimum, because as combustible as are the characteristic dusts of such places and as intimately mixed with oxygen as are the dust particles, combustion may be easily initiated by even a tiny spark. Industrial plants which burn large quantities of fuel find that it saves much on the fuel bill if smoke (which consists largely of unburned carbon particles) is held at a minimum, and plants which turn out products in the form of dusts note a great saving when the dust that would otherwise escape as an aerosol is collected. It is reported that one cement plant in California in a 12-year period collected 350,000 tons of cement dust which would otherwise have been lost.

There are a number of ways in which the smoke and dust nuisance may be lessened, but even in the best-regulated plants and factories a certain amount of both will form. To collect this minimum, the *Cotrell precipitator* may be used.

It consists of a series of plates alternately charged with a high voltage, or of one or more grounded metal tubes down whose center passes a highly charged wire. As dust or smoke particles pass through the strong electrical field thus generated, they become strongly charged and are attracted to the plate of opposite charge, or to the walls of the tube. The precipitated solid may be recovered from the collecting chamber at the bottom of the device.

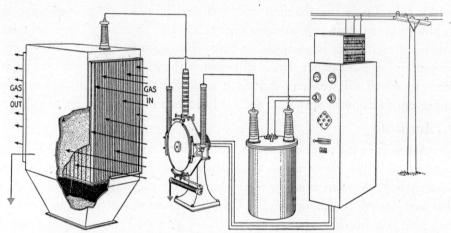

DIAGRAM OF THE ESSENTIAL PARTS OF THE COTTRELL PRECIPITATOR. The electrical equipment at the right is for the purpose of establishing a strong charge on the plates of the precipitator. Particles borne by the in-flowing gases are precipitated and collected in the dust bin below the plates. (Courtesy, Western Precipitation Corp.)

Silicosis is a disease which miners often contract as a result of breathing the finely divided particles of siliceous material borne in the air after blasts have been set off in the underground workings of the mine.

In the protection of orchards from frost, in the preparation of military smoke screens, in commercial sky-writing for advertising purposes, and in the dusting of crops as a means of pest control, the formation of smokes and dusts is highly important.

Fogs, mists, and clouds are looked upon as liquid aerosols, yet investigation reveals that the liquid droplets which make up such aerosols have been formed by the condensation of liquids upon dust or smoke particles as nuclei. Essentially, therefore, there is little distinction to be made between liquid and solid aerosols; cognizance is taken of this fact in certain industrial cities where the winter skies are described as being *smog* filled.

Medicinal aerosols have been introduced recently for the purpose of killing air-borne bacteria. For example, a concentration of 1 part of triethylene glycol

EFFECT PRODUCED BY THE COTTRELL PRECIPITATOR. The stack at the right is equipped with this device; the one at the left is not. (Courtesy, Western Precipitation Corp.)

dispersed in 200,000 parts of air is effective in sterilizing air. Inhalations of certain medicinal aerosols, notably penicillin, are often effective in destroying potent germs which have settled in the respiratory organs of human beings.

10. The Importance of Colloid Chemistry

Emphasis upon the importance of this branch of chemistry cannot be too strong. Many books and still more papers dealing with both its theoretical and practical aspects have been written, and many investigations whose aim is the increasing of our understanding of it are presently in progress. Bancroft says, "Colloid chemistry is the chemistry of everyday life."

Life itself is very dependent upon colloidal dispersions. The cells of which plant and animal organisms are composed are filled with a fluid which contains both dissolved and colloidally dispersed substances; the foods which man consumes are largely colloidal in nature; their digestion undoubtedly proceeds by processes closely associated with the colloidal condition of matter; and bile functions as a protective colloid in the prevention of the formation of gallstones.

Indirectly, man is even more dependent upon the behavior of colloidal dispersions. For his food he is dependent upon agriculture, which in turn is dependent upon soils. These must have not only the proper mineral content but also the proper colloidal nature. Soils contain many colloidal particles formed by the weathering of minerals. These particles are stabilized by the organic matter called "humus," which acts as a protective colloid, and upon their surfaces are adsorbed the necessary salts and moisture. Without the proper admixture of humus, soils of a claylike nature pack, do not retain moisture well, and do not retain salts well when rain water percolates through them.

Also dependent upon the colloidal nature of clays is their ability to be made into pottery, china, bricks, and tile. If the colloidal particles in the clay are too few, a weak, flaky product is obtained, while if they are too numerous, a product which shrinks and warps upon firing is formed.

The manufacture of fruit jellies involves the incorporation of sugar, fruit juices, and a substance called pectin, which occurs naturally in many fruits and vegetables, into a sol which, when concentrated to the proper degree and cooled, sets to a hydrogel. The formation of thin films and tiny fibers of the dispersed substances establishes an interlocking network of minute cells in which the liquid is held. Fruit juices which contain no pectin must have this substance added before they can be made into jellies.

Soap acts as a cleaning agent both because it lowers the surface tension of water so that it may readily emulsify oily substances, and because it acts as a peptizing and adsorbing agent for earthy dirt.

If space permitted, an almost endless list of substances and processes which are in some way dependent upon the colloidal condition could be given. The manufacture of breads, cakes, glasses, enamels, paints, glues, plastics, rubber and rubber substitutes, inks, varnishes, soaps, lacquers, paper, butter, cheese, and a host of other products belong in this category, as do laundering, cleaning, catalysis, tanning, dyeing, water purification, photography, and an almost interminable list of processes. Without colloids and the processes dependent upon them, this world would be a vastly different place.

(*See Appendix for Exercises*)

COLLATERAL READINGS

Alexander: *Colloid Chemistry*, 4th ed., New York, D. Van Nostrand Co., 1937.

Bancroft: *Applied Colloid Chemistry*, New York, McGraw-Hill Book Co., 1932.

Chapin and Steiner: *Second Year College Chemistry*, 5th ed. revised, New York, John Wiley & Sons, Inc., 1943.

Crossan and Abrahams: Colloidal metals in nonaqueous solvents by the Bredig method, *J. Chem. Education*, **23**, 289 (1946).

Gortner: Colloids in biochemistry, *J. Chem. Education*, **11**, 279 (1934).

Hatschek: *An Introduction to the Chemistry and Physics of Colloids*, 5th ed., The Blakiston Company, 1926.

Helbig: Activated carbon, *J. Chem. Education*, **23,** 98 (1946).

Hildebrand: *Principles of Chemistry*, New York, The Macmillan Co., 1941.

Holmes: *Introductory Colloid Chemistry*, New York, John Wiley & Sons, Inc., 1934.

Lewis, Squires, and Broughton: *Industrial Chemistry of Colloidal and Amorphous Materials*, New York, The Macmillan Co., 1944.

Lohse: *Catalytic Chemistry*, New York, Chemical Publishing Co., 1945.

Marshall: *Colloids in Agriculture*, New York, Longmans, Green, & Co., 1935.

McBain: Some recent advances in colloids, *J. Chem. Education*, **17,** 109 (1940).

Weiser: *Colloid Chemistry*, New York, John Wiley & Sons, Co., 1939.

Young and Coons: *Surface Active Agents*, New York, Chemical Publishing Co., 1945. Fun with colloids, *Popular Science*, **140:** HW 60, June (1942).

Phosphorus and Its Compounds

1. Introduction

Phosphorus is the fifth element of the third period. It is nonmetallic in both appearance and behavior, and is so active that it is never found free in nature. The free element and its compounds are of interest from industrial and commercial viewpoints as well as from the theoretical. Its atomic weight is 30.978 at. wt. units.

The atomic number of phosphorus is 15, and the distribution of its extranuclear electrons among the first three energy levels is 2, 8, 5. From a consideration of this distribution of electrons in the atom, one would expect it to react by gaining three electrons or by sharing electrons in such a manner as to acquire an interest in three. It does both of these things, to form compounds in which the oxidation number of the element is -3. The five valence electrons of the third main energy level are further distributed in the sub-levels of that main level, two existing in the 3_0 level and three in the 3_1 level. It is possible for the atom to share either its three 3_1 electrons or all five of its valence electrons with nonmetals; when it so behaves, it exhibits oxidation numbers of $+3$ and $+5$, respectively. The principal oxidation numbers shown by phosphorus are thus -3, $+3$, and $+5$. Intermediate oxidation numbers are shown in a few compounds, but, as will be shown later, there is no significant difference in the manner in which the atom is combined in these compounds.

The phosphorus atom, because of its more highly charged nucleus, attracts its valence electrons in the third main level even more strongly than does the silicon atom, and is, in consequence, smaller than the latter. Because of its strong attraction for electrons, phosphorus is much more inclined to gain electrons, or to share them, than it is to lose them. With five outer electrons, this atom is approaching the structure of the inert gas, argon. These changes manifest themselves in the ability of the atom to form more stable and more important compounds with the metals and with hydrogen, and to form oxides which are less stable but which are more numerous and which give rise to a wider variety of hydroxides which act as acids.

2. Physical Properties

Elementary phosphorus exists in a considerably wider variety of allotropic forms than does its predecessor in the third period, silicon. The two common varieties of the element seen in most laboratories are the *yellow* and the *red*. Studies of these two modifications have revealed that they are not homogeneous but appear to be mixtures of a very active *colorless* allotrope and a stable *violet* allotrope. In the yellow variety, the colorless modification predominates, while, in the much less active red variety, the violet predominates. Exposure of yellow phosphorus to light gradually converts it into the red. The violet allotrope is difficult to prepare in a pure state but is reported to be obtained by crystallization from a solution of phosphorus in molten lead. A fifth allotrope, black phosphorus, is obtained by heating any of the other modifications to a temperature of 200° C. under a pressure of 4,000 atmospheres. Some of the more prominent physical properties of the two common modifications are tabulated below.

Table 17

PHYSICAL PROPERTIES OF PHOSPHORUS

Property	Yellow Phosphorus	Red Phosphorus
Appearance....................	Moderately soft, yellow, waxy solid	Dull brownish-red powder
Odor........................	Somewhat garliclike	Odorless
Luminosity....................	Glows in air	Nonluminous
Melting point at standard pressure.	44° C.	Sublimes at 280° C.
Boiling point at standard pressure.	280° C.	Sublimes
Density.......................	1.82 g./ml.	No definite density; ranges from 2.05 to 2.34 g./ml.
Solubility.....................	Soluble in CS_2, turpentine, ether, and other organic liquids	Insoluble in all liquids
Toxicity.......................	Very poisonous: 0.01 to 0.15 g. fatal dose	Only slightly poisonous

Determination of the molecular weight of yellow phosphorus from its solutions in organic solvents indicates that its formula is P_4. Molecular weight determinations made upon the vapor of the yellow modification also indicate a formula P_4, with some dissociation into P_2 at temperatures above 1500° C. In writing equations, however, it is customary to represent elementary phosphorus by its symbol, P. The red modification lends itself to neither of the above determinations.

When red phosphorus is sublimed at reduced pressures below 100° C., the

(*Top*) A MILL FOR THE PROCESSING OF PHOSPHATE ORES.
(*Bottom*) A PHOSPHATE ROCK MINE.
(Courtesy, The Phosphate Mining Co.)

condensation product is also red, but at higher temperatures the condensate is the yellow variety.

3. Occurrence

Although it is never found in the elementary condition, phosphorus is, nevertheless, widely distributed in nature. Its most important mineral is *phosphorite*, commonly called *phosphate rock*, which contains principally slightly soluble calcium phosphate, $Ca_3(PO_4)_2$. This mineral is found in quantity in the southeastern states of Florida, Georgia, and the Carolinas, and in Tennessee, Montana, and Idaho. It is also found in Spain, northern Africa, and many other parts of the world. *Apatite, chlorapatite,* and *monazite* are also important minerals. The first of these has the approximate formula $3Ca_3(PO_4)_2.CaF_2$ and is found in considerable quantities in Canada. Chlorapatite has the formula $3Ca_3(PO_4)_2.CaCl_2$ and is found in many rocks, while monazite contains phosphates of cerium, thorium, and a number of rare metals. Monazite is found in sands in North Carolina, Idaho, Brazil, India, and elsewhere.

Since the bones of all animals are made up largely of calcium phosphate and calcium carbonate, a growing child needs foods which contain both calcium and phosphorus, but without the aid of vitamin D he will be unable to utilize these elements in the building of bone. The solubilizing action of natural waters containing small quantities of dissolved carbon dioxide gradually dissolves phosphate minerals, of the type discussed in the previous paragraph, carrying the dissolved matter into the streams and seas where it is utilized by marine life in the building of bone. Protoplasm and nerve tissues also contain combined phosphorus, as do milk, eggs, and seeds such as peas, beans, and whole grains. It is estimated that the production of a ton of wheat requires about 5.7 lb. of phosphorus in the form of its salts.

4. Preparation

Phosphorus is usually prepared by heating together a mixture of phosphate rock, sand, and coke in an electric furnace. The reaction may be thought of as taking place in two steps, the equations for which upon addition give the equation for the overall reaction:

$$Ca_3(PO_4)_2 + 3SiO_2 \xrightarrow{\Delta} 3CaSiO_3 + P_2O_5$$

$$P_2O_5 + 5C \xrightarrow{\Delta} 2P \uparrow + 5CO \uparrow$$

$$\overline{Ca_3(PO_4)_2 + 3SiO_2 + 5C \xrightarrow{\Delta} 3CaSiO_3 + 2P \uparrow + 5CO \uparrow}$$

The phosphorus vapor, which must be protected from air to prevent its spontaneous union with oxygen, is drawn off to be condensed under water. The liquid is cast into molds, which form the sticks of yellow phosphorus commonly seen in the laboratory. The carbon monoxide formed may be burned as a fuel, and the calcium silicate is drawn from the furnace as a liquid which hardens to a glassy slag.

Yellow phosphorus is so active that even the sticks ignite spontaneously when exposed to air, hence they are usually kept submerged in a container of water. Sticks so kept usually become covered with an opaque coating which is made up largely of the more stable modification.

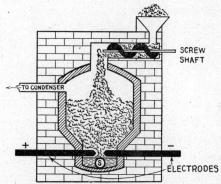

At the temperature of the electric furnace, the product is always yellow phosphorus. The red modification is prepared by heating the yellow to 240° C. in large iron pots which have only a narrow vent. Iodine serves as a catalyst for the conversion. The initial oxygen in the vessel is removed by the burning of sufficient of the phosphorus to combine with it. The product is washed with a hot solution of sodium hydroxide to remove any oxide formed, as well as any of the unconverted starting material.

DIAGRAM OF THE ELECTRIC FURNACE USED FOR THE PREPARATION OF PHOSPHORUS. Phosphorus vapor passes to the condenser and slag(s) is removed from time to time through a tap hole near the bottom of the furnace.

This element was discovered in 1669 by the German alchemist, Brandt, who, in seeking to prepare the Philosopher's Stone, heated with charcoal in a clay retort the residue he obtained by evaporating urine. To his surprise, the substance he obtained glowed when exposed to the air. To it he gave the name *phosphorus*, which he derived from two Greek words, and which means *light-bearer*. A normal adult excretes about 0.95 g. of phosphorus per day in the form of its compounds.

5. Chemical Properties

The type of reaction into which phosphorus enters most readily is combination. Because of its activity and its ability to share electrons, it enters, as might be expected, into a wide variety of such unions.

The most striking of its combinations is that with oxygen. If a stick of yellow phosphorus is exposed to the air, white fumes of phosphorus trioxide

An Artist's Conception of the Discovery of Phosphorus. (Courtesy, Fisher Scientific Co.)

soon begin to form, some ozone (O_3) is simultaneously formed, and the stick glows with a ghostly light. The light evolved is believed to be due to the conversion of some of the energy of reaction directly into light. The production of light in such a manner is known as *chemiluminescence*. In pure oxygen, or in air at increased pressures, yellow phosphorus forms the pentoxide and no glow is observed. The yellow modification of the element bursts into flame at 45° C., while the red ignites at 260° C. A gram-atomic weight of the yellow liberates about 4300 cal. more of heat when it burns than does a like weight of the red. This further serves to point to the stability of the red. In an excess of oxygen, both varieties form phosphorus pentoxide,

$$4P + 5O_2 \rightarrow 2P_2O_5$$

while, in a deficiency of air both burn to form a mixture of the pentoxide and the trioxide,

$$4P + 3O_2 \rightarrow 2P_2O_3$$

Phosphorus also combines readily with other nonmetals, the yellow variety always reacting more vigorously than the red. Both varieties react with the halogens to form two series of compounds of the general formula PX_3 and PX_5, where X stands for any halogen atom. When heated with sulfur, the yellow modification of the element reacts explosively. A mixture of the red modification and sulfur must be warmed for the reaction to begin, but, once started, it liberates sufficient heat to continue with no further assistance. By using the proper quantities of the two elements, the sulfides P_4S_3, P_2S_5, P_4S_7, P_2S_3, and P_3S_6 may be prepared. This behavior of phosphorus and sulfur illustrates the well-known fact that the closer two elements are to each other in the periodic chart, the greater the number of binary compounds which they form, if they will combine at all. Only the first two of the sulfides are stable enough to be recrystallized from their solutions in carbon disulfide. Phosphorus does not combine directly with hydrogen, though it does form several hydrides indirectly.

Phosphorus combines directly with many metals upon the heating of a mixture of the two to form metallic phosphides. These are usually contaminated by the presence of the oxide of phosphorus, metallic oxide, and small quantities of the unreacted elements. Phosphides of magnesium and aluminum have been mentioned in previous chapters, and phosphides of calcium and the heavier metals are easily prepared. A phosphide of tin is used in the manufacture of phosphorbronze, an alloy of copper and tin which contains a small quantity of phosphorus. Phosphides may also be prepared by three other methods: (a) Heating phosphorus and the oxide of the metal together; (b) the action of phosphorus upon solutions of certain metallic salts; and (c) the action of phosphine (PH_3) upon solutions of certain metallic salts. The last two methods are best suited for salts of the heavy metals.

6. *Phosphorus Pentoxide*

This compound is the most important of the oxides of phosphorus. It is easily formed by burning any variety of the element in an abundance of oxygen or air. It appears as a fine white powder which is usually contaminated with traces of P_2O_3 and of metaphosphoric acid, HPO_3, which is formed by the action of moisture on the pentoxide. These impurities are removed by heating the mixture in an iron tube through which a stream of dry oxygen is passing. The trioxide is burned to the pentoxide, which sublimes, and the acid remains unvolatilized. By heating the powdery pentoxide to 440° C., a crystalline mass which is less volatile than the powder is obtained.

The heat of formation of the pentoxide is high:

$$4P + 5O_2 \rightarrow 2P_2O_5 + 730,400 \text{ cal.}$$

The evolution of so much heat would lead one to expect this compound to be very stable with respect to decomposition into its constituent elements, and such is the case. Molecular weight determinations made upon the vapor indicate a formula of P_4O_{10}. At temperatures in excess of 1500° C., there is some dissociation of P_4O_{10} into P_2O_5, but even at extremely high temperatures there is apparently little tendency for phosphorus and oxygen to form. In equations, the formula P_2O_5 is generally used, since no one knows how many molecules may be further associated in the solid.

As very hot phosphorus pentoxide vapor is cooled, the P_2O_5 molecules recombine to form the P_4O_{10} molecules:

$$2P_2O_5 \rightarrow P_4O_{10}$$

This change affords a good example of the phenomenon known as *polymerization*, which is defined as *any process in which two or more simple molecules of the same kind unite to form a more complex molecule*. In such a large molecule, the ratio of the elements will, of course, be the same as in the smaller molecule.

The pentoxide has such a strong affinity for water that it is used both as a drying agent and as a dehydrating agent. These are, in fact, its principal uses. In the laboratory, it is used as a drying agent in the vessels known as *desic-*

cators, one of which is pictured in the accompanying illustration. It is also used for drying gases with which it will not react, and is frequently used in organic chemistry as a dehydrating agent in the preparation of a number of compounds:

$$CH_3CONH_2 + P_2O_5 \xrightarrow{\Delta} CH_3CN + 2HPO_3$$

$$C_2H_5OH + P_2O_5 \xrightarrow{\Delta} C_2H_4 + 2HPO_3$$

It will also remove water from concentrated sulfuric acid, with the liberation of sulfur trioxide:

$$H_2SO_4 + P_2O_5 \xrightarrow{\Delta} SO_3 \uparrow + 2HPO_3$$

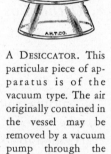

Phosphorus pentoxide is also used in the preparation of a new type of chemically resistant glass in which it is used to replace the silicon dioxide of ordinary glass.

A Desiccator. This particular piece of apparatus is of the vacuum type. The air originally contained in the vessel may be removed by a vacuum pump through the stopcock in the cover. (Courtesy, Arthur H. Thomas Co.)

7. *The Phosphoric Acids*

Phosphorus pentoxide is unlike the oxide of its predecessor in the third period, silicon, in that it combines readily, and even violently, with water to form three well-defined, moderately strong acids. It is thus an acid anhydride, and the formation of the acids from it may be represented by the following equations:

$$P_2O_5 + 3H_2O \rightarrow 2H_3PO_4$$
$$P_2O_5 + 2H_2O \rightarrow H_4P_2O_7$$
$$P_2O_5 + H_2O \rightarrow 2HPO_3$$

The first of these acids is the most highly hydrated form of the oxide; hence, as usual, it is known as *orthophosphoric acid*. The third contains one less molecule of water per molecule of the acid than does the first; hence, it is named *metaphosphoric acid*. The second, since it may be prepared by heating the ortho acid, is known as *pyrophosphoric acid* (*pyro* derives from the Greek word for *fire*). The oxidation number of the phosphorus is $+5$ in all of these acids.

When P_2O_5 is added to water, there is a hissing sound and also evolution of much heat. The product first formed is HPO_3, the meta acid, but upon standing with an excess of water, or upon being boiled with water, this yields the ortho acid, H_3PO_4.

In the ortho acid the phosphorus atom apparently shares three of its valence electrons with the oxygen atoms of three hydroxyl groups, and uses its two remaining electrons to form a covalent bond with a fourth oxygen atom:

$$
\begin{array}{c}
H \\
\cdot\!\times \\
:O: \\
\cdot\cdot \quad \circ\cdot \quad \cdot\cdot \\
H\!\times\!O\!\overset{\cdot}{\circ}\!P\!\overset{\cdot}{8}\!O: \\
\cdot\cdot \quad \cdot\circ \quad \cdot\cdot \\
:O: \\
\times\cdot \\
H
\end{array}
$$

8. Orthophosphoric Acid and Its Salts

Commercial orthophosphoric acid is usually made by treating the mineral phosphorite with sulfuric acid,

$$Ca_3(PO_4)_2 + 3H_2SO_4 + 6H_2O \rightarrow 2H_3PO_4 + \underline{3(CaSO_4.2H_2O)}$$

The calcium sulfate dihydrate, which is known as *gypsum*, is insoluble and may be removed by filtration. The solution of the acid is concentrated by evaporation to a strength of 85 per cent and a density of about 1.7 g./ml. This solution is a colorless syrupy liquid which is sold as *syrupy phosphoric acid*. A more nearly pure variety of the acid is prepared by treating red phosphorus with pure nitric acid. This reaction is generally carried out in two steps:

$$P + H_2O + HNO_3(\text{dil.}) \rightarrow H_3PO_3 + NO$$
$$H_3PO_3 + 2HNO_3(\text{conc.}) \rightarrow H_3PO_4 + 2NO_2 + H_2O$$

The intermediate product, H_3PO_3, is orthophosphorous acid, which will be discussed shortly.

As is the case with other polybasic acids, the first of the three ionizable hydrogens of this acid is removed more easily than the second, and the second more easily than the third (cf. section 9, Chapter 17). To say the same thing in another way, it may be stated that the primary degree of ionization is moderately strong, the secondary degree weak, and the tertiary degree very weak. The acid will give up all of its hydrogens with strong bases, but with weaker bases it does not react so extensively unless insoluble tertiary phosphates may be formed. With strong bases, it reacts to form three series of salts:

$$H_3PO_4 + \quad NaOH \rightarrow \quad H_2O + NaH_2PO_4 \quad \text{(primary sodium phosphate)}$$
$$H_3PO_4 + 2NaOH \rightarrow 2H_2O + Na_2HPO_4 \quad \text{(secondary sodium phosphate)}$$
$$H_3PO_4 + 3NaOH \rightarrow 3H_2O + \quad Na_3PO_4 \quad \text{(tertiary sodium phosphate)}$$

The first two of these compounds are acid salts, as is readily seen, while the last is a normal salt. Primary sodium phosphate gives an acid reaction in solution because of its hydrolysis, while the secondary and tertiary sodium phosphates yield basic solutions for the same reason. These three sodium orthophosphates are all of value. The secondary salt crystallizes from solution below 35° C. with 12 molecules of water, but in the air it gradually effloresces to yield the heptahydrate, and in very dry air it may lose water even to the extent of forming the dihydrate.

Sodium ammonium hydrogen orthophosphate ($NaNH_4HPO_4$), commonly called *microcosmic salt*, is a common laboratory reagent, and the calcium phosphates are of considerable importance.

A knowledge of the acids or bases of a given element is always of importance because these compounds are looked upon as being the parents of a whole series of salts. Thus orthophosphoric acid is the parent of all of the orthophosphate salts. The soluble orthophosphates are usually prepared by adding the acid to the proper metallic hydroxide or carbonate. Among the common normal orthophosphates, only the sodium, potassium, and ammonium salts are soluble, but many of the primary and secondary salts are soluble to varying degrees. The insoluble salts are usually prepared by the metathetical reactions of solutions containing the proper ions in suitable concentrations.

9. Pyrophosphoric Acid and Its Salts

Pyrophosphoric acid may be prepared according to the following equation:

$$2H_3PO_4 \xrightarrow[215°C]{\Delta} H_4P_2O_7 + H_2O$$

When dissolved in cold water, this acid reacts very slowly to return to the ortho acid, but in hot water it reacts much more quickly. The acid is tetrabasic, but its first degree of ionization is weak, and its fourth degree extremely weak. The acid is of little importance, but several of its salts, the pyrophosphates, are important. These are usually not prepared from the acid.

The tertiary orthophosphates are quite stable to heat, but the primary and secondary salts of orthophosphoric acid are not. For example, when secondary sodium phosphate is heated, sodium pyrophosphate is formed:

$$2Na_2HPO_4 \xrightarrow{\Delta} Na_4P_2O_7 + H_2O$$

Magnesium and manganese pyrophosphates are of some importance analytically, as will be discussed in a subsequent section. These are usually prepared by heating the corresponding mixed ammonium phosphates:

$$2MnNH_4PO_4 \rightarrow Mn_2P_2O_7 + H_2O \uparrow + 2NH_3 \uparrow$$

Most of the pyrophosphates are only slightly soluble.

10. Metaphosphoric Acid and Its Salts

This acid may be prepared, as has been pointed out, by the partial hydration of phosphorus pentoxide, or it may be prepared by heating either the ortho or the pyro acid to 316° C. Further ignition does not produce the anhydride, nor does it serve to volatilize the meta acid. After ignition, the product cools to a transparent, glassy mass, which accounts for the trade name, *glacial phosphoric acid*. In cold water, the acid reacts but slowly to reform the ortho acid; in hot water, the transformation is much more rapid. Molecular weight determinations made by observation of its effect upon the freezing point of water show it to be highly polymerized, so that it might be most accurately represented by the formula $(HPO_3)_x$.

Sodium metaphosphate is easily prepared by heating either NaH_2PO_4 or $NaNH_4HPO_4$:

$$NaH_2PO_4 \overset{\Delta}{\rightarrow} NaPO_3 + H_2O \uparrow$$

and

$$NaNH_4HPO_4 \overset{\Delta}{\rightarrow} NaPO_3 + H_2O \uparrow + NH_3 \uparrow$$

Other metaphosphates may be prepared in a similar fashion, or they may be prepared by the action of fresh cold solutions of the meta acid on the proper reagents.

Microcosmic salt is used as an analytical reagent in the phosphate bead tests. When a small loop of red-hot platinum wire is plunged into this reagent, some of it adheres to the wire. Introduced into the flame, this material reacts as shown in the equation above to form a molten droplet of sodium metaphosphate. If this is now touched to a metallic oxide or to a volatile salt of a metal and returned to the flame, a bead of sodium metal orthophosphate is formed:

$$NiO + NaPO_3 \rightarrow NaNiPO_4$$

For many metals, these beads are of characteristic colors which serve to identify the metal. In some cases, the bead formed by a given metal will be of one color if formed in the reducing flame, another if formed in the oxidizing flame; thus nickel gives a green bead in the oxidizing flame and a gray one in the reducing flame. The gray color is due to the reduction of nickel compounds to the free metal.

Sodium hexametaphosphate is formed by heating sodium metaphosphate or microcosmic salt to red heat for an hour or more and then quickly cooling the mass. It seems to have the formula $(NaPO_3)_6$ and is useful for uniting with the ions which cause "hardness" in water, thus preventing their usual reactions.

11. Analytical Tests for the Various Phosphate Ions

Attention has already been called to the fact that the majority of the metallic ortho-, pyro-, and metaphosphates are insoluble. The acids and the soluble salts furnish in solution their characteristic ions which show the following reactions. The orthophosphate ion gives a yellow precipitate with silver nitrate, while the other two phosphate ions give white precipitates. A solution of pyrophosphate ions acidified with acetic acid and treated with zinc acetate gives a white precipitate while solutions of the other two ions do not. A solution of the metaphosphate ions acidified with acetic acid gives a white precipitate when treated with a solution of albumen, while the other ions do not. Upon treatment with a solution of magnesium chloride and ammonium chloride in ammonium hydroxide, only the orthophosphate gives a fine, colorless, crystalline precipitate, and with nitric acid and a solution of ammonium molybdate only the orthophosphate ion forms a bright yellow precipitate of ammonium phosphomolybdate, $(NH_4)_3PO_4.12MoO_3$. Arsenate ions $(AsO_4)^{-3}$ interfere with both of these last tests by giving precipitates similar in appearance to those formed by the orthophosphate ion.

Quantitatively, phosphates are often precipitated in the final step of the analysis as $MgNH_4PO_4.6H_2O$ which is then ignited to $Mg_2P_2O_7$ and weighed.

12. Phosphorus Trioxide

At about 20° C., this oxide is a colorless solid which melts if the temperature is raised to 23.8° C. and boils at a temperature of 173° C. It is prepared by burning phosphorus in a deficiency of air and filtering the product while it is still a liquid through glass wool to remove any of the solid pentoxide which may be formed simultaneously. Determinations of its molecular weight in the gaseous state and by its effect upon the freezing point of benzene indicate a formula of P_4O_6. In equations, the formula is usually written P_2O_3, and it is usually referred to as the trioxide, although it is more properly known as phosphorus sesquioxide since oxygen is present in the ratio of one and one-half atoms to one atom of phosphorus. The compound is very unstable with respect to oxygen, gradually changing to the pentoxide at about 20° C. and bursting into flame if heated to 70° C. in the presence of air:

$$P_2O_3 + O_2 \rightarrow P_2O_5$$

When added to hot water, this oxide undergoes simultaneous oxidation and reduction, usually referred to as autooxidation-reduction, to form orthophos-phoric acid and phosphine (PH_3):

$$2P_2O_3 + 6H_2O \rightarrow 3H_3PO_4 + PH_3 \uparrow$$

13. The Naming of Acids and Their Salts

A number of elements give rise to more than one oxygen-containing acid, which acids of course give rise to corresponding salts. The common acid which has the highest state of oxidation is usually named by substituting for the characteristic ending of the name of the central element the suffix -ic. Thus we have phosphoric acid, in which the oxidation number of the phosphorus atoms is +5. The salts of such oxygen acids have names which terminate in -ate; e.g., the phosphates. The most common acid in which the oxidation number of the central element is less than in the -ic acid is given the ending -ous; thus there is phosphorous acid, H_3PO_3, in which the oxidation number of the phosphorus is +3. Acids whose names end in -ous form salts whose names end in -ite; thus Na_2HPO_3 is sodium phosphite. The prefix hypo- attached to the name of an acid indicates that the oxidation number of the central element is lower than would be indicated by the simple name without this prefix, while the prefix per- indicates a higher valence than would be indicated by the suffix used. The following table will serve further to illustrate the preceding statements.

Table 18

THE NAMING OF ACIDS AND THEIR SALTS

Oxid. No. Central Element	Formula of Acid	Name of Acid	Formula of Salt	Name of Sodium Salt
+1	H_3PO_2	Hypophosphorous acid	NaH_2PO_2	Sodium hypophosphite
+3	H_3PO_3	Phosphorous acid	Na_2HPO_3	Sodium phosphite
+4	$H_4P_2O_6$	Hypophosphoric acid	$Na_4P_2O_6$	Sodium hypophosphate
+5	H_3PO_4	Phosphoric acid	Na_3PO_4	Sodium phosphate
+7	H_3PO_5	Perphosphoric acid	Na_3PO_5	Sodium perphosphate

14. *The Phosphorous Acids and Their Salts*

If phosphorus trioxide is added to cold water, rather than to hot as described in section 12, it will gradually react by addition to form orthophosphorous acid (H_3PO_3):

$$3H_2O + P_2O_3 \rightarrow 2H_3PO_3$$

This acid is more commonly prepared by the action of phosphorus trichloride on water:

$$PCl_3 + 3H_2O \rightarrow H_3PO_3 + 3HCl$$

The hydrochloric acid so produced may be largely expelled by boiling, and if the aqueous solutions prepared by either of the foregoing methods are evaporated, the orthophosphorous acid may be obtained as colorless, deliquescent crystals. Just as phosphorus pentoxide is the anhydride of two phosphoric acids which are less highly hydrated than is the ortho acid, so phosphorus trioxide is also the anhydride of a pyro- and a metaphosphorous acid. Pyrophosphorous acid is obtained when more PCl_3 is added to a solution of the orthophosphorous acid:

$$H_3PO_3 + PCl_3 + 2H_2O \rightarrow H_4P_2O_5 + 3HCl$$

Pyrophosphites are prepared by heating orthophosphites:

$$2Na_2HPO_3 \xrightarrow{\Delta} Na_4P_2O_5 + H_2O \uparrow$$

Metaphosphites apparently result when acid orthophosphites are heated:

$$NaH_2PO_3 \xrightarrow{\Delta} NaPO_2 + H_2O \uparrow$$

In all of these acids and their salts, the oxidation number of the phosphorus is $+3$ as it is in the trioxide. Only the ortho acid and its salts are of any pronounced importance.

Despite the fact that it contains three hydrogen atoms in its structure, orthophosphorous acid is only dibasic and hence should more properly have the formula $H_2(HPO_3)$. A discussion of the reason for this behavior will be found in a subsequent section of this chapter. Having only two replaceable hydrogens, the acid forms two series of salts; Na_2HPO_3 is thus normal sodium phosphite and NaH_2PO_3 is sodium hydrogen phosphite. Despite the phosphorus having a lower oxidation number in H_3PO_3 than in H_3PO_4, the former is the stronger acid in its primary stage of ionization. A reason for this behavior will also be discussed in the section referred to above. Most of the metallic phosphites, save those of the I A family of metals, are only sparingly soluble. The majority of them form well-defined crystals.

All phosphorus compounds in which the oxidation number of phosphorus is less than five are readily oxidized in solution to the $+5$ condition, thus forming orthophosphoric acid or orthophosphates. When they are so oxidized, reduction must occur at the same time, hence all such compounds are good reducing agents. Orthophosphorous acid and its salts conform to this general rule, reducing the salts of many of the heavy metals to salts of a lower valence state of the metal or to the free metal:

$$2AuCl_3 + 3H_3PO_3 + 3H_2O \rightarrow 3H_3PO_4 + \underline{2Au} + 6HCl$$
$$2HgCl_2 + H_3PO_3 + H_2O \rightarrow H_3PO_4 + \underline{Hg_2Cl_2} + 2HCl$$

If a solution of the acid is heated strongly, it even reduces itself to afford another example of autooxidation-reduction:

$$4H_3PO_3 \rightarrow 3H_3PO_4 + PH_3 \uparrow$$

In this reaction for each phosphorus atom which has its oxidation number reduced from $+3$ to -3, a total change of six, three atoms have to be raised from $+3$ to $+5$ to afford an equal and opposite change; thus it is that the equation is balanced.

Upon standing, solutions of orthophosphorous acid are gradually oxidized by atmospheric oxygen to orthophosphoric acid.

15. *Hypophosphorous Acid and Its Salts*

Unlike the preceding acids, hypophosphorous acid has no known anhydride. Its formula is H_3PO_2, and it usually is prepared by boiling yellow phosphorus with aqueous barium hydroxide and then treating the barium hypophosphite so formed with sulfuric acid, which liberates the acid and forms a readily removable precipitate of barium sulfate:

$$8P + 3Ba(OH)_2 + 6H_2O \rightarrow 3Ba(H_2PO_2)_2 + 2PH_3 \uparrow$$
$$Ba(H_2PO_2)_2 + H_2SO_4 \rightarrow \underline{BaSO_4} + 2H_3PO_2$$

As will be noted, the above reaction for the preparation of barium hypophosphite and the hydride of phosphorus is another example of autooxidation-reduction. Similar reactions occur when yellow phosphorus is boiled with other bases.

Hypophosphorous acid is peculiar in two respects: (1) it is a monobasic acid [$H(H_2PO_2)$] despite its three hydrogens; and (2) its salts, contrary to the behavior of many of the other compounds of phosphorus, are not poisonous and are used in internal medicines. The acid is somewhat stronger than orthophosphorous acid, again contrary to normal expectation.

The acid and its salts, as is to be expected, are strong reducing agents, being themselves oxidized.

$$4AgCl + H_3PO_2 + 2H_2O \rightarrow \underline{4Ag} + H_3PO_4 + 4HCl$$

Upon standing, solutions of the acid are gradually oxidized to orthophosphoric acid, and if heated too strongly (above 130° C.), the acid undergoes autooxidation:

$$2H_3PO_2 \rightarrow H_3PO_4 + PH_3 \uparrow$$

Solutions of the salts behave similarly. Solutions of the acid may be concentrated below 130° C. to a syrupy liquid which upon cooling yields a glacial mass.

16. Hypophosphoric Acid

This acid is prepared by the slow oxidation of phosphorus in a limited supply of moist air:

$$14P + 18H_2O + 12O_2 \rightarrow 8H_3PO_3 + 3H_4P_2O_6$$

The acid may also be prepared by the action of bleaching powder ($CaClOCl$) on red phosphorus, and by an electrolytic process. The acid is removed from the reaction mixture by precipitation as the salt $Na_2H_2P_2O_6.6H_2O$. In agreement with its formula ($H_4P_2O_6$), hypophosphoric acid is tetrabasic. It and its salts are unstable to heat,

$$4H_4P_2O_6 + 4H_2O \overset{\Delta}{\rightarrow} 7H_3PO_4 + PH_3 \uparrow$$

but they do not reduce salts of the heavy metals; they act as reducing agents only on the strongest oxidizing agents. In general, the acid and its salts, most of which are only slightly soluble, are relatively unimportant.

17. The Perphosphoric Acids

There are two perphosphoric acids: permonophosphoric acid, H_3PO_5, and perdiphosphoric acid, $H_4P_2O_8$. These compounds have the typical peroxide configuration (cf. section 12 in Chapter 7), characterized by oxygen to oxygen unions.

$$\begin{array}{ccc}
\text{H} & \text{H} & \text{H} \\
\times\bullet & \times\bullet\ \bullet & \times\bullet \\
:\text{O}: & :\text{O}: & :\text{O}: \\
\cdot\cdot\ \cdot\cdot\ \cdot\text{o}\ \cdot\cdot & \cdot\cdot\ \cdot\text{o}\ \cdot\cdot\ \cdot\cdot\ \cdot\text{o}\ \cdot\cdot \\
\text{H}\times\text{O}:\text{O}\substack{\circ}\text{P}\substack{\circ}_{8}\text{O}: \quad\text{and}\quad :\text{O}\substack{\circ}_{8}\text{P}\substack{\circ}_{6}\text{O}:\text{O}\substack{\circ}\text{P}\substack{\circ}_{8}\text{O}: \\
\cdot\cdot\ \cdot\cdot\ \cdot\text{o}\cdot\ \cdot\cdot & \cdot\cdot\ \cdot\text{o}\cdot\ \cdot\cdot\ \cdot\cdot\ \cdot\text{o}\cdot\ \cdot\cdot \\
:\text{O}: & :\text{O}: \quad :\text{O}: \\
\cdot\times & \cdot\times \quad \cdot\times \\
\text{H} & \text{H} \quad \text{H}
\end{array}$$

These acids may be prepared by the action of hydrogen peroxide (H_2O_2) on phosphorus pentoxide, though commercially they are prepared by the electrolysis of solutions of orthophosphates. High current densities favor the production of permonophosphoric acid, while lower ones favor the formation of perdiphosphoric acid. These acids and their salts find use principally as oxidizing agents, and when so used they form orthophosphate ions.

18. Phosphorus Tetroxide

When heated in a sealed tube to about 300° C., phosphorus trioxide yields elementary phosphorus and phosphorus tetroxide, whose formula is usually written P_2O_4 despite the fact that its vapor density indicates a formula of P_8O_{16}. This compound exists as brilliant, colorless crystals which are highly hygroscopic and which sublime readily in a vacuum. By application of the zero valence rule, the oxidation number of phosphorus in this oxide is calculated to be $+4$, but apparently the substance is better thought of as a compound of P_2O_3 with P_2O_5, so that in reality phosphorus in both the $+3$ and the $+5$ states is present. This view is supported by the ready reaction of the oxide with water to form both orthophosphorous and orthophosphoric acids:

$$P_2O_4 + 3H_2O \rightarrow H_3PO_3 + H_3PO_4$$

Since this oxide yields two acids upon hydration, it is apparent that it is not an anhydride.

19. The Valences, Oxidation Numbers, and Coördination Numbers of Phosphorus in Its Various Acids

The structures assumed for the various acids of phosphorus are:

$$\begin{array}{ccc}
 & \text{H} & \text{H}\quad\text{H} \\
 & \cdot\times & \cdot\times\quad\cdot\times \\
\text{H} & :\text{O}: & :\text{O}::\text{O}: \\
\cdot\cdot\ \text{ox}\ \cdot\cdot & \cdot\cdot\ \cdot\text{o}\ \cdot\cdot & \cdot\cdot\ \text{o}\cdot\quad\text{o}\cdot\ \cdot\cdot \\
\text{H}\times\text{O}\substack{\circ}_{8}\text{P}\substack{\circ}_{8}\text{O}: & \text{H}\times\text{O}\substack{\circ}\text{P}\substack{\circ}_{8}\text{O}: & \text{H}\times\text{O}\substack{\circ}_{6}\text{P}\ \substack{8}\ \text{P}\substack{\circ}\text{O}\times\text{H} \\
\cdot\cdot\ \text{xo}\ \cdot\cdot & \cdot\cdot\ \text{xo}\ \cdot\cdot & \cdot\cdot\ \infty\quad\infty\ \cdot\cdot \\
\text{H} & \text{H} & :\text{O}::\text{O}: \\
\textbf{Hypophosphorous} & \textbf{Orthophosphorous} & \textbf{Hypophosphoric} \\
\textbf{acid} & \textbf{acid} & \textbf{acid}
\end{array}$$

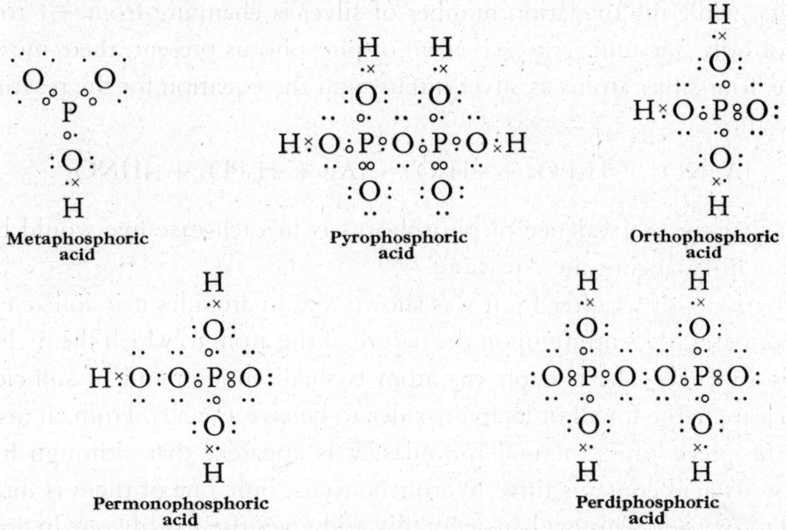

Metaphosphoric acid

Pyrophosphoric acid

Orthophosphoric acid

Permonophosphoric acid

Perdiphosphoric acid

It will be noted that in each of these formulas the phosphorus atom is sharing all five of its outermost electrons, and that in each case, save in that of metaphosphoric acid, the phosphorus atom is surrounded by four other groups. The real valence of phosphorus is, therefore, in each instance five, while its coördination number is in each case four, save in the case of metaphosphoric acid in which it is three. The various oxidation numbers which may be calculated for phosphorus in these compounds are:

Hypophosphorous acid, H_3PO_2, $+1$
Orthophosphorous acid, H_3PO_3, $+3$
Hypophosphoric acid, $H_4P_2O_6$, $+4$
Metaphosphoric acid, HPO_3, $+5$
Pyrophosphoric acid, $H_4P_2O_7$, $+5$
Orthophosphoric acid, H_3PO_4, $+5$
Permonophosphoric acid, H_3PO_5, $+7$
Perdiphosphoric acid, $H_4P_2O_8$, $+6$

From the above structures, it is apparent that these numbers are imaginary, since they represent no real valence. Even so, however, they are useful in classifying the compounds of phosphorus and their reactions, and they are especially useful in balancing oxidation-reduction equations for such reactions in which they participate. For example, when hypophosphorous acid reduces silver nitrate to free silver, orthophosphoric acid is formed. In this reaction, the oxidation number of the phosphorus is changing from $+1$ to $+5$, a change of four units, while the oxidation number of silver is changing from $+1$ to 0, a change of only one unit. For each atom of phosphorus present, there must be, therefore, four silver atoms as silver nitrate, and the equation for the reaction is balanced thus:

$$4AgNO_3 + H_3PO_2 + 2H_2O \rightarrow \underline{4Ag} + H_3PO_4 + 4HNO_3$$

The fact that the real valence of phosphorus is in each case five would be of little value in balancing the equation.

In section 7 of Chapter 15, it was shown that hydroxides may ionize either as acids or bases, depending upon the nature of the atom to which the hydroxyl radical is attached. The phosphorus atom is small enough and of sufficiently high nuclear charge for all of its hydroxides to behave as acids. From an inspection of the preceding structural formulas, it is apparent that although hypophosphorous acid contains three hydrogen atoms, only one of them is directly attached to oxygen. This explains why this acid gives rise to only one hydrogen ion per molecule. Similarly, the structural formula for orthophosphorous acid shows why it is dibasic. The number of hydrogen ions each acid is capable of furnishing may be determined by counting the number of hydroxyl groups in the molecule of that acid.

Mention has been made of the fact that the strength of hypophosphorous, orthophosphorous, and orthophosphoric acids as acids increases as the oxidation numbers of the central phosphorus atoms decrease. This is contrary to the usual state of affairs because usually larger oxidation numbers indicate smaller, more highly charged ions whose hydroxides ionize more strongly as acids. In the cases of these three acids, the actual valence of the phosphorus remains the same, but the number of hydroxyl groups decreases from orthophosphoric acid to hypophosphorous acid so that the extent of the primary stage of ionization increases in that order.

20. The Properties of Oxides

A review of the properties of the oxides of phosphorus and of the elements which precede it in the third period reveals that all are solids, but that a very definite change of properties occurs from member to member. Sodium oxide is an ionic compound of high melting and boiling points, which is stable to heat and which reacts with water to form a single, strongly ionized, basic hydroxide. In passing through the other oxides of the period to phosphorus and on to the end of the period with chlorine, the properties listed for sodium oxide gradually change. The oxides become less ionic and more molecular. When there is no longer an ionic lattice to tear down, the melting and boiling points are found to be decreased; thus the oxides of phosphorus while still solids at about 20° C. are either easily melted or easily sublimed. With this increasing volatility, it may be assumed that some of the oxides of the following two elements, sulfur and chlorine, may be liquids and gases at room temperature. The oxides of phosphorus are still stable to heat, but it is to be anticipated that the oxides of the remaining elements of the period will show a decreasing stability. As one progresses through the period the elements show an increasing tendency to form oxides whose strength as bases decreases while the strength as acids increases. In summation, then, it may be said that as one passes from left to right through a given period of the chart, the elements tend to form a greater number of oxides, whose ionic nature decreases as their molecular nature increases, whose stability decreases, whose tendency to form hydrates increases, and whose hydrates decrease in strength as bases as their strength as acids increases.

21. *Hydrides*

Like silicon, phosphorus forms no hydrides by direct union, but it does form several such binary compounds indirectly. Collectively, these compounds are known as *phosphines*, and the simplest, PH_3, is also the most important. It has already been pointed out that this compound is usually one of the products when phosphorus compounds of intermediate valence undergo autooxidation-reduction, and that it is produced along with a metallic hypophosphite when yellow phosphorus is boiled with a basic solution. In essence, this latter reaction is comparable to the reaction of chlorine with water (cf. section 5, Chapter 10) whereby a hypochlorite and a hydride of

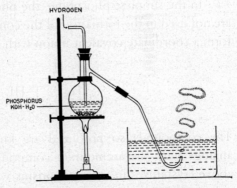

APPARATUS FOR THE LABORATORY PREPARATION OF PHOSPHINE. Either hydrogen or natural gas may be used to sweep the residual oxygen from the generator.

chlorine are produced. By this latter reaction, traces of another hydride, P_2H_4, which is a liquid at about 20° C., are produced. This hydride inflames spontaneously upon contact with air while the hydride PH_3 inflames only in pure oxygen under reduced pressures. If the gaseous phosphine prepared by the action of phosphorus and caustic be allowed to bubble up through water, the bubbles inflame upon reaching the air (because of the P_2H_4 present), forming beautiful symmetrical smoke rings composed of phosphoric acid particles:

$$PH_3 + 2O_2 \rightarrow H_3PO_4$$

The unstable P_2H_4 may be removed by condensation in a tube surrounded by a freezing mixture, or, if exposed to light, it will gradually decompose thus:

$$5P_2H_4 \xrightarrow{\text{u.v.}} 6PH_3 + P_4H_2$$

The latter product is a solid and is not spontaneously combustible. It, too, is sometimes formed in small quantities along with the simpler PH_3. The phosphines are poisonous and should be handled with care. The simplest phosphine may also be formed by the action of acidified water upon a metallic phosphide in a manner similar to that in which the silicon hydrides were prepared:

$$Ca_3P_2 + 6HCl \rightarrow 3CaCl_2 + 2PH_3 \uparrow$$

Cans of calcium phosphide which may be punctured to admit sea water are sometimes used as floating signal flares at sea. The phosphine generated ignites spontaneously to furnish a light which neither wind nor water will extinguish.

22. Phosphonium Compounds

In the simplest phosphine, the phosphorus atom has two electrons which are not used in the formation of the compound. These electrons may be used to form a coördinate covalent union with hydrogen ions:

$$
\begin{array}{ccc}
\text{H} & & \text{H} \\
\text{ox} & & \text{ox} \quad\quad .. \\
\text{H\,\%P\,\%} + \text{HI} \rightarrow & & \text{H\,\%P\,\%H\,\%I:} \\
\text{xo} & & \text{xo} \quad\quad .. \\
\text{H} & & \text{H}
\end{array}
$$

The compounds so produced are known as phosphonium compounds in analogy with the ammonium compounds. The phosphonium iodide formed above crystallizes in colorless prisms which sublime at 62° C. It is a powerful reducing agent and is easily decomposed into phosphine and hydriodic acid by the action of water. This suggests that phosphine does not react with water to form a phosphonium hydroxide. With solutions of salts of certain of the heavy metals, phosphine reacts to precipitate the corresponding metallic phosphides.

23. Halides

Phosphorus forms two series of halides in which it shows its two principal oxidation numbers. These compounds have the general formulas PX_3 and PX_5, where X stands for any halogen atom. Iodine, however, does not form a pentaiodide, forming instead the compound P_2I_4. These halides and their physical states and colors are given in the following table.

Table 19

THE HALIDES OF PHOSPHORUS

PF_3, colorless gas	PCl_3, colorless liquid	PBr_3, colorless liquid	P_2I_4, orange solid
PF_5, colorless gas	PCl_5, colorless solid	PBr_5, yellow solid	PI_3, red solid

It should be noted that, as the weight of these compounds increases, their state at about 20° C. passes from gas to liquid to solid. Of the group, the chlorides are the most important, with the tribromide running a poor third.

The trichloride is prepared by passing a stream of dry chlorine over yellow phosphorus. The heat of the reaction causes the product, whose boiling point is 76° C., to distil from the reaction vessel. This liquid may be purified by standing in contact with yellow phosphorus and subsequent redistillation.

$$2P + 3Cl_2 \rightarrow 2PCl_3$$

If dry chlorine gas is passed into the liquid trichloride in a well-cooled container, the pentachloride will be formed:

$$PCl_3 + Cl_2 \rightarrow PCl_5$$

This compound is a colorless solid which fumes profusely in moist air and sublimes readily. The halides show the tendency to decreased rigidity and increased volatility more markedly than do the corresponding oxides because in the halides the more positive atoms are attached to more of the negative atoms than is the case in the oxides. Both of the chlorides hydrolyze easily to yield acids of phosphorus and hydrochloric acid:

$$PCl_3 + 3HOH \rightarrow H_3PO_3 + 3HCl$$
$$PCl_5 + 4HOH \rightarrow H_3PO_4 + 5HCl$$

The pentachloride has a great affinity for oxygen. It reacts mole for mole with water to form phosphoryl chloride (phosphorus oxychloride), a compound which it forms readily when added to other oxygen-containing compounds:

$$PCl_5 + HOH \rightarrow POCl_3 + 2HCl$$
$$PCl_5 + SO_2 \rightarrow POCl_3 + SOCl_2$$
$$PCl_5 + C_2H_5OH \rightarrow POCl_3 + C_2H_5Cl + HCl$$

All of the phosphorus halides may be prepared by direct union, with the violence of the reaction decreasing as the weight of the halogen used increases. As might be inferred from this statement, the stability of the compounds decreases as the weight of the halogen present increases.

24. Uses of Phosphorus

Free phosphorus is now prepared in large quantities and is often shipped in tank car lots. During World War II it was used extensively in the preparation of incendiary bombs, tracer bullets, and smoke screens. Large quantities of it are burned to phosphorus pentoxide which is used in the preparation of a wide variety of compounds. Rat biscuits are prepared by grinding yellow phosphorus with flour and grease. It is also used in the preparation of certain alloys and a variety of metallic phosphides.

Formerly, yellow phosphorus mixed with lead dioxide, glass, and glue was used in the manufacture of matches. Such matches were very poisonous and the workers who made them, as a result of the continued breathing of phosphorus vapor, were subject to "phossy jaw," a decomposition of the bone of the lower jaw. Such matches are now prohibited by law in most countries.

25. Uses of Phosphorus Compounds

The most widely used compounds of this important element are the phosphates. Agriculture, our largest industry, uses a great tonnage of calcium acid phosphate as *superphosphate* fertilizer. This commodity is prepared by treating crushed phosphate rock with sulfuric acid.

$$Ca_3(PO_4)_2 + 2H_2SO_4 + 5H_2O \rightarrow Ca(H_2PO_4)_2.H_2O + 2(CaSO_4.2H_2O)$$

The mixture of primary calcium phosphate and gypsum is applied directly to the land. The secondary and tertiary phosphates are too insoluble to be of ready use as a plant food. A superphosphate fertilizer containing a greater percentage of phosphorus is now prepared by making orthophosphoric acid from phosphate rock, then using this acid instead of sulfuric for treating a second portion of the rock.

$$Ca_3(PO_4)_2 + 3H_2SO_4 + 6H_2O \rightarrow 3(CaSO_4.2H_2O) + 2H_3PO_4$$
$$Ca_3(PO_4)_2 + 4H_3PO_4 + 3H_2O \rightarrow 3[Ca(H_2PO_4)_2.H_2O]$$

Use of this latter preparation effects a considerable saving in freight bills.

Other phosphates and their uses are:

Formula	Name	Uses
$Na_3PO_4.12H_2O$	Tertiary sodium phosphate	Water softener, cleaning agent
$Na_2HPO_4.12H_2O$	Secondary sodium phosphate	Reagent, weighting of silk
$Na_4P_2O_7.10H_2O$	Sodium pyrophosphate	Stabilizing agent for peroxides
$Na_2H_2P_2O_7.6H_2O$	Secondary sodium pyrophosphate	Baking powders
$Na_6P_6O_{18}$	Sodium hexametaphosphate	Water softener, cleaning agent
$Ca_3(PO_4)_2$	Tertiary calcium phosphate	Manufacture of bone china
$CaHPO_4.2H_2O$	Secondary calcium phosphate	Abrasive in tooth cleaners, stock food, yeast food
$Ca(H_2PO_4)_2$	Primary calcium phosphate	Fertilizer, baking powder
$(NH_4)_2HPO_4$	Secondary ammonium phosphate	Yeast food, fireproofing, fertilizer
$NH_4H_2PO_4$	Primary ammonium phosphate	Yeast food, fireproofing

The phosphates used in baking powder hydrolyze to act as an acid upon the sodium bicarbonate present. Carbon dioxide is thus liberated.

Present-day matches are of two general varieties: the *strike-anywhere* type and the *safety* type. Both varieties are made upon small pine sticks which have been impregnated with ammonium phosphate to prevent afterglow and then dipped in molten paraffin. To make matches of the first kind there is added to the stick a head of oxidizing agent ($KClO_3$ or PbO_2) and oxidizable material (rosin or sulfur) held together with glue, and to this head is added a tip of ground glass and P_4S_3. When struck, the heat of friction ignites the P_4S_3, which, in turn, ignites the head. The head of the *safety* match is made of a mixture of oxidizing agent ($KClO_3$, K_2CrO_4, or PbO_2), antimony trisulfide (Sb_2S_3), and glue. The striking surface on the box is coated with a mixture of pulverized glass, antimony trisulfide, red phosphorus, and glue. When the match is struck, friction converts some of the red phosphorus to the yellow variety and the burning of this ignites the match head.

The sulfide P_2S_5 is used to some extent in the preparation of organic sulfur compounds.

Uses of other phosphorus compounds have been mentioned throughout the chapter.

(*See Appendix for Exercises*)

COLLATERAL READINGS

Chamberlain: *Chemistry in Agriculture*, New York, Chemical Foundation, 1926.
Crass: A history of the match industry, *J. Chem. Education*, **18**, 116, 277 (1941).

Curtis and Co-workers: Fertilizer from rock phosphates, *Ind. and Eng. Chem.*, **29,** 766 (1937).

Ephraim: *Inorganic Chemistry*, 3d Eng. ed., London, Gurney and Jackson, 1939.

Kirkpatrick: Phosphorus for progress, *Chem. and Met. Eng.*, **44,** 643 (1937).

Latimer and Hildebrand: *Reference Book of Inorganic Chemistry*, New York, The Macmillan Co., 1941.

Moore: *History of Chemistry*, New York, McGraw-Hill Book Co., 1939.

Weeks: *Discovery of the Elements*, 5th ed., Mack Printing Co., 1945.

Yost and Russell: *Systematic Inorganic Chemistry*, New York, Prentice-Hall, Inc., 1944.

21

Sulfur and Its Compounds

1. Introduction

Sulfur is the sixth element of the third period and is unique in that it is the only element of the period which occurs naturally in the free state. It is non-metallic both in appearance and in behavior, and is moderately active, though far less so than either phosphorus or chlorine, its nearest neighbors in the period. As a constituent of many proteins, sulfur is necessary to the life of humans and the higher animals, and is of importance both commercially and theoretically. The element is an isotopic mixture of the atomic species whose weights are 32, 33, 34, and 36 at. wt. units, and whose proportions in the mixture are always such that its average atomic weight is 32.06 at. wt. units.

The atomic number of sulfur is 16, and the distribution of its extranuclear electrons among the first three energy levels is 2, 8, 6. As a consequence of having six electrons in its outermost energy level, the atom will react by gaining two electrons to show a negative valence of two; it will share electrons in such a fashion as to gain an interest in two electrons to show a valence of two and an oxidation number of -2, and it will form coördinate linkages by sharing with other nonmetals either its four 3_1 electrons or all six of its valence electrons to show oxidation numbers of $+4$ and $+6$, respectively. The principal oxidation numbers of the element are thus -2, $+4$, and $+6$, but in certain of its less common compounds intermediate oxidation states are represented, though in most of these there is no significant difference in the manner in which the atom is held in union.

Because of its increased nuclear charge, the sulfur atom is smaller than the phosphorus atom. It is therefore a strong attractor of electrons and forms many important compounds with the metals. It also forms a wide variety of oxides, which are acidic in nature, and an even wider variety of acids, many of whose salts are of considerable importance.

2. Physical Properties

Like phosphorus, sulfur exists in a variety of allotropic forms. As commonly found in nature and in the laboratory, the element is a yellow solid which has little odor, is soluble in carbon disulfide but not in water, whose crystals belong to the rhombic system (cf. section 16, Chapter 11), whose density is 2.07 g./ml., and whose melting point is 112.8° C. Rhombic sulfur, or alpha sulfur, S_α, is stable at any temperature below 96° C. Above this temperature, monoclinic crystals form. These are known as beta sulfur, S_β, and are most readily prepared by carefully melting sulfur and allowing it to cool slowly. The long, transparent yellow needles which form are perfectly stable at temperatures between 96° C. and the melting point, but below the transition tem-

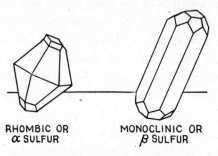

RHOMBIC OR
α SULFUR

MONOCLINIC OR
β SULFUR

SULFUR CRYSTALS.

perature they gradually become opaque due to their cracking into many tiny rhombic crystals. The change of the rhombic crystals to the monoclinic ones is, as might be expected, endothermic:

$$S_r + 69 \text{ cal.} \rightleftarrows S_m \quad \text{or} \quad S_\alpha + 69 \text{ cal.} \rightleftarrows S_\beta$$

In the monoclinic form, sulfur has a density of 1.96 g./ml. and a melting point of 119.2° C., although it will melt at 114.5° C. to form a mixture of liquid allotropes. Rhombic crystals of a fair size are best obtained by dissolving solid sulfur in carbon disulfide and allowing the solvent to evaporate slowly.

When either of the solid allotropes of sulfur is heated gently just above the melting point, a thin, straw-colored liquid is formed which becomes both darker in color and more viscous as the temperature is raised. In the neighborhood of 200° C., the liquid is a dark brown and so viscous that it shows very little tendency to flow from an inverted container. As the temperature is raised, the liquid becomes more fluid again, though it remains dark, and at 444.6° C. it boils. Liquid sulfur contains three molecular species which are interconvertible, and whose proportions in the mixture are dependent largely upon its temperature. These forms and their formulas are $S_\lambda(S_8)$, $S_\pi(S_4)$, and S_μ (formula unknown). The percentage of each in liquid sulfur at all temperatures from the melting point to the boiling point is given by the following graph.

It will be noted that, above 280° C., the composition remains virtually constant. The transformation of one liquid allotrope into another is not instantaneous, and the speed of conversion is greatly affected by both positive and negative catalysts.

Measurements made upon sulfur vapor just above its melting point reveal that the gas has a molecular weight which indicates a formula of S_8. At more

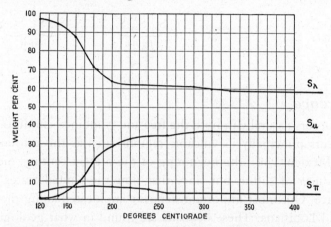

WEIGHT-PER CENT OF THE COMPONENTS OF LIQUID SULFUR FROM
120° to 400° C.

elevated temperatures, the formula of the gas is found to be S_6; at 1000° C., dissociation into S_2 molecules is almost complete; and at 2000° C., about 45 per cent of these molecules have dissociated into monatomic molecules, S.

If sulfur is heated nearly to its boiling point and then suddenly cooled by being poured into a vessel of cold water, there is formed a dark, gummy mass known as *plastic sulfur*. This mass is amorphous because its molecules were cooled so rapidly that they did not have time to assume their proper places in the characteristic rhombic crystals. If this supercooled liquid is allowed to stand for several days, its color becomes much lighter, and examination with a lens shows that it has become a mass of tiny interlocking rhombic crystals and fragments of crystals. Plastic sulfur is only partially soluble in carbon disulfide, and the insoluble portion changes to the rhombic state only with extreme slowness.

A third solid allotrope of sulfur has been prepared by heating the element to 180° C., cooling the melt quickly, and dissolving it in carbon disulfide.

The solution is chilled to $-80°$ C., at which temperature a majority of the solute precipitates. This precipitate is removed by filtration, and the filtrate is allowed to evaporate slowly. Intensely yellow crystals of the S_π referred to above as having a formula of S_4 are formed. A fourth allotrope whose formula appears to be S_6 has also been reported.

The relationship of the various allotropes of the element is summarized in the following chart.

$$S_{(rhombic)} \xrightleftharpoons[\text{}]{96° C.} S_{(monoclinic)} \xrightleftharpoons[\text{}]{114.5° C.} \underbrace{S_\lambda, S_\mu, S_\pi,}_{\text{liquid}} \xrightleftharpoons[\text{}]{\substack{\text{above} \\ 444.6° C}} \underbrace{S_8, S_6, S_2, S}_{\text{vapor}}$$

quick cooling → plastic sulfur

3. Occurrence

Sulfur occurs naturally in both the free and combined conditions. The free element occurs principally in volcanic regions such as those found in Sicily, Japan, and Mexico. Until the beginning of the present century, Sicily was the biggest producer of sulfur, but since that time the United States has moved into first place. Our most important deposits are located along the Gulf coast of Texas and Louisiana. These deposits are found in what geologists call salt domes, and they are not of volcanic origin; the exact nature of their origin is, in fact, still a matter of conjecture.

In combination, sulfur occurs in greatest quantity as the insoluble sulfides of the heavy metals. Many metallic sulfides are important ores of the metals so combined. Among these are Ag_2S, *argentite;* $CuFeS_2$, *chalcopyrite;* HgS, *cinnabar;* PbS, *galena;* and ZnS, *zinc blende.* Large deposits of a number of these sulfides are found in the mountainous regions of the western United States. A few sulfates are sufficiently insoluble for deposits of them to be found. Notable among these are barium sulfate, *barite;* calcium sulfate, *gypsum;* and strontium sulfate, *celestite.* Deposits of the more soluble magnesium sulfate are also found in Germany and elsewhere.

Many of the compounds of carbon contain sulfur. Reference has already been made to its presence in protein. Much of the unpleasant odor of putrefying plant and animal matter is due to the conversion of these sulfur-bearing proteins into other compounds of the element. It is present in the human organism to the extent of about 0.26 per cent. Petroleum from many sources contains sulfurous compounds which must be removed at considerable expense before the oil can be used as motor fuel. Coal also frequently contains sulfur compounds which form unpleasant sulfur dioxide gas when the fuel is burned. Organic sulfur compounds are of little value as an industrial source of the element.

4. Production

Volcanic gases frequently contain the gases hydrogen sulfide, H_2S, and sulfur dioxide, SO_2. It is believed that deposits of the free element in volcanic regions result from the interaction of these two substances:

$$2H_2S + SO_2 \rightarrow \underline{3S} + 2H_2O$$

Such sulfur is always contaminated with earthy material from which it is removed by heating the ore in a kiln in which some of the sulfur is allowed to burn to supply the necessary heat. This is a wasteful practice. The element melts and drains away while the earthy material does not. Being still somewhat impure, the material so obtained is loaded into iron retorts, from which it is distilled in the absence of air to prevent combustion. The vapor is cooled in large brick vaults, or chambers. If the chamber walls are cold, the condensate takes the form of a finely divided powder which is the *flowers of sulfur* of commerce; if the chamber is allowed to reach a temperature above the melting point of the element, the condensate is liquid sulfur which is poured into round molds where it solidifies to a yellow solid which is quite hard and which is sold as *roll sulfur*, or *brimstone* (burning stone), to use its oldest name.

Deposits of sulfur in Texas and Louisiana lie approximately 900 ft. underground, and often occur where swamps, quicksand, and other nonrigid subsurface structures render the sinking of shafts to the deposits highly impractical. The problem of reaching these rich beds was finally solved in 1902 by Frasch, who had evolved a scheme of sinking a series of four concentric pipes, the largest of which is about 8 in. in diameter, into the layer of sulfur-bearing limestone ($CaCO_3$) which forms a layer above the salt domes characteristic of the region. Water superheated under pressure to a temperature of about 180° C. is forced downward through the two outer pipes. The outermost pipe carries the hot water to the top of the deposit, while the second pipe carries water to the bottom of the deposit. The heat thus delivered is sufficient to melt any nearby sulfur, which then collects in a pool at the bottom of the pipes. Hot compressed air is forced downward through the fourth or innermost pipe, and the molten sulfur and water which have collected are forced upward through the third pipe. At the surface the mixture is run into large pens walled with

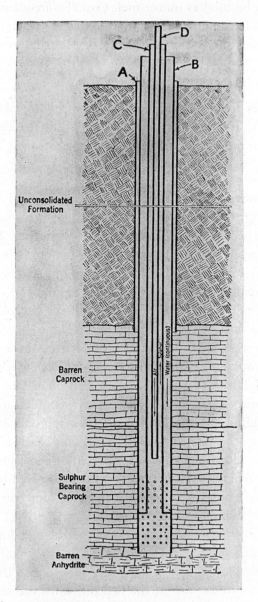

A SULFUR WELL WITH THE FRASCH DEVICE IN
PLACE. (Courtesy, Freeport Sulfur Co.)

boards, from which the water seeps away as the sulfur hardens. Huge piles of sulfur, some containing as much as 100,000 tons, are thus built up. The board walls may be removed and set up elsewhere. An estimate of the sulfur production in the United States in 1945 was 3,753,188 long tons. Late in the same year, the price of sulfur at the mines was $16 per ton.

DISCHARGE FROM A SULFUR WELL POURING INTO A STORAGE VAT.
(Courtesy, Texas Gulf Sulfur Co.)

Countries which have no deposits of free sulfur supply a portion of their needs by securing it as a by-product in the refining of sulfide ores, in the coking of coal, and in the refining of petroleum.

5. Chemical Properties

As was the case with phosphorus, the common method of reaction for sulfur is combination. Having six electrons in its outermost energy level, the sulfur atom will react with anything which will furnish it two electrons. In consequence, it combines directly with all metals save platinum and gold. When it is rubbed with mercury in a mortar, the sulfide of that element is formed, but heat is necessary to bring about its combination with most metals. Large quantities of iron sulfide are prepared by heating together the elements in proper quantities. In all of its binary compounds with metals, the element exhibits an electrovalence of -2.

Unlike silicon and phosphorus, sulfur will combine directly with hydrogen when the gas is passed over boiling sulfur, but the yield of hydrogen sulfide is too small for the process to be of practical value.

In the open air or in an atmosphere of oxygen, elementary sulfur burns with a blue flame largely to produce the dioxide, SO_2, along with traces of the trioxide, SO_3. Here the maximum state of oxidation is not so easily reached as was the case with phosphorus. Sulfur combines readily with fluorine, chlorine, and bromine, but not with iodine, and only with the very active electron-taker fluorine does it show its maximum oxidation number. With the molten element, dry chlorine gas reacts,

$$2S + Cl_2 \rightarrow S_2Cl_2$$

to form sulfur monochloride which is a yellow liquid. As might be expected from their nearness in the third period, sulfur and chlorine also form several

HUGE STOCK PILES OF SULFUR. (Courtesy, Texas Gulf Sulfur Co.)

other chlorides: SCl_2, SCl_4, and S_3Cl_4. These latter are prepared by direct combination under special conditions, and are, in general, of slight importance. The formation of the sulfides of phosphorus—P_4S_3, P_2S_5, P_4S_7, P_2S_3, and P_3S_6— has already been dealt with in the preceding chapter. When coke and sulfur are heated together to a high temperature in the electric furnace, the product is carbon disulfide, CS_2, which is condensed to a colorless, highly volatile liquid. Large quantities of it are prepared for commercial and laboratory use. All of these binary compounds of sulfur and other nonmetals are covalent in nature, but the oxidation numbers of the elements in the various compounds may be counted in the usual manner.

Aqueous solutions of very strong oxidizing agents oxidize sulfur to sulfuric acid:

$$S + 6HNO_3 \xrightarrow[\text{sol.}]{\text{aq.}} H_2SO_4 + 6NO_2 \uparrow + 2H_2O$$

Sulfur reacts with alkaline solutions when boiled with them and with pure alkalies when melted with them. In each case, the products are a complex mixture. Lime-water and sulfur, when boiled together, yield such a mixture, known as *liquid lime-sulfur*. It is used as a fungicidal orchard spray.

6. Hydrogen Sulfide

This compound is the first hydride of any very marked importance to be encountered in the study of the compounds of the first six elements of the third period. Its greater stability is indicated by the fact that it may be prepared, albeit in poor yield, by the direct union of the elements. Its stability is still of a low order, however, as is further shown by the fact that its heat of formation is only 5260 cal./mole. It is decomposed by heat, and above 1700° C. is completely dissociated:

$$S_r + H_2 \rightleftharpoons H_2S + 5260 \text{ cal.}$$

Because of the poor yield obtained by direct union, this hydride is usually prepared by an indirect method similar to that used for the production of the hydrides of silicon and phosphorus; namely, the action of an acid on a metallic binary compound of the element:

$$FeS + 2HCl \rightarrow FeCl_2 + H_2S \uparrow$$

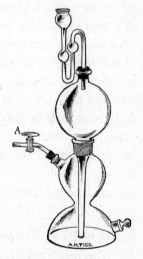

Synthetic ferrous sulfide, referred to in the preceding section, and hydrochloric acid are usually the reagents employed. In smaller laboratories, the gas is usually prepared in the device known as a Kipp generator, which is useful in the preparation of any gas by the action of a liquid on a coarse solid. Sufficient liquid is employed to fill the lower chamber and to extend into the middle chamber to a height sufficient to wet the solid contained there. The gas produced collects in the middle chamber until it exerts sufficient pressure to force the liquid from that compartment. The upper compartment serves as a reservoir to contain the liquid forced from the two lower chambers by pressure of the gas. When gas is withdrawn through the delivery tube at A, the pressure is relieved, the liquid rises into the

A KIPP GENERATOR FOR THE PRODUCTION OF A GAS BY THE ACTION OF A LIQUID ON A SOLID. (Courtesy, Hackh-Grant: "Chemical Dictionary," Philadelphia, The Blakiston Company.)

middle chamber, and more gas is generated until the pressure is again sufficient to separate the reagents. For micro and semi-micro work, smaller generators (cf. the Starkey generator) which operate on the same principle are used, and for the generation of large quantities of the gas, larger generators are employed. Large laboratories frequently purchase cylinders of liquefied hydrogen sulfide from commercial manufacturers.

Laboratory quantities of the gas are sometimes prepared by heating together a mixture of sulfur, paraffin, and shredded asbestos fibers. When the heating is stopped, evolution of the gas ceases. The prepared mixture may be purchased under the trade name of "Aitch-tu-ess."

Hydrogen sulfide is of practical importance as a reagent chemical and it is of theoretical importance because it may be thought of as the fundamental compound of the -2 oxidation state of sulfur and the parent of the family of metallic sulfides.

7. Physical Properties of Hydrogen Sulfide

Since the boiling point of this compound is $-61.8°$ C., at standard pressure it exists as a gas at about $20°$ C. In the lay mind (and perhaps in others as well), its outstanding property is a strong odor highly reminiscent of rotten eggs. As a matter of fact, rotten eggs owe much of their unpleasant odor to hydrogen sulfide which is produced by the anaerobic decomposition of sulfur-bearing proteins in the egg. The freezing point of hydrogen sulfide is $-82.9°$ C. Because of its rather high critical temperature of $100.4°$ C. at standard pressure, it is easily liquefied. The liquid is a nonconductor of electricity. As may be inferred from its gram-molecular weight of 34.08 g., it is more dense than air. The solubility of the gas in 1 ml. of water when under standard pressure is 3.40 ml. at $10°$ C., 2.58 ml. at $20°$ C., and 2.04 ml. at $30°$ C. Boiling completely removes the gas from solution. There are many natural springs whose waters, containing the dissolved gas, are highly valued for their medicinal action. The gas is also soluble in alcohol and other covalent liquids.

8. Chemical Properties of Gaseous Hydrogen Sulfide

The reactions of gaseous hydrogen sulfide are neither numerous nor of great practical importance. Attention has already been directed to the fact that it is somewhat more stable than phosphine. As might be expected from the position of sulfur in the period between phosphorus and chlorine, the gas is less stable than the hydride of chlorine, HCl. Also noted is the reaction between the gas and gaseous sulfur dioxide by which free sulfur is formed. This reaction accents the ability of hydrogen sulfide to act as a reducing agent. When the gas is ignited, it burns readily in an adequate supply of air or oxygen to form sulfur dioxide and water,

$$2H_2S + 3O_2 \rightarrow 2H_2O + 2SO_2$$

but in a limited supply of oxygen the product is finely divided sulfur,

$$2H_2S + O_2 \rightarrow 2H_2O + \underline{2S}$$

Even when sufficient oxygen for complete combustion is at hand, a cold object held in the flame will receive a coating of sulfur. This is believed to be due to the thermal decomposition of the gas into its elements in the interior of the flame. At elevated temperatures, metals which form stable sulfides react with hydrogen sulfide:

$$Cu + H_2S \rightarrow CuS + H_2 \uparrow$$

Hydrogen is a by-product of the reaction, and, since metallic sulfides heated in a stream of hydrogen are reduced to the metal, one more properly writes:

$$Cu + H_2S \rightleftarrows CuS + H_2 \uparrow$$

Even at about 20° C., silver reacts superficially with the gas to form the film of silver sulfide which is the bane of every housewife. Silver alloyed with a small fraction of a per cent of the metal beryllium is reported to be immune to such tarnishing.

Gaseous hydrogen sulfide, because of its paralyzing action upon the respiratory nerve centers, is a dangerous poison. Concentrations of as little as 1 to 3 parts of the gas in 1,000 parts of air are reported to produce death when breathed for any considerable period. Larger concentrations produce their effect in short order, and it is reported that the maximum concentration which the average individual can tolerate for an exposure of one hour is 2 to 3 parts in 10,000 parts of air. Exposure to the gas may produce headaches and nausea. Fainting, which may result in a bad fall, follows continued exposure. The gas is burned into waste products in the blood stream, so usually fresh air produces a complete recovery. Advanced cases of hydrogen sulfide toxemia may require artificial respiration, the administration of oxygen containing 5 per cent of carbon dioxide, and the customary treatment for shock.

9. Chemical Properties of Aqueous Solutions of Hydrogen Sulfide

The solubility of hydrogen sulfide in water has already been noted. When so dissolved it acts both as a very weak acid and as a reducing agent.

A. As an Acid. From the solubility data given in the section on physical properties, it may be calculated that aqueous solutions of the gas at about 20° C. and under standard pressure are about 0.1 molar. Such solutions conduct the electric current poorly, indicating a low degree of ionization (which is, however, sufficient to turn blue litmus red). By analogy to hydrogen chloride and hydrochloric acid, the aqueous solutions of hydrogen sulfide are sometimes referred to as *hydrosulfuric acid*. Ionization occurs as the result of the action of the water dipoles and proceeds in two steps:

$$H_2S \rightleftharpoons H^+ + HS^- \rightleftharpoons 2H^+ + S^{--}$$

The hydrogen ions are, of course, hydrated so that they exist as hydronium ions, H_3O^+. In the 0.1 M solution, only about 0.1 per cent of the molecules undergo the primary degree of ionization, and, as might be anticipated, a much smaller percentage undergoes the second degree. Strong bases react with the aqueous solution to produce two series of salts:

$$NaOH + \quad H_2S \rightarrow NaSH + H_2O$$

and

$$NaOH + NaSH \rightarrow \quad Na_2S + H_2O$$

Such salts, being the salts of strong bases and a very weak acid, are highly hydrolyzed so that their solutions react strongly basic. Solutions of the bases and salts of the metals whose sulfides are insoluble react with aqueous hydrogen sulfide to produce precipitates of the insoluble metallic sulfides. In this case, the small concentration of S^{--} ions in the solution is removed by precipitation, thus disrupting the equilibrium so that more of the HS^- ions and in turn more of the H_2S molecules are dissociated in an attempt to restore the disrupted equilibrium.

B. As a Reducing Agent. In view of the relative instability of hydrogen sulfide with respect to decomposition into its elements, it is not strange that it is readily oxidized by a wide variety of oxidizing agents; or, to say the same thing in reverse, it is not strange that it is a reducing agent with respect to a wide variety of substances which may be reduced. In most cases the sulfide ion is oxidized to free sulfur, a change involving two electrons or two units of valence. Very strong oxidizing agents may oxidize the sulfide ion to an even higher oxidation state. Equations representing some of these characteristic reductions are:

$$H_2S + I_2 \rightarrow 2HI + \underline{S}$$

$$5H_2S + 2KMnO_4 + 6HCl \rightarrow 2KCl + 2MnCl_2 + 8H_2O + \underline{5S}$$

$$3H_2S + 2K_2CrO_4 + 10HCl \rightarrow 4KCl + 2CrCl_3 + 8H_2O + \underline{3S}$$

$$H_2S + 2FeCl_3 \rightarrow 2FeCl_2 + 2HCl + \underline{S}$$

and

$$3H_2S + 2HNO_3(dil.) \rightarrow 2NO \uparrow + 4H_2O + \underline{3S}$$

10. Sulfides

Most of the natural sulfides are the result of the direct union of sulfur and metals when they were heated together. Sulfides may also be prepared by the reduction of sulfates,

$$Na_2SO_4 + 4C \rightarrow Na_2S + 4CO \uparrow$$

a process which is sometimes employed in the preparation of soluble sulfides. A third method of preparation, and the one most frequently employed in the laboratory, is the metathetical reaction of aqueous hydrogen sulfide and a soluble compound of the metal in question. This latter process is, however, suitable for use only with metals which form strong bases or which form insoluble sulfides. Consider, for example, the case of aluminum sulfide, which is soluble. It is a salt of a base weak to the point of being amphoteric and of a very weak acid. Salts which have one or more weak parents have been shown to be susceptible to hydrolysis (cf. section 18, Chapter 17); hence, even if the solid formed by direct union were placed in water, it would be decomposed immediately by hydrolysis to yield $Al(OH)_3$ and H_2S, its slightly ionized parents. In solution, it could not be formed by union of the Al^{+3} and S^{--} ions because these unite instead with the H^+ and OH^- ions of water to form the slightly ionized $Al(OH)_3$ and H_2S. The case of other metallic ions whose bases are weak and whose sulfides are soluble is similar.

Because of its ability to precipitate a great many metallic ions as their insoluble sulfides, hydrogen sulfide finds its greatest use as a laboratory reagent in qualitative chemistry, whose chief concern is the separation and identification of ions. Many of the metallic ions so precipitated have bases which are weak or insoluble, but, because of the greater insolubility of the precipitated sulfides, hydrolysis may not occur to an appreciable extent. The solubility in acid of the water-insoluble sulfides varies considerably. Even in a weakly acidic solution, the sulfides of zinc, iron, cobalt, nickel, and manganese will not precipitate, while the sulfides of lead, mercuric mercury, bismuth, copper, cadmium, arsenic, antimony, and tin precipitate readily. In basic solution, however, the five ions which will not precipitate in acid solution are readily precipitated upon the introduction of hydrogen sulfide. The gas thus serves as a reagent for bringing about an initial separation of metallic ions into three major groups: (a) Those whose sulfides precipitate in acid solution, (b) those whose sulfides are precipitated in alkaline solution, and (c) those whose sulfides are precipitated in neither. Many sulfides are black, but there are a number whose colors are useful in identifying them: manganous sulfide is pale pink; zinc sulfide is white; antimony sulfide is a brilliant orange.

11. Polysulfides

When the soluble normal sulfides of the stronger bases are boiled with free sulfur, there are formed a series of sulfides which contain more sulfur than would be predicted on the basis of the valence of the sulfide ion. Sodium compounds so prepared have the formulas Na_2S_2, Na_2S_3, and Na_2S_4. The compounds Na_2S_5 and Na_2S_6 have been reported, but some investigators believe that the excess sulfur above four atoms is held mechanically. Such compounds may be prepared also by boiling together sulfur and an aqueous solution of the basic hydroxide. Since several of these higher sulfides usually occur together in varying amounts, the formula for the mixture is usually written as Na_2S_x, $(NH_4)_2S_x$, etc., and they are referred to as polysulfides; thus we have sodium polysulfide and ammonium polysulfide, etc. Solutions of the polysulfides vary in color from yellow to brown as their sulfur content is increased. They are unstable, decomposing slowly into free sulfur. They also serve as mild oxidizing agents, and when so used yield some free sulfur. When acid is added to the polysulfides, hydrogen sulfide and free sulfur are formed,

$$Na_2S_4 + 2HCl \rightarrow 2NaCl + H_2S \uparrow + \underline{3S}$$

but under carefully controlled conditions some of the corresponding hydrogen polysulfides are produced. These are foul-smelling, yellow liquids which decompose readily into H_2S and free sulfur.

Liquid lime-sulfur, referred to in section 5, is a mixture of the polysulfides of calcium, which decompose after being sprayed on vegetation to leave a fine deposit of sulfur.

12. Analytical Tests for the Sulfides

The strong, characteristic odor of hydrogen sulfide serves to establish its presence even when it is present in only small amounts. Very small quantities may be detected by the use of filter paper soaked with a solution of lead acetate; a positive test consists of the formation of a lustrous brownish to black film of lead sulfide on the paper.

Soluble sulfides produce a characteristic dark stain on a bright silver surface upon which a drop of their solutions has been placed.

Insoluble sulfides may be treated with hydrochloric acid and a piece of lead acetate test paper, as described above, held in the evolved gas:

$$FeS + 2HCl \rightarrow FeCl_2 + H_2S \uparrow$$

Extremely insoluble sulfides should be treated with zinc and hydrochloric acid. The hydrogen produced by the reaction of these two substances is a powerful reducing agent. Again the lead acetate test paper may be employed:

$$CuS + 2HCl + Zn \rightarrow ZnCl_2 + \underline{Cu} + H_2S \uparrow$$

13. Halides

Most important among the halides of sulfur is the monochloride whose preparation from the elements was referred to in section 5. It may also be prepared by passing dry chlorine gas into carbon disulfide containing a little iodine:

$$CS_2 + 3Cl_2 \rightarrow CCl_4 + S_2Cl_2$$

Both products are liquids; they can be separated by fractional distillation since the former boils at 76.8° C. while the latter boils at 135.6° C. without decomposition. The freezing point of sulfur monochloride is $-80°$ C.; its density is 1.678 g./ml. It has a highly unpleasant odor and fumes in moist air.

Pronounced susceptibility to hydrolysis accounts for the fumes mentioned above. With water, the chloride reacts to form HCl, SO_2, S, and other sulfur-containing compounds. Vapor density measurements show the molecular formula to be S_2Cl_2, and investigations indicate that both chlorine atoms are attached to the same sulfur atom. At temperatures between 6° and 10° C. it reacts with more chlorine to form the dichloride, SCl_2, and below $-22°$ C. it reacts with still more chlorine to form the tetrachloride, SCl_4.

Sulfur monochloride reacts with ethylene to produce mustard gas, a substance introduced into warfare by the Germans at the battle of Ypres during World War I:

$$S_2Cl_2 + 2C_2H_4 \rightarrow (C_2H_4)_2Cl_2S + \underline{S}$$

Mustard *gas* is not a gas but a liquid which is *atomized* to produce a fine mist.

In contact with the skin and mucous membranes it causes severe burns. Its chemical name is β-β'-dichlorodiethylsulfide.

The monochloride of sulfur is a good solvent for sulfur, iodine, and a wide variety of other substances. Solutions of sulfur in it are commonly used in the vulcanization of rubber.

14. Oxides of Sulfur

Six oxides of sulfur are known; namely, SO, sulfur monoxide; S_2O_3, sulfur sesquioxide (*sesqui-* is derived from the Latin and means one and a half); SO_2, sulfur dioxide; SO_3, sulfur trioxide; S_2O_7, sulfur heptoxide; and SO_4, sulfur tetroxide. Of these compounds, only the dioxide and trioxide are common enough and of sufficient general importance to warrant their discussion in some detail in an elementary text. Some sulfur monoxide is produced along with sulfur dioxide when sulfur is burned in oxygen. The yield is reported to increase as the pressure under which the reaction is carried out is reduced, reaching a maximum of 40 per cent at a pressure of 5 mm. of mercury. It is a colorless gas, reportedly stable at room temperature but decomposing into its constituent elements when heated. The sesquioxide is obtained as bluish-green crystals by the reaction of sulfur with anhydrous sulfur trioxide. This substance is very unstable, and, in consequence, highly reactive. It hydrolyzes even in cold water with the liberation of free sulfur and the formation of a mixture of the oxygen acids of sulfur. There is some question as to whether the heptoxide is a true compound, since its chemical behavior would indicate that it may be an addition product of either the trioxide and oxygen, or the trioxide and the tetroxide. It is prepared by the action of ozonized oxygen on either the dioxide or the trioxide. It crystallizes at $0°$ C. and decomposes readily unless kept cold. Upon addition to water, it hydrolyzes to liberate oxygen and to form a mixture of the oxygen acids of sulfur. The tetroxide is reported as being formed when a silent electric discharge is passed through a $1:10$ mixture of sulfur dioxide and oxygen at a pressure of 0.5 mm. of mercury. Colorless crystals are said to form at $3°$ C., and at about $20°$ C. the substance decomposes into oxygen, ozone (O_3), and S_2O_7, which undergoes further decomposition as mentioned above.

15. Sulfur Dioxide

The strong odor characteristic of burning sulfur is that of sulfur dioxide, which is produced by the combustion. The burning of sulfur—or brimstone, as it has long been called—has been known since prehistoric times, and the gas produced has long been used as both a fumigating and a bleaching agent. The colorless gas so produced was first recognized as a definite compound by Priestley in 1775, and its formula, SO_2, was established by Lavoisier in 1777.

At normal pressures, the gas liquefies at $-10°$ C., but it is easily liquefied at about $20°$ C., since its critical temperature is $157.2°$ C. The liquid, which is an excellent polar solvent, freezes to a snowy solid at $-72.7°$ C. Freezing may be brought about by allowing the liquid to evaporate rapidly. Shortly, the temperature is lowered sufficiently to cause the crystallization of the remaining liquid. Sulfur dioxide gas has a density of 2.9269 g. per liter, from which it may be calculated that it is 2.26 times as heavy as air, and may therefore be collected in an upright container. Because of its solubility, the gas cannot be caught by displacement of water. At $0°$ C., the solubility of the gas in 1 ml. of water is 79.9 ml., and at $20°$ C., 39.4 ml., the gas volumes being calculated at S.T.P. The gas reacts slightly with the water to form sulfurous acid, but is expelled completely when the solution is boiled. Liquefied sulfur dioxide has a density of 1.46 g./ml. at its boiling point. Because of its relatively low vapor pressure, it may be stored and transported in comparatively light metal cylinders. The high critical temperature of the gas, its relatively low vapor pressure at about $20°$ C., its high heat of vaporization (87.7 cal. per gram), its low cost, and its inertness toward metals when dry, make sulfur dioxide an excellent refrigerant for home-type refrigerators. *Freon* (difluorodichloromethane), however, is gradually displacing it in small refrigerators.

16. Preparation of Sulfur Dioxide

Although the gas is found free in volcanic regions and dissolved in the hot springs of such localities, this does not constitute a practical source. On a commercial scale, the three principal sources are:

(*a*) *the burning of sulfur,*

$$S + O_2 \rightarrow SO_2 \uparrow$$

(*b*) *the burning of pyrite* (*FeS*$_2$), large deposits of which occur in some of our western states,

$$4FeS_2 + 11O_2 \xrightarrow{\Delta} 2Fe_2O_3 + 8SO_2 \uparrow$$

(*c*) *the roasting of sulfide ores*, in which process the gas is obtained as a by-product in the refining of the ores, for example,

$$2ZnS + 3O_2 \rightarrow \underline{2ZnO} + 2SO_2 \uparrow$$

Collection and use of the gas produced by this last method has relieved a number of communities where such refineries are located of a scourge which in the past has killed vegetation for miles around. In this country, the major portion of commercial SO_2 is produced by the burning of sulfur. It is calculated that more sulfur is contained in the SO_2 evolved in the refining of sulfide ores than is mined in Texas and Louisiana in a like period; most of these by-product gases are still wasted, constituting a nuisance and a health hazard and causing still further losses.

In general, the foregoing methods are not suitable for the production of small quantities of the gas for laboratory use. Methods commonly employed there are:

(*a*) *the reduction of sulfuric acid by a number of reducing agents*, the commonest of which are copper and carbon,

$$2H_2SO_4 + Cu \rightarrow CuSO_4 + SO_2 \uparrow + 2H_2O$$
$$2H_2SO_4 + C \rightarrow CO_2 \uparrow + 2SO_2 \uparrow + 2H_2O$$

and (*b*) *the decomposition of soluble sulfites and bisulfites by acids*,

$$Na_2SO_3 + 2HCl \rightarrow 2NaCl + SO_2 \uparrow + H_2O$$
$$NaHSO_3 + HCl \rightarrow NaCl + SO_2 \uparrow + H_2O$$

When larger quantities are needed in the laboratory, it is customary to buy a cylinder of the liquefied substance from a commercial producer.

17. *Chemical Properties of Sulfur Dioxide*

Sulfur dioxide is very stable to decomposition by heat. Even at temperatures in excess of 2000° C. it is dissociated to only a slight extent. With oxygen it shows little tendency to react save in the presence of a catalyst; in this respect, it differs markedly from the intermediate oxide of phosphorus, P_2O_3, which is easily oxidized to P_2O_5. Upon being heated with a number of oxides, however, it forms sulfates, for example,

$$PbO_2 + SO_2 \xrightarrow{\Delta} PbSO_4$$

With anhydrous chlorine, the anhydrous dioxide reacts to form *sulfuryl chloride* (SO_2Cl_2),

$$SO_2 + Cl_2 \xrightarrow{\Delta} SO_2Cl_2$$

The reaction is catalyzed by camphor and requires the energizing effect of ultraviolet light. Phosphorus pentachloride reacts upon SO_2 in its usual manner to remove oxygen forming *thionyl chloride* and *phosphoryl chloride*,

$$SO_2 + PCl_5 \xrightarrow{\Delta} SOCl_2 + POCl_3$$

The products, which are both liquids, are separated by fractional distillation. Both the sulfuryl and thionyl chlorides find considerable use in organic chemistry. Dissolved in water, the dioxide reacts slightly to form a weak solution of sulfurous acid:

$$SO_2 + H_2O \rightleftharpoons H_2SO_3$$

18. *Sulfurous Acid*

This acid belongs to the group of *hypothetical acids*, since it cannot be isolated in pure form. Attempts to concentrate its solutions by evaporation result only in the reversal of the equilibrium given above and the subsequent total decomposition of the acid. That the solution contains an acid may be shown by its action on litmus and other indicators, and that the acid is sulfurous acid is shown by the fact that upon the addition of bases, sulfites, which may be isolated, are formed. The principal chemical behaviors of the solution of SO_2 in water (sulfurous acid) are:

A. As an Acid. As an acid it is dibasic. The primary degree of ionization is moderately strong, while the secondary degree is very weak. There are thus possible two series of salts—the normal sulfites and the acid sulfites or bisulfites—but only the strong bases and those which form insoluble sulfites will yield the normal salt:

$$H_2SO_3 + NaOH \rightarrow NaHSO_3 + H_2O$$

and

$$H_2SO_3 + 2NaOH \rightarrow Na_2SO_3 + 2H_2O$$

Being salts of strong bases and a weak acid, these compounds are highly hydrolyzed in solution.

B. As a Reducing Agent. It is readily seen that, in sulfurous acid, the oxidation number of the sulfur atom is $+4$, a state intermediate between the highest and lowest of which the element is capable. Conceivably, then, the compound could be converted to others in which the oxidation number of sulfur might be either higher or lower. Such is the case. The acid is easily oxidized, acting itself as a reducing agent, and though it is less readily reduced it may be so treated, in which case it acts as an oxidizing agent. The direction of the change depends largely upon the nature and strength of the reagents employed. It is a good reducing agent with soluble permanganates, chromates and dichromates, hydrogen peroxide, chlorine, and other strong oxidizing agents, and is always converted by such agents to sulfates, in which the oxidation number of the sulfur atom is $+6$:

$$5H_2SO_3 + 2KMnO_4 \rightarrow 2H_2SO_4 + K_2SO_4 + 2MnSO_4 + 3H_2O$$
$$3H_2SO_3 + 2K_2CrO_4 + 4HCl \rightarrow Cr_2(SO_4)_3 + 4KCl + 5H_2O$$
$$H_2SO_3 + H_2O_2 \rightarrow H_2SO_4 + H_2O$$
$$H_2SO_3 + Cl_2 + H_2O \rightarrow H_2SO_4 + 2HCl$$

In the presence of ultraviolet light, the acid solution gradually undergoes auto-oxidation-reduction:

$$3H_2SO_3 \rightarrow 2H_2SO_4 + \underline{S} + H_2O$$

c. As an Oxidizing Agent. There are only a few common examples of this behavior of the acid, since it occurs only with substances which are easily oxidized—that is, with strong reducing agents. The two reactions chosen show that in some instances the sulfur is reduced to the zero valence state while in others it is reduced to the -2 state:

$$H_2SO_3 + 2H_2S \rightarrow \underline{3S} + 3H_2O$$

and

$$H_2SO_3 + 3Zn + 6HCl \rightarrow H_2S \uparrow + 3ZnCl_2 + 3H_2O$$

d. As a Toxic Agent. Solutions of sulfurous acid formed by the absorption of gaseous sulfur dioxide are poisonous to plants and to animals ranging in size from microörganisms to man. It is less poisonous than hydrogen sulfide to humans; furthermore, it is so irritating that few individuals ever absorb enough of the gas to suffer any very serious consequences. Small quantities of the gas are added to molasses and other canned foods to kill bacteria which might otherwise cause decomposition to take place. Sulfur is often burned as a fumigant, and the action of sulfur dioxide on plant life near smelter towns has been cited.

e. As a Bleaching Agent. With many synthetic and natural coloring matters, sulfur dioxide reacts in the presence of water to remove the color—apparently by forming more or less stable addition compounds which are colorless. Paper, wool, straw, and other substances which might be injured by more acidic agents are bleached in this way. Materials so bleached upon exposure to light and air usually regain their yellowish color slowly. Some foods, such as dried fruits, are bleached by the action of sulfur dioxide. Even though most of the sulfur compounds are removed after treatment, too frequent consumption of such foods is discouraged by some medical authorities.

19. Sulfites and Bisulfites

As has been noted, sulfurous acid forms two series of salts. In general, the important salts of both series are those of the metals of the I A and II A families. For the most part, these salts are water-soluble, though the sulfite of barium is only sparingly soluble. A number of the salts of the heavier metals are not soluble in water, but all members of both series are soluble in dilute acid, with which they react to liberate sulfur dioxide. Upon being heated, solutions of sodium bisulfite yield first the normal sulfite, SO_2, and water:

$$2NaHSO_3 \xrightarrow{\Delta} Na_2SO_3 + H_2O + SO_2 \uparrow$$

Upon further heating, the normal sulfite decomposes thus:

$$4Na_2SO_3 \xrightarrow{\Delta} 3Na_2SO_4 + Na_2S$$

undergoing autooxidation-reduction. Most of the normal sulfites decompose when heated to give normal sulfates and other products which vary with the specific nature of the heated salt.

Like their parent acid, the sulfites are easily oxidized and hence are good reducing agents. Their aqueous solutions are oxidized by the air to sulfates:

$$2Na_2SO_3 + O_2 \rightarrow 2Na_2SO_4$$

The speed of this reaction is affected by a wide variety of both positive and negative catalysts. Mild oxidizing agents react with neutral or slightly alkaline solutions of sodium sulfite to form dithionates instead of the sulfates. Such a reaction occurs when the bisulfite is used to remove deposits of insoluble manganese dioxide from glassware or the skin:

$$MnO_2 + 2NaHSO_3 \rightarrow MnS_2O_6 + 2NaOH$$

When sodium hydroxide solution is treated with an excess of sulfur dioxide, upon evaporation of the water there are obtained crystals of sodium metabisulfite, $Na_2S_2O_5$, which is widely used in photographic development. This salt may be considered to be the dehydration product of sodium bisulfite, hence the use of the prefix meta:

$$2NaHSO_3 - H_2O \rightarrow Na_2S_2O_5$$

Sulfites find considerable use in the laboratory and in the chemistry of the photographic darkroom. Aqueous solutions of calcium bisulfite, $Ca(HSO_3)_2$, are used in huge volumes in the sulfite process for making paper, the bisulfite dissolving the lignin from wood to leave cellulose. Sulfite solutions are also used on a commercial scale to separate the protein and carbohydrate portions of wheat and other grains.

20. Sulfur Trioxide

Sulfur trioxide is noteworthy as the anhydride of sulfuric acid, which is one of the most important of industrial reagents; otherwise, however, it finds little use. At about 20° C., it is a colorless liquid which fumes readily in moist air. Its boiling point is 44.8° C., and, when heated further, the gas shows a tendency to dissociate into oxygen and sulfur dioxide. (Contrast this behavior with that of P_2O_5, the corresponding oxide of phosphorus.) Upon being cooled, the liquid forms transparent, glacial crystals (α-sulfur trioxide) whose melting point is 16.83° C. These crystals also fume in moist air, and, upon standing, gradually change into an opaque mass of fibrous, asbestos-like crystals of which there appear to be two modifications (β- and γ-sulfur trioxide). The properties of the solid, therefore, vary somewhat as the quantities of the three polymorphic forms present vary.

21. Preparation of Sulfur Trioxide

While sulfur dioxide and oxygen will unite in the absence of a catalyst, the reaction is much too slow to be of any practical value. Under proper conditions of temperature, and with a suitable catalyst, the reaction proceeds rapidly to give good yields; the process is of great commercial value:

$$2SO_2 + O_2 \leftrightarrows 2SO_3 + 44,400 \text{ cal.}$$

In the presence of a platinum catalyst, the gaseous mixture which issues from an industrial sulfur burner and contains about 10 per cent oxygen, 7 per cent sulfur dioxide, and 83 per cent nitrogen (inert in the reaction) produces at 434° C. an optimum yield of the trioxide equal to 99 per cent of the theoretical. Inferior yields are obtained at lower and at higher temperatures. At 250° C., the yield is 45 per cent of the theoretical, while, at 1000° C., the yield is zero. Since the production of the trioxide is essentially for the manufacture of sulfuric acid, details of its commercial preparation will be discussed in the section describing the manufacture of that important compound.

In the laboratory, small quantities of sulfur trioxide may be obtained by:

(*a*) *dehydrating sulfuric acid with phosphorus pentoxide,*

$$H_2SO_4 + P_2O_5 \xrightarrow{\Delta} SO_3 \uparrow + 2HPO_3$$

(*b*) *heating a sulfate of a weak base* (in general, these are the sulfates of the heavy metals),

$$Fe_2(SO_4)_3 \xrightarrow{\Delta} Fe_2O_3 + 3SO_3 \uparrow$$

(*c*) *distilling pyrosulfuric acid,*

$$H_2S_2O_7 \xrightarrow{\Delta} H_2SO_4 + SO_3 \uparrow$$

22. Chemical Properties of Sulfur Trioxide

That the trioxide when heated will decompose into the dioxide and oxygen has already been noted. With phosphorus pentachloride it reacts to form sulfuryl chloride:

$$SO_3 + PCl_5 \rightarrow SO_2Cl_2 + POCl_3$$

The two oxychlorides thus formed are liquids at about 20° C. and may be separated by fractional distillation. Many metallic oxides and hydroxides unite with the trioxide to form sulfates and bisulfates:

$$BaO + SO_3 \rightarrow BaSO_4$$

and

$$NaOH + SO_3 \rightarrow NaHSO_4$$

This illustrates the point that salts may be thought of not only as the metathetical products of acids and bases, but also as the combination products of nonmetallic oxides and metallic oxides, or of acid anhydrides and basic anhydrides. The most important reaction of sulfur trioxide is that with water to form sulfuric acid:

$$SO_3 + H_2O \rightarrow H_2SO_4 + 40,000 \text{ cal.}$$

Because the reaction is so highly exothermic, each particle of the trioxide tends to become surrounded by a jacket of steam which separates it from the water, thus delaying its dissolution. To obviate this difficulty, the SO_3 is usually dissolved in concentrated sulfuric acid to form pyrosulfuric acid, which is then allowed to react with the water requisite for the formation of sulfuric acid:

$$SO_3 + H_2SO_4 \rightarrow H_2S_2O_7$$

and

$$H_2S_2O_7 + H_2O \rightarrow 2H_2SO_4$$

Traces of water cause the polymerization of SO_3 to S_2O_6, which is a white solid at about $20°$ C.

It will be recalled that several different hydration products of phosphorus pentoxide are known, and mention has already been made of two acids derived

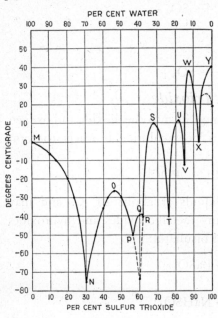

from this corresponding oxide of sulfur. Other hydrates also are known. Their existence is conveniently shown by the freezing-point method. On the diagram of the freezing-point curve of various mixtures of sulfur trioxide and water, the freezing point of pure water is represented by the point M and that of the pure trioxide by the point Y. The maxima in the curve represent the composition of single compounds while the minima are the eutectic points between adjacent pairs of compounds. The eutectic temperature for any pair of compounds represents the lowest freezing point of any mixture of the two. Below that temperature, the two substances crystallize out in such proportions that the concentration of the liquid mixture from which they are freezing re-

FREEZING-POINT DIAGRAM OF THE HYDRATES OF SULFUR TRIOXIDE.

mains the same. By application of this method it is possible to determine the composition of the compounds formed by two reagents without isolating and analyzing each of them. From the accompanying diagram, it will be noted that the various hydrates formed are:

$$\text{At point O} \quad 1SO_3 + 5H_2O = H_{10}SO_8$$
$$\text{``} \quad \text{``} \quad Q \quad 1SO_3 + 3H_2O = H_6SO_6$$
$$\text{``} \quad \text{``} \quad S \quad 1SO_3 + 2H_2O = H_4SO_5$$
$$\text{``} \quad \text{``} \quad U \quad 1SO_3 + 1H_2O = H_2SO_4$$
$$\text{``} \quad \text{``} \quad W \quad 2SO_3 + 1H_2O = H_2S_2O_7$$

Of these hydrates, H_2SO_4 and $H_2S_2O_7$ are of greatest practical importance.

23. Physical Properties of Sulfuric Acid

Anhydrous hydrogen sulfate (H_2SO_4) is a colorless, syrupy liquid whose density at 20° C. is 1.8305 g./ml. It solidifies to give crystals whose melting point is 10.5° C., but it is so hygroscopic that its actual freezing point is usually lower. Upon being heated, it begins to decompose, losing principally the trioxide. Boiling begins in the neighborhood of 270° C. The evolution of the trioxide continues, and the boiling point rises until it reaches 338° C., at which temperature it becomes constant (cf. section 17 of Chapter 12). The constant boiling sulfuric acid contains 98.3 per cent of hydrogen sulfate, and has a density of 1.835 g./ml. The heat of hydration of hydrogen sulfate is large. In an excess of water this heat has been measured to be 21,000 cal./mole. Because of this liberation of heat, water, which is less dense than the acid, should never be poured into the acid. The steam developed may throw hot water and acid back on the worker. *Sulfuric acid should always be poured into the water.*

24. Manufacture of Sulfuric Acid

Two methods of manufacturing this important reagent find general application. The older of these processes is the *lead chamber process;* the more modern is the *contact process.*

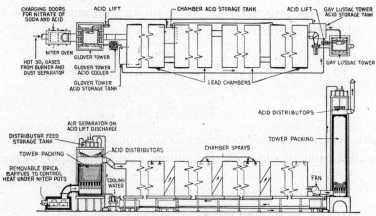

DIAGRAM OF A LEAD CHAMBER SULFURIC ACID PLANT.

A. THE LEAD CHAMBER PROCESS. The essential reactions of this method are carried out in the gaseous phase; hence, on the commercial scale, a very large apparatus is required. To provide the requisite space, large rooms lined with sheet lead have been found most satisfactory; from this has come the name of the process. Lead is chosen as a lining material because, although it reacts with sulfuric acid, it soon becomes coated with a closely adhering layer of lead sulfate which serves to prevent further action. Usually six or eight lead chambers are used, but for purpose of elucidation a four-chamber plant is represented in the accompanying diagram. Usually, the chambers are arranged in the form of a ⊔ with the two towers side by side.

In a rotary kiln, or burner, sulfur dioxide is produced by one of the three commercial methods cataloged in section 16. The hot gas thus produced passes over the niter pot, where it becomes mixed with gaseous hydrogen nitrate which is produced in the pot by the following reaction:

$$NaNO_3 + H_2SO_4 \rightarrow NaHSO_4 + HNO_3$$

This mixture of gases then rises through the Glover tower, heating the siliceous checker work there and forming some sulfuric acid as it cools:

$$3SO_2 + 2HNO_3 + 2H_2O \rightarrow 3H_2SO_4 + 2NO$$

Water for the reaction arises from concentration of the previously prepared acid, as will be seen shortly, and oxides of nitrogen collected at the end of the process are also added here. The moderately concentrated acid which collects in the bottom of the tower is drained into a pressure storage tank.

From the Glover tower a mixture of the gases SO_2, NO_2, NO, and air enters the chambers into which jets of steam are also injected. The reactions which occur in the chambers are, in essence:

$$2NO + O_2 \rightarrow 2NO_2$$
$$NO_2 + SO_2 \rightarrow SO_3 + NO$$

and

$$SO_3 + H_2O \rightarrow H_2SO_4$$

Also there occurs a series of complicated reactions which are not thoroughly understood, by one of which nitrosyl sulfuric acid, $H(NO)SO_4$, is formed.

$$2SO_2 + NO_2 + NO + O_2 + H_2O \rightarrow 2SO_2 \begin{smallmatrix} \diagup OH \\ \diagdown O\text{---}NO \end{smallmatrix}$$

In the presence of sufficient water, this substance is decomposed thus,

$$2H(NO)SO_4 + H_2O \rightarrow 2H_2SO_4 + NO\uparrow + NO_2\uparrow$$

but if too little water is present it forms crystals which collect on the chamber walls. The chamber acid has a concentration of 60 per cent to 70 per cent of H_2SO_4, and is drawn off into pressure storage tanks.

It will have been noted that the oxides of nitrogen are being used, regenerated, and again recycled; they are thus functioning as a homogeneous catalyst. From the last chamber some of them emerge as gases and would be lost were it not arranged to collect them. They are, therefore, led into the bottom of a tower, the Gay-Lussac tower, which is filled with a checker work over which the moderately concentrated acid from the pressure tank at the foot of the Glover tower is falling. The counter current of gases is cooled and nitrosyl sulfuric acid is formed. It collects in a third pressure storage tank. From there, it is forced by air pressure to the top of the Glover tower where it descends through the tower to be decomposed again into sulfuric acid and the oxides of nitrogen, which may then reënter the chambers. Dilute acid from the second pressure storage tank is also forced to the top of the Glover tower, and as it descends over the heated checkerwork water is given off in the form of steam which is carried into the chambers, while concentrated acid descends to the bottom of the tower.

The acid so produced is first concentrated by evaporation in lead vats until its density is about 1.7 g./ml. Further concentration is conducted in duriron vats. The concentrated acid of commerce has a density of 1.83 to 1.84 g./ml., is known as *oil of vitriol*, and is shipped in iron tank cars. The concentrated acid has little action on iron because of the formation of a protective coat of iron sulfate crystals.

B. THE CONTACT PROCESS. In this process, sulfur is usually the source of the sulfur dioxide used. The gas produced by the burning of the sulfur is first run through a precipitator which removes colloidal dust particles; it is then washed with water and next dried in a tower over whose siliceous checker work concentrated sulfuric acid trickles. It next enters a device which further assists in the removal of any arsenic which might be present, and lastly it is preheated before it enters with a stream of purified air into the series of two towers which contain the catalyst. The catalyst formerly used was finely divided platinum, but it was very expensive and easily "poisoned" by arsenic and other impurities which might be present. At the present time, the catalyst used is usually vanadium pentoxide, V_2O_5, which is much cheaper and not susceptible to poisoning by arsenic. These catalysts are of the heterogeneous, or contact, type, hence the name of the process. The gaseous SO_3 formed is dissolved in concentrated sulfuric acid and this is diluted as discussed in section 22. Solu-

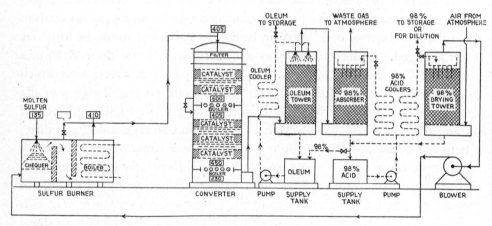

DIAGRAM OF A CONTACT PLANT FOR THE CONVERSION OF SULFUR TO SULFURIC ACID. (Courtesy, C. M. Dean.)

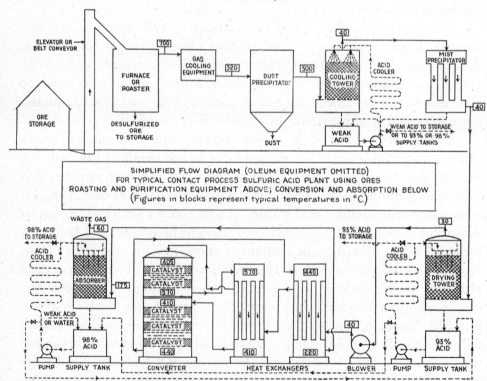

DIAGRAM OF A PLANT FOR THE CONVERSION OF SULFUR DIOXIDE OBTAINED IN THE REFINING OF ORES TO SULFURIC ACID BY THE CONTACT PROCESS. (Courtesy, C. M. Dean.)

tions of sulfur trioxide in concentrated sulfuric acid are known commercially as *oleum, fuming sulfuric acid,* and *Nordhausen acid.*

The acid produced by this process is more nearly pure than that of the chamber process, and it has the added advantage of not requiring to be concentrated. Most of the newer plants are of the contact type, but more than half of the United States production of sulfuric acid is still by the chamber process.

25. *Chemical Properties of Sulfuric Acid*

The instability of the acid to heat has already been noted. Its other chemical properties are related to the fact that it is (a) a strong acid of low volatility, (b) a good oxidizing agent, and (c) a good drying and dehydrating agent, when concentrated.

Sulfuric acid, while in water less highly ionized than hydrochloric acid, is classed, nevertheless, as a moderately strong acid. In dilute solutions its primary stage of ionization is almost complete. Its second stage of ionization is much weaker, and in concentrated solutions it is very slight. Because it may ionize thus in two stages, it forms two series of salts: (1) the normal sulfates and (2) the acid sulfates, or bisulfates, representative of which are the sodium salts Na_2SO_4 and $NaHSO_4$. Because of its low volatility, the concentrated acid reacts with the salts of many volatile acids to liberate the free acids. (Cf. the production of HCl, section 6, Chapter 10.)

$$NaNO_3 + H_2SO_4 \rightarrow NaHSO_4 + HNO_3 \uparrow$$

and

$$NaC_2H_3O_2 + H_2SO_4 \rightarrow NaHSO_4 + HC_2H_3O_2 \uparrow$$

As solutions of the acid become more concentrated, its ionization decreases (cf. section 7, Chapter 14) and its properties as an oxidizing agent become more prominent. When acting in this latter capacity, it is reduced to the dioxide by moderately strong reducing agents but to free sulfur or a sulfide by stronger ones. It converts metallic reducing agents to sulfates, while nonmetallic agents are usually oxidized to their oxides or to the free element.

$$Cu + 2H_2SO_4 \rightarrow CuSO_4 + SO_2 \uparrow + 2H_2O$$
$$C + 2H_2SO_4 \rightarrow CO_2 \uparrow + 2SO_2 \uparrow + 2H_2O$$

and

$$8HI + H_2SO_4 \rightarrow 4I_2 + H_2S \uparrow + 4H_2O$$

The hot acid is much more reactive as an oxidizing agent than is the cold.

Because of the affinity of hydrogen sulfate for water, strong solutions of it are frequently used in desiccators, drying trains, etc., to absorb water vapor, and in many reversible reactions in which water is one of the products it is also used as a drying agent. The highly concentrated acid also acts as a dehydrating agent upon many substances, including wood, table sugar ($C_{12}H_{22}O_{11}$), alcohol, etc.:

$$C_{12}H_{22}O_{11} \xrightarrow{H_2SO_4} 12C + 11H_2O$$

and

$$C_2H_5OH \xrightarrow{H_2SO_4} C_2H_4 + H_2O$$

26. Sulfates

As a class, the sulfates may be considered to be rather soluble, and for that reason various ones of them find wide use. The least soluble of the group is that of barium, with that of lead a none-too-close second. Most of them crystallize from solution with several molecules of water of crystallization: $CaSO_4.2H_2O$, $MgSO_4.7H_2O$, $Al_2(SO_4)_3.18H_2O$. Natural deposits of the sulfates of the metals of the II A family are found, but those of the other metals are usually obtained by the action of sulfuric acid on a compound of the metal in question. Sodium sulfate is derived principally as a by-product in the manufacture of hydrochloric acid from salt. In solution, these salts have no oxidizing ability, but when dry they react with certain strong reducing agents, on heating, as has been noted in the case of carbon:

$$Na_2SO_4 + 4C \rightarrow Na_2S + 4CO \uparrow$$

When heated, the bisulfates form the corresponding pyrosulfates:

$$2NaHSO_4 \xrightarrow{\Delta} Na_2S_2O_7 + H_2O \uparrow$$

These revert to sulfates as soon as they are dissolved in water, but in the dry state they are useful for converting insoluble, basic oxides to soluble salts:

$$3Na_2S_2O_7 + Al_2O_3 \rightarrow Al_2(SO_4)_3 + 3Na_2SO_4$$

Some sulfates and their uses are:

$Al_2(SO_4)_3.18H_2O$..Aluminum sulfate octadecahydrate..Mordant; water purification

$ZnSO_4.7H_2O$......Zinc sulfate heptahydrate.........Wood preservative

$MgSO_4.7H_2O$.....Magnesium sulfate heptahydrate....Medicine; source of (Epsom salt)   magnesium

$CuSO_4.5H_2O$......Cupric sulfate pentahydrate........Copper plating; wet batteries

27. *Analytical Tests for the Sulfate Ion*

The SO_4^{--} ion is usually tested for qualitatively by adding a solution of a barium salt to its solution. Barium ions and sulfate ions unite instantaneously to form a white, finely divided precipitate of insoluble barium sulfate. Insoluble sulfates may be reduced with carbon, as mentioned in the preceding section, to form sulfides, solutions of which when added to a bright silver coin produce a stain of silver sulfide. This latter reaction is known as the *hepar test.*

Quantitatively, the sulfur in most sulfur compounds is determined by oxidizing it to the sulfate ion, which is then precipitated as barium sulfate which may be collected and weighed; or the solution containing the sulfate ion may be titrated with a standard solution of barium chloride and with the organic compound tetrahydroxyquinone as an indicator. It turns pink at the end-point due to the presence of free barium ions.

28. *Uses of Sulfuric Acid*

From the standpoint of quantity consumed, sulfuric acid is one of the most important of the heavy industrial chemicals. The industries and processes

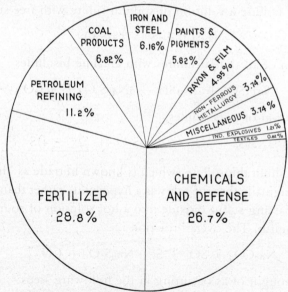

CONSUMPTION OF SULFURIC ACID BY INDUSTRIES IN THE
UNITED STATES FOR 1944.

in which it is used are far too numerous to list, let alone to discuss. In 1943, 13,917,000 short tons of sulfuric acid of a density of 1.526 g./ml. were consumed in the United States alone.

29. *Thiosulfuric Acid and the Thiosulfates*

Theion is the Greek word for sulfur. Its use in the foregoing terms is intended to convey the idea that one of the oxygen atoms of the sulfate radical, SO_4^{--}, has in these compounds been replaced by a sulfur atom (note the relative positions of oxygen and sulfur in the periodic chart) to give the radical $S_2O_3^{--}$. Thiosulfuric acid is a hypothetical acid which cannot be isolated because its solutions, upon being heated, immediately undergo decomposition to yield water, sulfur dioxide, and sulfur:

$$H_2S_2O_3 \overset{\Delta}{\rightarrow} H_2SO_3 + \underline{S} \rightarrow H_2O + SO_2 \uparrow + S$$

Sulfur monoxide is held to be the anhydride of the acid:

$$2SO + H_2O \rightarrow H_2S_2O_3$$

A number of the salts of the acid, the thiosulfates, are known. The thiosulfates of a majority of the heavy metals are unstable to both water and heat. The most important of the metallic salts is sodium thiosulfate, which in the laboratory may be made by boiling a solution of sodium sulfite with free sulfur,

$$Na_2SO_3 + S \rightarrow Na_2S_2O_3$$

by the interaction of alkaline bisulfites with alkaline bisulfides

$$4NaHSO_3 + 2NaSH \rightarrow 3Na_2S_2O_3 + 3H_2O$$

and by the oxidation of polysulfides,

$$2Na_2S_x + 3O_2 \rightarrow 2Na_2S_2O_3 + \underline{(2x - 4)S}$$

Commercially, sodium thiosulfate (which is known in trade as "hypo" because it was thought originally that the salt was a hyposulfite rather than a thiosulfate) is produced by passing sulfur dioxide into a hot solution of sodium carbonate containing free sulfur. The overall reaction is

$$Na_2CO_3 + SO_2 + S \rightarrow Na_2S_2O_3 + CO_2 \uparrow$$

which may be thought of as occurring in the following steps:

$$H_2O + SO_2 \rightarrow H_2SO_3$$
$$H_2SO_3 + Na_2CO_3 \rightarrow Na_2SO_3 + H_2O + CO_2 \uparrow$$
$$Na_2SO_3 + S \rightarrow Na_2S_2O_3$$

The salt so produced crystallizes from solution in large colorless crystals of the formula $Na_2S_2O_3.5H_2O$. The melting point of the hydrate is 48° C., and in the liquid state it is easily supercooled. When acidified, the salt decomposes rapidly into sulfur and sulfur dioxide; presumably the unstable acid is first formed:

$$Na_2S_2O_3 + 2HCl \rightarrow 2NaCl + H_2S_2O_3 \rightarrow 2NaCl + H_2O + SO_2 \uparrow + \underline{S}$$

Even carbonic acid, as weak as it is, is sufficiently strong to displace thiosulfuric acid from its salts.

The uses of sodium thiosulfate, "hypo," are:

A. AS A FIXING AGENT IN PHOTOGRAPHY. When an exposed film is "developed," the silver halides on that part of the film which was exposed to light are reduced to free silver. The developer does not affect the unexposed halides. It is the function of the "fixer" to remove these unreacted salts from the film. Sodium thiosulfate achieves its purpose by combining with the silver halides to form soluble, complex silver salts.

B. AS AN ANTICHLOR IN BLEACHING PROCESSES. Cotton cloth, paper, and a number of other products are bleached by the use of chlorine. When the process is complete, it is necessary to remove remaining chlorine and acids of chlorine to prevent their rotting the product. Sodium thiosulfate is used for this purpose. The chlorine and its compounds are converted into salt, NaCl. With very strong oxidizing agents the thiosulfates yield sulfates mixed with less simple derivatives of sulfur.

C. AS A TITRATING AGENT IN IODIMETRY. When thiosulfates are oxidized by free iodine, the only sulfur product obtained is sodium tetrathionate,

$$2Na_2S_2O_3 + I_2 \rightarrow 2NaI + Na_2S_4O_6$$

The iodine is quantitatively reduced to the iodide ion. Solutions of iodine may thus be standardized by titration with standard solutions of the thiosulfate. Starch, which turns blue in the presence of free iodine, may be used as an indicator. This reaction is also useful for removing iodine stains.

30. Hyposulfurous Acid and the Hyposulfites

Hyposulfurous acid, $H_2S_2O_4$, is also hypothetical. It appears to be formed in small quantities around the cathode during the electrolysis of solutions of sulfurous acid. When its salts, the colorless hyposulfites, are acidified, there develops an intense orange coloration which very shortly disappears. The color is presumed to be associated with the free acid. The most important of the hyposulfites (or hydrosulfites, as they are sometimes called) is that of sodium. In the laboratory, it may be prepared by the action of sulfur dioxide on either the hydride of sodium or free sodium suspended in an organic liquid:

$$2NaH + 2SO_2 \rightarrow Na_2S_2O_4 + H_2 \uparrow$$

and

$$2Na + 2SO_2 \xrightarrow[\text{solvent}]{\text{organic}} Na_2S_2O_4$$

Commercially, the salt is prepared by passing sulfur dioxide into a suspension of finely divided zinc in a solution of sodium bisulfite:

$$2NaHSO_3 + SO_2 + Zn \rightarrow Na_2S_2O_4 + ZnSO_3 + H_2O$$

To the resulting solution a calculated quantity of lime-water is added,

$$Na_2S_2O_4 + ZnSO_3 + Ca(OH)_2 \rightarrow Na_2S_2O_4 + \underline{Zn(OH)_2} + \underline{CaSO_3}$$

and the precipitated salts removed. The hyposulfite is then crystallized from solution. The crystals, which have the formula $Na_2S_2O_4.2H_2O$, cannot be kept well, because they react so readily with the oxygen of the air. The anhydrous salt is prepared by washing the hydrate first with a mixture of water and acetone, then with pure acetone, after which it is dried *in vacuo* at 60° C. As long as it remains dry, the salt keeps very well.

The principal use of the salt is as a reducing agent. Because fresh solutions of it absorb oxygen almost quantitatively, it is used in gas analysis and to remove oxygen from gaseous mixtures:

$$2Na_2S_2O_4 + O_2 \rightarrow 2Na_2S_2O_5$$

It reduces salts of the noble metals and a number of other heavy metals to the free metals. Many dyes as they ordinarily exist are insoluble in water, and thus may not be applied to the fabric. Sodium hyposulfite reduces many such dyes, including indigo, to pale straw-colored substances which are water-soluble. In this condition, they are applied to the fabric. The oxygen of the air, or other oxidizing agents, will convert the dye to its original condition, thus precipitating it in the fibers. Such dyes are known as "vats" or "vat dyes," and the hyposulfite is therefore said to be a good "vatting agent." The salt is more soluble in hot water than cold, but is more effective as a reducing agent in the latter. Continued heating of a solution of the sodium salt produces decomposition into the thiosulfate and bisulfite:

$$2Na_2S_2O_4 + H_2O \rightarrow Na_2S_2O_3 + 2NaHSO_3$$

31. The Polythionic Acids

Thiosulfuric acid afforded an example of an acid in which sulfur atoms were directly attached to each other. There are a number of other acids of sulfur in which similar unions exist. Collectively, these acids are known as the *polythionic acids*, and they are represented by the type formula $H_2S_nO_6$, where *n* may have any value from 2 to 6, inclusive. Their names are respectively dithionic acid, trithionic acid, tetrathionic acid, pentathionic acid, and hexathionic acid. The formation of manganese dithionate has been referred to in section 19, that of sodium tetrathionate in section 29; the parent acids of both are unstable. Of the free acids, the dithionic is the most stable, being very slightly affected even by strong oxidizing agents. The higher members of the family are much less stable, are known only in solution, and upon their decomposition always yield free sulfur along with other sulfur-bearing products. On strong oxidation, sulfates are the final product along with sulfur, and usually some SO_2.

Wachenroder's solution, prepared by passing H_2S into a cold solution of sulfurous acid, is reported to contain, in addition to the colloidal sulfur whose formation might be expected, the tetra- and pentathionic acids along with traces of trithionic and sulfuric acids. Importance does not warrant and space will not permit the discussion of the preparation and properties of the individual acids. Their structures are not fully established, but it is believed that the di- and tri- acids have the following structures,

$$\text{:O::O:} \qquad \qquad \text{:O: :O:}$$
$$\text{H}\overset{\times}{\text{O}}\overset{\cdot}{\text{S}}\ 8\ \text{S}\overset{\cdot}{\text{O}}\overset{\times}{\text{H}} \quad \text{and} \quad \text{H}\overset{\times}{\text{O}}\overset{\cdot}{\text{S}}8\text{S}8\text{S}\overset{\circ}{\text{O}}\overset{\times}{\text{H}}$$
$$\text{:O::O:} \qquad \qquad \text{:O: :O:}$$

respectively, with the higher members of the series having their remaining sulfur atoms attached by covalence to the central S atom of the tri-acid.

32. The Persulfuric Acids

It will be recalled that phosphorus formed two *per-* acids. Sulfur behaves in an analogous fashion, forming permonosulfuric acid, H_2SO_5, commonly called Caro's acid, and perdisulfuric acid, $H_2S_2O_8$, in which the oxidation number of the sulfur is $+8$ and $+7$, respectively. Both are true *per-* acids in that they contain oxygen atoms linked to each other. Their structures are believed to be

$$\text{:O:} \qquad \qquad \text{:O: :O:}$$
$$\text{H}\overset{\times}{\text{O}}\text{:O}\overset{\cdot}{\text{O}}\overset{\cdot}{\text{S}}\overset{\circ}{\text{O}}\overset{\times}{\text{H}} \quad \text{and} \quad \text{H}\overset{\times}{\text{O}}\overset{\cdot}{\text{O}}\text{S}\overset{\circ}{\text{O}}\text{:O}\overset{\cdot}{\text{O}}\text{S}\overset{\circ}{\text{O}}\overset{\times}{\text{H}}$$
$$\text{:O:} \qquad \qquad \text{:O: :O:}$$

KARL WILHELM SCHEELE

(1742–1786, Swedish)

An apothecary blessed with great natural powers of observation and unusual experimental skill, Scheele discovered the elements chlorine and oxygen; was the first investigator to study the compounds of tungsten and molybdenum; established that graphite is a form of carbon; discovered arsine, hydrocyanic acid, copper arsenite (Scheele's green), and a host of organic compounds; and was the first investigator to make a thorough study of hydrogen sulfide. His methods of isolating organic acids from natural sources and of purifying them are still in common use. Throughout his life he had poor health which led to his early death. Much of the recognition that was due him was not accorded until after his death. (Courtesy, *Journal of Chemical Education.*)

respectively, which indicate their relationship to H_2SO_4 and $H_2S_2O_7$, respectively. The pure acids are crystalline at about 20° C. and may be kept indefinitely if dry. Both are strong oxidizing agents and also strong drying and dehydrating agents. Contrary to expectation, the oxides SO_4 and S_2O_7 do not seem to be the anhydrides of these acids. Both acids may be made by the action of hydrogen peroxide on sulfur trioxide:

$$H_2O_2 + SO_3 \rightarrow H_2SO_5 \quad \text{and} \quad H_2O_2 + 2SO_3 \rightarrow H_2S_2O_8$$

In practice, solutions of the perdisulfuric acid are usually prepared by the low-temperature electrolysis of sulfuric acid of a density of 1.35 to 1.45 g./ml. The acid is reported to be completely decomposed at 60° C., yielding largely sulfuric acid and oxygen. The potassium and ammonium salts, $K_2S_2O_8$ and $(NH_4)_2S_2O_8$, are prepared by low-temperature electrolysis of their respective bisulfates. The salts are powerful oxidizing agents, and as such are used in the laboratory, in medicine, in photography, in batteries as depolarizers, and as bleaching agents. In aqueous solution, these salts hydrolyze to form sulfates and hydrogen peroxide:

$$K_2S_2O_8 + 2H_2O \rightarrow K_2SO_4 + H_2SO_4 + H_2O_2$$

Caro's acid is formed when $K_2S_2O_8$ is treated with cold concentrated sulfuric acid,

$$K_2S_2O_8 + H_2O \xrightarrow{H_2SO_4} H_2SO_5 + K_2SO_4$$

The acid is also formed during the electrolytic production of perdisulfuric acid. Of its salts, little is known. Upon hydrolysis, it yields sulfuric acid and hydrogen peroxide.

33. Uses of Sulfur

A major portion of all sulfur mined is converted into sulfur dioxide, which, in turn, is used for the production of sulfuric acid, in the preparation of sul-

THE DOMESTIC PRODUCTION OF SULFUR.

fites for the manufacture of paper by the sulfite process, in bleaching, in refrigeration, etc. Large quantities of the element also find use in the vulcanizing of rubber, in the manufacture of carbon disulfide and other reagents, in the preparation of the red pigment vermilion and the blue pigment ultramarine, and in the production of matches, enamel, and black gunpowder, which is essentially a mixture of sulfur, carbon, and potassium nitrate. A cement is

The Vulcanizing of a Rubber Automobile Tire. (Courtesy, Goodyear Tire & Rubber Co.)

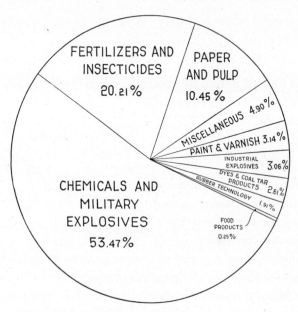

Consumption of Sulfur by Industries in the United States for 1944.

prepared from sand and molten sulfur; a synthetic stone known as *petrasul* and used as a substitute for slate is prepared from asbestos fibers, cement, and sulfur; and vessels to contain corrosive liquids are made of *lavasul*, which in turn is made of powdered coke and sulfur. Sulfur is also used as a fungicide, as an electrical insulator, and in the manufacture of a number of important organic compounds, among which are the important class of dyestuffs known as the *sulfur colors*. In short, sulfur is one of the most important of the elements.

(See Appendix for Exercises)

COLLATERAL READINGS

Badger and Baker: *Inorganic Chemical Technology*, New York, McGraw-Hill Book Co., 1941.

Fairlie: *Sulphuric Acid Manufacture*, New York, Reinhold Publishing Corp., 1936.

Foster: *The Romance of Chemistry*, New York, D. Appleton-Century Co., 1937.

Furnas: *Roger's Industrial Chemistry*, Vols. I & II, New York, D. Van Nostrand Co., 1943.

Haynes: *The Stone that Burns*, New York, D. Van Nostrand Co., 1942.

Johnstone: Sulphur dioxide, *Ind. and Eng. Chem.*, **34,** 1017 (1942).

Weeks: *Discovery of the Elements*, 5th ed., Easton, Pa., Mack Printing Co., 1945.

Yost and Russell: *Systematic Inorganic Chemistry*, New York, Prentice-Hall, Inc., 1944

Sulphur and national defense, *Chem. and Met. Eng.*, **48,** 70 (1941).

WILLIAM ALBERT NOYES
(1857–1941, *American*)

A great research chemist, a great teacher, and a great editor was W. A. Noyes. His works include determination of the atomic weights of oxygen, hydrogen, and chlorine, the evolution of methods for the analytical determination of phosphorus, sulfur, and manganese in iron, the study of the oxidation of benzene derivatives by potassium ferricyanide, and studies on valence and polarity. He is the author of textbooks in the fields of organic, inorganic, and analytical chemistry, and he served as editor of the *Journal of the American Chemical Society, Chemical Reviews, Scientific Monographs*, and *Chemical Abstracts*. He was editor of the *Journal* for 15 years, and was instrumental in the founding of *Chemical Abstracts*. After taking his Ph.D. at Johns Hopkins in 1882, holding several other professorships, and serving as the first chief chemist of the National Bureau of Standards, he became head of the department of chemistry of the University of Illinois in 1907, serving in that capacity until his retirement in 1926. He was the recipient of many honors, including the Gibbs, Nichols, and Priestley Medals.

22

The Oxygen Compounds of Chlorine

1. Introduction

The binary compounds of chlorine in which the element exhibits its characteristic oxidation number of -1 have already been discussed in Chapter 10. Since the chlorine atom contains seven electrons in its highest energy level, it is to be expected that its most common behavior will be to gain or share one electron, but, by reference to the behavior of phosphorus and sulfur, it might be anticipated also that the atom may be induced, under special conditions, to share some or all of its valence electrons, thereby establishing coördinate linkages. Such is the case, but it must be emphasized that the element is loath to form compounds in which it exhibits positive oxidation numbers, and that in general these compounds tend to be unstable. As might be further anticipated as a result of the study of the positive oxidation states of phosphorus and sulfur, the oxygen compounds of chlorine in which it shows its maximum oxidation number of $+7$ are most stable.

2. The Oxides of Chlorine

Four oxides of chlorine are well known. Their formulas and names are:

Cl_2O	ClO_2	Cl_2O_6	Cl_2O_7
Chlorine monoxide	Chlorine dioxide	Chlorine hexoxide	Chlorine heptoxide

None of these oxides may be made by direct union of the elements, and all are unstable—the first three dangerously so. The oxidation numbers shown by chlorine in each case in the order listed is $+1$, $+4$, $+6$, and $+7$. As will be seen in subsequent sections, the monoxide and the heptoxide are anhydrides, while the dioxide and hexoxide each react with water to undergo autooxidation-reduction by which a mixture of two acids is produced.

3. Chlorine Monoxide

This compound is prepared by passing a slow stream of dried chlorine through a tube containing finely divided (precipitated) yellow oxide of mercury which has been partially deactivated by having been heated to a temperature of 300° C.:

$$2Cl_2 + 2HgO \rightarrow HgO \cdot HgCl_2 + Cl_2O \uparrow$$

The oxide forms as a brownish-yellow gas which is condensed to an orange liquid in a tube surrounded by a salt-ice mixture. All vessels used must be scrupulously cleaned, since the product is a strong oxidizing agent whose decomposition might be initiated by a particle of dust or other easily oxidizable organic matter. The liquid boils at 3.8° C. and explodes violently when warmed, decomposing into its elements with the evolution of heat:

$$2Cl_2O \rightarrow 2Cl_2 \uparrow + O_2 \uparrow + \text{heat}$$

It is soluble in water at 0° C. to the extent of 200 ml. per milliliter of water, the two substances reacting to form hypochlorous acid:

$$Cl_2O + H_2O \rightarrow 2HClO$$

4. Preparation of Hypochlorous Acid

Very pure solutions of this acid may be prepared from its anhydride, as indicated above. Less pure solutions are more easily prepared by one of the following methods. (a) The hydrolysis of chlorine yields an equilibrium mixture of four substances,

$$Cl_2 + H_2O \rightleftarrows HCl + HClO$$

whence it is apparent that hydrochloric and hypochlorous acids react to produce chlorine. In sunlight, or in artificial ultraviolet light, the HClO is gradually converted to HCl, and the equilibrium is thus shifted to the right. The equilibrium is also shifted to the right by the addition of a base to neutralize the acids formed. (b) The acid is also prepared by passing chlorine into a suspension of finely divided calcium carbonate. Presumably, chlorine is again hydrolyzed, but the relatively insoluble carbonate is attacked only by the stronger acid, HCl, which leaves a solution of the hypochlorous acid:

$$2Cl_2 + H_2O + \underline{CaCO_3} \rightarrow CaCl_2 + 2HClO + CO_2 \uparrow$$

(c) When chlorine is passed into a cold solution of sodium hydroxide, a mixture of the chloride and hypochlorite of sodium is formed. If the solution is treated with a weak acid or with a very dilute solution of one of the stronger acids, weakly ionized hypochlorous acid is formed in preference to the more highly ionized hydrochloric acid:

$$2NaOH + Cl_2 \rightarrow NaCl + NaClO + H_2O$$

and
$$NaCl + NaClO + H_2SO_4 \rightarrow NaCl + NaHSO_4 + HClO$$

5. *Chemical Properties of Hypochlorous Acid*

At the outset, the acid is a weak one, hence its most important salts are those of the stronger bases of the metals of the I A and II A families. Furthermore, it is a hypothetical acid, since it is known only in weak aqueous solutions. Efforts to concentrate its solutions by evaporation usually result in its

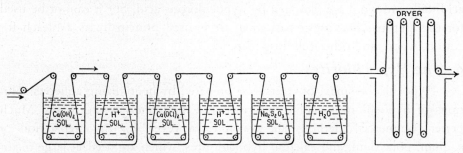

DIAGRAMMATIC REPRESENTATION OF A MACHINE FOR THE BLEACHING OF FABRICS BY CHLORINE DERIVED FROM HYPOCHLORITES.

decomposition into the anhydride and water when the concentration of HClO exceeds 5 per cent:
$$2HClO \xrightarrow{\Delta} H_2O + Cl_2O \uparrow$$

If the aqueous solution is warmed slowly, a second type of decomposition occurs,
$$3HClO \xrightarrow{\Delta} 2HCl + HClO_3$$

by which a portion of the acid is reduced to hydrochloric acid while the remainder is oxidized to chloric acid. When exposed to the sun's rays, or to ultraviolet light, or when treated with one of a number of contact catalysts, the acid undergoes a third type of decomposition by which hydrochloric acid and oxygen are formed:
$$2HClO \rightarrow 2HCl + O_2 \uparrow$$

The acid is a powerful oxidizing agent. It oxidizes both free bromine and free iodine to their $+5$ oxidation states, yielding bromic and iodic acids respectively,
$$Br_2 + 5HClO + H_2O \rightarrow 2HBrO_3 + 5HCl$$

and it oxidizes many metals which form more than one variety of ion from their lower to their higher valence states,

$$2FeCl_2 + HClO + HCl \rightarrow 2FeCl_3 + H_2O$$

Because of its ability as an oxidizing agent, the acid is a good germ killer and a strong bleaching agent. The bleaching action of chlorine is due to its reaction with moisture to form hypochlorous acid. This statement is borne out by the fact that dry chlorine does not cause bleaching. Printer's ink (carbon) and other substances which are oxidized with difficulty are not bleached by the acid. Silk and wool are bleached by hypochlorous acid, but it cannot be used for this purpose because it rots them. It is used principally as a bleach for cotton, wood, and other cellulose materials.

6. The Hypochlorites

Hypochlorites may, of course, be prepared by neutralizing aqueous solutions of hypochlorous acid with strong and moderately strong bases. Much better commercial methods are available, however, for the preparation of sodium, potassium, and calcium hypochlorites, which are used in large quantities. When chlorine is passed into cold aqueous sodium hydroxide, the hypochlorite is formed along with the chloride:

$$2NaOH + Cl_2 \rightarrow NaCl + NaClO + H_2O$$

If the temperature is allowed to rise, the following autooxidation-reduction occurs:

$$3NaClO \rightarrow 2NaCl + NaClO_3$$

In practice, cooled solutions of sodium chloride are electrolyzed and the chlorine produced is allowed to mix with the solution of sodium hydroxide which is being formed. (Cf. section 14, Chapter 7.) Solutions of potassium salts may be prepared in a similar fashion. Chlorine passed into lime water produces a similar mixture of the salts of calcium, which, upon treatment with sodium carbonate, is converted to the corresponding mixture of sodium salts from whose solution the precipitated calcium carbonate may be removed by filtration. Dilute solutions of sodium hypochlorite are sold under various trade names and are used as disinfectants and bleaching agents. Such solutions are known collectively as *Javelle water*. When used as an antiseptic for the irrigation of open wounds, a dilute solution of the two sodium salts is known after the discoverers of the method as *Carrel-Dakin solution*. Solid sodium hypochlorite crystallizes from cold, concentrated solutions as the hexahydrate, $NaClO.6H_2O$.

When chlorine is led over trays upon which dry slaked lime is spread, there is formed a product known both as *bleaching powder* and *chloride of lime*.

It is usually represented by the formula $Ca\diagdown^{Cl}_{OCl}$, which would indicate that it is a mixed chloride and hypochlorite of calcium; actually, it seems to be a mixture of the two compounds $Ca(ClO)_2.3H_2O$ and $CaCl_2.Ca(OH)_2.H_2O$:

$$3Ca(OH)_2 + 2Cl_2 + 2H_2O \rightarrow Ca(ClO)_2.3H_2O + CaCl_2.Ca(OH)_2.H_2O$$

When treated with acidified water, the compound yields chlorine and calcium hydroxide:

$$Ca(Cl)ClO + H_2O \rightarrow \underline{Ca(OH)_2} + Cl_2 \uparrow$$

It is a powerful bleaching agent and disinfectant. More powerful in these respects is the straight hypochlorite, $Ca(ClO)_2$, which was put on the market some years ago. It is known as H.T.H. (high-test hypochlorite) and dissolves to give a clear solution.

7. *Chlorine Dioxide*

The dioxide of chlorine is a yellow gas which is easily condensed to a brownish-red liquid whose boiling point is 9.9° C. It has a strong odor, and is a violent oxidizing agent which reacts explosively with any easily oxidizable substance. It will cause table sugar to burst into flame. It is decomposed into its elements by heat and by exposure to ultraviolet light. Much heat is liberated by the reaction. One milliliter of water at 0° C. will dissolve 20 ml. of the gas. There ensues, then, a reaction by which chlorous and chloric acid are formed:

$$2ClO_2 + H_2O \rightarrow HClO_2 + HClO_3$$

With strong bases, the dioxide reacts to form a mixture of chlorites and chlorates:

$$2ClO_2 + 2NaOH \rightarrow NaClO_2 + NaClO_3 + H_2O$$

There are a number of ways of preparing the dioxide:
(*a*) *by the reaction of a soluble chlorate and a strong, concentrated acid,*

$$3KClO_3 + H_2SO_4 \rightarrow KClO_4 + 2ClO_2 \uparrow + K_2SO_4 + H_2O$$

(*b*) *by the heating of a mixture of potassium chlorate, oxalic acid, and water to 60° C.,*

$$2KClO_3 + 2H_2C_2O_4 \rightarrow K_2C_2O_4 + 2CO_2 \uparrow + 2ClO_2 \uparrow + 2H_2O$$

Single Tower Chlorine-chlorite Solution Generator. (Courtesy, Mathieson Alkali Works.)

(c) by the electrolysis of a solution containing salt and sodium chlorite,

$$2NaClO_2 + 2H_2O \xrightarrow{NaCl} 2ClO_2 \uparrow + 2NaOH + H_2 \uparrow$$

a process whose conditions must be very carefully controlled; and *(d) by the action of chlorine upon a solution of sodium chlorite or upon the moistened solid,*

$$Cl_2 + 2NaClO_2 \rightarrow 2NaCl + 2ClO_2 \uparrow$$

When carried out in a generator of special design, this latter reaction serves as a source of the dioxide which is delivered in an air mixture in which its partial pressure is about 30 mm. of mercury. It seems to be safe in such a mixture, unless heated too strongly.

Industrially, the dioxide is used as a bleaching agent for flour, soap, paper, starch, textiles, etc. Water treated with it is said to taste better than water treated with chlorine, and it is reported to be useful in the preservation of fruits and vegetables from molds.

8. *Chlorous Acid and Its Salts*

Chlorous acid, $HClO_2$, while stronger in its ionization than either hypochlorous acid or carbonic acid, is still a very weak acid. Its aqueous solutions may be concentrated a bit more than can those of the hypochlorous acid without decomposition occurring, but it is, nevertheless, a hypothetical acid and of little importance. Its salts of the lighter metals are readily soluble, while a number of those of the heavier metals are only slightly soluble. The sodium salt is manufactured in industrial quantities.

The formation of a mixture of chlorites and chlorates when chlorine dioxide is passed into a basic solution has already been noted. If a peroxide has been added previously to the basic solution, only the chlorite is formed:

$$Ba(OH)_2 + H_2O_2 + 2ClO_2 \rightarrow Ba(ClO_2)_2 + 2H_2O + O_2 \uparrow$$

The addition of a calculated quantity of sulfuric acid to barium chlorite yields a solution of the free acid and a precipitate of barium sulfate which may be removed by filtration. The use of sodium peroxide produces the sodium salt.

$$Na_2O_2 + 2ClO_2 \rightarrow 2NaClO_2 + O_2 \uparrow$$

The sodium salt is used in bleaching cotton cloth and other cellulose products, since it is strong enough as an oxidizing agent to serve this purpose without being strong enough to damage the fibers. It will act in this capacity in either an acid or a basic solution. Its use as a source of the dioxide has been noted.

When heated slowly, sodium chlorite undergoes autooxidation-reduction to give sodium chlorate and the chloride:

$$3NaClO_2 \rightarrow 2NaClO_3 + NaCl$$

Molten sodium chlorite is a powerful and dangerous oxidizing agent. Some of the chlorites of the noble metals explode when heated, and some explode even when struck.

9. *Chloric Acid*

It has been noted that chlorine dioxide reacts with water to yield a mixture of chlorous and chloric acids. The latter acid has the formula $HClO_3$ and contains chlorine whose oxidation number is $+5$. No anhydride of the acid is known. In the laboratory, it is most conveniently prepared by the action of sulfuric acid on barium chlorate or by the action of fluosilicic acid on potassium chlorate:

$$Ba(ClO_3)_2 + H_2SO_4 \rightarrow \underline{BaSO_4} + 2HClO_3$$

and
$$2KClO_3 + H_2SiF_6 \rightarrow \underline{K_2SiF_6} + 2HClO_3$$

In each case, the precipitated by-product may be removed by filtration.

Aqueous solutions of the acid are colorless and have an odor reminiscent of that of nitric acid. As an acid, it is much more highly ionized than either chlorous or hypochlorous acid, as is borne out by the fact that aqueous solutions of sodium and potassium chlorates react neutral to litmus. The stability of chloric acid is somewhat greater than that of its two predecessors in the family of oxygen acids of chlorine. Its aqueous solutions may be concentrated to a strength of 40 per cent by the use of reduced pressure and temperatures below 40° C. At about 20° C., by use of a vacuum desiccator kept in the dark, the concentration may be increased to 50 per cent. When warmed, both of these solutions decompose into perchloric acid, oxygen, and chlorine. Solutions of lower concentration decompose in the cold in a like manner when exposed to ultraviolet radiations:

$$3HClO_3 \overset{\Delta}{\rightarrow} HClO_4 + 2ClO_2 \uparrow + H_2O \rightarrow HClO_4 + Cl_2 \uparrow + 2O_2 \uparrow + H_2O$$

The concentrated acid is a strong oxidizing agent which readily oxidizes the active metals, iodine, and a host of organic materials, among which wood and paper may be noted.

10. The Chlorates

In section 6, attention was directed to the fact that, when solutions of hypochlorites are boiled, chlorates and chlorides are formed. Use is made of this knowledge in the preparation of the metallic chlorates. The usual procedure is to pass chlorine into a solution or suspension of the proper base maintained at a temperature of about 90° C.:

$$6KOH + 3Cl_2 \underset{90°\,C.}{\overset{\Delta}{\rightleftarrows}} KClO_3 + 5KCl + 3H_2O$$

The chlorate thus formed is separated from the simultaneously produced chloride by fractional crystallization. Since there is a greater difference in solubility between the chlorate and chloride of potassium than between the like salts of the other common metals, potassium chlorate is the most easily prepared of the chlorates, and therefore finds the widest use. The sodium salt is so soluble that it is difficult to recover.

It is apparent from the above equation that potassium chloride, which is more cheaply obtained from natural deposits, is produced in larger quantity than the desired product. To overcome this difficulty, a commercial process has been developed which consists of electrolyzing hot, slightly acidic, saturated solutions of potassium chloride. Some chlorate is formed by the interaction of the chlorine produced at the anode and the potassium hydroxide produced at the cathode. When the solution reaches a concentration of 3 per cent of the chlorate, it is chilled and the crystalline product withdrawn. The mother solution of potassium chloride is warmed and electrolysis resumed. This cycle of operations proceeds indefinitely, with KCl being added to the solution from time to time to replace the converted material.

Crystals of potassium chlorate are broad, colorless plates which contain no water of crystallization and which melt at 368.4° C. When heated, the dry salt may decompose according to one of the following equations:

$$2KClO_3 \xrightarrow{\Delta} 2KCl + 3O_2 \uparrow$$

and

$$4KClO_3 \xrightarrow{\Delta} KCl + 3KClO_4$$

The former reaction is favored by temperatures considerably in excess of the melting point, but even then the evolution of oxygen is slow. The presence of manganese dioxide, MnO_2, as a catalyst greatly increases the speed at which the oxygen is given off, and makes the reaction suitable for the laboratory production of small quantities of the gas. The latter reaction is favored by temperatures just slightly in excess of the melting point. With a strong acid, the salt reacts to form chlorine dioxide which decomposes with a slight popping sound as it is formed. The principal use of potassium chlorate is as a dry oxidizing agent in matches, explosives, and fireworks. The storage of such materials is very hazardous, since the development of an acid would liberate ClO_2, which is spontaneously explosive. Care should be taken never to grind the salt with any oxidizable material, since a violent explosion may result. Even dust particles in a mortar may be the cause of such an explosion. The molten salt in an extremely violent oxidizing agent. As an oxidizing agent the salt also finds use in the manufacture of aniline black and a number of other dyes. Medicinally, the salt finds use in the preparation of throat lozenges.

Solutions of the chlorates of sodium, calcium, and magnesium find some use as weed killers. Such use is dangerous, however, since organic matter (clothing or dead weeds) encrusted with the dry salts is easily ignited, even by slight friction, and burns violently.

11. Chlorine Hexoxide

This substance is a red, oily, unstable liquid which freezes at $-1°$ C.; it has been known since 1843. At first it was not regarded as a true compound, but, with Bodenstein's investigation of it in 1925, it was found to have the formula Cl_2O_6 in the liquid state. It may be formed by the irradiation of either the dioxide or a mixture of chlorine and ozone, O_3. At ordinary temperatures, the substance decomposes into chlorine, chlorine dioxide, and oxygen. It decomposes violently at more elevated temperatures, as it does when mixed with organic substances, upon which it acts as an oxidizing agent. Its stability is markedly decreased by the presence of the other oxides of chlorine. It reacts with water to produce a mixture of chloric and perchloric acids:

$$Cl_2O_6 + H_2O \rightarrow HClO_3 + HClO_4$$

12. Perchloric Acid

Perchloric acid is not a *per-* acid in the sense that perphosphoric and persulfuric acids are, for it contains no oxygen atoms bonded to each other. In this case, *per-* is used simply to designate a state of oxidation higher than that shown in the *-ic* acid. The oxidation number of chlorine in $HClO_4$ is readily calculated to be $+7$. Perchloric is the strongest and most stable of the oxygen acids of chlorine. It is much more stable than even chloric acid, since it may be prepared in the anhydrous form, albeit with some danger. Being more stable, it acts less readily as an oxidizing agent, especially in aqueous solution. As an acid, its strength is comparable to that of sulfuric.

The acid may be prepared by the careful distillation of chloric acid, as indicated in the equation given at the end of section 9. It may also be prepared by the distillation under reduced pressure of a mixture of sulfuric acid and potassium perchlorate,

$$KClO_4 + H_2SO_4 \xrightarrow{\Delta} KHSO_4 + HClO_4 \uparrow$$

and by the treatment of barium perchlorate with a calculated quantity of sulfuric acid,

$$Ba(ClO_4)_2 + H_2SO_4 \rightarrow \underline{BaSO_4} + 2HClO_4$$

Aqueous solutions of the acid form a constant boiling mixture whose boiling point is 203° C., and which contains 72.4 per cent of $HClO_4$. This solution is the concentrated acid of commerce. The remaining water may be removed by further evaporation at reduced pressure followed by distillation, also under diminished pressure, with phosphorus pentoxide. The anhydrous acid is a colorless, mobile liquid which fumes readily in moist air and explodes violently if heated above its boiling point, 92° C. During distillation, it partially decomposes into water and its anhydride, chlorine heptoxide. As in the case of concentrated sulfuric acid, dissolution of the anhydrous acid in water is accompanied by the evolution of a large quantity of heat.

Other forms of the acid, such as oxonium perchlorate (H_3OClO_4) and dioxonium perchlorate ($H_5O_2ClO_4$), are known. These may be prepared according to the following scheme:

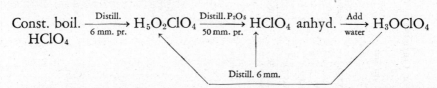

Because of its properties, perchloric acid is a useful laboratory reagent which may be used to replace sulfuric acid in many processes. The anhydrous acid is a dehydrating and oxidizing agent, but, because of its danger, it is seldom used in the laboratory. The 72 per cent constant boiling acid is the customary reagent. It is a strong acid of low volatility, and it is not reduced by hydrochloric acid or active metals, although it is reduced by titanous sulfate, sodium hyposulfite, and other very strong reducing agents. The acid is much more readily reduced when hot. Since its potassium salt is only very slightly soluble, it may be used as a precipitating agent for potassium ions.

13. The Perchlorates

It has already been noted that the metallic chlorates, when maintained at temperatures just above their respective melting points, gradually undergo autooxidation-reduction:

$$4KClO_3 \rightarrow 3KClO_4 + KCl$$

In the case of the potassium salts, the chloride is so much more soluble than the perchlorate that the products are easily separated.

Commercially, sodium and potassium perchlorates are prepared by electrolysis of slightly acidic solutions of their respective chlorides. The reaction is reported as being favored by high currents, low temperatures, and a longer time of reaction than is used in the electrolytic preparation of chlorates. Because

Table 20

RÉSUMÉ OF OXYGEN COMPOUNDS OF CHLORINE

Stability increases →
Oxidizing ability decreases →

Oxid. No.	Oxides	Stability of Oxides	Acids	Preparation of Acids	Decomposition Acids and Salts	Strength of Acids	Stability of Acids	Salts	Important Salts	Use of Salts
+1	Cl_2O, brown gas	Very unstable	$HClO$	$Cl_2 + H_2O \rightleftarrows HCl + HClO$. $2Cl_2 + H_2O + CaCO_3 \rightarrow CaCl_2 + 2HClO + CO_2$. $Ba(ClO)_2 + H_2SO_4 \rightarrow BaSO_4 + 2HClO$.	$2HClO \xrightarrow{\Delta} H_2O + Cl_2O$. $2HClO \xrightarrow{Conc. Cat.} 2HCl + O_2$. $3HClO \xrightarrow{\Delta} 2HCl + HClO_3$. $3NaClO \xrightarrow{\Delta} 2NaCl + NaClO_3$.	Very weak	Unstable in conc. greater than 5%	Only of strong bases	Na^+, K^+, Ca^{++}	Oxidizing agents in solution
+3			$HClO_2$	$2ClO_2 + H_2O \rightarrow HClO_2 + HClO_3$. $2ClO_2 + H_2O_2 \rightarrow 2HClO_2 + O_2$. $Ba(ClO_2)_2 + H_2SO_4 \rightarrow BaSO_4 + 2HClO_2$.	$4HClO_2 \rightarrow 2H_2O + 2Cl_2 + 3O_2$. $3NaClO_2 \rightarrow NaCl + 2NaClO_3$.	Weak	Stable only in very dilute solutions	Only of strong bases and bases forming insolb. salts	Na^+	Oxidizing agents in solution; source ClO_2
+4	ClO_2, yellow gas	Very unstable								
+5			$HClO_3$	$Ba(ClO_3)_2 + H_2SO_4 \rightarrow BaSO_4 + 2HClO_3$. $2KClO_3 + H_2SiF_6 \rightarrow K_2SiF_6 + 2HClO_3$.	$3HClO_3 \xrightarrow{\Delta} HClO_4 + 2O_2 + Cl_2 + H_2O$. $2KClO_3 \xrightarrow{\Delta} 2KCl + 3O_2$. $4KClO_3 \xrightarrow{\Delta} KCl + 3KClO_4$.	Moderately strong	Unstable in conc. greater than 50%	Of most bases	K^+, Na^+, Ca^{++}, Mg^{++}	Dry oxidizing agents. Weed killers
+6	Cl_2O_6, reddish liquid	Very unstable								
+7	Cl_2O_7, oily colorless liquid	Unstable	$HClO_4$	$3HClO_3 \rightarrow HClO_4 + 2O_2 + Cl_2 + H_2O$. $KClO_4 + H_2SO_4 \rightarrow KHSO_4 + HClO_4$. $Ba(ClO_4)_2 + H_2SO_4 \rightarrow BaSO_4 + 2HClO_4$.	$2HClO_4 \xrightarrow{P_2O_5} H_2O + Cl_2O_7$. $4HClO_4 \rightarrow 2H_2O + 2Cl_2 + 7O_2$. $NaClO_4 \rightarrow NaCl + 2O_2$.	Strong	Fairly stable at about 20° C. when 100% conc.	Of most bases	K^+, Na^+, NH_4^+, Ba^{++}, Mg^{++}	Dry oxidizing agents. Weed killers. Mg and Ba drying agents

of its slight solubility, the potassium salt is easily recovered while the very soluble sodium salt is recovered only from its concentrated solution. Slightly soluble ammonium perchlorate is easily precipitated by adding ammonium chloride to solutions of the sodium salt:

$$NH_4Cl + NaClO_4 \rightarrow \underline{NH_4ClO_4} + NaCl$$

As a class, the perchlorates are generally soluble, dissolving not only in water but also in many nonaqueous liquids. The least soluble members of the family are the salts of potassium, rubidium, cesium, and ammonium.

The perchlorates are much more stable than the salts of the other oxygen-acids of chlorine, but upon strong heating they do evolve oxygen:

$$NaClO_4 \xrightarrow{\Delta} NaCl + 2O_2 \uparrow$$

Because of this ability to evolve oxygen, they find use as dry oxidizing agents in the manufacture of fireworks, explosives, and matches. Since the salts yield no chlorine, chlorine dioxide, or oxygen upon contact with acid, they and products containing them are much more safely stored than are the chlorates and products containing them. Sodium perchlorate is a safe weed killer, since it establishes no fire hazard, and anhydrous barium and magnesium perchlorates are both good drying agents.

14. Chlorine Heptoxide

This oxide has the formula Cl_2O_7 and is the anhydride of perchloric acid. It is most readily obtained by the dehydration of the acid with phosphorus pentoxide.

$$2HClO_4 + P_2O_5 \rightarrow Cl_2O_7 + 2HPO_3$$

The acid is chilled to $-10°$ C., whereupon the pentoxide is slowly added. The mixture is maintained at this low temperature for some 20 to 24 hrs., after which it is distilled. The heptoxide is a colorless, oily liquid which boils at $82°$ C. under standard pressure. It decomposes slowly at about $20°$ C., and does not explode when added to organic substances. When struck or ignited, however, it explodes violently. With water it reacts slowly to regenerate perchloric acid.

15. Odd Molecule Oxides

It has been shown that atoms enter into reactions apparently as a result of their efforts to achieve outer-electronic structures similar to those of the inert gases, which contain even numbers of electrons in their outermost levels. In compounds in which each atom of the molecule has attained such a structure, the sum of the valence electrons (those in the outermost level) of all the atoms of the molecule will be an even number: for NaCl, $1 + 7 = 8$; for CCl_4, $4 + 4(7) = 32$; and for Na_2SO_4, $2(1) + 6 + 4(6) = 2 + 6 + 24 = 32$. There are, however, a very few molecules the valence electrons of whose atoms do not add up to an even number. Such substances are referred to as *odd molecules*. Thus far, we have encountered three nonmetallic oxides—$PO_2(P_2O_4)$, ClO_2, and $ClO_3(Cl_2O_6)$—which very well illustrate the characteristic properties of such compounds, which are: (a) instability, (b) a tendency to polymerize, (c) a tendency to show color, and (d) a tendency, in the case of nonmetallic odd-molecule oxides, to react with water to form two acids as a result of what appears to be autooxidation-reduction. The property of instability results from the fact that the atoms present are still striving to acquire an inert gas structure, and the tendency to polymerize results from the same thing; thus PO_2 and ClO_3 (which exist at higher temperatures) polymerize into P_8O_{16} and Cl_2O_6, respectively, which are no longer odd-molecule oxides. Apparently ClO_2 does not polymerize. Color results from the fact that the atoms are less firmly bound together in odd molecules. Their electrons are, therefore, less firmly bound and vibrate at a slower rate, which enables the molecule to absorb visible light. Phosphorus tetroxide is an exception in this respect. By autooxidation-reduction of such compounds, *even* molecule compounds result.

16. *The Third Period*

After chlorine, there remains in the third period only the gaseous element, argon, which enters into no chemical reactions. The study of the chemistry of the elements of this period, therefore, comes to an end with the foregoing survey of the oxygen-containing compounds of chlorine. To fix this material firmly in mind, at this juncture the student should review the chapters dealing with the elements of the period and their compounds. To emphasize the gradual change of properties from element to element, as well as the general trend of these changes, it is suggested that the student make a list of physical and chemical properties to be studied, and then opposite each one note that property for the elements from sodium to chlorine. A form which might be used is suggested in Table 21. This form may be extended to cover properties not listed, and to cover hydrides and other compounds not included. Such a study will help to fix general relationships in mind, thus eliminating to some extent the necessity for depending upon the retention by the memory of each property of each element as a separate and unrelated bit of information.

Table 21

Period III

Elements	Na	Mg	Al	Si	P	S	Cl	A
Atomic number								
Electronic distribution								
Common oxidation number								
State								
Color								
Melting point, °C.								
Boiling point, °C.								
Class								
Size of ions								
Formulas of common oxides								
Chlorides: Formula								
State								
Color								
Reactivity with H_2O								
Polarity								
Melting point, °C.								
Stability to heat								
Hydroxides: Formula								
State								
Color								
Nature of solutions								
Strength								

(See Appendix for Exercises)

COLLATERAL READINGS

Creighton and Koehler: *Electrochemistry*, 4th ed., Vol. II, New York, John Wiley & Sons, Inc., 1944.

Emeleus and Anderson: *Modern Aspects of Inorganic Chemistry*, London, Routledge, George & Sons, Ltd., 1938.

Latimer and Hildebrand: *Reference Book of Inorganic Chemistry*, New York, The Macmillan Co., 1941.

Murray: Alkali-chlorine developments, *Chem. & Met. Eng.*, **47,** 396 (1940).

Riegel: *Industrial Chemistry*, New York, Reinhold Publishing Corp., 1937.

Vincent, *et al.:* Two new chlorine compounds, *J. Chem. Education*, **22,** 283 (1945).

Woodward: Generating chlorine dioxide, *Chem. and Eng. News*, **22,** 1092 (1944).

Yost and Russell: *Systematic Inorganic Chemistry*, New York, Prentice-Hall, Inc., 1944.

Chemistry of chlorites, *Ind. and Eng. Chem.*, **34,** 782 (1942).

23

Hydrogen and Its Compounds

1. Introduction

In the preceding chapters, it has been necessary to refer repeatedly to acids, basic hydroxides, water, and other hydrogen compounds. The material already presented will be organized and augmented in this chapter with other pertinent information concerning this element. Hydrogen as a component of water, of foods, and of all plant and animal tissues is of special importance to everyone.

Hydrogen was known to Paracelsus in the sixteenth century, but was first investigated carefully by Cavendish in 1766. The name *hydrogen* was first applied to the element by Lavoisier in 1783. It is derived from two Greek words and means *water-former*. The element is an isotopic mixture of the three atomic species whose weights are 1, 2, and 3 at. wt. units, respectively, and whose proportions in the mixture are such that the average atomic weight is 1.008 at. wt. units. The atomic number of the element is 1. Having thus one valence electron in the first main energy level, its atoms may react in various ways: (1) by losing that one electron to an atom which attracts electrons more strongly, (2) by sharing that electron with an atom which will also furnish one electron to the shared pair, or (3) by gaining an electron to attain the structure of helium, the nearest inert gas. As a result of these various methods of reacting, the element may show valences of $+1$, 1, and -1. Its covalent compounds and those in which it has a valence of $+1$ are much more common than are those in which it shows a valence of -1.

2. Physical Properties

Hydrogen is the lightest of the elements. At about 20° C., it is a colorless, odorless, tasteless gas whose density at S.T.P. is 0.08987 g./l., or approximately $\frac{1}{15}$ that of air. Its critical temperature is $-241°$ C., or 32° K. Because the gas must be cooled first to such a low temperature, its condensation is accomplished only with difficulty. It was first liquefied by Dewar, who used a device similar to that used in liquefying air (cf. section 12, Chapter 11). The liquid, which is also colorless, boils at $-252.7°$ C. and freezes to a colorless solid at

$-259.14°$ C. Freezing is produced by rapid evaporation of the liquid under reduced pressure.

The gas is only slightly soluble in water. Its solubility under standard pressure in 100 ml. of water is 1.93 ml. at $0°$ C. and 1.8 ml. at $25°$ C. A number of metals have the ability to adsorb hydrogen in a monomolecular layer on their surfaces. Among these are iron, gold, platinum, and palladium, of which palladium possesses the ability in the highest degree. One volume of the latter at about $20°$ C. is reported as being able to adsorb as much as 870 volumes of the gas. The quantity adsorbed varies with the physical condition of the metal and with the existing temperature and pressure. When hydrogen is adsorbed on spongy platinum, sufficient heat is liberated to ignite a mixture of hydrogen and oxygen. This knowledge is used to advantage in the construction of automatic gas lighters. Finely divided palladium is used to remove hydrogen from gaseous mixtures in gas analysis. It should also be noted that heated containers made of the metals which adsorb hydrogen will gradually permit the gas to diffuse through their walls.

Hydrogen exists as diatomic molecules H_2, H:H, hence its molecular weight is approximately 2 at. wt. units. Its molecules travel at a high rate of speed because of their extreme lightness (cf. the kinetic-molecular theory and Graham's law). A high rate of diffusion permits it to escape rapidly from a cracked container or from a container of the type mentioned in the preceding paragraph. It will also diffuse through the walls of a quartz vessel.

Because of the lightness of the hydrogen molecules and their consequent slight attraction for each other, the gas behaves as a little more than "perfect." That is, its gram-molecular volume is slightly greater than 22.4 l., and when the gas expands it becomes warmed slightly instead of cooled, as is the case with air and other gases which are less than "perfect."

In 1929, Bonhoeffer discovered that there are two types of hydrogen molecules: orthohydrogen and parahydrogen. His explanation of their existence is that in the ortho type the nuclear protons of both atoms are spinning in the same direction while in the para type they are spinning in opposite directions. At ordinary temperatures, gaseous hydrogen appears to contain about 75 per cent of the ortho molecules and 25 per cent of the para. At lower temperatures in the presence of a charcoal catalyst, the ortho molecules tend to change to the para type. A few of the physical properties of the two types, notably their specific heats, differ, but their chemical properties appear to be identical.

3. Deuterium and Tritium

Deuterium, the isotope of hydrogen of weight 2, was discovered by use of the spectroscope in 1932 by Professor H. C. Urey of Columbia University, who was awarded the Nobel prize in 1934 for his achievement. A method of producing the isotope was shortly perfected. The double-weight isotope appears to be present in ordinary hydrogen in the proportion of about 1 to 5,000. It is usually represented by the symbol D or by the symbol ^2H. In 1934, a third isotope of weight 3 was discovered and christened *tritium*. It is represented by the symbol ^3H and is reported to be present in ordinary hydrogen in the proportion of about 1 part per million. The nucleus of the deuterium atom contains one proton and one neutron, while the nucleus of the tritium atom contains one proton and two neutrons. Deuterium has proved to be a valuable tool in the study of the mechanism of reactions—especially those which occur in plant and animal organisms.

4. Occurrence

Hydrogen is found in the free state only in minute quantities because of its marked chemical activity. In the combined condition, it occurs principally as its oxide, water, H_2O, whose universality on our planet is well known. Also occurring in large quantities are the hydrides of carbon, the *hydrocarbons*, which in varying mixtures make up the vast reserves of petroleum oils and gases. Natural gas consists principally of the simplest hydrocarbon, methane, whose formula is CH_4. Since nearly all carbon compounds contain hydrogen, all animal and plant structures and their products may be thought of as representing the natural occurrence of the element. Small quantities of the free gas issue from volcanoes and from oil wells, and its presence in seams in coal beds often constitutes a fire hazard in coal mines. Meteorites containing bubbles of hydrogen have been found, and the spectroscope shows the presence of the element in the hot gases of the sun and other stars.

5. Production

Hydrogen is usually prepared in the laboratory by its liberation from acids, bases, or water. Some of these methods are:

(a) the electrolysis of water whereby oxygen gas is also obtained,

$$2H_2O \rightarrow 2H_2 \uparrow + O_2 \uparrow$$

(b) the action of active metals on water as discussed in the chapter on sodium,

$$2Na + 2HOH \rightarrow 2NaOH + H_2 \uparrow$$

(c) the action of less active metals on steam,

$$3Fe + 4HOH \rightleftarrows Fe_3O_4 + 4H_2 \uparrow \quad (cf.\ Table\ 6,\ Chapter\ 7)$$

(d) the action of metals above hydrogen in the activity series upon solutions of acids,

$$Zn + 2HCl \rightarrow ZnCl_2 + H_2 \uparrow$$

(A Kipp generator may be used for preparing a relatively large volume of gas by the above method.) (e) the action of water upon the saltlike hydrides of the active metals,

$$NaH + H_2O \rightarrow NaOH + H_2 \uparrow$$

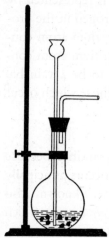

and (f) the action of silicon and of metals whose hydroxides are amphoteric upon solutions of a strong base. The action of silicon upon sodium hydroxide has been referred to in section 5 of Chapter 18. The behavior of aluminum when placed in solutions of sodium hydroxide has also been discussed (cf. section 5 of Chapter 15). Zinc and other metals whose hydroxides are amphoteric behave similarly:

$$Zn + 2NaOH \rightarrow Na_2ZnO_2 + H_2 \uparrow$$

LABORATORY APPARATUS FOR THE GENERATION OF HYDROGEN BY THE ACTION OF ACID ON ZINC. A delivery tube may be attached and the gas collected over water.

At ordinary temperatures, aluminum which has been amalgamated (alloyed with mercury) will displace hydrogen from water. Amalgamation prevents the formation of a protective coat of oxide on the surface of the aluminum.

6. Polarization

The most commonly employed laboratory method for the production of hydrogen is the action of either dilute hydrochloric acid or dilute sulfuric acid upon either zinc or iron. If the zinc employed is highly purified, the liberation of the gas begins vigorously enough, but soon slows down, largely because a film of the gas collects upon the metal surface so that metal and acid are no longer in contact. This covering of the metal surface with a film of gas is known as *polarization*. If, now, a piece of platinum, or some other less active metal, is placed in contact with the zinc, liberation of the gas will again proceed rapidly. The liberation of the gas is essentially the removal of electrons from zinc atoms and their addition to hydrogen ions:

$$Zn - 2\epsilon \rightarrow Zn^{++} \quad \text{or} \quad Zn \rightarrow Zn^{++} + 2\epsilon$$

A Portable Hydrogen Generating Plant. (Courtesy, The Girdler Corp.)

and

$$2H^+ + 2\epsilon \rightarrow H_2$$

The metal placed in contact with the zinc serves to conduct the liberated electrons away from it so that the hydrogen molecules do not form on its surface to blanket it. Pairs of metals thus employed are known as *couples*. Usually, commercial zinc contains sufficient metallic impurities to be already in essence a conglomerate of many small couples. If it is not, a few milliliters of a solution of copper sulfate may be added. The zinc, being more active than the copper, displaces it from solution, and a copper-zinc couple is thus formed:

$$Cu^{++} + \underline{Zn} \rightarrow Zn^{++} + \underline{Cu}$$

When hydrogen is prepared by electrolysis, the metallic cathode at which the gas is liberated often becomes coated with a film of it. This is also *polarization*, and to force the reaction to continue it is necessary to increase the voltage of the current supplied. The difference between the voltage actually required to cause a reaction to proceed and the theoretical voltage calculated for the process is known as the *overvoltage* of that reaction on the particular variety of electrode used.

Substances used in cells to remove gas films which cause polarization are known as *depolarizers*.

7. Industrial Production

Hydrogen is prepared in large quantities because of its many industrial uses. The principal commercial source of the gas is the so-called *water-gas reaction*. By this method, steam is blown against red-hot coke, and hydrogen and carbon monoxide are produced:

$$C + H_2O \xrightarrow{\Delta} CO\uparrow + H_2\uparrow$$

The mixture of gases is known as water gas, and may be burned as a fuel,

$$CO + H_2 + O_2 \xrightarrow{\Delta} CO_2\uparrow + H_2O\uparrow$$

but, if the hydrogen is desired, it may be separated by liquefying the carbon monoxide, which is much more easily condensed. Another method of removing the hydrogen consists of passing the water gas and an excess of steam over a catalyst containing the oxides of chromium, iron, and thorium maintained at a temperature of 500° C.:

$$CO + H_2 + H_2O \xrightarrow{\Delta} CO_2\uparrow + 2H_2\uparrow$$

The carbon dioxide, being more soluble than hydrogen, is usually removed by dissolving it in water.

Some industrial hydrogen is obtained as a by-product in the preparation of sodium hydroxide and chlorine by the electrolysis of brine (cf. section 14 of Chapter 7). A third source is the dry distillation of coal for the production of coke. Hydrogen is present to the extent of some 50 per cent in the mixture of gases driven off, with carbon monoxide and methane accounting for a major portion of the remainder. These gases are more easily liquefied than the hydrogen whose separation is based upon this fact.

Relatively small quantities of the gas are sometimes generated on the spot by the action of silicon on sodium hydroxide solution. Portable generators which employ the following catalytic reaction of methanol are also used:

$$CH_3OH + H_2O(\text{steam}) \underset{\text{cat.}}{\overset{\Delta}{\rightleftarrows}} CO_2\uparrow + 3H_2\uparrow$$

8. Chemical Properties

Free hydrogen, as it normally exists, is made up of diatomic molecules, H:H. The gas is not inordinately active at about 20° C. in the molecular condition, but, when the molecules are broken into their constituent atoms, the substance becomes very active. The union between hydrogen atoms is so strong that large quantities of energy are required for their separation. By passing the molecules through an electric arc or through a silent electrical discharge at low pressures, or by subjecting them to the influence of x-ray radiations or radium emanations, they may be dissociated into their constituent atoms. Hydrogen so treated is said to be activated. When adsorbed on a metal surface, the gas is activated to some extent. As soon as the element passes from the influence of the activating force, the atoms formed tend to recombine with each other or to combine with any other active substance which may be present. When the atoms recombine with each other, they release the quantity of energy which was absorbed when the original molecules were dissociated:

$$H_2 + 102,600 \text{ cal.} \rightleftarrows 2H$$

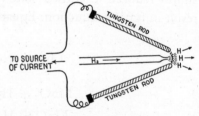

DIAGRAMMATIC REPRESENTATION OF THE ATOMIC HYDROGEN TORCH.

Use is made of this process in atomic-hydrogen welding. A stream of the molecular gas is passed through an electric arc onto the metal pieces which are to be welded. Upon striking the metal, the atoms separated in the arc reunite, giving up their heat to the metal and raising its temperature at the point of impingement to as much as 4000° to 5000° C. The process is especially desirable for some types of welding, because no oxidation of the heated parts occurs in the atmosphere of hydrogen produced and thus no flux is required.

Hydrogen will combine directly with a number of elements, though the majority of hydrides are prepared by indirect methods such as those mentioned for the preparation of the silicides, phosphine, hydrogen sulfide, and hydrogen chloride. The most notable of these elementary combinations is that with oxygen. A mixture of the two gases is stable at about 20° C., but, as the temperature is raised, the speed of reaction increases, until above 700° C. it proceeds with explosive violence and the liberation of a large quantity of heat:

$$2H_2 + O_2 \rightarrow 2H_2O + 136,774 \text{ cal.}$$

Hydrogen mixed with oxygen is burned in a special torch for oxyhydrogen welding. The temperature of the flame produced is reported to be about 2500° C.

The union of hydrogen with sodium to form a saltlike hydride has been referred to in Chapter 7. Calcium and others of the active metals behave in a similar fashion. The union of hydrogen and sulfur has been described as slow and incomplete, and the union with nitrogen is incomplete even in the presence of a catalyst.

Chemically, hydrogen also acts as a reducing agent—a behavior which it exhibits most commonly with the oxides and chlorides of the less active metals. Usually, the substance to be reduced is heated to redness in a tube through which the gas is permitted to flow in a slow stream. Water is formed in the case of the oxides, while in the case of the chlorides one product is HCl, hence these reactions may also be thought of as displacements. The compounds so treated are in some instances reduced to the free metal while in others they are simply reduced to a lower state of oxidation. An increase in temperature may result in further reduction. Equations of typical reactions are:

$$CuO + H_2 \xrightarrow{\Delta} Cu + H_2O \uparrow$$

$$MnO_2 + H_2 \xrightarrow{\Delta} MnO + H_2O \uparrow$$

$$MnO + H_2 \xrightarrow[\text{temp.}]{\text{higher}} Mn + H_2O \uparrow$$

$$Fe_3O_4 + H_2 \xrightarrow{\Delta} 3FeO + H_2O \uparrow$$

$$2TiCl_4 + H_2 \xrightarrow{700° C.} 2TiCl_3 + 2HCl \uparrow$$

Elementary hydrogen bubbled into aqueous solutions of oxidizing agents has no effect, but hydrogen produced in solution by the action of a metal on an acid acts to reduce many soluble oxidizing agents. When so produced and used, hydrogen is usually described as *nascent*.

In the presence of a suitable catalyst, molecular hydrogen will combine with a number of compounds. Much of our present-day wood alcohol (CH$_3$OH, methanol) is prepared by the Patart synthesis whereby carbon monoxide and hydrogen (water gas) are forced to unite under pressure in the presence of a catalyst.

$$2H_2 + CO \underset{\text{cat.}}{\overset{\text{pr.}}{\rightleftarrows}} CH_3OH$$

The union of hydrogen with unsaturated organic compounds is also of con-

APPARATUS USED FOR INDUSTRIAL SCALE HYDROGENATION OF VEGETABLE OILS. (Courtesy, The Procter & Gamble Co.)

THE DESTRUCTION OF THE VON HINDENBURG—A HYDROGEN-FILLED DIRIGIBLE. (Courtesy,
Acme Newspictures, Inc.)

siderable practical importance. (An unsaturated organic compound is one in
which a pair, or several pairs, of carbon atoms are held together by more than
one pair of shared electrons.) When two carbon atoms are thus held, all but
one of the shared pairs is easily broken, and under pressure and in the presence
of a catalyst hydrogen will cause such ruptures and form shared pairs with the
displaced electrons. For example, ethylene and hydrogen react thus:

$$\begin{matrix} \text{H} & \text{H} \\ \text{C} & \text{C} \end{matrix} + \text{H}_2 \xrightarrow[\text{cat.}]{\text{pr.}} \begin{matrix} \text{H} & \text{H} \\ \text{H:C:C:H} \\ \text{H} & \text{H} \end{matrix}$$

Cottonseed oil, peanut oil, and other liquid fats consist largely of unsaturated
organic compounds which upon saturation with hydrogen yield solid fats.
By partial saturation of such oils, creamy mixtures of liquid and solid fats,
which make excellent shortenings, are obtained. Crisco, Snowdrift, Humko,

and other shortenings are prepared in this manner. Finely divided nickel is the catalyst usually employed. Platinum and palladium serve well in this capacity, but are much more expensive than nickel.

9. Uses

Elementary hydrogen is used in large quantities for the production of lard substitutes from liquid fats as discussed above. It is also used in the commercial synthesis of ammonia, NH_3, hydrogen chloride, and methanol, CH_3OH. It finds further application as a reducing agent, for welding, for the cooling of electric motors and generators, and for filling balloons. As the lightest of all gases it is well suited for this last purpose, but, because it is easily ignited, it is dangerous to use. The destruction of the dirigible *Von Hindenburg* well illustrates the reality of this danger. The use of water gas as a fuel was mentioned in section 7.

10. Hydrides

The binary compounds of hydrogen, the hydrides, fall readily into three distinct groups. The first of these groups is that of the saltlike hydrides. When the metals of the I A family and those of the II A family, with the exception of beryllium and magnesium, are heated to between 400° and 600° C. in a stream of hydrogen, there are formed colorless crystalline compounds which in the molten condition conduct electricity readily. Hydrogen is liberated at the positive electrode of the cell so it must have been present as the H^- ion. Hydrides of this type are decomposed by water with the evolution of hydrogen:

$$CaH_2 + 2H_2O \rightarrow Ca(OH)_2 + 2H_2 \uparrow$$

Such compounds are powerful reducing agents.

A second class of hydrides consists of those which are volatile and contain covalent linkages. Members of this group are formed by the elements of the IV A, V A, VI A, and VII A families of elements and by boron. Many of these elements do not combine directly with molecular hydrogen. Fluorine, chlorine, and oxygen combine most readily with the element, and nitrogen combines sufficiently well in the presence of a catalyst for the process to be of great commercial value. The other members of the group are best prepared by indirect means. Discussion of the preparation of the individual hydrides will be found in the chapters dealing with the other element of the combination. At this juncture it will be sufficient to say that the most widely applicable indirect method of producing them is the hydrolysis of the binary compounds of the elements in question with more positive elements:

$$Mg_2Si + 4H_2O \xrightarrow{H^+} 2Mg(OH)_2 + SiH_4 \uparrow$$
$$Al_4C_3 + 12H_2O \xrightarrow{H^+} 4Al(OH)_3 + 3CH_4 \uparrow$$
$$Mg_3N_2 + 6H_2O \xrightarrow{H^+} 3Mg(OH)_2 + 2NH_3 \uparrow$$
$$Ca_3P_2 + 6H_2O \xrightarrow{H^+} 3Ca(OH)_2 + 2PH_3 \uparrow$$
$$FeSe + 2H_2O \xrightarrow{H^+} Fe(OH)_2 + H_2Se \uparrow$$

and

$$PBr_3 + 3H_2O \xrightarrow{H^+} H_3PO_3 + 3HBr \uparrow$$

A number of these hydrides may also be prepared by reduction of other compounds of their principal element with *nascent* hydrogen. The stability of these hydrides increases from left to right across a given period of the chart and from bottom to top of a given column. In this group only the hydrides of the halogens and of nitrogen are readily soluble in water, while those of silicon are slowly decomposed by it. The acid character of these hydrides increases from left to right in a given period, and increases slightly as one passes down a given column of the chart. The hydrides of chlorine, bromine, and iodine ionize as acids due to the influence of the water dipoles, while aqueous solutions of ammonia, NH_3, are weakly basic as will be discussed in the chapter on nitrogen.

The third class of binary compounds of hydrogen consists of the so-called metallic hydrides which are formed by the elements which do not form hydrides of the other two classes. Notable among these elements are the transition metals of the long periods. These metals will absorb varying amounts of hydrogen with apparently little effect upon their properties. In some instances, it appears that the maximum amount which may be taken up is of the proper magnitude to represent a definite formula. Thus palladium, whose ability as an absorber of hydrogen has already been referred to, appears to form the unstable compound Pd_2H.

11. Water

By far the most important of the hydrides is that of oxygen, commonly called *water*. So universal and so important is this compound that to discuss it in all of its connections would require volumes. It is contained in plant and animal structures and in many minerals. The human body, for example, is about 70 per cent water, while tomatoes contain about 94 per cent and potatoes about 78 per cent. Great bodies of water cover much of the earth's surface; water vapor is contained in the atmosphere; and much water is contained in the soil and subsoil. In these connections, it has much to do with our weather, our transportation, our agriculture, and, in short, our very being. Water is both interesting and important in all of its associations, and it is unfortunate that space does not permit further discussion. Water is of greatest value from the chemical standpoint as a solvent. In this capacity, it has the ability to dissolve a wide variety of solids, liquids, and gases, and it is in aqueous solution that a majority of reactions occur. Many reactions will not take place at all without the presence of at least traces of water.

12. *Physical Properties of Water*

At ordinary temperatures, water is a transparent, odorless, tasteless liquid which is almost colorless. Deep layers of the fluid have a slight bluish tint. At standard pressure, the freezing point of pure water is 0° C. and its boiling point 100° C. That these transition temperatures are abnormally high for a compound whose molecular weight is only 18 at. wt. units, and that they are so because of association due to the polar nature of the compound, was pointed out in section 10 of Chapter 11. Like other liquids, water may be supercooled to temperatures below its freezing point. It has its greatest density at 3.98° C., at which temperature 1 ml. of the fluid has a mass of 1 g. Ice thus has a lower density than water, and for that reason will float in the liquid. The volume increases as the temperature is varied in either direction from 3.98° C., and the density, therefore, decreases to values less than 1 g./ml. The specific heat of the compound is 1.0000 cal./g. at 14.5° C., and for all other temperatures it is approximately 1. A majority of other substances have specific heats whose values are less than that of water. The heat of vaporization of the liquid at 100° C. is 539.55 cal./g., and the heat of fusion of the solid at 0° C. is 79.71 cal./g.

Ice crystals belong to the hexagonal system, as is strikingly and beautifully demonstrated in the six-pointed stars and other figures of six sides to be found among snowflakes. When subjected to high pressures, ice changes into several allotropic forms which are not stable at ordinary pressures. Since liquid water occupies a smaller volume than its solid, moderate pressures tend to cause ice to melt, as would be predicted by the application of the principle of Le Chatelier.

Both liquid and solid water have a tendency to escape into the gaseous state. This tendency and the pressure exerted by water vapor at various temperatures were discussed in sections 7 and 20 of Chapter 11. The critical temperature of the substance is 374° C.

13. *Preparation of Water*

Since water exists naturally in such abundance, its preparation is of scientific interest only. Earlier in this chapter, the combustion of hydrogen in air or oxygen was discussed:

$$2H_2 + O_2 \rightarrow 2H_2O$$

That two volumes of hydrogen and one of oxygen are involved in the preparation of water is strikingly demonstrated, qualitatively at least, by its electrolytic

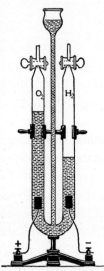

decomposition in an apparatus of the design illustrated herewith. In this apparatus, the volume of the hydrogen may readily be seen to be virtually twice that of the oxygen. The mechanism of the reaction by which the two gases combine directly is not yet understood fully.

Water is also prepared by the union of hydrogen (hydronium) and hydroxyl ions in neutralization reactions,

$$H_3O^+ + OH^- \rightarrow 2H_2O$$

by the reduction of oxides with hydrogen,

$$CuO + H_2 \rightarrow Cu + H_2O$$

and by a number of other reactions.

APPARATUS FOR THE LAB-ORATORY DEMONSTRA-TION OF THE ELECTROLY-SIS OF WATER.

The study of the exact composition of water has engaged some of the best scientific minds down through the years, and the establishment of its formula as H_2O was of great theoretical importance.

14. *Purification of Water*

Natural waters contain more or less dissolved mineral matter, and in addition they may contain suspended colloidal particles of soil and of organic matter, bacteria, and floating particles of trash. The principal criteria of good drinking water are its palatability and its freedom from harmful bacteria. Drinking water and other waters for domestic use are usually first piped into large settling basins where as much of the suspended matter as will is allowed to settle. Finely divided particles which show little inclination to settle, and some of the bacteria, are then removed by the addition of lime and ferrous or aluminum sulfate, or other chemicals, which form a heavy gelatinous precipitate that carries these small particles down with it as it settles.

$$3Ca(OH)_2 + Al_2(SO_4)_3 \rightarrow \underline{3CaSO_4} + \underline{2Al(OH)}_{3(gel.)}$$

Next comes filtration through beds of sand, gravel, and sometimes charcoal. Lastly, as the water enters the storage tanks, or during its storage, it is treated to kill any remaining bacteria. Hypochlorites are often added in small systems, but in the larger plants ozone, ultraviolet rays, chlorine dioxide, and chlorine are the usual germicides. Chlorine is the agent most commonly used.

None of these treatments removes dissolved minerals to any marked degree. Unless present in excessive quantities, the ordinary mineral impurities of water do not render it unfit for drinking, but some of them may render it

unfit for washing, for industrial proc- esses, or for use in boilers. Removal of these undesirable substances whose presence causes water to be classed as "hard" will be discussed in a later chapter.

For laboratory use, water must fre- quently be entirely devoid of impurities. Such water is usually prepared by dis- tillation (cf. section 15, Chapter 12). By

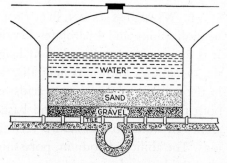

A WATER FILTRATION UNIT.

simple distillation, all nonvolatile impurities are left behind in the boiler, but traces of carbon dioxide, ammonia, and other volatile substances are usually carried over with the distillate. One method of eliminating these substances is to permit only partial condensation, so that they are swept out with the uncondensed steam. A more certain method is to treat the water to be distilled with sodium hydroxide and potassium permanganate. The distillate is then made faintly acid with sulfuric acid, and redistilled. Water thus carefully puri- fied should be kept in containers made of quartz or lined with block tin, since glass and many other substances are slightly soluble in water.

15. Chemical Properties of Water

The chemical behavior of water is related to its stability to heat, to its only slight ability to dissociate into ions, to its dipolar nature, and to its ability to act in what appears to be a catalytic capacity.

A. STABILITY TO HEAT. It was noted in section 8 that, when hydrogen and oxygen combine, the reaction is highly exothermal. From this, it will be inferred that, to decompose water into its elements, an equally large quantity of heat would have to be absorbed. Langmuir reports that water is decomposed into its elements to the extent of only 0.000745 per cent at 927° C.; 0.0920 per cent at 1427° C.; and 11.1 per cent at 2727° C. The elementary substances formed recombine, with evolution of the heat absorbed, as the temperature is lowered. It is because of its slight instability at elevated temperatures that water is able to react with various relatively inactive substances to form their oxides and to liberate hydrogen. The water-gas reaction and the action of iron and steam are examples of this behavior:

$$C + H_2O \rightleftarrows CO + H_2 \uparrow$$

and

$$3Fe + 4H_2O \rightleftarrows Fe_3O_4 + 4H_2 \uparrow$$

B. WEAKNESS AS AN ELECTROLYTE. Water is of special importance in neutralizations and hydrolyses because of its ability to ionize very slightly. It is due to the withdrawal of hydrogen and hydroxyl ions by each other that the metatheses known as neutralizations may proceed virtually to completion in the cases involving strong acids and bases. The hydrolysis of salts, one or both of whose parent acid and base are weak, is also made possible by the ability of water to maintain a very tiny concentration of both H^+ and OH^- ions. The ability of sodium, potassium, and other very active elements to displace hydrogen from cold water is, in a large measure, dependent upon the slight ionization of water as well as upon the activity of the metals involved:

$$2Na + 2HOH \rightarrow H_2 \uparrow + 2Na^+ + 2OH^-$$

C. DIPOLAR NATURE. The ability of water to dissolve a wide variety of substances has already been noted. This ability is due largely to the dipolar nature of the water molecules, and the heat of hydration of many ionic substances is due to the strong attraction between the ions and the water dipoles. In solution, ions are hydrated by a variable number of dipoles, but, as has been shown, many ions, when withdrawn from solution into a crystal lattice, carry a definite number of water molecules with them into the structure. Presumably, these molecules are held by coördination valence. It would be well to review at this point previous discussions of hydrates and their efflorescence and deliquescence.

Related to the hydration of ions is the hydration of metallic and nonmetallic oxides to form compounds which may act as acids, bases, or ampholytes. In essence, the addition of water results in the formation of hydroxides whose subsequent behavior is determined largely by the ionic potential of the element whose oxide has become hydrated. At this juncture, the discussion of the ionization of hydroxides (section 7, Chapter 15) should be reviewed.

D. CATALYTIC ACTIVITY. There are many reactions which will proceed readily, some even violently, if only a trace of water is present, but which will not proceed at all if that trace of moisture is absent. It is reported that dry sodium and anhydrous hydrogen sulfate do not react, that dry sulfur may be vaporized in dry oxygen without reaction, that anhydrous hydrogen chloride and anhydrous ammonia do not react, that mixtures of anhydrous hydrogen and anhydrous oxygen do not react even when heated to high temperatures, and that anhydrous chlorine shows little of the reactivity that chlorine exhibits in the presence of moisture. Water undoubtedly does behave as a catalyst in many of these reactions, but in others, while its exact function is not exactly known, indications are that its behavior is not simply that of a catalyst.

To obtain absolutely dry substances is very difficult. Moisture is always present in the air to a greater or lesser degree, so that everything exposed to the air usually becomes contaminated with water. Substances which have been dried carefully take up moisture eagerly upon exposure to the air. Even substances which are ordinarily considered to be anhydrous are rarely absolutely dry. The boiling point of benzene (C_6H_6) is usually given as 80.09° C., but experiments performed at the Johns Hopkins University have established the boiling point of benzene which has been dried by long contact with phosphorus pentoxide as 106° C. This would indicate that perhaps even the slightest traces of moisture permit the formation of molecular arrangements which are not possible in their absence.

16. Heavy Water

Deuterium oxide, D_2O, is commonly known as *heavy water*. The mixed oxide of hydrogen and deuterium, HDO, is also a heavy water. Deuterium oxide is present in ordinary water to the extent of about one part in 5,000 to 7,000 parts, and is less susceptible to electrolysis than is H_2O. By careful electrolysis of water containing a small concentration of sodium hydroxide, the residual liquid gradually becomes richer in D_2O. Much current is required in the preparation of even a small volume of heavy water, so its price is high; nevertheless, considerable quantities of it have been used in scientific research. As little as one part of it in 100,000 parts of water may be detected, hence it is of considerable value in following vital processes in plant and animal organisms. Whether the higher animals could exist on D_2O instead of ordinary water is not known, but some microörganisms are killed by it and certain seeds do not germinate in it.

Some of its properties as compared with the corresponding ones of ordinary water are given in the following table.

Table 22

COMPARISON OF PROPERTIES OF WATER AND DEUTERIUM OXIDE

Property	For H_2O	For D_2O
Molecular weight....................	18.02	20.03
Density at 20° C.....................	0.9982	1.1059
Temp. of maximum density.............	3.98° C.	11.6° C.
Freezing point......................	0.0° C.	3.82° C.
Boiling point.......................	100.0° C.	101.42° C.

17. Hydrogen Peroxide

Hydrogen forms a second oxide, H_2O_2, which is a typical peroxide in that the oxygen atoms are attached to each other. The compound was discovered in 1818 by Thenard. Subsequent elementary analyses showed the atomic ratio of the elements to correspond to the formula HO, while molecular-weight determinations revealed a weight of 34 at. wt. units, which figure indicates the formula H_2O_2. The configuration of the molecule is generally taken as

H ̈×O ̈:O ̈×H, though there is reason for believing that some of the molecules

$$\begin{array}{c} H \\ {}^{\cdot\times} \quad {}^{\cdot\cdot} \end{array}$$

have the isomeric structure H×O:O: The compound is so active and so unstable that only minute traces of it are found in nature, usually in snow, rain, or dew. Its presence there is accounted for by the action of ultraviolet light on the oxygen and moisture of the air:

$$\text{u.v.}$$
$$2H_2O + O_2 \rightleftarrows 2H_2O_2$$

18. Physical Properties of Hydrogen Peroxide

The pure compound is a colorless, sirupy liquid with an irritating odor and an acrid, astringent taste. Its density is 1.442 g./ml. at 20° C., and its boiling point under a pressure of 21 mm. of mercury is 62.8° C. It explodes violently under normal pressure before its boiling temperature is reached. The pure liquid is fairly stable if kept away from oxidizable material and if preserved in the dark in containers whose walls are smooth. Even so, oxygen is slowly evolved. It is possible to prepare needlelike crystals of the substance whose melting point is −1.70° C. It mixes in all proportions with water, alcohol, or ether. In ether it is more soluble and more stable than in water. Its specific heat is 0.579 cal./g. Lastly, it ionizes slightly as a weak dibasic acid whose primary ionization constant is 1.5×10^{-12}.

19. Preparation of Hydrogen Peroxide

This interesting compound is most easily prepared in the laboratory by the action of sulfuric acid on barium peroxide:

$$BaO_2 + H_2SO_4 \rightarrow \underline{BaSO_4} + H_2O_2$$

Instead of sulfuric acid, one may substitute phosphoric acid or even the aqueous solutions of carbon dioxide commonly called carbonic acid:

$$BaO_2 + H_2CO_3 \rightarrow \underline{BaCO_3} + H_2O_2$$

Commercially, phosphoric acid is preferred since it helps to stabilize the product.

In the laboratory, one may also dissolve sodium peroxide in water just above its freezing point (to retard the decomposition of the Na_2O_2 into NaOH and O_2) and then add hydrochloric acid:

$$Na_2O_2 + 2HCl \rightarrow 2NaCl + H_2O_2$$

Alcoholic solutions of sodium peroxide react with concentrated mineral acids to yield $NaHO_2$, sodium hydroperoxide. The product may be extracted from its aqueous solutions by ether and separated from the latter liquid by fractional distillation under reduced pressure.

On a large industrial scale, the method of preparation is the hydrolysis of perdisulfuric acid or its salts, whose electrolytic preparation was discussed in section 32 of Chapter 21. Permonosulfuric acid is an intermediate product of the hydrolysis:

$$H_2S_2O_8 + 2H_2O \rightarrow 2H_2SO_4 + H_2O_2$$

The product is separated by fractional distillation in a fused quartz still under reduced pressure, and, because of its purity, the 30 to 35 per cent aqueous solution so obtained keeps much better than the product obtained by the metathesis of metallic peroxides. A 27.6 per cent solution finds wide industrial use. During World War II, the Germans perfected methods of preparing highly concentrated hydrogen peroxide for use as a source of oxygen in their jet-propelled bombs and planes. Decomposition is always favored by nearly all foreign substances, rough surfaces, and ultraviolet light.

The commercial product is shipped in aluminum drums and tank cars, and sometimes preservatives such as glycerol, alcohol, acetanilide, or quinine sulfate are added in small amounts.

20. Chemical Properties of Hydrogen Peroxide

In view of the fact that the formation of hydrogen peroxide is a highly endothermic reaction, it is not strange that it decomposes easily, and in so doing liberates heat:

$$2H_2O_2 \rightarrow 2H_2O + O_2 \uparrow + 47,800 \text{ cal.}$$

The ease with which this reaction occurs has been referred to in preceding sections, and it may be added here that finely divided metals, bases, many salts, and manganese dioxide also foster the decomposition. Acids tend to retard it, especially phosphoric acid.

The pure compound acts principally as an oxidizing agent. Cotton and other easily oxidizable materials are so strongly attacked by it that they may burst into flame. Weaker solutions also act as oxidizing agents, converting nitrous acid to nitric acid, sulfurous acid to sulfuric acid, hydrogen iodide to free iodine, and sulfides to sulfates:

$$HNO_2 + H_2O_2 \rightarrow HNO_3 + H_2O$$
$$2HI + H_2O_2 \rightarrow 2H_2O + I_2$$

and

$$PbS + 4H_2O_2 \rightarrow PbSO_4 + 4H_2O$$

Also because of their oxidizing action, weak aqueous solutions (3 per cent) are used to disinfect wounds. Much more dependable antiseptics are to be had, however. Solutions whose strength is about 30 per cent are used as oxidizing agents to bleach the color from cloth, hair, silk, feathers, ivory, and straw. It is much safer to use on these materials than is chlorine, since water, the only by-product, is not acidic and hence will foster little decomposition. Solutions of this strength may burn the skin and will surely cause spots if spilled on clothing.

Beside acting as an oxidizing agent, dilute solutions of hydrogen peroxide will also act as a reducing agent. This dual behavior might have been predicted from the fact that the oxidation number of oxygen in H_2O_2 is -1, a value midway between the zero oxidation number of elementary oxygen and the -2 oxidation number which it shows in ordinary oxides. The peroxide acts as a reducing agent with substances whose oxidizing powers are greater than its

HENRY CAVENDISH
(1731–1810, English)

Though he is sometimes erroneously credited with
the discovery of hydrogen, Cavendish was, nevertheless, the first investigator to study that gas carefully and thoroughly. For this work he is remembered
best. In many respects he was the most singular of all
scientists. Despite the fact that he was very wealthy,
he lived the life of a recluse, devoting all of his time
to scientific research. Many stories are told of his
shyness and eccentricities. He was an excellent mathematician, and his scientific interests were many. In
addition to his researches of a chemical nature, he
conducted studies in the fields of astronomy, electricity, geology, metallurgy, meteorology, and
mineralogy.

HAROLD CLAYTON UREY
(1893–   , American)

After receiving the Ph.D. degree in chemistry at the
University of California in 1923, Urey spent a year
at the University of Copenhagen where he worked in
the laboratory of Niels Bohr. Returning to the United
States, he was appointed to the faculty of Johns
Hopkins University and in 1929 to the faculty of
Columbia University, but is now at the University
of Chicago. He is known principally for his discovery in 1932 of deuterium (heavy hydrogen);
however, he has worked on the kinetics of reactions,
Raman spectra, the thermodynamic properties of
gases, the structures of atoms and molecules, etc.
For his discovery of deuterium he received the Nobel
Prize in 1934. He is the author of many scientific
papers and several books, and has edited the *Journal
of Chemical Physics*. (Courtesy, *Journal of Chemical
Education.*)

own, and when it so acts, elementary oxygen, as indicated above, is one of the products. It reduces the oxides of silver, platinum, and other of the heavy metals as well as acidified solutions of potassium permanganate:

$$Ag_2O + H_2O_2 \rightarrow \underline{2Ag} + H_2O + O_2 \uparrow$$

and

$$2KMnO_4 + 5H_2O_2 + 6HCl \rightarrow 2MnCl_2 + 2KCl + 8H_2O + 5O_2 \uparrow$$

Whether H_2O_2 acts as an oxidizing or reducing agent depends not only on the specific nature of the substance with which it is placed in contact, but also upon the hydrogen-ion concentration of the medium. For example, it reacts with manganese dioxide in acidic solution to reduce it to the manganous condition, but in basic solution it will effect the reverse reaction, converting manganous salts to manganese dioxide:

$$MnO_2 + H_2O_2 + 2H^+ \rightarrow Mn^{++} + 2H_2O + O_2 \uparrow$$

and

$$Mn^{++} + H_2O_2 + 2OH^- \rightarrow \underline{MnO_2} + 2H_2O$$

Hydrogen peroxide in aqueous solution may also exhibit its ability to act as a weak acid. With such solutions, the slightly soluble hydroxides of barium and strontium react to form the corresponding metallic peroxides, which are also but slightly soluble:

$$Ba(OH)_2 + H_2O_2 \rightarrow \underline{BaO_2} + 2H_2O$$

After the fashion in which water unites with acid anhydrides to form acids, hydrogen peroxide unites with many of the same anhydrides to form the corresponding *per-* acids.

$$H_2O + SO_3 \rightarrow H_2SO_4$$
$$H_2O + 2SO_3 \rightarrow H_2S_2O_7$$
$$3H_2O + P_2O_5 \rightarrow 2H_3PO_4$$
$$H_2O_2 + SO_3 \rightarrow H_2SO_5$$
$$H_2O_2 + 2SO_3 \rightarrow H_2S_2O_8$$
$$2H_2O_2 + H_2O + P_2O_5 \rightarrow 2H_3PO_5$$

Some ions which are capable of combining with molecules of water of hydration are also capable of combining with molecules of hydrogen peroxide in a similar fashion to form perhydrates. Salts containing H_2O_2 held in such a manner will be encountered in later chapters.

21. Uses of Hydrogen Peroxide

The principal use of this compound is as a commercial bleaching agent for the materials already referred to and for a wide variety of organic materials. Its 3 per cent solution is used rather widely as a mild antiseptic and germicide, and solutions of varying strength are used in the laboratory as oxidizing and reducing agents. Its solutions also find some use as oxidizing agents in the dyeing industry. The preparation of medicinals and pharmaceuticals also uses large quantities of it. Because its solutions will oxidize dark lead sulfide to the colorless sulfate, they are sometimes used to restore darkened oil paintings. The use of the highly concentrated reagent in jet-propelled devices has already been mentioned. Complex organic peroxides are often used as a bleach for flour.

22. Analytical Tests for Hydrogen Peroxide

Like a number of other oxidizing agents, including the *per*- acids, hydrogen peroxide will cause starch-iodide paper to turn blue. A specific test consists of adding the liquid to be tested to a solution of titanic sulfate, $Ti(SO_4)_2$. If hydrogen peroxide is present, an intense and stable orange-yellow color will develop. The color is that of pertitanic acid. A second specific test consists of adding the liquid to be tested to a solution of potassium dichromate acidified with sulfuric acid. If the peroxide is present, a delicate and evanescent blue color develops. The color is believed to be that of an unstable perchromic acid. This substance may be extracted by shaking its aqueous solution with ether, in which it is quite soluble and considerably more stable than in water. The true *per*- acids give neither of these tests.

Quantitatively, hydrogen peroxide is determined by titration of its acidified aqueous solution with standard potassium permanganate solution.

(See *Appendix for Exercises*)

COLLATERAL READINGS

Bartlett: Flames of atomic hydrogen, *J. Chem. Education*, **4,** 38 (1927).
Findlay: *The Spirit of Chemistry*, New York, Longmans, Green & Co., 1934.
Furnas: *Roger's Industrial Chemistry*, Vol. I, New York, D. Van Nostrand Co., 1943.
Hazen: *Clean Water and How to Get It*, New York, John Wiley & Sons, Inc., 1914.
Latimer and Hildebrand: *Reference Book of Inorganic Chemistry*, New York, The Macmillan Co., 1941.

Reichert: Hydrogen peroxide, *Chem. and Eng. News*, **21,** 480 (1943).

Smith: *The Effects of Moisture on Chemical and Physical Changes*, New York, Longmans, Green & Co., 1929.

Taylor: *Industrial Hydrogen*, New York, Reinhold Publishing Corp., 1925.

Urey: Significance of the hydrogen isotopes, *Ind. and Eng. Chem.*, **26,** 803 (1934).

Weeks: *Discovery of the Elements*, 5th ed., Mack Printing Co., 1945.

White: Concentrated hydrogen peroxide, *Chem. and Eng. News*, **23,** 1626 (1945).

Yost and Russell: *Systematic Inorganic Chemistry*, New York, Prentice-Hall, Inc., 1944.

Nitrogen and the Members of the V A Family

1. Introduction

Considerable time and space have been devoted in preceding chapters to the discussion of the manner in which the properties of the elements vary from left to right across a given period of the periodic chart. Let us now discuss the manner in which the properties of the elements of a given family vary as one passes from top to bottom down the column of the chart which they occupy. Since the members of the V A family of elements show this variation perhaps more strikingly than do those of any other family, they have been chosen for initial study. The V A family consists of nitrogen, phosphorus, arsenic, antimony, and bismuth, all of which possess five valence electrons but whose respective atomic sizes increase as their atomic weights increase. As one passes down the column, then, the size of the individual atoms increases, and hence the basic and metallic properties of the elements increase in the same order. Nitrogen, the lightest member of the family, is definitely a nonmetal, a gas of low reactivity, while bismuth, the heaviest member of the family, is a metal of moderate to strong activity. In between these extremes are phosphorus, a very active nonmetal, arsenic, a moderately active nonmetal, and antimony, whose appearance is distinctly metallic but whose behavior is amphoteric.

In this family, as in others, the greatest difference in properties between successive elements lies between those of the second and third periods; thus, there is more difference in behavior between nitrogen and phosphorus than between any other two consecutive members of the family. Because of that difference, it will be necessary to discuss the properties of nitrogen rather fully, but, since the chemistry of phosphorus was discussed at some length in Chapter 20, and since the compounds of the remaining elements of the family are of less general importance from the practical standpoint, these other members of the group will be discussed more briefly.

Having five valence electrons, two of which are in the zero sub-level and three of which are in the number one sub-level, these elements, as might be anticipated, show in their compounds the regular oxidation numbers $+5$, $+3$, and -3. The importance of these regular oxidation states varies somewhat with the different members of the family, and nitrogen in particular shows other intermediate oxidation numbers in its compounds.

Upon concluding this chapter, the student should be able to use his knowledge of the variation of properties in a period and in a family to predict the properties of any of the regular "A" family elements.

I. NITROGEN

2. *Physical Properties*

Nitrogen was first recognized as a distinct chemical entity by the Scottish botanist, Rutherford, in 1772. Lavoisier established that it was an element, and later, when it was found to be a constituent of *niter*, KNO_3, Chaptal suggested that it be called nitrogen (*niter former*). At ordinary temperatures, it is a gas which is colorless, odorless, and tasteless. Having a critical temperature of $-147.1°$ C., it is liquefied only with difficulty, but, once formed, the liquid boils at $-195.8°$ C. and freezes to a colorless solid at $-209.86°$ C. At S.T.P., 1 l. of the gas weighs 1.2506 g., which places its density just slightly below that of air and indicates that its molecules are diatomic and of the formula N_2. The density of the liquid is 0.808 g./ml. Under standard pressure, the solubility of the gas in 1 ml. of water is 0.023 ml. at $0°$ C. and 0.015 ml. at $20°$ C. Naturally occurring nitrogen is an isotopic mixture of the atomic species whose weights are 14 and 15, respectively, and in which the former predominates.

3. *Occurrence*

Among the lighter and commoner elements, nitrogen is unusual in that it occurs principally in the uncombined form. This statement emphasizes its relatively low activity. The atmosphere, of which it constitutes about four-fifths by volume, is the great reservoir of nitrogen from which compounds are prepared by electrical, bacterial, and chemical means, and to which the free element is returned as a result of the decomposition of nitrogenous compounds. It has been estimated that there are more than 20,000,000 tons of the free element over each square mile of the earth's surface.

Nitrogen also occurs in combination. Every living cell contains compounds of carbon, hydrogen, oxygen, and nitrogen, and all animal and plant proteins contain these four elements. Among the products of the destructive distillation of coal is ammonia, NH_3, a hydride of nitrogen, and the same substance and some of its derivatives are formed by the putrefaction of protein matter.

The principal naturally occurring inorganic compounds of the element are potassium nitrate, KNO_3, which is also known both as *niter* and as *saltpeter*, and sodium nitrate, $NaNO_3$, which is commonly known as *Chile saltpeter*. Both of these compounds are highly soluble and are found, therefore, only where their deposits are well protected from moisture. Extensive beds of the latter salt are found in the ultra-dry Atacama Desert of northern Chile.

4. Production

Industrially, pure nitrogen is obtained by the fractional distillation of liquid air (cf. section 12, Chapter 11). The nitrogen, having a lower boiling point, boils away more readily than does the oxygen, and is collected and recompressed into steel cylinders for shipment.

In the laboratory, nitrogen is most easily obtained in moderate quantities by the pyrolytic decomposition of ammonium nitrite:

$$NH_4NO_2 \overset{\Delta}{\rightarrow} 2H_2O \uparrow + N_2 \uparrow$$

In practice, a mixture of sodium nitrite and ammonium chloride is generally used because ammonium nitrite is too unstable to keep well.

$$NaNO_2 + NH_4Cl \overset{\Delta}{\rightarrow} NaCl + 2H_2O \uparrow + N_2 \uparrow$$

The water vapor is removed by passing the gas through a drying tube filled with anhydrous calcium chloride. Other laboratory methods consist of: (a) the oxidation of ammonia by copper oxide, nitric oxide, or a hypochlorite,

$$2NH_3 + 3CuO \overset{\Delta}{\rightarrow} 3H_2O + 3Cu + N_2 \uparrow$$
$$4NH_3 + 6NO \rightarrow 6H_2O + 5N_2 \uparrow$$

and

$$2NH_3 + 3NaOCl \rightarrow 3NaCl + 3H_2O + N_2 \uparrow$$

and (b) the passage of air through a tube containing hot copper. In the latter process, the oxygen of the air combines with the copper, allowing nitrogen containing a small percentage of argon and other inert gases to pass on through.

5. Chemical Properties

It is more difficult to separate the atoms which form the nitrogen molecule than it is to separate those which form the hydrogen molecule (cf. section 8, Chapter 23):

$$N_2 + 208,000 \text{ cal.} \rightleftarrows 2N$$

Because of this disinclination of its elementary molecules to dissociate, nitrogen shows but slight chemical activity. As might be expected, its compounds are quite active, represent a wide variety of oxidation states of the element, and are among the most important of chemical substances.

Nitrogen does not burn, but, when passed with oxygen through a powerful electric arc, it unites with the latter to form nitric oxide, NO:

$$N_2 + O_2 \overset{arc}{\rightleftarrows} 2NO \uparrow$$

It does not combine directly with the halogens, but with hydrogen under high pressure and in the presence of a suitable catalyst it does combine to a slight extent:

$$N_2 + 3H_2 \overset{pr.}{\underset{cat.}{\rightleftarrows}} 2NH_3 \uparrow$$

This reaction will be discussed further in connection with the preparation of ammonia.

With a few very active elements, notable among which are magnesium, aluminum, lithium, titanium, calcium, and boron, the element unites directly at high temperatures to form their respective nitrides:

$$6Li + N_2 \rightarrow 2Li_3N$$

and

$$3Ca + N_2 \rightarrow Ca_3N_2$$

These nitrides are easily hydrolyzed into ammonia, NH_3, and the hydroxide of the more positive element:

$$Ca_3N_2 + 6HOH \rightarrow \underline{3Ca(OH)_2} + 2NH_3 \uparrow$$

Nitrogen is too inactive to enter into displacement reactions.

6. Nitric Acid

Nitric acid, which is one of the oldest and most important members of the class of compounds known as acids, is an aqueous solution of hydrogen nitrate, HNO_3. Pure hydrogen nitrate is a colorless liquid which fumes in moist air and has a density of 1.502 g./ml. at 20° C. It boils under standard pressure at 86° C., undergoing the while some decomposition into its anhydride, nitrogen pentoxide, N_2O_5,

$$2HNO_3 \rightleftarrows H_2O + N_2O_5$$

which, in turn, is decomposed into nitrogen dioxide and oxygen:

$$2N_2O_5 \rightarrow 4NO_2 + O_2$$

It will be noted that nitrogen pentoxide forms principally metanitric acid, while phosphorus pentoxide is more commonly associated with orthophosphoric acid rather than with the meta acid. By means of the freezing-point method (cf. section 22, Chapter 21) it can be shown, however, that nitrogen pentoxide is also the anhydride of several less common acids. Either concentrated or dilute solutions of hydrogen nitrate when boiled lose the component that is present in excess of the proportions required for the establishment of

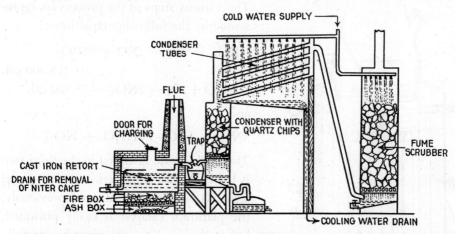

DIAGRAM OF A PLANT FOR THE PREPARATION OF NITRIC ACID. In the retort sodium nitrate and sulfuric acid are heated and the evolved hydrogen nitrate is condensed in the condenser tubes over which cold water flows. As the condensate flows downward over the quartz chips the rising hot fumes remove dissolved oxides of nitrogen. Storage is in the tank at the bottom of the tower. The fume scrubber with its descending spray of water removes the last traces of hydrogen nitrate which escape from the condenser.

an azeotropic mixture whose boiling point under standard pressure is 121° C., whose density is 1.42 g./ml., and whose percentage of hydrogen nitrate is 68. This acid is the concentrated acid of the laboratory.

Until the present century, nitric acid was usually prepared both commercially and in the laboratory by the action of concentrated sulfuric acid on sodium nitrate, a method which still finds wide use:

$$\overset{\Delta}{NaNO_3 + H_2SO_4 \rightarrow NaHSO_4 + HNO_3 \uparrow}$$

The acid is distilled from the reaction mixture as it is formed.

A more modern process whose use shows a steady increase is the oxidation of ammonia. By this method (commonly referred to as the Ostwald process), gaseous ammonia, NH_3, and about ten times its own volume of air are preheated to about 600° C. and then passed over a red-hot platinum gauze. The reaction whereby nitric oxide is produced is exothermic, so that the reaction once begun is able to maintain the gauze at red heat and to heat the incoming

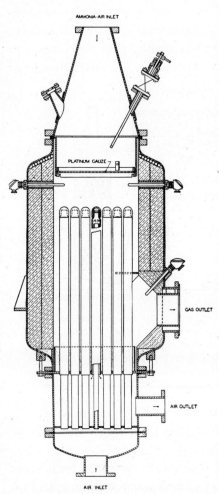

AMMONIA-AIR INLET

PLATINUM GAUZE

GAS OUTLET

AIR OUTLET

AIR INLET

A REACTION CHAMBER FOR THE CATALYTIC OXIDATION OF AMMONIA. (Courtesy, Chemical Construction Corp.)

reaction mixture to approximately 1000° C. Upon contact with excess oxygen, the nitric oxide reacts to form nitrogen dioxide, which is then dissolved in hot water. The various steps of the process are represented by the following equations:

$$4NH_3 + 5O_2 \rightarrow 4NO + 6H_2O$$
$$+ 215,000 \text{ cal.}$$
$$2NO + O_2 \rightarrow 2NO_2 + 27,800 \text{ cal.}$$

and

$$3NO_2 + H_2O \rightarrow 2HNO_3 + NO \uparrow$$

The nitric oxide liberated in the third step is led back into the reaction in the second step. As has been mentioned previously, the platinum catalyst is easily poisoned, hence the reaction gas must be carefully purified before coming in contact with it.

7. Chemical Properties of Nitric Acid

At the outset, nitric acid is a strong acid which exhibits all the properties that have come to be associated with acids; furthermore, as was pointed out in the preceding section, it is unstable, and, because of this instability, even in its dilute solutions it acts as a strong oxidizing agent upon a wide variety of elements and compounds.

With all metals except gold, platinum, and a few others of the noble metals the acid reacts, forming nitrates of the metals, save in the case of tin, antimony, molybdenum, and tungsten whose oxides are formed. It might be expected that metals above hydrogen in the activity series would react to liberate hydrogen from the acid, but, since its properties as an oxidizing agent are even more pronounced than are its properties as an acid, most of the hydrogen liberated is oxidized immediately to water. Metals below hydrogen in the series are oxidized directly to nitrates, save as noted. When dilute nitric acid is used, it is usually reduced to nitric oxide, NO, while the concentrated acid is usually reduced to nitrogen dioxide, NO_2:

$$3Mg + 8HNO_3 \text{ (dil.)} \rightarrow 3Mg(NO_3)_2 + 2NO \uparrow + 4H_2O$$
$$3Cu + 8HNO_3 \text{ (dil.)} \rightarrow 3Cu(NO_3)_2 + 2NO \uparrow + 4H_2O$$
$$Cu + 4HNO_3 \text{ (conc.)} \rightarrow Cu(NO_3)_2 + 2NO_2 \uparrow + 2H_2O$$

and

$$2Sb + 10HNO_3 \text{ (conc.)} \rightarrow Sb_2O_5 + 10NO_2 \uparrow + 5H_2O$$

Although NO and NO_2 are the usual products of the reduction of the acid, other reduction products may be obtained. These vary with the nature of the substance to be oxidized, the strength of the acid, the temperature, and other conditions. Thus, zinc is able to reduce the nitrogen of very dilute nitric acid all the way from its $+5$ oxidation state to its -3 state:

$$4Zn + 10HNO_3 \rightarrow 4Zn(NO_3)_2 + NH_4NO_3 + 3H_2O$$

The acid reacts with most nonmetals to form their oxides, which may or may not combine with the water also produced to form acids. Again, the dilute acid usually is converted to NO and the concentrated to NO_2:

$$C + 4HNO_3 \text{ (conc.)} \rightarrow CO_2 \uparrow + 4NO_2 \uparrow + 2H_2O$$
$$P + HNO_3 \text{ (dil.)} + H_2O \rightarrow H_3PO_3 + NO \uparrow$$
$$P + 5HNO_3 \text{ (conc.)} \rightarrow H_3PO_4 + 5NO_2 \uparrow + H_2O$$

Nitric acid oxidizes many compounds. Its action on hydrogen sulfide, other compounds of sulfur, and a number of the compounds of phosphorus has already been noted. With hydrochloric acid it reacts to form chlorine, nitrosyl chloride, and water:

$$3HCl + HNO_3 \rightarrow Cl_2 \uparrow + NOCl \uparrow + 2H_2O$$

The mixture of nitric and hydrochloric acids in the ratio of 1 to 3 is known as *aqua regia* (royal water), because it is strong enough as an oxidizing agent to dissolve gold, platinum, and others of the *royal* or *noble* metals which are not attacked by simple acids.

A wide variety of the compounds of carbon also reacts with nitric acid, forming in some instances nitrates and in other instances nitro compounds.

Nitro compounds contain the group $-N\diagup_{\diagdown O}^{O}$. With the protein of skin, lean meat, egg white, wool, etc., nitric acid develops a yellow color. This *xantho-proteic acid* test is very sensitive so that protein is easily identified by it.

Reactions in which nitric acid acts as an oxidizing agent occur much more rapidly in the presence of traces of nitrous acid than they do in their absence, hence nitrous acid is a positive catalyst for these reactions. As it happens, nitrous acid is usually produced during the course of oxidations by nitric acid. Reactions which produce their own catalysts are said to be *autocatalytic*. It is characteristic of such reactions that they start slowly, pick up speed as the catalyst is produced, and gradually slow down as the substance from which the catalyst comes is consumed. Hydrogen peroxide destroys nitrous acid and hence may be used to slow the oxidizing action of nitric acid.

8. Nitrates

Besides acting upon many metals to produce nitrates, nitric acid reacts by metathesis with their oxides, hydroxides, carbonates, sulfites, and other compounds to produce nitrates. As a class, the nitrates are among the most soluble of inorganic salts, with all normal members of the group being water-soluble. All nitrates decompose upon being heated and hence serve well as dry oxidizing agents. Black gunpowder is a mixture of sulfur, charcoal, and potassium nitrate, and steel when dipped into molten potassium nitrate is given a bluish, protective coat of metallic oxide. The manner in which nitrates decompose upon heating are: (a) salts of active metals yield nitrites when heated for a long time at red heat:

$$2NaNO_3 \overset{\Delta}{\rightarrow} 2NaNO_2 + O_2 \uparrow$$

—the reaction is hastened by the addition of some substance to combine with the evolved oxygen; (b) salts of the heavy metals are more readily decomposed yielding their oxides, nitrogen dioxide, and sometimes oxygen,

$$2Pb(NO_3)_2 \overset{\Delta}{\rightarrow} 2PbO + 4NO_2 \uparrow + O_2 \uparrow$$

$$2Cu(NO_3)_2 \overset{\Delta}{\rightarrow} 2CuO + 4NO_2 \uparrow + O_2 \uparrow$$

and

$$Mn(NO_3)_2 \overset{\Delta}{\rightarrow} MnO_2 + 2NO_2 \uparrow$$

—silver nitrate is an exception to the rule since it yields free silver, NO_2, and

O_2; and (c) ammonium nitrate decomposes into water and nitrous oxide,

$$NH_4NO_3 \rightarrow 2H_2O + N_2O \uparrow$$

In alkaline solution, nitrates are reduced to ammonia by zinc or aluminum:

$$NaNO_3 + 4Zn + 7NaOH \rightarrow 4Na_2ZnO_2 + NH_3 \uparrow + 2H_2O$$

9. Uses of Nitric Acid and the Nitrates

Nitric acid ranks high among the leading industrial chemicals. It finds wide use both as an acid and as an oxidizing agent in the laboratory as well as

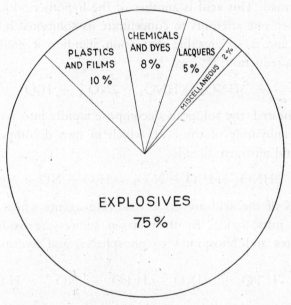

AVERAGE CONSUMPTION OF NITRIC ACID IN THE UNITED
STATES BY USES.

in industry. It is used in the production of all commercial explosives and in the manufacture of chemicals, dyes, medicinals, and fertilizers. The nitrates are important dry oxidizing agents and fertilizers.

10. Nitrogen Pentoxide

Nitrogen pentoxide is a colorless solid which fumes in moist air, melts with some decomposition at 30° C., and is in general very unstable, as noted in section 6. It is usually prepared by the dehydration with phosphorus pentoxide of nitric acid, whose anhydride it is:

$$2HNO_3 + P_2O_5 \rightarrow N_2O_5 + 2HPO_3$$

Nitric acid whose N_2O_5 content has been increased by partial dehydration resulting from distillation with concentrated sulfuric acid is known as *fuming nitric acid*. It is usually reddish in color due to redissolved NO_2 formed by decomposition of some of the N_2O_5.

11. Nitrous Acid

When sodium or potassium nitrite, made by heating their respective nitrates, is dissolved in water and acidified, a pale blue solution of nitrous acid, HNO_2, is formed. This acid is another of the hypothetical acids, since it decomposes when one attempts to concentrate its solutions. It is a very weakly ionized acid and is so unstable that upon standing it gradually undergoes autooxidation-reduction:

$$3HNO_2 \rightarrow HNO_3 + 2NO \uparrow + H_2O$$

Upon being heated, the solutions decompose rapidly into water and nitrogen trioxide, the anhydride of the acid, which in turn decomposes rapidly into nitric oxide and nitrogen dioxide:

$$2HNO_2 \rightarrow H_2O + N_2O_3 \rightarrow H_2O + NO + NO_2$$

Solutions of the acid are good oxidizing agents which upon reduction usually yield nitric oxide. By their action sulfites are oxidized to sulfates, hypophosphites and phosphites to phosphates, and hydriodic acid to free iodine:

$$H_3PO_3 + 2HNO_2 \rightarrow H_3PO_4 + 2NO \uparrow + H_2O$$

Since the nitrogen of nitrous acid has the intermediate oxidation number of $+3$, the acid may also act as a reducing agent when treated with active oxidizing agents; and when it so acts it is usually oxidized to nitric acid, which may or may not form salts:

$$HNO_2 + H_2O_2 \rightarrow HNO_3 + H_2O$$

$$5HNO_2 + 2KMnO_4 + 3H_2SO_4 \rightarrow 5HNO_3 + K_2SO_4 + 2MnSO_4 + 3H_2O$$

12. Nitrites

Since nitrous acid is weak, its most important salts are those of the strong bases, and these salts of course, are strongly hydrolyzed in solution. As a class, the salts are soluble, though silver nitrite, which finds some use in organic chemistry, is only sparingly so. The most important salts are those of potassium and sodium. They are usually made by heating the corresponding nitrate slowly with finely divided lead:

$$NaNO_3 + Pb \rightarrow NaNO_2 + PbO$$

The reaction mixture when cool is added to water, the lead oxide removed by filtration, and the filtrate evaporated. The salts are used in large quantities in the manufacture of dyes.

Nitrites are also reduced to ammonia by zinc or aluminum in sodium hydroxide solution.

13. *Analytical Tests for Nitrates and Nitrites*

Both nitric and nitrous acids are reduced to nitric oxide by ferrous ion, Fe^{++}. The NO then reacts with excess ferrous ion to form the ferrous nitrosyl ion, $Fe(NO)^{++}$, which is brown in color. The test is made by adding solid ferrous sulfate to the unknown solution contained in a test tube. Concentrated sulfuric acid is then added carefully to the inclined tube so that it forms a layer beneath the unknown fluid. If nitrites or nitrates are present, a brown ring is formed at the interface between the two layers. Concentrated acetic acid gives the *brown ring test* with nitrites, but not with nitrates. Solid nitrites, or their concentrated solutions, yield brown fumes with concentrated

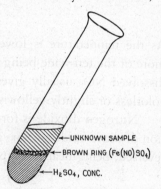

←UNKNOWN SAMPLE
←BROWN RING (Fe(NO)SO₄)
←H₂SO₄, CONC.

THE BROWN RING TEST FOR NITRATES AND NITRITES.

sulfuric acid and decolorize acidified potassium permanganate, while nitrates and their concentrated solutions do not.

Quantitatively, nitrates and nitrites are usually reduced to nitric oxide, which is carefully collected and measured in a gas buret.

14. *Nitrogen Trioxide*

The decomposition of nitrous acid into its anhydride, nitrogen trioxide, has already been noted. A more satisfactory manner of obtaining this oxide of nitrogen is to pass an equimolar mixture of nitric oxide and nitrogen dioxide through a tube chilled to a temperature below 3.5° C., the boiling point of the liquid trioxide:

$$NO + NO_2 \rightleftharpoons N_2O_3$$

Oxygen and nitric oxide also combine at low temperatures to form the trioxide:

$$4NO + O_2 \rightarrow 2N_2O_3$$

The product is a deep blue liquid. Upon evaporating, it decomposes by reversing the reaction of its formation. If the liquid is chilled slightly below $-100°$ C., it forms a blue, crystalline solid. With water, the liquid reacts to form unstable solutions of nitrous acid. Stability of the oxide is greater in glacial acetic acid and in other solvents than in water. The decomposition of the trioxide is another of those reactions upon which traces of moisture have a great influence; perfectly dry N_2O_3 is reported to be stable at about $20°$ C.

15. Nitrogen Dioxide

At ordinary temperatures, nitrogen dioxide is a brown gas which is partly polymerized into nitrogen tetroxide,

$$2NO_2 \rightleftarrows N_2O_4$$

As the temperature is lowered, the equilibrium is shifted to the right with more of the tetroxide being formed. It is a colorless liquid when pure, though dissolved NO_2 usually gives it a yellowish color. It freezes at $-9.3°$ C. to a colorless or slightly yellowish solid.

Nitrogen dioxide is formed at about $20°$ C. by the spontaneous combination of nitric oxide and oxygen, but as the temperature is raised the reaction is reversed, being nearly completely so at $620°$ C. and above:

$$2NO + O_2 \rightleftarrows 2NO_2 + 27,800 \text{ cal.}$$

In the laboratory, the dioxide is most easily prepared by the action of concentrated nitric acid on copper or any one of a considerable variety of other mild reducing agents (cf. section 7), or by the decomposition of the nitrates of the heavier metals (cf. section 8). Because of its instability, it is an excellent oxidizing agent. Flaming carbon or flaming phosphorus will continue to burn vigorously in it, and it will oxidize hydrogen sulfide and a variety of other substances. Because nitrogen in the dioxide is in an intermediate state, the latter may also act as a reducing agent when placed with very strong oxidizing agents whose ability in that capacity is greater than its own. As is characteristic of an odd-molecule oxide, it unites with cold water to form two acids, nitrous and nitric,

$$2NO_2 + H_2O \rightarrow HNO_2 + HNO_3$$

Its behavior with hot water has been noted in section 6.

The breathing of nitrogen dioxide causes water to be discharged into the lungs from their mucous linings; death, therefore, may eventually result from drowning.

16. Nitric Oxide

The preparation of nitric oxide by the reduction of dilute nitric acid (cf. section 7), by the reduction of nitrous acid and nitrites (cf. section 11), and by the direct union of the elements (cf. section 5) has already been mentioned. It is the only one of the oxides of nitrogen which may be made by direct union of the elements:

$$N_2 + O_2 + 43,200 \text{ cal.} \rightleftarrows 2NO \uparrow$$

Because its formation is endothermic, the high temperature of the electric arc is required for its manufacture, and at lower temperatures it is unstable, although at about 20° C. its rate of decomposition is slow enough for it to be considered relatively stable. Its spontaneous union with oxygen to form NO_2 has been noted above.

Although it is an odd-molecule oxide, nitric oxide is colorless and not appreciably polymerized. Its dissociation at temperatures between that of the average room and that of the electric arc permits it to act as an oxidizing agent in that temperature range. Flaming phosphorus will continue to burn in it, but flaming sulfur and carbon are extinguished. By virtue of containing nitrogen in an intermediate state of oxidation, this oxide may also act as a reducing agent, being itself oxidized. It so acts with oxygen and with acidified permanganate solutions,

$$5NO + 3KMnO_4 + 9HCl \rightarrow 5HNO_3 + 3KCl + 3MnCl_2 + 2H_2O$$

The formation of NO_2 by concentrated nitric acid is due to the oxidizing action of the strong acid upon the NO originally formed. The action of this oxide with ferrous salts was noted in section 13.

17. Hyponitrous Acid

In aqueous solution, either sodium nitrate or sodium nitrite is reduced by sodium amalgam to sodium hyponitrite, $Na_2N_2O_2$:

$$2NaNO_2 + 4Na + 2HOH \rightarrow Na_2N_2O_2 + 4NaOH$$

If the resulting solution is neutralized with acetic acid and treated with a solution of silver nitrate, a yellow precipitate of silver hyponitrite is formed. This salt, upon treatment with hydrogen chloride in ether, yields the free acid which may be obtained by filtering to remove silver chloride and evaporating the solvent. It is an explosively unstable, colorless, deliquescent solid of the formula $H_2N_2O_2$. It is a very weak acid whose fresh solutions reduce acidified permanganate,

$$5H_2N_2O_2 + 8KMnO_4 + 24HCl \rightarrow 10HNO_3 + 8KCl + 8MnCl_2 + 12H_2O$$

but upon standing gradually decompose into water and nitrous oxide:

$$H_2N_2O_2 \rightarrow H_2O + N_2O$$

18. Nitrous Oxide

This oxide of nitrogen, in which the element has an oxidation number of $+1$, is a colorless gas with a faintly sweetish odor and taste, whose density is greater than that of air and whose solubility in water is appreciable. Its critical temperature is $35°$ C. Despite its formation by the decomposition of hyponitrous acid, it does not unite with water to yield that acid. It is most readily prepared by the pyrolytic decomposition of ammonium nitrate:

$$NH_4NO_3 \xrightarrow{\Delta} 2H_2O + N_2O$$

Inhalation of the gas is followed by a temporary paralysis of some of the nerve centers, which may result in hysterical giddiness. To this physiological action, discovered by Sir Humphry Davy, the substance owes its soubriquet, *laughing gas*, and its use as an anesthetic, particularly in dental surgery.

This lowest oxide of nitrogen is endothermal and therefore unstable, but its decomposition proceeds very slowly below $500°$ C. Most burning material introduced into it continues to burn as in oxygen; its odor, however, readily distinguishes it from the latter substance.

19. Hydrides

Nitrogen and hydrogen form three binary compounds whose names and formulas are: ammonia, NH_3; hydrazine, N_2H_4; and hydrazoic acid, HN_3. Of these compounds, ammonia is the oldest in man's knowledge, the most stable, and the most important. It and hydrazine react with many substances to form a variety of derivatives, while hydrazoic acid forms unstable metallic salts known as azides. Each hydride will be considered in turn. Their electronic formulas are:

H	H	
·×	·· ·×	·· ··
H×N×H	H×N:N×H	H×N::N::N:
··	×· ··	
	H	
Ammonia	**Hydrazine**	**Hydrazoic acid**

20. *Physical Properties of Ammonia*

At about 20° C., ammonia is a colorless gas of a strong characteristic odor. Having a critical temperature of 132.4° C., it is easily condensed to a colorless liquid which boils at −33.4° C. and freezes at −77.7° C. A liter of the gas at S.T.P. weighs 0.771 g., hence is much lighter than air. It is highly soluble in water, the concentrated ammonia water of commerce containing about 28 per cent by weight of the solute. Its density is about 0.9 g./ml. The gas may be completely dispelled by boiling the solution. The gas is also soluble in alcohol and ether. Its unusually high heat of vaporization, 327 cal./g., makes ammonia especially useful as a refrigerating gas (cf. section 13, Chapter 11). Its rather high critical pressure makes the use of strong, bulky equipment necessary.

The ammonia molecule, H ⦂ N ⦂, is unsym-

$$\overset{\text{H}}{\underset{\text{H}}{\text{H} \overset{\cdot}{\underset{\cdot}{\times}} \text{N} :}}$$

metrical, and hence dipolar. As a result of this polarity, liquid ammonia is a good solvent for many electrolytes.

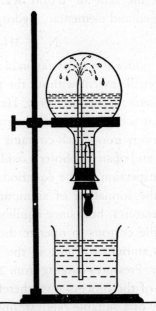

AN AMMONIA FOUNTAIN. At the outset the flask is filled with gaseous ammonia. When a few drops of water are admitted to the flask from the medicine dropper, solution of the gas is sufficient to create a partial vacuum which permits water from the beaker to be forced upward by atmospheric pressure into the flask.

21. *Commercial Production of Ammonia*

Ammonia has been known since the eighth century of the Christian era, and perhaps longer, but until relatively recent times it was manufactured principally by the pyrolytic decomposition of hoofs, horns, scraps of hide, hair, and the dried blood of animals; hence its old name, *spirits of hartshorn.*

A more recent method, and one still in use where coke is prepared in by-product ovens, is the pyrolytic decomposition of coal in the absence of air. Coal tar and a considerable volume of mixed gases of which ammonia accounts for some 50 per cent are the principal products of distillation. The ammonia so obtained is caused to react with sulfuric acid to form a crude grade of ammonium sulfate which is sold for use as fertilizer and for other purposes. The average yield of the sulfate per ton of coal is 20 to 25 pounds. Great quantities of valuable by-products were wasted by the use of the old "beehive" type of coke oven which had no facilities for collecting these substances.

At present, the most widely used method of manufacturing ammonia in industrial quantities is the *Haber process*. This method came into use in Germany about the time of World War I and consists of the reaction of elementary nitrogen and elementary hydrogen in the presence of a catalyst:

$$N_2 + 3H_2 \rightleftharpoons 2NH_3 + 24,400 \text{ cal.}$$

Even under the most favorable conditions, the reaction will not occur to an appreciable extent without the presence of a catalyst. The process is named for the German chemist, Fritz Haber, because he developed the first successful catalyst for the reaction. The most satisfactory catalyst now appears to be one of spongy iron which contains small amounts of a highly basic oxide, such as K_2O, and of an amphoteric oxide, such as Al_2O_3. The oxides serve as promoters, *q.v.* Inspection of the equation and reference to Le Chatelier's principle show that the formation of ammonia will be favored by high pressures and low temperatures, but, since equilibrium is reached so slowly at low temperatures, it is the custom to operate the catalytic units at about 500° C. Many small yields amount to more in the long run than one larger yield obtained more slowly. Pressures ranging from 200 to 1,000 atmospheres are used. The development of the process was, therefore, delayed not only by the slowness of discovery of a suitable catalyst, but also by the slowness of development of steels of a strength to withstand such enormous pressures.

Also finding considerable use in the modern production of ammonia is the *cyanamide process*. Calcium carbide, CaC_2, is prepared by heating together coke and lime made by the calcining of limestone; this substance is then heated to about 1100° C. in an atmosphere of nitrogen to form a mixture of calcium cyanamide and carbon which is sold for use as fertilizer as *nitrolime:*

$$CaC_2 + N_2 \overset{\Delta}{\rightarrow} CaCN_2 + C$$

In the preparation of ammonia, this crude product is treated first with cold water to decompose any unreacted carbide, and then with steam:

$$CaCN_2 + 3H_2O \overset{\Delta}{\rightarrow} CaCO_3 + 2NH_3 \uparrow$$

The heat evolved by the reaction causes its speed to increase, and the heat and flow of steam serve to expel the gas evolved.

Considerable ammonia is obtained also as a by-product of the Serpek process (cf. section 4, Chapter 15).

22. Laboratory Preparation of Ammonia

Small quantities of ammonia are readily obtained in the laboratory by boiling the aqueous solutions of the gas usually available, or by heating a mixture of sodium hydroxide and an ammonium salt, such as the chloride or sulfate:

$$NaOH + NH_4Cl \xrightarrow{\Delta} NaCl$$
$$+ HOH\uparrow + NH_3\uparrow$$

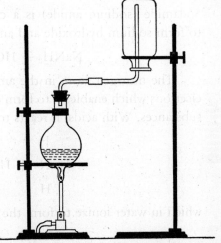

The gas cannot be collected over water because of its solubility, and, because of its reaction with them, it cannot be dried over phosphorus-pentoxide, sulfuric acid, or anhydrous calcium chloride. It is usually dried over soda-lime, a mixture of $NaOH$ and CaO.

23. Chemical Properties of Ammonia

Ammonia is chemically active and widely employed in both the liquid and the gaseous states.

EQUIPMENT FOR THE LABORATORY PREPARATION OF AMMONIA AND ITS COLLECTION BY THE DOWNWARD DISPLACEMENT OF AIR.

As was noted in the discussion of its preparation from its elements, the compound is unstable to heat, being largely decomposed at elevated temperatures. Because of this instability, the hot gas is an excellent reducing agent:

$$3CuO + 2NH_3 \xrightarrow{\Delta} 3Cu + N_2\uparrow + 3H_2O\uparrow$$

This instability also accounts for its ability to burn in an atmosphere of pure oxygen, chlorine, or bromine:

$$4NH_3 + 3O_2 \xrightarrow{\Delta} 2N_2\uparrow + 6H_2O\uparrow$$
$$2NH_3 + 3Cl_2 \xrightarrow{\Delta} N_2\uparrow + 6HCl\uparrow$$

The oxidation of the gas by air in the presence of a platinum catalyst has already been discussed in section 6.

With the metals which react with nitrogen to form nitrides (cf. section 5), ammonia also reacts at high temperatures to form nitrides:

$$6Li + 2NH_3 \rightarrow 2Li_3N + 3H_2 \uparrow$$

With sodium and potassium, only a portion of the hydrogen is replaced and metallic amides are formed:

$$2Na + 2NH_3 \xrightarrow{\Delta} 2NaNH_2 + H_2 \uparrow$$

Sodamide (sodium amide) is a colorless solid which hydrolyzes explosively to form sodium hydroxide and ammonia:

$$NaNH_2 + HOH \rightarrow NaOH + NH_3 \uparrow$$

The nitrogen atom in the ammonia molecule possesses a pair of unused electrons which enables it to form coördinate covalent unions with a number of substances. With acids, it reacts to form salts,

$$
\begin{array}{ccc}
\overset{H}{\underset{H}{H \overset{\cdot\times}{\underset{\times\cdot}{N}} \colon}} + \overset{\cdot\cdot}{\underset{\cdot\cdot}{H \overset{\times}{\cdot} Cl \colon}} & \rightarrow & \overset{H}{\underset{H}{H \overset{\cdot\times}{\underset{\times\cdot}{N}} \colon H \overset{\times}{\cdot} \overset{\cdot\cdot}{\underset{\cdot\cdot}{Cl}} \colon}}
\end{array}
$$

which in water ionize to form the positively charged ammonium radical,

$$NH_4Cl_{(s)} \rightarrow NH_4^+ + Cl^-_{(in\ sol.)}$$

Ammonia dipoles attach themselves to many salts, apparently in the same manner that water dipoles attach themselves. When so held in crystal structures, it may be thought of as ammonia of crystallization. Definite numbers of ammonia molecules attach themselves to many of the ions of metals of the "B" families to form the so-called *complex ions* whose salts are for the most part quite soluble:

$$Cu^{++} + SO_4^{--} + 4NH_3 \rightarrow Cu(NH_3)_4^{++} + SO_4^{--}$$
$$AgCl_{(s)} + 2NH_3 \rightarrow Ag(NH_3)_2^+ + Cl^-$$

The ions formed in these equations are known respectively as the cupric-tetrammino and the silverdiammino ion.

24. *Liquid Ammonia*

Liquid ammonia is like water not only in its dipolar nature, but also in its ability to ionize slightly:

$$NH_3 \rightleftharpoons H^+ + NH_2^-$$

The degree of ionization is even less than that of water, but it is sufficient to account for a part of the chemical properties of the substance. Sodamide is also formed when sodium metal is dissolved in the liquid. At first, the solution is blue and apparently contains colloidally dispersed sodium, but, upon standing, the blue color disappears slowly as hydrogen is evolved and the amide formed. This solution is a good conductor of electricity. Sodamide is a strong base in a solution of liquid ammonia, just as NaOH in water is a strong base. This serves to emphasize one aspect of a modern concept of bases; namely, that strong bases are substances which furnish the same negative ion as the solvent in which they are dissolved.

The slight ionization of ammonia permits it to enter into reactions which, because of their analogy to hydrolysis, may be termed *ammonolysis:*

$$HgCl_2 + 2NH_3 \rightarrow Hg(NH_2)Cl + NH_4Cl$$

The mercury compound formed is known as mercuric amido-chloride or ammonobasic mercuric chloride. A number of similar reactions are known.

25. *Ammonium Hydroxide*

The solubility of ammonia in water has been noted. Such solutions feel and taste soapy, act weakly basic, and upon neutralization with acids yield ammonium salts, hence some ammonium hydroxide, NH_4OH, formed by the union of the water and ammonia molecules through the unused pair of electrons of the latter, must be present; however, most aqueous solutions of ammonia contain this substance largely as NH_3 and not as NH_4OH. This knowledge notwithstanding, aqueous solutions of ammonia are commonly referred to as solutions of ammonium hydroxide. The hydroxide is a hypothetical base since attempts to concentrate its solutions result in their decomposition by the evolution of gaseous NH_3. The hydroxide, besides entering into neutralization reactions, will react to form complex ions, and its stronger solutions will cause ammonolysis to take place. The concentrated solutions also react with chlorine and also with aqueous solutions of iodine and potassium iodide to form in the first case nitrogen chloride, NCl_3, a yellow oil, and in the second case nitrogen iodide, NI_3, a dark solid. Both are explosive in the extreme, and therefore very dangerous.

Large quantities of the aqueous solutions of ammonia are used in the laboratory, in industry, and by the housewife as a cleaning agent.

26. *Hydrazine*

Under standard pressure, and at about 20° C., hydrazine, N_2H_4, is a colorless and extremely poisonous liquid which freezes at 1.4° C. and boils at 113.5° C.

Its hydrate is prepared by passing nitric oxide into an aqueous solution of potassium sulfite containing sodium amalgam. Hydrogen liberated by the action of sodium upon the water is the active reducing agent, although the sulfite ion also acts in this capacity. Distillation of the hydrate with the oxide of either barium or calcium liberates the hydrazine:

$$K_2SO_3 + 2NO + 3H_2 \rightarrow N_2H_4.H_2O + K_2SO_4$$

$$N_2H_4.H_2O + CaO \xrightarrow{\Delta} N_2H_4 \uparrow + \underline{Ca(OH)_2}$$

Like ammonia, hydrazine combines with acids to form salts and with water to form a base, but, since its molecule contains two nitrogen atoms each possessed of a pair of unused electrons, it may form two series of salts—for example, with HCl it may form N_2H_5Cl and $N_2H_6Cl_2$. Hydrazine inflames spontaneously in pure oxygen, and its salts are powerful reducing agents, which are themselves oxidized to free nitrogen:

$$4AgNO_3 + N_2H_4 \rightarrow \underline{4Ag} + N_2 \uparrow + 4HNO_3$$
$$5N_2H_4 + 4KMnO_4 + 12HCl \rightarrow 5N_2 \uparrow + 4KCl + 4MnCl_2 + 16H_2O$$

It reacts with nitrous acid to form hydrazoic acid, HN_3:

$$N_2H_4 + HNO_2 \rightarrow HN_3 + 2H_2O$$

Phenylhydrazine, $C_6H_5N_2H_3$, is an important reagent in organic chemistry.

27. Hydrazoic Acid

This substance is a colorless liquid which freezes at $-80°$ C. and boils at $37°$ C. and is weakly ionized as an acid in aqueous solution. Its odor is nauseous. In addition to the preparation given above, its formation from sodamide may be mentioned:

$$NaNH_2 + N_2O \rightarrow NaN_3 + H_2O$$

and

$$NaN_3 + H_2SO_4 \xrightarrow[\text{low pr.}]{\Delta} HN_3 + NaHSO_4$$

The solution may be concentrated under reduced pressure and the remaining water removed with anhydrous calcium chloride. Being highly endothermal, the acid decomposes violently into its elements with the evolution of much energy:

$$2HN_3 \rightarrow 3N_2 \uparrow + H_2 \uparrow + 123,200 \text{ cal.}$$

Its salts are also very unstable. The lead salt, $Pb(N_3)_2$, is used in detonating caps for dynamite, shells, and other explosives.

28. Hydroxylamine

Hydroxylamine, NH_2OH, appears to be a hydroxy-substituted ammonia. It is a colorless solid whose melting point is 33° C., and it is prepared by the reactions represented by the following equations:

$$HNO_2 + 2NaHSO_3 \rightarrow (NaSO_3)_2NOH + H_2O$$

and

$$(NaSO_3)_2NOH + 2H_2O \xrightarrow[H^+]{warm} 2NaHSO_4 + H_2NOH$$

It is weakly basic, reacting with acids by means of the unused pair of electrons of the nitrogen atom to form salts. It and its salts are easily oxidized, and hence are active reducing agents, though they themselves may be reduced by very strong reducing agents. Derivatives of hydroxylamine are of special importance in organic chemistry.

29. The Fixation of Nitrogen

Any process by which atmospheric nitrogen is incorporated into useful nitrogenous compounds is referred to as a method of "fixing" the element. Among such methods have been noted the arc process, the Haber process, the cyanamide process, and the Serpek process. There are other commercial processes of less importance which also enjoy some use. The arc process is usually known as the Birkland-Eyde process, though in various countries it goes by other names. Lightning bolts are accompanied by the formation of some nitric

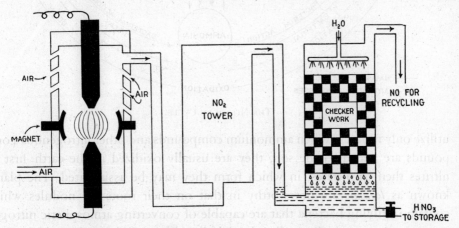

DIAGRAM OF THE BIRKLAND-EYDE PROCESS OF NITROGEN FIXATION.

oxide which dissolves in rainwater to form dilute nitric acid, which, in the course of a year, makes a valuable contribution of available nitrogen to the agriculture of the world.

30. *Nitrogen and Plant Growth*

Nitrogen is essential to the growth of plants, but the majority of these cannot utilize the free element—in fact, the majority of plants can directly

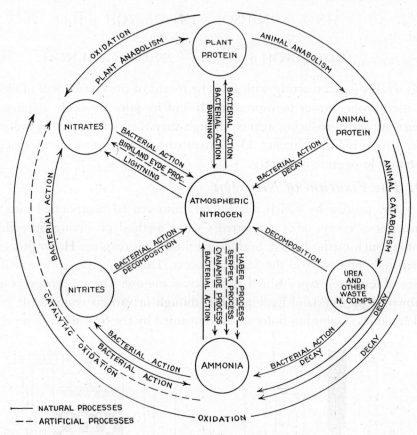

THE NITROGEN CYCLE.

utilize only nitrates. When ammonium compounds and other nitrogenous compounds are added to the soil, they are usually oxidized in the earth first to nitrites then to nitrates, in which form they may be assimilated. The plants known as *legumes* are noteworthy in that on their roots are nodules which contain nitrifying bacteria that are capable of converting atmospheric nitrogen into compounds which are directly assimilated by the plants. Peas, beans, and alfalfa are representative members of the class. The decomposition of plant and animal matter and the discharge of nitrogenous excrements by animals return to the soil a considerable quantity of the nitrogen removed from it. This removal of the nitrogen from the soil and its return to the soil for reuse is referred to generally as the *nitrogen cycle*.

31. Use of Nitrogen and Its Compounds

The uses of nitrogen are principally those connected with its fixation, although it does find some application where a cheap gas of low activity is

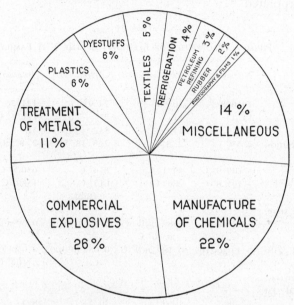

DOMESTIC INDUSTRIAL CONSUMPTION OF NITROGENOUS
COMPOUNDS.

required. Light bulbs, for example, are often filled with it to retard evaporation of the white-hot filament. The uses of the principal compounds have been mentioned in the discussions of them.

II. ARSENIC, ANTIMONY, AND BISMUTH

32. Physical Properties

Arsenic, like phosphorus, is capable of existing in several allotropic modifications, but at about 20° C. only the gray form is stable. As commonly observed, it is a gray, crystalline solid with a metal-like luster. It is easily sublimed to a yellow gas of high toxicity and of an alliaceous odor. Antimony is also allotropic, but is commonly observed as a brilliant silvery-white metal. It is unusual in that it expands upon solidifying. Bismuth is a silvery metal with a distinct reddish cast. It also expands upon solidification and has an unusually low melting point for a heavy metal. All of these elements are insoluble in water, all crystallize as rhombohedrons, and all are diamagnetic, bismuth being the most pronouncedly diamagnetic of all elementary substances.

Other physical properties of these elements are summarized in the accompanying table, in which the similar properties of nitrogen and phosphorus are also incorporated.

Table 23

PHYSICAL PROPERTIES OF ELEMENTS OF THE V A FAMILY

Property	Nitrogen (N)	Phosphorus (P)	Arsenic (As)	Antimony (Sb)	Bismuth (Bi)
Atomic weight........	14.008	30.98	74.91	121.76	209.00
Isotopes.............	14, 15	31	75	121, 123	209
Atomic number.......	7	15	33	51	83
Electronic distribution	2, 5	2, 8, 5	2, 8, 18, 5	2, 8, 18, 18, 5	2, 8, 18, 32, 18, 5
Melting point.......	−209.9° C.	44.1° C.	814° C.	630.5° C.	271.3° C.
Boiling point.........	−195.8° C.	280° C.	615° C. (subl.)	1380° C.	1470° C.
Density, solid state, g./ml.............	1.026 at −252° C.	1.82 (yellow) at 20° C.	5.73 at 14° C.	6.69 at 25° C.	9.78 at 20° C.
Specific heat, cal./g...	0.39 at 210° C.	0.189 at 9° C.	0.082 (0–100° C.)	0.050 (20–100° C.)	0.029 at 20° C.
Ionizing potential, volts, removal 1st electron............	14.48	10.9	10.5	8.5	8.0

33. Occurrence and Preparation

Arsenic occurs free, and in combination in its sulfides, in mixed sulfides, and in traces in many metallic ores. When some of the mixed sulfides are roasted, free arsenic sublimes; others, upon roasting, yield the trioxide, As_2O_3, which is then reduced by heating with coke. Sweden leads in the production of the element. Arsenic takes its name from the Greek name for the mineral orpiment, which contains the trisulfide, As_2S_3. The same Greek word also means *male* and was applied in token of the efficacy of the substance. Free arsenic, in so far as is known, was first prepared by Albertus Magnus about 1250.

Antimony is also found free, but its prime source is the ore *stibnite*, Sb_2S_3, which occurs principally in China and Mexico, and in Bolivia and other South

American countries. Stibnite is refined either by heating it with scrap iron,

$$Sb_2S_3 + 3Fe \xrightarrow{\Delta} 2Sb + 3FeS$$

or by roasting the ore to form the corresponding oxide which is then reduced with coke,

$$2Sb_2S_3 + 9O_2 \xrightarrow{\Delta} 2Sb_2O_3 + 6SO_2 \uparrow$$

and

$$Sb_2O_3 + 3C \xrightarrow{\Delta} 2Sb + 3CO \uparrow$$

The free metal has been known since prehistoric times and derives its name from the name *antimonium* applied by Geber to the sulfide mineral stibnite. The symbol, Sb, comes from the name *stibium* which Pliny applied to the same ore and which derives from the Latin verb *to mark*.

Bismuth is found in the free condition, though in small amounts. Its principal ores are its oxide and sulfide. Bolivia leads in its production, though Canada, Australia, and other countries have lesser deposits. The ores are refined in manners similar to those employed for the corresponding ores of antimony. The discovery of bismuth is lost in antiquity, but it was accurately described for the first time, in so far as is known, in 1739 by Pott. The name *bismuth* is believed to be derived from two German words whose meanings are *white mass* or *white matter*.

34. *Chemical Properties*

Arsenic and bismuth tarnish in moist air while antimony does not, but all three burn when heated in oxygen to form trioxides, As_2O_3, Sb_2O_3, and Bi_2O_3. All three of the elements unite directly with the halogens. Arsenic, when heated with many metals, reacts to form arsenides, but, because of their increasingly positive natures, antimony and bismuth do not behave similarly. This increasingly positive nature is well demonstrated by the behavior of the elements with concentrated nitric acid; phosphorus and arsenic yield the acids H_3PO_4 and H_3AsO_4, respectively, of which the latter is the weaker; antimony forms the weak and unstable orthoantimonic acid $H[Sb(OH)_6]$; and bismuth forms only its nitrate $Bi(NO_3)_3$. Arsenic and antimony show the oxidation numbers characteristic of the family -3, $+3$, and $+5$, but bismuth shows principally only the $+3$ number in its common compounds.

35. *Oxides*

A. ARSENIC. The principal oxides of arsenic are the trioxide and the pentoxide, As_2O_3 and As_2O_5, though the tetroxide, As_2O_4, is known. The trioxide is formed whenever arsenic or its combustible compounds are burned in air or oxygen. It is extremely poisonous, but a tolerance for it may be built up. It dissolves slightly in water to form orthoarsenous acid, H_3AsO_3, which is known only in solution. Salts of ortho-, pyro-, and metaarsenous acids are known. Worthy of mention among these is *Paris green*, whose formula is generally taken as $Cu_3(AsO_3)_2.Cu(C_2H_3O_2)_2$, and whose use is as an insecticide. Attempts to concentrate the arsenous acids result only in their dehydration to As_2O_3.

Arsenic pentoxide is made only by indirect methods, and, unlike phosphorus pentoxide, is quite unstable, decomposing easily when heated into the trioxide and oxygen. It is the anhydride of ortho-, pyro-, and metaarsenic acids, of which the first is the most common. This acid is usually prepared by the oxidation of the trioxide with nitric acid or hypochlorous acid. Crystals of the formula $2H_3AsO_4.H_2O$ separate from the concentrated solution. When one heats these to about 150° C., the pyro acid, $H_4As_2O_7$, forms, and this upon being heated to 200° C. yields the meta acid, $HAsO_3$, which upon further heating yields the anhydride, As_2O_5. Arsenic acid, unlike phosphoric, is an oxidizing agent. Secondary sodium arsenate, Na_2HAsO_4, is used in calico printing, and a number of the heavy metal arsenates are used as dusting insecticides.

B. ANTIMONY. Antimony also forms a trioxide, a tetroxide, and a pentoxide. The trioxide is only slightly soluble and is not an acid anhydride. It reacts with the halogen acids to form the corresponding trihalides, and with other acids it also forms salts, such as $Sb(NO_3)_3$. As might be expected, pentavalent antimony is more nonmetallic in its behavior than is the trivalent, since its particle size is smaller. The pentoxide is prepared by dehydration of the orthoantimonic acid (orthostibic acid) which is obtained when the trioxide or trichloride is oxidized with concentrated nitric acid. The ortho acid has the formula $H[Sb(OH)_6]$. Other antimonic acids, if they exist, are little known. Orthoantimonic acid is rather weak and not very stable. It reacts with strong bases to form the corresponding salts, of which the sodium salt is only sparingly soluble and is used in testing for the sodium ion.

C. BISMUTH. Oxides of bismuth of the formulas BiO, Bi_2O_3, Bi_2O_4, and Bi_2O_5 have been described, but only the trioxide is of general interest. It is more basic than Sb_2O_3, and, with mineral acids, forms the corresponding bismuth salts such as $Bi(NO_3)_3$ and $Bi_2(SO_4)_3$. The addition of soluble bases to solutions of bismuth ions causes the precipitation of the trihydroxide $Bi(OH)_3$, which is almost exclusively basic in its behavior. In a solution of sodium hydroxide, bismuth hydroxide is oxidized by hypochlorites to form sodium metabismuthate, $NaBiO_3$, which is not obtained pure but is nevertheless an excellent oxidizing agent. Orthobismuthates are not known, though it is entirely likely that the tetroxide is a bismuth bismuthate.

D. GENERAL. The oxides of nitrogen, phosphorus, and arsenic are exclusively acidic in nature. The higher oxide of antimony is acidic, the lower one amphoteric though more pronouncedly basic, and the lower oxide of bismuth is almost exclusively basic. Stability of the oxides varies. Pentavalent oxides of nitrogen, arsenic, and bismuth are unstable, while that of phosphorus is extremely stable and that of antimony relatively so. This illustrates the general rule that the oxides of highest valence of elements of a given family are usually more stable in the odd-numbered periods than in the even-numbered ones. It is to this instability that nitric and arsenic acids and the bismuthates owe their ability as oxidizing agents.

36. Sulfides

Attention has already been directed to the fact that phosphorus forms more different sulfides than does any other member of the V A family, as it has to the fact that nitrogen forms a number of sulfides all of which are unstable. The sulfides of arsenic are less numerous than those of phosphorus, but more numerous than might be predicted on the basis of the common valences of the family. Three of these—the disulfide, As_2S_2, known as *realgar;* the trisulfide, As_2S_3, known as *orpiment;* and the pentasulfide, As_2S_5—are well known. Less well known is As_4S_3. Realgar and orpiment occur naturally. The former is of a brilliant red color, while the latter is yellow. The trisulfide and the pentasulfide are precipitated as yellow solids when hydrogen sulfide is passed into acidified solutions of arsenous and arsenic compounds, respectively. The pentasulfide precipitates much more slowly than the trisulfide, but the latter is inclined to form a colloidal suspension. Neither is soluble in concentrated hydrochloric acid.

Antimony forms the sulfides Sb_2S_3, Sb_2S_4, and Sb_2S_5. The trisulfide and the pentasulfide appear as orange-red precipitates when hydrogen sulfide is passed into acidified solutions of the tri- and pentachlorides, respectively. The pentasulfide is easily reduced to the trisulfide, and both compounds are soluble in solutions of hydrochloric acid whose concentration is greater than 2.5 N. The naturally occurring trisulfide of the mineral stibnite is black.

Bismuth forms only the trisulfide, Bi_2S_3, which occurs in nature and may be precipitated as a dark, chocolate-colored substance from weakly acidic solutions of bismuth salts. It is readily soluble in more strongly acidic solutions.

Attention previously has been directed to the facts that many salts may be made by the fusion of basic and acidic oxides, and that all salts may be thought of as having such parents. In an analogous fashion, *thio-* or *sulfo-* salts may be formed by the union of metallic and nonmetallic sulfides. Thus, the basic sulfides of sodium, potassium, ammonium, and other elements unite with the acidic and amphoteric sulfides of arsenic and antimony to form thio-salts in which sulfur atoms as indicated by the prefix *thio-* may be thought of as having replaced a like number of oxygen atoms:

$$As_2S_3 + 3Na_2S \rightarrow 2Na_3AsS_3, \text{ sodium thioarsenite}$$
$$As_2S_5 + 3Na_2S \rightarrow 2Na_3AsS_4, \text{ sodium thioarsenate}$$
$$Sb_2S_3 + 3Na_2S \rightarrow 2Na_3SbS_3, \text{ sodium thioantimonite}$$

and

$$Sb_2S_5 + 3Na_2S \rightarrow 2Na_3SbS_4, \text{ sodium thioantimonate}$$

Polysulfides oxidize the lower sulfides to the higher ones and then form the corresponding thioarsenate and thioantimonate. Acidification of these soluble thiosalts reprecipitates the parent sulfides save in the case of the thioantimonate, which yields the tetrasulfide:

$$2Na_3SbS_4 + 6HCl \rightarrow 6NaCl + 3H_2S\uparrow + \underline{S} + \underline{Sb_2S_4}$$

This compound may be thought of as antimonous thioantimonate. Bismuth is too metallic in behavior for its sulfide to form thiosalts.

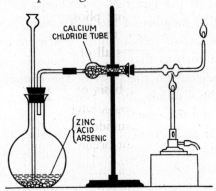

APPARATUS FOR THE GENERATION OF ARSINE OR STIBINE.

37. *Hydrides*

Of the elements of the V A family, only nitrogen will combine directly with hydrogen. The preparation and proper-ties of phosphine were discussed in section 21 of Chapter 20. Arsine, AsH_3, and stibine, SbH_3, are gases at about $20°$ C. and are very toxic. Arsine may be pre-pared by the action of an acid on metallic arsenides such as Mg_3As_2, and either compound may be made by the reduction of arsenic and antimony compounds, respectively, with nascent hydrogen generated by the action of dilute mineral acid on zinc. The dried gases may be ignited. The products are water and the

FRITZ HABER

(1868–1934, German)

Haber is best known as the originator of the process which bears his name and by which ammonia may be synthesized directly from the elementary nitrogen of the air. For this achievement he received the Nobel Prize in 1918. He also conducted important studies on the synthesis of nitric oxide by the arc method, the electrolytic reduction of nitrobenzene, and other electrochemical processes. Less commendable are his development of the methods by which poisonous gases were first used for military purposes and other applications of chemistry to warfare. Among his publications are several books in the field of chemical engineering.

corresponding oxide, but if a cold dish is held in the flame, a deposit of the free element will form. Arsenic stains are usually a lustrous brown, while those of antimony are black. Deposits of arsenic are readily soluble in sodium hypochlorite, while those of antimony are insoluble. When used analytically, this procedure is known as the Marsh-Berzelius test. Bismuthine is too unstable to be of any import. Little is known of it.

38. Hydrolysis of the Salts of Antimony and Bismuth

The trivalent salts of antimony are the derivatives of an amphoteric hydroxide, while those of bismuth are the salts of a very weakly basic hydroxide. It is to be expected, therefore, that both series of salts should hydrolyze; this they do, but not so completely as, for instance, do the halides of phosphorus. Equations representing typical overall reactions are:

$$SbCl_3 + H_2O \rightleftarrows \underline{SbOCl} + 2HCl$$
$$BiCl_3 + H_2O \rightleftarrows \underline{BiOCl} + 2HCl$$

and

$$Bi(NO_3)_3 + H_2O \rightleftarrows \underline{BiONO_3} + 2HNO_3$$

Hydrolysis is fostered by the formation of an insoluble product, but, as indicated in the equations, the addition of acid reverses the reactions, dissolving the precipitates. The names of the compounds are, in order: antimony oxychloride or antimonyl chloride; bismuth oxychloride or bismuthyl chloride; and bismuth oxynitrate or bismuthyl nitrate. In pharmacy, compounds containing the BiO^+ radical are known as bismuth sub- (e.g., bismuth subnitrate) and are used in treating stomach disorders and in external remedies.

39. Use of the Elements and Their Compounds

Arsenic to the extent of about 0.5 per cent is alloyed with lead in the preparation of shot, because a harder and more spherical product is thus obtained. It is sometimes alloyed with copper to harden it. Arsenites and arsenates are used as insecticides, and various arsenic compounds are used in the manufacture of glass and dyes. Arsenic trioxide and a wide variety of other arsenicals are used in medicine for a variety of purposes. Dosage, of course, must be carefully controlled.

Antimony is used principally for alloying with other metals to produce type metal, bearing metal, metal sheathing for cables, battery plates, etc. Its sulfide is used in the preparation of matches and as a filler in the manufacture of reddish rubber. Tartar emetic, potassium antimonyl tartrate, $KSbOC_4H_4O_6$, is used in medicine as an emetic and in dye technology as a mordant.

Bismuth also finds its principal use in the preparation of alloys, notably alloys of low melting points which are used as fuses and as safety plugs for boilers, sprinkler systems, fire-door retainers, etc. Wood's alloy (Bi 50 per

AERIAL DUSTING OF COTTON WITH CALCIUM ARSENATE FOR BOLL WEEVIL CONTROL. (Courtesy, U.S. Department of Agriculture.)

AN AUTOMATIC SPRINKLER HEAD CONTROLLED BY A BISMUTH ALLOY PLUG. (Courtesy, Grinnell Corp.)

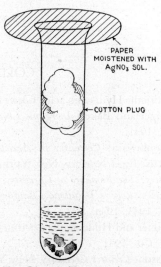

THE GUTZEIT TEST FOR ARSENIC.

cent, Pb 25 per cent, Sn 12.5 per cent, and Cd 12.5 per cent), for example, melts at 60.5° C. Compounds of the element are used as medicines and in the preparation of paints, pottery glazes, and some kinds of glass.

40. *Analytical Tests of the Elements*

Arsenic may be identified by the insolubility of its yellow sulfides in concentrated hydrochloric acid, by the formation of a brown precipitate of silver orthoarsenate, Ag_3AsO_4, by the precipitation of a yellow ammonium arsenomolybdate (cf. ammonium phosphomolybdate), by the precipitation of a yellow silver orthoarsenite, and by the action of arsine on a crystal of silver nitrate to turn it first yellow then black (the Gutzeit test).

Antimony is usually identified, after the removal of any arsenic, by buffering the acidic solution with ammonium oxalate and adding hydrogen sulfide. The formation of an orange-red precipitate of its sulfides is a sufficient test. The Marsh-Berzelius test may be used for either arsenic or antimony, or both.

Bismuth is usually confirmed by precipitating it from solution, after the removal of interfering ions, as its hydroxide by the addition of ammonium hydroxide. The addition of sodium stannite, $NaHSnO_2$, to the filtered precipitate reduces it to a lustrous jet-black deposit of elementary bismuth:

$$2Bi(OH)_3 + 3NaHSnO_2 + 3NaOH \rightarrow \underline{2Bi} + 3Na_2SnO_3 + 6H_2O$$

(*See Appendix for Exercises*)

COLLATERAL READINGS

Audrieth: Hydrazoic acid, *Chem. Rev.*, **15**, 169 (1934).

Badger and Baker: *Inorganic Chemical Technology*, New York, McGraw-Hill Book Co., 1941.

Chamberlain: *Chemistry in Agriculture*, New York, Chemical Foundation, Inc., 1926.

Curtis: *Fixed Nitrogen*, New York, Reinhold Publishing Corp., 1932.

Foster: *The Romance of Chemistry*, New York, D. Appleton-Century Co. 1937.

Furnas: *Roger's Industrial Chemistry*, Vols. I & II, New York, D. Van Nostrand Co., Inc., 1943, 1944.

Latimer and Hildebrand: *Reference Book of Inorganic Chemistry*, New York, The Macmillan Co., 1941.

Slosson: *Creative Chemistry*, New York, Century Co., 1923.

Vickers: *Metals and Their Alloys*, New York, H. C. Baird & Co., Inc., 1923.

Weeks: *Discovery of the Elements*, 5th ed., Mack Printing Co., 1945.

Yost and Russell: *Systematic Inorganic Chemistry*, New York, Prentice-Hall, Inc., 1944.

Nitrogen, *Fortune*, **6**, 74 (1932).

25

Oxygen and Other Members of the VI A Family

1. Introduction

Oxygen, sulfur, selenium, tellurium, and polonium are the elements of the VI A family. As a group, these elements show the same characteristic variations that have been pointed out for the nitrogen family. Oxygen is a gaseous non-metal; sulfur is a typical solid nonmetal; selenium and tellurium are amphoteric substances which show increasingly metallic tendencies; and polonium is a rare, radioactive metal. All of these substances possess six valence electrons, and as a result show a pronounced tendency to react by gaining or sharing two electrons of more electropositive elements. Their commonest oxidation number in their compounds is, therefore, -2. In addition, however, as was pointed out in the chapter on sulfur, it might be expected that one or more of the six valence electrons would be lost or shared with a consequent development of a positive oxidation number. As with sulfur, the $+4$ and $+6$ oxidation states are most likely to be developed, and are therefore most important. Since oxygen has the smallest atom, it naturally attracts its planetary electrons most strongly, and is least likely to show positive oxidation numbers—in fact, no common compounds are known in which it shows an oxidation number other than -2. Sulfur, selenium, and tellurium in their compounds represent both positive and negative states of oxidation. These observations reëmphasize the fact that, in a given family, the greatest difference lies between the elements of the second and third periods. Because of this difference, because sulfur has already been discussed in detail, and because selenium and tellurium resemble sulfur closely in chemical behavior and are of less general importance, the major portion of this chapter will be devoted to oxygen.

I. OXYGEN

2. Physical Properties

Although oxygen had been investigated partially by a number of individuals and had been prepared by a number of earlier workers, including the

Swedish apothecary Scheele, its discovery is usually credited to Joseph Priestley, an Englishman, who in 1774 prepared it by the decomposition of mercuric oxide. Lavoisier, laboring under the misapprehension that it was a constituent of all acids, gave it the name oxygen which he derived from two Greek words which mean *acid former*. The element exists ordinarily as diatomic molecules of the formula O_2. At ordinary temperatures and pressures, it is a colorless, odorless, tasteless gas. Having a critical temperature of $-118.8°$ C., it is liquefied only with difficulty and at the expense of considerable work. The liquid, which is of a pale blue color, boils at $-183°$ C. and at $-218.4°$ C. freezes to a pale blue solid which, upon further cooling, passes into other allotropic forms. At least three solid allotropes are known. At S.T.P., 1 l. of the gas has a mass of 1.429 g., and, therefore, has a density just slightly greater than that of air. Under standard pressure, 1 ml. of water dissolves 0.049 ml. of the gas at 0° C., and 0.030 ml. at 20° C. Oxygen is unusual in that even in the gaseous state it is paramagnetic, a property which is shown more strongly by the liquid and the solid. This property is associated with an odd number of electrons, hence it is presumed that the atoms of the diatomic molecule are paired in such a way as to give each atom one odd, or unpaired, electron. For many years, oxygen was regarded as being made up of only one variety of atom. In fairly recent years, it has been discovered that isotopes of atomic weights of 17 and 18, respectively, occur along with the usual atoms of weight 16. The two heavier isotopes are reported to be present in ordinary oxygen to the extent of one part in 1,250 parts and one part in 10,000 parts, respectively.

3. Occurrence

Oxygen is the most abundant of all the elements which constitute the earth's crust and atmosphere. Free oxygen makes up about 21 per cent of the volume of the atmosphere, and, in combination with a host of other elements, it is widely distributed in the earth's surface. Water contains 88.8 per cent of oxygen by weight, while sand contains 53.3 per cent. All living organisms contain compounds of oxygen, as do a majority of other organic substances. Altogether, oxygen accounts for about 49.5 per cent of the matter of the earth's crust and atmosphere.

4. Production

Industrially, oxygen is obtained along with nitrogen by the liquefaction of air and its subsequent fractional distillation. As has been noted, the nitrogen boils at a lower temperature, and hence tends to leave the oxygen behind when the mixture is warmed. After separation, the latter is vaporized and compressed into steel cylinders for distribution. Some industrial oxygen is also obtained by electrolysis, but, in general, the process is too expensive to compete with the liquid air process.

In the laboratory, oxygen is produced by several convenient methods. The commonest of these is the heating of potassium chlorate with manganese dioxide as

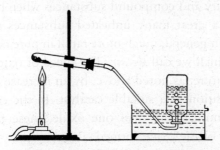

THE LABORATORY PREPARATION OF OXYGEN FROM POTASSIUM CHLORATE AND THE COLLECTION OF THE GAS OVER WATER.

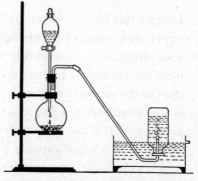

THE LABORATORY PREPARATION OF OXYGEN FROM OXONE AND THE COLLECTION OF THE GAS OVER WATER.

a catalyst. The reaction proceeds rapidly at about 270° C., and the gas evolved is easily caught over water:

$$2KClO_3 \xrightarrow[MnO_2]{\Delta} 2KCl + 3O_2 \uparrow$$

A number of other compounds also yield oxygen when heated:

$$2HgO \xrightarrow{\Delta} \underline{2Hg} + O_2 \uparrow$$

$$2KNO_3 \xrightarrow{\Delta} 2KNO_2 + O_2 \uparrow$$

and

$$2PbO_2 \xrightarrow{\Delta} 2PbO + O_2 \uparrow$$

The use of barium oxide, BaO, is of special interest. It combines with atmospheric oxygen at about 500° C. to form barium peroxide, BaO_2, which, when heated to about 700° C., loses oxygen to reform the normal oxide. Thus, by alternately heating and cooling this latter substance, oxygen is removed from the air. The liberation of oxygen by the action of sodium peroxide on water has been discussed in section 12 of Chapter 7. Crude sodium peroxide prepared for use in oxygen generators is sold under the trade name of *oxone*.

5. *Chemical Properties*

Like other diatomic molecules already discussed, the oxygen molecule is separated into its constituent atoms only at the expense of considerable energy, and is therefore stable at ordinary temperatures:

$$O_2 + 118,000 \text{ cal.} \leftrightharpoons 2O$$

Despite this fact, however, oxygen is an active element, for it combines rapidly with a wide variety of both elementary and compound substances when heated with them, and more slowly with a great many unheated substances which have been moistened. Oxidation is, in general, much more rapid in pure oxygen than in the gaseous solution of it which we call *the air*. The speed of oxidation is also increased by a rise in temperature, as noted above, by an increase in the pressure of the gas, and by the addition of a suitable catalyst. In the case of elements which are capable of forming more than one oxide, these factors may also influence the composition of the oxide formed.

Upon being heated with them, oxygen combines directly with all metals save silver, gold, platinum, and a few other less common inactive metals. Oxides of these noble metals may be formed, however, by indirect means. Many of the more active metals, such as sodium, iron, and aluminum, *rust* when left exposed to moist air. In the case of metals which are capable of forming more than one oxide, the compound which does form depends largely upon the conditions of the reaction.

A number of oxides of the nonmetals have been encountered in preceding chapters. All nonmetals save the halogens and the inert gases will unite directly with oxygen, and the oxides of the halogens may be prepared by indirect methods (cf. the oxides of chlorine, Chapter 22). The degree of activity of the nonmetals varies widely, however, and again conditions largely determine which of several possible oxides may be formed.

The burning of wood, gasoline, alcohol, natural gas, paper, etc., well illustrates the ability of oxygen to unite with compound substances. In general, the products of oxidation in such cases, especially if the process has been rapid, are the oxides of the elements of which the compounds were composed. For example, gasoline is a mixture of compounds each of which contains only hydrogen and carbon; the products of its complete combustion are carbon dioxide, CO_2, and water, while the products of its less complete combustion are carbon monoxide, CO, and water. Substances which are already in a high state of oxidation naturally show very little tendency to undergo further oxidation.

Oxygen is absorbed rapidly by moist ferrous hydroxide and by moist chromous hydroxide, which are oxidized by it to ferric and chromic hydroxides, respectively. It is also rapidly absorbed by basic aqueous solutions of the organic compound pyrogallol, $C_6H_3(OH)_3$. Because of this ability of pyrogallol and moist chromous salts to absorb oxygen, they are often used in gas analysis for its removal from gaseous mixtures.

In general, the formation of oxides is highly exothermic, so that many oxidations are carried on not for the sake of the products formed but for the sake of the energy evolved.

6. Oxides

Those oxides whose formation is highly exothermic are naturally quite stable, but those of the less active elements are fairly easily decomposed, and those which must be prepared by indirect methods are so easily decomposed that they are frequently dangerously and spontaneously explosive (cf. the oxides of chlorine, Chapter 22).

Quantities of the less soluble oxides—such as those of iron, aluminum, and carbon—are found in nature, and many of the metallic oxides are readily prepared from their oxygen-containing compounds. For instance, the hydroxides, carbonates, and nitrates of many metals yield the oxide upon being heated. Naturally, the oxide formed must be stable at the temperature of the reaction. In general, the temperature of decomposition becomes lower as the positive nature of the metal involved decreases:

$$2Cr(OH)_3 \xrightarrow{\Delta} Cr_2O_3 + 3H_2O \uparrow$$

$$MgCO_3 \xrightarrow{\Delta} MgO + CO_2 \uparrow$$

and

$$2Pb(NO_3)_2 \xrightarrow{\Delta} 2PbO + 4NO_2 \uparrow + O_2 \uparrow$$

In the solid state, those oxides in which the attraction between oxygen and the other element is not too large have crystal lattices whose points are occupied by ions. Molecular lattices result in those compounds in which the forces of attraction are large.

A number of elements—notably hydrogen, barium, and the metals of the I A family—form *peroxides* in which the bond between pairs of oxygen atoms is unbroken. These compounds are all more or less unstable, and therefore good oxidizing agents. Reference should be made at this time to the discussions of sodium peroxide and hydrogen peroxide presented in preceding chapters.

Several elements which are capable of exhibiting more than one valence will form, in addition to their regular oxides, one or more mixed oxides. Thus iron, whose regular valences are $+2$ and $+3$, will form the compound Fe_3O_4-$(FeO.Fe_2O_3)$ in addition to the oxides FeO and Fe_2O_3.

Examples of both the practical and theoretical importance of oxides have been noted in previous chapters. At this juncture, it would be well to review the material of those chapters which relate to the physical and chemical properties of the oxides of the elements of the third period and of the V A family, with special attention to the orderly variation of these properties as one progresses from left to right across the period and from top to bottom down the column.

7. Combustion

Combustion is a term which is rather loosely used, but in its stricter sense it is usually applied to any chemical reaction which is accompanied by the evolution of heat and light. The majority of the examples of combustion encountered by the average man are those of the rapid oxidation of easily ignited materials by atmospheric oxygen. Among these may be classed the burning of wood, coal, paper, gasoline, natural gas, oils, etc.

One usually associates flames with combustion. These are the result of a rapid reaction between two substances, both of which are in the gaseous state. Someone will suggest that wood and other solids inflame, but, in actuality, the flames are produced by the reaction of gases evolved by the solid under the influence of the high temperature maintained by the reaction. In starting a coal fire, one usually uses both paper and kindling wood. The temperature of a match flame is sufficiently high to bring about the partial decomposition of paper into combustible gases whose combustion liberates sufficient heat to perform the same function for the wood, whose combustion in turn liberates sufficient heat to begin the decomposition of the coal into gases.

The foregoing discussion brings to the fore the matter of kindling temperatures. *The kindling temperature of a given material is that temperature at which the reaction will proceed at a speed sufficient to liberate enough heat to keep the process going without the addition of heat from an external source.* Even for a specified material, however, the kindling temperature varies considerably with conditions, especially with the fineness of its own subdivision, for, as subdivision is continued, the amount of surface offered to the oxidizing agent by a given mass of material is increased. A one-inch board, for example, is not usually ignited by a match, but shavings from the board are easily ignited by it. It is because the kindling temperature becomes lower as the fineness of subdivision increases that dust suspensions in the air are so easily ignited and so dangerous.

Each unit of mass of a pure substance which enters into combustion with oxygen evolves a characteristic quantity of energy. Wood, coal, and the majority of the ordinary fuels are not pure substances but variable mixtures; hence, in purchasing these materials in any quantity, it is highly desirable to know the quantity of heat that may be obtained from each gram, or each pound, purchased. Oakwood has a heat of combustion of about 8,300 B.t.u. per pound, while high-grade bituminous coal is rated at about 14,000 B.t.u. per pound. A large industrial user of coal will, for instance, find it greatly to his benefit to buy a coal whose heat of combustion is 14,150 B.t.u. per pound rather than a coal whose price is identical but whose heat of combustion is 13,840 B.t.u. per pound. Heats of combustion are determined in carefully insulated, oxygen-filled calorimeters.

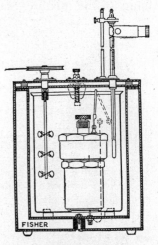

DETAILS OF A BOMB CALORIMETER. The material for combustion is placed in the bomb along with a suitable oxidizing agent and the bomb is submerged in a well-insulated container of water equipped with a stirrer. By observing the rise in temperature of the insulated system one may calculate the heat liberated by the combustion of the weighed sample. (Courtesy, Fisher Scientific Co.)

8. Spontaneous Combustion

Spontaneous combustion is self-initiating combustion. It occurs when a slow oxidation liberates heat which is not removed, or is removed but slowly, from the surrounding material. If the material is combustible and if it is surrounded by sufficient oxygen, combustion occurs when sufficient heat has accumulated to raise the material to its kindling temperature. Many carbon compounds undergo such slow oxidation. The drying of oil paints depends upon such a reaction between oxygen and the oil. Oily rags are, therefore, a particular fire hazard when allowed to accumulate in a pile, for the oil and oxygen supply the heat which is dissipated but slowly, since cloth is a poor conductor. Vegetable matter, such as hay, and piles of soft coal are also highly susceptible to spontaneous ignition and combustion.

9. *Explosions*

Mention has been made of the decrease of kindling temperature with the increase of subdivision of combustible material. If such a finely divided material be now suspended in air so that each particle is completely surrounded by oxygen, not only does it ignite more easily but it burns more rapidly, with the reaction spreading quickly from the point of ignition to the outermost limits of the mixture. Such a combustion is referred to as an explosion, and

DAMAGE WROUGHT BY A DUST EXPLOSION IN A GRAIN ELEVATOR. (Courtesy, National Safety Council.)

the more closely the explosive mixture is confined, the more violent it is apt to be. Explosions may occur in mixtures of gases or in suspensions of finely divided solids or liquids in a gas. Reference was made in section 9 of Chapter 19 to the danger of dust explosions in flour mills, planing mills, coal mines, and other industrial establishments. In an automobile engine, it is the function of the carburetor to vaporize the gasoline and to mix it with a proper quantity of air so that an explosive mixture will be insured.

The last-mentioned function of a carburetor is quite as important as the first, for explosions will not occur if either component of the explosive mixture is present in too small a concentration. For each pair of components there are limits of composition beyond which explosion will not occur. These are usually expressed in terms of the percentage of the combustible material and are known as *explosive limits*. Thus, for hydrogen and air, the approximate limits are 4 to 75 per cent, while for methane (the principal component of natural gas) and air, the limits are 5 to 15 per cent. In some mixtures, the rapidity of explosion is naturally greater than in others. Very rapid explosions in the cylinders of an internal combustion engine cause a knock or "ping" and exert a sudden violent thrust upon the pistons. The introduction of tetraethyllead and other antiknock agents into gasoline slows the explosion of its mixture, thereby eliminating the knock and causing a more gradual and steady pressure to be exerted on the pistons.

Explosions are best prevented by the removal of the material which is a source of danger, but a wise precaution is the surrounding of flames and hot objects with a wire

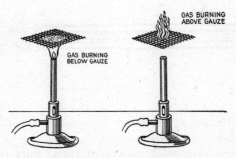

THE DAVY SAFETY LAMP.

DEMONSTRATION OF THE PRINCIPLE OF THE DAVY SAFETY LAMP.

gauze. The metal of the wire, being a better conductor of heat than the surrounding gases, tends to absorb the emitted energy, thus preventing the gases from doing so. Sir Humphry Davy used this principle in the construction of his miner's safety lamp, invented in 1815. It consisted of an ordinary oil lantern with a wire gauze cage to surround the flame.

10. Physiological Relationships

Oxygen bears an important relationship to both plant and animal life. In the case of animals, air is drawn into the body during respiration; oxygen is removed by iron-containing compounds in the blood and is then distributed to the tissues by the circulation of the blood. Slowly the carbon and hydrogen of compounds resulting from the digestion of food are oxidized to carbon dioxide and water, which are expelled. Heat to maintain body temperature and energy to permit the functioning of the organism are generated by this oxidation. Very nearly pure oxygen is often administered to victims of respiratory diseases, asphyxiation, drowning, and electrical shock. When so used, oxygen is usually admixed with about 5 per cent of carbon dioxide, which acts as a stimulant to the respiratory process.

During sunny hours, green plants take from the air the carbon dioxide exhaled by animals. By the process known as *photosynthesis*, they are able to convert this substance and water into sugars and starches. Oxygen is a by-product of the synthesis, and is returned to the air. Were this not the case, the oxygen of the air would be depleted rapidly. During hours of darkness, how-ever, plants like animals take in oxygen and give off carbon dioxide.

11. Uses

A number of the principal uses of this important element have already been noted. Of greatest import are its uses in sustaining life and in supporting the

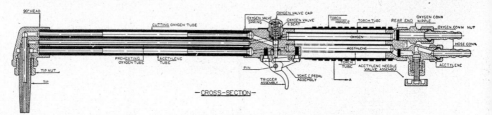

DETAILS OF THE OXYACETYLENE TORCH. (Courtesy, Air Reduction Sales Co.)

combustion of a wide variety of fuels. Pure oxygen is used in oxyacetylene and oxyhydrogen torches for the cutting and welding of metals, and it also finds a number of laboratory uses. Cylinders of it are used to support life in diving bells, submarines, and high-altitude airplanes. During general anesthesia oxygen is usually administered in carefully controlled quantities to the patient. It is also administered to victims of pneumonia and other respiratory diseases. Its uses in resuscitation have been noted above. Many combustible substances, when soaked in liquid oxygen, become violent explosives.

12. Analytical Tests

A glowing splint introduced into pure oxygen will burst into flame, but nitrous oxide will have the same effect. The odor of the latter gas, however, serves to distinguish it. A much more delicate test for oxygen is the production of a red color by the action of even minute quantities of the element upon an alkaline solution of catechol, $C_6H_4(OH)_2$, which contains ferrous ions, Fe^{++}. The removal of oxygen in the quantitative analysis of gaseous mixtures has been referred to in section 5. Solutions of cuprous chloride in hydrochloric acid may also be used for this purpose, though such solutions also absorb carbon monoxide, CO.

13. Ozone

Ozone is an allotrope of oxygen. Its formula is O_3. Its existence was first noted in 1785 by the Dutch chemist, van Marum, and the name *ozone*, derived from the Greek verb *to smell*, was applied many years later by Schönbein, who was impressed by the sharp odor of the substance.

14. Physical Properties of Ozone

At about 20° C., ozone is a pale blue gas of pungent odor. Its density at S.T.P. is 2.144 g./l., or one and one-half times that of oxygen under the same conditions. It is much more soluble in water than is oxygen, and in oil of cinnamon it is extremely soluble. It may be condensed to an intensely blue liquid which boils at −112° C. and freezes to a violet-black solid at −251° C.

15. Preparation of Ozone

The conversion of oxygen into ozone is strongly endothermic,

$$3O_2 + 68,800 \text{ cal.} \rightarrow 2O_3$$

hence large quantities of energy are necessary to bring about this change. The method most commonly used is the passage of low-temperature electrical

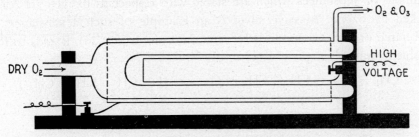

SILENT ELECTRICAL DISCHARGE APPARATUS USED FOR THE LABORATORY PREPARATION OF OZONE.

discharges through air or oxygen. The silent electrical discharge obtained by connecting two metallic plates through an induction coil with a source of current is eminently suited for this purpose. Carefully dried gases maintained at low temperatures give the best yield, but, even so, only a fraction of the available energy is utilized in the production of ozone. Commercial ozonizers, because of their complicated construction, are expensive.

Ozone is produced naturally by lightning flashes and by the action of the ultraviolet rays of sunlight upon the dry, dust-free air of the upper atmosphere. In the laboratory, it is produced in small amounts when a hot platinum wire is plunged into liquid oxygen, when phosphorus burns in oxygen or an excess of air, when a jet of hydrogen burns in oxygen, when fluorine acts on water, and when sulfuric acid acts on barium peroxide. The odor of ozone is usually quite distinct around operating electric generators and motors.

16. *Chemical Properties of Ozone*

As might be anticipated from a consideration of the fact that the formation of ozone is endothermic, this allotrope of oxygen is highly unstable with respect to its reconversion into O_2, save at advanced temperatures; though at very low temperatures the rate of decomposition is markedly decreased. Because of this instability and because of its high energy content, it is an excellent oxidizing agent which attacks a wide variety of both organic and inorganic materials. Usually, oxygen is a by-product of these reactions, since only the atomic oxygen produced by the following decomposition is used:

$$O_3 \rightarrow O_2 + O$$

In some instances, as for example the oxidation of sulfur dioxide, no oxygen is set free:

$$3SO_2 + O_3 \rightarrow 3SO_3$$

A number of substances which are stable with respect to oxygen are readily attacked by ozone. Massive silver is an example of such a substance. To unsaturated organic compounds (cf. section 8 of Chapter 23), it adds to form unstable ozonides,

$$CH_3 - CH = CH - CH_3 + O_3 \rightarrow CH_3 - \underset{\underset{O}{\overset{\displaystyle |}{O}}}{CH} - \underset{\underset{O}{\overset{\displaystyle |}{O}}}{CH} - CH_3$$

It reacts with neutral and basic aqueous solutions to form the perhydroxyl ion, O_2^-,

$$O_3 + 2OH^- \rightarrow H_2O + 2O_2^-$$

which, in acid solution, reacts to form hydrogen peroxide and oxygen.

17. *Uses of Ozone*

The uses of ozone are all based upon its ability as an oxidizing agent. Many natural and artificial coloring matters are readily oxidized by it to colorless substances, hence it is frequently used to bleach starch, flour, fabrics, oils, waxes, ivory, and a variety of other materials. It is also used to "season" tobacco, tea, leather, and wood, and to hasten the "drying" of paints and varnishes whose vehicle is of an oily nature. It finds use in the preparation of camphor and a number of other useful synthetic chemicals, and it is also in demand as a deodorant and disinfectant. Most air-borne odors are those of easily oxidized organic compounds. Ozone dissolved in water attacks both inanimate organic matter and microörganisms. The concentration of ozone in air is not great enough to have much effect upon bacteria which may be present, but it is used to help keep the air of subways and cellars both pleasant and healthful. Despite the cost of its production, ozone finds wide application, because its use leads to the formation of no undesirable by-products.

18. Analytical Tests for Ozone

It is reported that the odor of as little as one part of ozone in 10,000,000 parts of air can be detected by the average individual. Moistened starch-iodide paper turns blue in its presence, but this test is not specific, since chlorine, hydrogen peroxide, some of the oxides of nitrogen, and other substances have a like behavior. As noted above, it reacts directly upon massive silver. A black stain, presumably of silver peroxide, is produced:

$$2O_3 + 2Ag \rightarrow Ag_2O_2 + 2O_2 \uparrow$$

This stain must not be confused with the dark, brownish stain produced by hydrogen sulfide.

II. SELENIUM, TELLURIUM, AND POLONIUM

19. General

Of these three elements, tellurium was the first to be discovered. Although it had been known for a number of years, it was not named until 1798 when Klaproth christened it tellurium from the Latin word signifying *the earth*. In 1817, the great Berzelius discovered a new element which, because of its relation to the earthy tellurium, he named selenium from the Greek word for *moon*. Polonium was not discovered until 1898. Its discoverer, Madame Maria Sklodowska Curie, named it in honor of her native land, Poland. Polonium is a radioactive substance of weakly metallic properties. Because it is so rare, and because so little is known of it, little attention will be devoted to it here.

20. Physical Properties

At ordinary temperatures, selenium exists in the form of gray, rhombo-hedral, hexagonal crystals of semimetallic appearance which melt at 220° C.

and boil at 688° C. Like sulfur, this element also exists in a number of allotropic modifications; in addition to the gray crystalline variety there are two red varieties and a black, amorphous variety, reminiscent of amorphous sulfur. The red forms are soluble in carbon disulfide, while the gray form is not. Gaseous selenium is red in color and is extremely poisonous. At 1400° C., the vapor has the formula Se_2, but above 2000° C., its formula is Se.

The allotropism of tellurium is less pronounced than that of either sulfur or selenium. The molten element crystallizes as silvery-white, rhombohedral, hexagonal crystals which are isomorphic with those of gray selenium. A second crystalline variety has been reported, and an *amorphous form*, which is really finely crystalline, is known. The silvery variety melts at 452° C., boils at 1390° C., and has a density of 6.24 g./ml. Its vapor is of a golden-yellow color, and very poisonous. At about 1500° C., the formula of the vapor is Te_2, while above 2000° C., it is Te. The breathing of both selenium and tellurium may result in a peculiarly persistent and obnoxious variety of halitosis. Both elements are isotopic mixtures of a number of atomic species.

Several physical properties of the four most common elements of the VI A family are summarized in the accompanying table.

Table 24

PHYSICAL PROPERTIES OF THE ELEMENTS OF THE VI A FAMILY

Property	Oxygen (O)	Sulfur (S)	Selenium (Se)	Tellurium (Te)
Atomic weight.............	16.00	32.06	78.96	127.61
Mass of isotopes...........	16, 17, 18	32, 33, 34, 36	74, 76, 77, 78, 80, 82	120, 122, 123, 124, 125, 126, 128, 130
Atomic number............	8	16	34	52
Electronic distribution........	2, 6	2, 8, 6	2, 8, 18, 6	2, 8, 18, 18, 6
Melting point..............	−218.4° C.	112.8° C.	220° C. (gray)	452° C.
Boiling point..............	−183° C.	444.6° C.	688° C.	1390° C.
Density of common solid variety.................	1.429 g./ml. (−0° C.)	2.07 g./ml. (20° C.)	4.80 g./ml. (20° C.)	6.24 g./ml. (20° C.)
Specific heat of solid in cal./g.	0.336 at (−221.8° C.)	0.176 (15–96° C.)	0.077 at (20.5° C.)	0.0483 (15–100° C.)
Ionizing potential, volts, removal 1st electron........	13.55	10.30	9.70	8.96

21. Occurrence

Small quantities of free selenium are usually found in the majority of the deposits of free sulfur. In combination, it is found as the selenide of a number of the heavy metals, notable among which are lead, copper, and silver, and also to a lesser extent as the selenite of several of the heavy metals. Many plants growing in soils bearing selenium compounds contain the element in the form of its salts and protein complexes.

Only trifling quantities of free tellurium are found. It occurs principally as the telluride of copper, lead, silver, gold, and others of the heavy metals. Neither selenium nor tellurium is abundant in the earth's crust.

22. Production

Both of the elements are obtained principally from the anode mud of the cells used in the electrolytic refining of copper. Were there a demand for them, both elements could be obtained in quantity as by-products in a number of metallurgical processes and much selenium could be obtained from the flue dust of sulfur and pyrite burners.

23. Chemical Properties

Both metals burn in oxygen to form their corresponding dioxides:

$$Se + O_2 \rightarrow SeO_2$$

and

$$Te + O_2 \rightarrow TeO_2$$

Upon being heated with a wide variety of metals and nonmetals, both elements, after the fashion of sulfur, unite to form their respective binary compounds, the selenides and tellurides. Neither element combines with hydrogen to any marked extent, hence their hydrides are best prepared by the usual indirect methods (cf. section 6, Chapter 23).

In general, the reactions of both elements closely parallel the common reactions of sulfur. As one proceeds down column VI A, the size of the atoms increases, which change is accompanied by a corresponding increase in metallic properties; however, both elements are, in the main, nonmetallic in behavior. Selenium may take the place of sulfur in a wide variety of the compounds of the latter.

24. Hydrides

Both hydrogen selenide and hydrogen telluride are best prepared by the action of acid upon their respective metallic binary compounds:

$$FeSe + 2HCl \rightarrow H_2Se \uparrow + FeCl_2$$

Both hydrides are gaseous, inflammable, foul-smelling, and toxic. The breath-

JOSEPH PRIESTLEY
(*1733–1804, English*)

Although Scheele's preparation of oxygen undoubtedly antedated that of Priestley, the two discoveries were made independently of each other and Priestley is usually credited with the discovery of the element because of his earlier publication of his findings. He obtained the element by the thermal decomposition of mercuric oxide. A not very successful clergyman, Priestley devoted much of his time to scientific experimentation, writing, and teaching. His best scientific work was done upon various gaseous substances, at whose manipulation he was a master. Because he collected his gases by displacement of mercury rather than water, he was able to isolate the water-soluble gases ammonia, hydrogen chloride, sulfur dioxide, and several others. He also recognized the analogy between combustion and respiration, but missed the full significance of his discovery. Because of his unpopularity, which stemmed largely from his religious views and his openly stated sympathy for the aims of the French Revolution, he left England in 1794 to spend the last ten years of his life in Northumberland, Pa.

ing of even small quantities of them may result in the characteristic halitosis referred to above. Both dissolve in water to yield weakly acidic solutions, and each will precipitate from solutions containing metallic ions a wide variety of corresponding selenides or tellurides, as the case may be. Both are good reducing agents, for as the size of the ions of the VI A family increases, the stability of their hydrides decreases and their ability as reducing agents increases.

25. Oxides and Acids

The principal oxide of selenium is the dioxide, SeO_2. The trioxide, SeO_3, is little known, though its preparation has been reported. Free selenium or selenium compounds may be burned to yield the dioxide which is a white solid that sublimes readily and is reported to have the odor of "rotten horseradish." It dissolves slowly in water to yield weakly acidic solutions of selenious acid, H_2SeO_3, which may be obtained as a colorless solid upon evaporation of the water. The acid is the parent of the selenites and the acid selenites and is a powerful oxidizing agent, as are its salts:

$$H_2SeO_3 + 2H_3PO_3 \rightarrow 2H_3PO_4 + H_2O + \underline{Se}$$

It is decomposed into its anhydride by heat. It is most readily prepared by the action of nitric acid on elementary selenium.

Selenic acid, H_2SeO_4, may be prepared by the action of chlorine on selenious acid:

$$H_2SeO_3 + Cl_2 + H_2O \rightarrow H_2SeO_4 + 2HCl$$

The pure acid is a white solid whose aqueous solutions behave much like those of sulfuric acid, H_2SO_4. It is a moderately strong acid and a very strong oxidizing agent. Upon being heated strongly, it decomposes into water, oxygen, and SeO_2. The solubility of its salts, the selenates, closely resembles that of the sulfates.

Tellurium forms the oxides TeO, TeO_2, and TeO_3. The dioxide occurs to some extent in nature as the mineral *tellurite* and is formed as a white powder by the burning of the element. Upon being heated, the dioxide decomposes into oxygen and the monoxide, TeO. Since the dioxide is only slightly soluble, tellurous acid, H_2TeO_3, is best prepared by the action of nitric acid on the element:

$$4HNO_3 + 3Te + H_2O \rightarrow 3H_2TeO_3 + 4NO \uparrow$$

The pure acid is a white powder which is amphoteric in its behavior. It forms both normal and acid tellurites with strong bases, and with strong acids it forms salts of tetravalent tellurium such as tellurous sulfate, $Te(SO_4)_2$, or salts of the telluryl radical, TeO^{++}. The acid is a good oxidizing agent.

An unstable perselenic acid is known.

Upon treatment with very strong oxidizing agents, tellurous acid is oxidized to telluric acid, which has the formula H_6TeO_6 and is believed to exist as the hexahydroxide. It is a colorless solid of slight solubility, of extremely weakly acidic properties, and of strong ability as an oxidizing agent. Upon being heated, it decomposes thus:

$$H_6TeO_6 \xrightarrow{\Delta} 2H_2O + H_2TeO_4 \xrightarrow{\Delta} 3H_2O + TeO_3$$

The trioxide is an orange-colored powder which is insoluble in water. Normal and acid tellurates containing the radical TeO_4^{--} are known. Only the strongest bases form such salts.

26. Halides

A variety of halides of both selenium and tellurium are known. Selenyl and telluryl chlorides, $SeOCl_2$ and $TeOCl_2$, are also known.

27. Selenium and Agriculture

Plants grown on seleniferous soil tend to accumulate the element in their organisms. Cows and horses pastured on such land soon develop sore hoofs which may eventually be sloughed off, and they may also lose hair from their coats and tails. Cows may also lose their horns. Pigs and other animals experience comparable difficulties. The disease was originally known as "alkali disease," since it was erroneously believed to be caused by the stock drinking water containing alkali; it is also known as "bobtailed disease." In the United States seleniferous areas occur principally in the northern plains states and to a lesser degree in states of the Rocky Mountain area. If eaten by human beings, cereal grains grown in such regions may cause chronic illness, and even death. Examinations of the organs of laboratory animals fed on such grains have revealed badly degenerated livers.

28. Uses of Selenium and Tellurium

Because the conductivity of selenium increases greatly with its illumination, it finds use in the construction of photoelectric cells for the control of a wide variety of automatic devices. Colloidal suspensions of the element in glass give it a brilliant red color. It is also used in small quantities to counteract the color imparted to glass by iron impurities. It also finds use in the production of various enamels and paints, as it does in the production of various alloys. The machinability of various alloys of iron and of copper is improved by its presence. Its other uses form a list which is steadily growing.

In addition to improving the machinability of various alloys, tellurium increases the toughness, strength, and resistance to corrosion of lead, and also strengthens tin. Light emitted by the tellurium vapor lamp approaches sunlight in quality, but the high operating temperature of the lamp presents a practical difficulty. Because of the ease with which the element may be obtained, new uses are being sought for it.

29. Analytical Tests

Selenium and tellurium may be identified by oxidizing their compounds to the selenates and tellurates, respectively, from which the free elements are precipitated by the action of hydrogen sulfide. If the two elements are precipitated together, they may be separated by distilling the mixture with hydrogen bromide. The distillate consists of selenium tetrabromide, $SeBr_4$. Elementary selenium dissolves in concentrated sulfuric acid to yield a deep green solution of $SeSO_3$, which is a selenium-substituted sulfur sesquioxide, S_2O_3.

(*See Appendix for Exercises*)

COLLATERAL READINGS

Ellis and Kirkby: *Flame*, New York, Chemical Publishing Co., 1945.

Ephraim: *Inorganic Chemistry*, 3d Eng. ed., London, Gurney and Jackson, 1939.

Findlay: *The Spirit of Chemistry*, New York, Longmans, Green & Co., 1934.

Foster: *The Romance of Chemistry*, New York, D. Appleton-Century Co., 1937.

Jaffe: *Crucibles*, New York, Simon and Schuster, 1930.

Latimer and Hildebrand: *Reference Book of Inorganic Chemistry*, New York, The Macmillan Co., 1941.

Moore: *History of Chemistry*, New York, McGraw-Hill Book Co., 1939.

Price: Dust dangers in industrial plants, *Chem. and Met. Eng.*, **35,** 151 (1928).

Selwood, *et al.:* Electrolytic concentration of oxygen isotopes, *J. Am. Chem. Soc.*, **57,** 642 (1935).

Weeks: *Discovery of the Elements*, 5th ed., Mack Printing Co., 1945.

Worstell: Ozone, *J. Chem. Education*, **9,** 291 (1932).

Yost and Russell: *Systematic Inorganic Chemistry*, New York, Prentice-Hall, Inc., 1944.

Various bulletins of the South Dakota Ag. Expt. Station dealing with selenium in relation to soils, plants, and animals.

Oxygen, *Fortune*, **16,** No. 2, 61 (1937).

HENRI MOISSAN
(*1852–1907, French*)

Moissan is best known for his isolation of the element fluorine, but many other brilliant achievements are also his. While trying to prepare diamonds synthetically, he invented the electric furnace, by whose use he was able not only to prepare many new compounds, notable among which were the carbides, borides, and silicides, but also to melt many compounds which up to that time had been considered infusible. By means of his furnace, he was able to prepare vanadium, uranium, and tungsten, and to prepare a series of saltlike metallic hydrides. He held professorships in various French institutions of higher learning, and in 1900 became professor of general chemistry at the Sorbonne. He is the author of a number of books, and in 1906 he was awarded the Nobel Prize.

26

The Halogens, Members of
the VII A Family

1. Introduction

Fluorine, chlorine, bromine, iodine, and element 85, which has been named *alabamine* by Allison, are the members of the VII A family. Collectively, they are known as the *halogens* (Greek, *salt-formers*), because of the occurrence of their binary compounds in sea water. The atoms of each of these elements possess seven valence electrons so that their chemical behaviors are much alike, differing in degree rather than in kind. The differences to be noted are of the same type as those already recorded for preceding families and result from the gradual increase in size of the successively heavier atoms and the accompanying decrease in the attraction between nucleus and valence electrons. Decreasing ionization potentials emphasize this decrease in firmness of binding of the outermost electrons.

In general, the properties of the other members of this family are much like those of chlorine, discussed at some length in Chapters 10 and 22. Fluorine, the halogen of the second period, is, as might be expected, the member of the family which deviates most markedly in its behavior. Although the existence of alabamine has been reported as confirmed, the element has never been isolated and almost nothing is known of its compounds.

Since they are placed in the column just preceding that of the inert gases, and lack only one electron of having an inert gas structure, the halogens react most commonly by gaining or sharing one electron to show a valence number or oxidation number of -1. Further, bromine and iodine, like chlorine, form compounds in which they exhibit a variety of positive oxidation numbers. Fluorine, whose atoms are smallest, never exists in positive states of oxidation, while iodine, whose atoms are the largest, shows a strong tendency toward existence in positive states.

Careful study should be made of the trend of the various properties of these elements as compiled in the accompanying table.

Table 25

PROPERTIES OF THE HALOGENS

Property	Fluorine (F)	Chlorine (Cl)	Bromine (Br)	Iodine (I)
Atomic weight........	19.00	35.457	79.916	126.92
Mass of isotopes......	19	35,37	79,81	127
Atomic number.......	9	17	35	53
Distribution of planetary electrons.......	2, 7	2, 8, 7	2, 8, 18, 7	2, 8, 18, 18, 7
Physical state, at about 20° C..............	Gas	Gas	Liquid	Solid
Color...............	Pale yellow	Greenish-yellow	Brownish-red	Gray black (vapor, violet)
Melting point.........	−223° C.	−101.6° C.	−7.2° C.	113.5° C.
Boiling point.........	−187° C.	−34.6° C.	58.78° C.	184.35° C.
Density..............	1.695 g./l. (gas)	3.214 g./l. (gas)	3.12 g./ml. (liq.)	4.93 g./ml. (solid)
Solubility in water, at 20° C..............	Reacts with H_2O	2.2 ml./ml.	3.58 g./100 g.	0.029 g./100 g.
Molecular heat of dissociation..........	66,800 cal.	56,800 cal.	45,200 cal.	35,600 cal.
Heat of vaporization, cal./mol............	1,640	4,420	7,418	10,388
Heat of formation of HX at 18° C. and standard pressure....	63,991	22,030	8,650	−5,926
Ionizing potentials of gaseous atoms......	17.34 v.	12.95 v.	11.80 v.	10.6 v.

I. FLUORINE

2. Physical Properties

Despite the fact that compounds of fluorine had long been known, the element is so active that it was not obtained free in appreciable quantities until 1886. Its name is derived from the Latin verb meaning *to flow*, and was chosen because many of its compounds when heated with other minerals produce a fluid slag. Table 25 shows the element to be a pale yellow gas of strong odor, so active that it decomposes water and a number of other solvents. It is liquefied and solidified only with difficulty. The gas is more dense than air.

3. Occurrence

Fluorine occurs principally as calcium fluoride, CaF_2, which is found as the mineral *fluorspar*, or *fluorite*, and in combination with calcium phosphate in the mineral *apatite* (cf. section 3, Chapter 20). Fluorspar is widely distributed in nature. In the United States, it is mined in Illinois, Kentucky, Colorado, New Mexico, and other states. *Cryolite* is another of the important minerals of

A CRYSTAL OF FLUORITE. (Courtesy, American Museum of Natural History.)

fluorine. Its composition corresponds to the formula Na_3AlF_6. It is mined in Greenland and Iceland, and its principal use is as a flux in the refining of aluminum oxide (cf. section 4, chapter 15). A synthetic fluorine-containing flux is now manufactured for this purpose. Small quantities of the element are found in bones and teeth, and the diet must provide these small but essential amounts. Too large a quantity of fluorides in drinking water causes an unsightly brownish mottling of tooth enamel.

4. Preparation

The free element was first prepared in appreciable quantities by the French chemist, Moissan, who electrolyzed a solution of potassium acid fluoride, KHF_2, in hydrogen fluoride contained in a copper U-tube. The salt had to be used because hydrogen fluoride alone is virtually a nonconductor. Free fluorine is so reactive that there are relatively few materials of which the electrolytic cell may be made. Although copper is attacked, it proved to be suitable because the copper fluoride formed adheres tightly, thus protecting the underlying metal from further attack. The electrodes which Moissan used were of a platinum-iridium alloy. At present, fluorine is still prepared in virtually the same way, though the design of the copper cell has been changed and it has been found that an anode of graphite may be used. At the beginning of the reaction, the cell is heated to a temperature of about 22° C., which is gradually raised to about 300° C. as the electrolysis progresses.

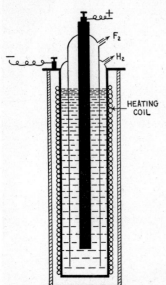

DIAGRAM OF AN ELECTROLYTIC CELL FOR THE PRODUCTION OF FLUORINE.

5. Chemical Properties

As might be predicted from its position in the periodic table at the head of the VII A column, fluorine is the most active of the electron-gainers, the nonmetals. It combines directly with practically all of the elements save oxygen, nitrogen, and the inert gases. It combines violently with hydrogen even in the dark if a trace of moisture is present; it combines spontaneously with the metals of the I A and II A families (the active electron-losers); with the other metals, including gold and platinum, it combines at temperatures in excess of 200° C.; and with the other halogens it also unites to form fluorides. Many of the nonmetallic elements also combine spontaneously with fluorine, bursting into flame in an atmosphere of it.

The free element reacts with water to form hydrogen fluoride and to liberate ozonized oxygen. The hydrogen of many other compounds is also removed in a similar fashion to form hydrogen fluoride. Fluorine displaces the other halogens from ionic halides, setting them free, and it behaves in a similar fashion with some of the covalent halides—for example, it liberates chlorine from carbon tetrachloride. It reacts with glass in the presence of a trace of moisture to form silicon tetrafluoride, SiF_4, but upon pure fused silica it has no action. Little is known of its behavior with the wide variety of plastics now available.

6. *Hydrogen Fluoride*

At about 20° C., anhydrous hydrogen fluoride is a colorless gas that is easily condensed to a colorless liquid which boils at 19.4° C. and freezes at −92.3° C. It is extremely soluble in water, but, unlike hydrogen chloride, is not strongly ionized in solution. The aqueous solutions are known as hydrofluoric acid, and at 120° C. an azeotropic mixture containing 35 per cent of the solute is formed. The anhydrous liquid is reported to be associated and of the formula H_6F_6. This would account for its relatively high boiling point.

A WAX BOTTLE USED FOR THE PACKING OF HYDROFLUORIC ACID. (Courtesy, J. T. Baker Chemical Co.)

The vapor also seems to be associated, but becomes less so as the temperature is raised. Above 88° C., the formula of the gas is HF, and this formula is used to represent the aqueous solutions.

Hydrogen fluoride is easily prepared by heating a mixture of calcium fluoride and concentrated sulfuric acid, or by heating potassium hydrogen fluoride:

$$CaF_2 + H_2SO_4 \xrightarrow{\Delta} \underline{CaSO_4} + 2HF \uparrow$$

and

$$KHF_2 \overset{\Delta}{\rightarrow} \underline{KF} + HF \uparrow$$

The gas may be dried thoroughly and condensed or it may be led into water to prepare hydrofluoric acid.

Being less highly ionized than the other hydrohalic acids, hydrofluoric acid reacts with metals and bases much less vigorously than they; nevertheless, it reacts to produce fluorides. These salts are usually the acid fluorides, since the solutions characteristically contain the HF_2^- ion which results from the union of an F^- ion with an HF molecule:

$$:\overset{..}{\underset{..}{F}}:^- + H \overset{..}{\underset{..}{\times F}}: \rightarrow :\overset{..}{\underset{..}{F}}:H \overset{..}{\underset{..}{\times F}}:^-$$

The outstanding property of the acid is its ability to attack sand, glass, and other silicates (cf. section 18, Chapter 18). Gaseous silicon tetrafluoride is formed, but it may react with moisture present to form a mixture of silicic and fluosilicic acids. Because of this behavior, the acid must be kept in wax, hard-rubber, or plastic bottles, and is used to etch glass and to destroy siliceous matter in analytical samples, as well as to prepare other fluorides.

Attention must be directed to the facts that hydrogen fluoride is toxic and that it and its solutions cause painful burns on the skin.

7. Fluorides

The most widely used fluorides are those which occur naturally, but others are prepared from hydrogen fluoride and from its aqueous solutions. The solubilities of these salts usually are just contrary to those of the other halides. The majority of the metallic fluorides are insoluble, with the calcium salt being among the least soluble. Among the soluble ones are those of silver, sodium, potassium, and ammonium. The fluorides are used as fluxes and in the manufacture of ceramics, and certain of them are used as mordants in dyeing. The mixed fluoride and chloride of carbon, CCl_2F_2, commonly known as *freon* (difluorodichloromethane) is used as a refrigerant, and NH_4HF_2 is used to etch glass.

8. The Fluoacids

Reference to fluosilicic acid has already been made (cf. section 14, Chapter 18). Boron, titanium, and other elements also form *fluo*-acids. These compounds may be thought of as normal oxygen acids in which each oxygen atom has been substituted by two monovalent fluorine atoms, though they are not prepared by direct substitution. They will be discussed in connection with the chemistry of their central elements.

In conclusion, it may be said that much work needs to be done to increase the knowledge of fluorine and its chemistry. As this work is accomplished, a wider use of it and its compounds may be expected.

II. BROMINE

9. General

Although bromine had been prepared by other workers, its discovery is usually attributed to Balard, who recognized it as a new element when he chanced to prepare it in 1826. The name *bromine* (from the Greek meaning *a stench*) is due also to Balard and was applied in token of its choking and unpleasant odor.

The student should note the close resemblance in the behavior of bromine and iodine and that of chlorine, also the contrast between these three substances and fluorine.

10. Physical Properties

At about 20° C., bromine is a dark red liquid of high vapor pressure. Because of this latter property, it evaporates readily, yielding clouds of dense brownish-red fumes whose formula at ordinary temperatures seems to be Br_2. The density and other physical properties of the element are given in Table 25. Saturated aqueous solutions of bromine are widely used in both laboratory and factory, but the element is much more soluble in carbon tetrachloride, chloroform, alcohol, ether, and other organic liquids than it is in water. Stronger aqueous solutions may be prepared by first adding potassium bromide. The bromine is removed from plain aqueous solutions by heating or by bubbling air through the liquid.

11. Occurrence

Bromine is far less plentiful than either chlorine or fluorine, but, like them, it is never found free in nature, and its compounds are widely distributed. Until relatively recent years, the majority of the bromine and bromides of commerce were prepared from the bromides of potassium, magnesium, and sodium which occur in the salt deposits of Stassfurt in Germany and in solution in the waters of the salt wells of Michigan, Ohio, and neighboring states in this country. At present, great quantities of the element are obtained from the small concentration of dissolved metallic bromides contained in the water of the oceans. Some marine plants and animals contain bromides also derived from this latter source.

12. *Preparation*

Elementary bromine is prepared by treating acidified sea water or other acidified solutions of bromides with free chlorine:

$$2KBr + Cl_2 \rightarrow Br_2 + 2KCl$$

Acid is necessary to prevent the reaction of the liberated bromine with the slightly basic solution. Usually, the acidified solution trickles down a tower

SEA-WATER INTAKE CANAL FOR A MODERN BROMINE PLANT. (Courtesy, The Dow Chemical Co.)

containing baffles. The gaseous chlorine is admitted well above the bottom of the tower and steam or air is introduced at the bottom to sweep the liberated bromine upward. The liberated element may be collected directly, or it may be absorbed in a solution of sodium carbonate,

$$3Br_2 + 3Na_2CO_3 \rightarrow 5NaBr + NaBrO_3 + 3CO_2 \uparrow$$

from which the free bromine is liberated by treatment with sulfuric acid,

$$5NaBr + NaBrO_3 + 3H_2SO_4 \xrightarrow{\Delta} 3Na_2SO_4 + 3H_2O + 3Br_2 \uparrow$$

Some bromine is also prepared by the electrolysis of the salt-well brines from which most of the chlorides have been removed by crystallization. Since bromine is less reactive than chlorine, it is liberated from its binary compounds by a voltage too small to liberate chlorine also.

In the laboratory, bromine may be prepared by displacement from bromides by chlorine or by the action of sulfuric acid and manganese dioxide on a bromide:

$$2NaBr + MnO_2 + 2H_2SO_4 \xrightarrow{\Delta} Na_2SO_4 + MnSO_4 + 2H_2O + Br_2 \uparrow$$

A Plant for the Removal of Bromine from Sea Water. (Courtesy, The Dow Chemical Co.)

13. Chemical Properties

The chemical behavior of bromine closely resembles that of chlorine, although, having a larger atom than chlorine, it gains an electron less readily and holds on to it less tightly once it has been gained. Mixtures of hydrogen and bromine vapor do not unite spontaneously, and when the reaction has been started by the addition of a catalyst or of energy, the reaction does not proceed as violently as the union of chlorine and hydrogen. At higher temperatures and with a catalyst, the reaction proceeds rapidly. Bromine combines directly to form bromides with the more active

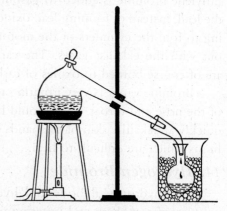

Apparatus for the Laboratory Preparation of Bromine.

metals such as sodium, magnesium, and calcium, and with the more active nonmetals such as phosphorus. It is thus a good oxidizing agent.

Bromine also reacts less readily with water than does chlorine; however, bromine water does contain some hypobromous acid, HBrO, and some hydrobromic acid, HBr:

$$Br_2 + HOH \rightleftharpoons HBrO + H^+ + Br^-$$

The addition of a base to remove the H^+ ions as water naturally shifts the equilibrium to the right, permitting the formation of a hypobromite and a bromide:

$$Br_2 + 2KOH \rightarrow KBrO + KBr + H_2O$$

Bromine reacts with a wide variety of organic compounds. With saturated organic substances (cf. section 8, Chapter 23), it reacts by *substitution* to replace one or more hydrogen atoms,

$$\underset{\text{(Ethane)}}{C_2H_6} + Br_2 \rightarrow \underset{\text{(Ethyl bromide)}}{C_2H_5Br} + HBr$$

while with unsaturated organic compounds it reacts by *addition*,

$$\underset{\text{(Ethylene)}}{H_2C{=}CH_2} + Br_2 \rightarrow \underset{\text{(Ethylene bromide)}}{BrCH_2{-}CH_2Br}$$

Such organic bromides find a wide use. For example, ethyl bromide or the corresponding ethyl chloride may be used to prepare lead tetraethyl which is used in large quantities as an antiknock compound in gasolines:

$$4C_2H_5Br + 4NaPb \rightarrow (C_2H_5)_4Pb + 4NaBr + 3Pb$$

Ethylene bromide is added to gasolines along with the lead tetraethyl so that the lead, instead of forming lead oxide when the gasoline is burned and remaining to foul the cylinders of the motor, will form lead bromide which is blown out with the exhaust gases. The carbon and hydrogen of these compounds are of course burned to oxides of carbon and to water.

Bromine vapor is very irritating to the eyes and to the mucous membranes of the nose and throat. Care should be taken to avoid breathing it. The liquid quickly attacks the skin of the hands or other parts of the body, causing severe burns which are difficult to heal.

14. Hydrogen Bromide

Like hydrogen fluoride and hydrogen chloride, hydrogen bromide is a colorless gas of sharp and irritating odor at about 20° C. It may be condensed to a colorless, anhydrous liquid whose boiling point is −67° C. and whose freezing point is −88.5° C. The gas is extremely soluble in water; under standard conditions, 1 ml. of water will dissolve 611 ml. of it, or 100 g. of water will dissolve 221 g. of it. The aqueous solution of hydrogen bromide is known as hydrobromic acid, and, like the other hydrohalic acids, it forms an azeotropic mixture. Under standard pressure, this constant boiling mixture contains 47.8 per cent of HBr and boils at 126° C.

In the laboratory, hydrogen bromide is most conveniently prepared on a small scale by the hydrolysis of phosphorus tribromide,

$$PBr_3 + 3HOH \rightarrow H_3PO_3 + 3HBr \uparrow$$

On a larger scale, the anhydrous gas may be prepared by passing hydrogen and vaporized bromine through a hot tube containing siliceous baffles or a suitable catalyst such as palladium or platinum.

Aqueous solutions are prepared by passing either hydrogen sulfide gas or sulfur dioxide gas into a vessel containing cracked ice over which bromine has been poured:

$$Br_2 + H_2S \xrightarrow{H_2O} 2HBr + \underline{S}$$

and

$$Br_2 + 2H_2O + SO_2 \xrightarrow{H_2O} 2HBr + H_2SO_4$$

The action of sulfuric acid, or other oxidizing acid, on metallic bromides is not a suitable method of preparing hydrogen bromide, because bromine is liberated from them by the action of the oxidizing agent. This behavior serves to emphasize the decreasing strength of the union between hydrogen and the increasingly heavy halogen atoms. Reference to the decreasing heats of formation of the hydrogen halides as listed in Table 25 would have implied this decreased stability.

The decreasing strength of union also accounts for the fact that hydrobromic acid is even more highly ionized than hydrochloric acid, and is, similarly, a more powerful reducing agent. Generally, though, the chemical behavior of these two acids is entirely analogous, differing in degree rather than in kind (cf. section 9, Chapter 10). Likewise, the chemical behavior of gaseous hydrogen bromide and gaseous hydrogen chloride is very similar.

15. The Bromides

These salts are usually prepared by the direct action of bromine or by displacements or metatheses involving hydrobromic acid. Bromides closely resemble the chlorides in appearance and behavior. The bromide ion is colorless and highly soluble, as are most of its binary compounds. Least soluble of the common metallic bromides are those of silver, mercurous mercury, and lead.

This solubility is in contrast with that of the fluorides. Certain of the metallic bromides, notably those of sodium, potassium, calcium, and strontium, are used medicinally as nerve sedatives, and silver bromide is manufactured in large quantities for use as the light-sensitive substance with which photographic

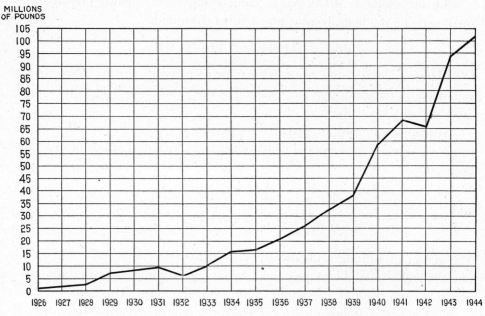

THE INCREASE IN THE DOMESTIC PRODUCTION OF BROMINE FROM 1926 TO 1944.

films, plates, and papers are coated. The most useful of the nonmetallic bromides are those of phosphorus and those of the carbon compounds. Various ones of these latter brominated organic substances find a wide use in synthesis, as dyes, as medicinals, and as lachrymal, or tear, gases. Ethyl bromide and ethylene bromide were referred to specifically in section 13.

16. The Positive Oxidation States of Bromine

Bromine forms no stable oxides; however, the very unstable oxides Br_2O and BrO_2 have been reported as having been prepared by indirect methods. Among the oxygen acids of the element hypobromous acid, HBrO, and bromic acid, $HBrO_3$, are known. Bromous acid, $HBrO_2$, has been prepared, but it is so unstable that its existence is brief; no perbromic acid is known. Contrast this behavior with that of both fluorine and chlorine. The limited formation of hypobromous acid by the hydrolysis of the element was dealt with in section 13. While still a good oxidizing agent, it is weaker in this respect than is hypochlorous acid, and is much less stable with respect to its conversion by autooxidation-reduction into hydrobromic and bromic acids:

$$3HBrO \rightarrow 2HBr + HBrO_3$$

Its salts also readily undergo this change, slowly in solution at about 20° C. and rapidly when warmed in solution or when heated in the dry condition:

$$3NaBrO \overset{\Delta}{\rightarrow} 2NaBr + NaBrO_3$$

Bromic acid, because of its instability, cannot be prepared in the pure condition, but aqueous solutions are readily prepared by methods analogous to those used for the preparation of chloric acid (cf. section 9, Chapter 22), or by the action of chloric acid, nitric acid, hydrogen peroxide, or other strong oxidizing agent upon elementary bromine. The acid is highly ionized and is a good oxidizing agent, though it does not oxidize hydrochloric acid as does chloric acid. Most of the metallic bromates are only slightly soluble, being less soluble than the corresponding chlorates. Chlorate and bromate ions may be distinguished by the fact that silver chlorate is soluble while silver bromate is not. Upon being heated, bromates do not form perbromates, but rather lose oxygen to form bromides,

$$2KBrO_3 \rightarrow \underline{2KBr} + 3O_2 \uparrow$$

In some cases, both oxygen and bromine are lost with an oxide being formed,

$$2Ca(BrO_3)_2 \rightarrow \underline{2CaO} + 2Br_2 \uparrow + 5O_2 \uparrow$$

As oxidizing agents, the bromates find a limited use both in the laboratory and in industry.

III. IODINE

17. General

Iodine has been known slightly longer than bromine. So far as is known, it was first isolated in 1812 by the French chemist, Courtois, who obtained it from the ashes of burned seaweed. Somewhat later it was named *iodine* (from the Greek word signifying *a violet color*) by Gay-Lussac, who was impressed by the beautiful violet color of the vapor of the new element. The chemistry of iodine and bromine are similar, though not identical.

18. Physical Properties

At about 20° C., iodine is a grayish-black solid with a semimetallic luster. Because of its high vapor pressure, it sublimes readily. Its vapor is dense, and has an intense violet color which becomes blue as the temperature is raised. The formula of the vapor appears to be I_2, but, as the temperature is raised, the diatomic molecules dissociate into their atoms much more readily than do the molecules of the lighter halogens. Lustrous rhombic plates are formed when the vapor is cooled. The density and other physical properties of the element are listed in Table 25. There the solubility in water is listed as being very low. The addition of potassium iodide to the water greatly increases the solubility of the element, for a reason which will be discussed in connection with its chemical properties. Its solubility in alcohol, ether, carbon tetrachloride, carbon disulfide, and a host of other organic liquids is much greater than in plain water. In liquids such as alcohol, C_2H_5OH, water, and ether, $(C_2H_5)_2O$, which contain oxygen in their formulas, its solutions are brown in color, while in liquids which contain no oxygen, its solutions vary with concentration from pink to deep purple. The brown color in liquids of the first type is believed to result from a very weak type of union between solute and solvent.

Free iodine is easily identified because it produces an intense blue coloration when brought in contact with starch paste. This color is believed to be due to the adsorption of iodine on the colloidal particles of starch; iodide ions participate in the reaction, however. When the paste is diluted to transparency and heated, the color disappears, but, upon cooling, it regains its blue color. As little as one part of iodine in 5,000,000 parts of water is said to give the test. In reverse, the test may be used to identify starch.

19. Occurrence

Iodine, while less active chemically than the other members of the halogen family, is still sufficiently active never to be found free in nature. It occurs to about the same extent in the earth's crust as does bromine, and its compounds are widely and thinly distributed. For many years, the chief source of the element has been the sodium iodate, $NaIO_3$, which occurs to the extent of about 0.2 of 1 per cent in the deposits of sodium nitrate of Chile's northern deserts. An important domestic source of iodine is the brine from certain of the California and Louisiana oil wells. Soluble iodides are to be found in sea water, but to a lesser extent than are the bromides. The seaweed known as *kelp* removes iodine from sea water, and when these plants are burned the ash is found to contain appreciable quantities of iodides, principally potassium iodide. Oysters, sponges, and other marine animals are found to be particularly rich in the element. Iodine is essential to all of the higher animals. In man, it occurs principally in the thyroid gland at the base of the neck. The function of this gland is to manufacture the iodine-containing compound known as *thyroxine*, which controls the rate of metabolism of ingested food.

20. Preparation

Sodium iodate remains in the mother liquors when sodium nitrate is crystallized from concentrated solutions of the crude Chile saltpeter. Iodine is precipitated when these liquors are treated with a mixture of sodium sulfite and sodium bisulfite. The precipitate is collected, dried, mixed with a little potassium iodide, and purified by sublimation:

$$2NaIO_3 + 3Na_2SO_3 + 2NaHSO_3 \rightarrow 5Na_2SO_4$$
$$+ H_2O + \underline{I_2}$$

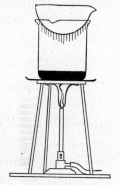

The element is set free by displacement with elementary chlorine from the iodides of oil-well brines. The freed iodine is adsorbed on activated charcoal which, according to the patent taken on the process, is compressed and used as a cathode in an electrolytic cell. The product is collected at the anode and may be further purified by sublimation.

THE LABORATORY PURIFICATION OF IO- DINE BY SUBLIMATION.

Iodine is liberated from the iodides of kelp ash by their oxidation with either free chlorine or a mixture of manganese dioxide and sulfuric acid. If chlorine is used, care must be taken that the proper quantity is employed, for either too much or too little will leave combined iodine in the solution of the ashes:

$$2KI + Cl_2 \rightarrow 2KCl + \underline{I_2}$$
$$2KI + MnO_2 + 3H_2SO_4 \rightarrow 2KHSO_4 + MnSO_4 + 2H_2O + \underline{I_2}$$

In both cases, the crude product is purified by sublimation.

In 1946, the wholesale price of resublimed iodine was about $2 per pound. This price, despite a wartime rise, is a figure considerably lower than that quoted for the years prior to the initiation of domestic production.

Iodine may be prepared in the laboratory from iodates or iodides by the first, third, and fourth of the foregoing procedures.

21. Chemical Properties

Although less active than bromine, iodine enters into reactions a majority of which are counterparts of those of that element. Iodine unites spontaneously with phosphorus, sodium, and a few of the more reactive elements. It combines with many of the less active elements when mixtures of the two are heated.

Such is the case with mixtures of hydrogen and iodine whose union is further aided by the presence of a suitable catalyst, but, even under optimum conditions, the reaction is both slow and reversible. Mercuric iodide, HgI_2, is formed when its constituent elements are rubbed together in a mortar, and iodine chloride, ICl, is formed as a reddish-brown liquid by direct combination.

Free iodine and its aqueous solutions are good oxidizing agents, and standard solutions of iodine are often used in this capacity in quantitative analysis. Free iodine is always titrated with solutions of sodium thiosulfate with starch as an indicator:

$$I_2 + 2Na_2S_2O_3 \rightarrow 2NaI + Na_2S_4O_6$$

Volumetric, quantitative analysis which employs standard solutions of free iodine is usually referred to as *iodimetry*, while analysis which involves the oxidation of iodides to free iodine which is subsequently titrated with standard thiosulfate is frequently referred to as *iodometry*. Because iodine will add to unsaturated organic compounds, it is used in the analysis of unsaturated plant and animal oils. The number of grams of iodine absorbed by 100 g. of a given oil is known as its *iodine number*.

Attention has already been directed to the fact that iodine is much more soluble in aqueous solutions of potassium iodide than it is in pure water. This increased solubility is due to the interaction of the iodide ion and free iodine to form the complex ion I_3^-:

$$I^- + I_2 \rightleftarrows I_3^-$$

The equation indicates that the reaction is reversible, and that, as the free iodine always present is destroyed, more of the I_3^- ion will decompose, tending to restore equilibrium. Ultimately, only iodide ions, I^-, will remain. Complex ions of the type of I_3^-, which are composed of atoms all of which are alike, are known as *homoatomic ions*.

Iodine reacts only slightly with water to form hydriodic acid and hypoiodous acid, but with strong bases it reacts readily to form a mixture of the corresponding salts. As usual for such hydrolyses, the reaction is reversible.

22. Hydrogen Iodide

Pure hydrogen iodide at about 20° C. is a colorless gas of sharp, irritating odor. It may be condensed to a colorless anhydrous liquid which boils at −35.4° C. and freezes at −50.8° C. Like the other hydrogen halides, it is highly soluble in water and therefore fumes in moist air. At 10° C. and standard pressure, one volume of water will dissolve 425 volumes of the dry gas. Aqueous hydrogen iodide is highly ionized, and its solutions are known as hydriodic acid. Like the other hydrohalic acids, this one forms an azeotropic mixture. The constant boiling acid boils at 127° C. under standard pressure, and contains 57 per cent of hydrogen iodide.

Being oxidized to free iodine by sulfuric acid and other oxidizing agents, and because the union of hydrogen and iodine is both slow and reversible, hydrogen iodide is best prepared by methods analogous to those used for the preparation of hydrogen bromide:

$$PI_3 + 3HOH \rightarrow H_3PO_3 + 3HI \uparrow$$
$$I_2 + H_2S \rightarrow \underline{S} + 2HI \uparrow$$

and

$$I_2 + SO_2 + 2HOH \rightarrow H_2SO_4 + 2HI \uparrow$$

Hydriodic acid is the least stable, the most highly ionized, and the strongest reducing agent of the hydrohalic acids; otherwise, its reactions are similar to those of hydrobromic and hydrochloric acids. Its heat of formation is negative, representing an endothermal reaction and indicating less stability than the other hydrogen halides possess. The behavior of gaseous hydrogen iodide is much like that of hydrogen bromide and hydrogen chloride.

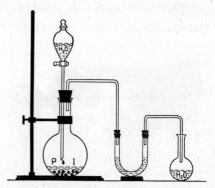

APPARATUS FOR THE LABORATORY PREPARATION OF HYDRIODIC ACID. A small quantity of water contained in the U tube serves to remove free iodine which contaminates the evolved hydrogen iodide gas.

Table 26

THE HYDROGEN HALIDES

Formula	Constant Boiling Aqueous Solutions				Solubility in Water at 1 atm. and 20° C. in moles per liter	Degree of Ionization 0.5 N sol. at 25° C.	Electrode Potentials (Oxidation of Halide to Halogen)
	Boiling Point °C.	Density g./ml.	Per Cent HX	Normality			
HF	120°	1.14	35.37	20.	Decomposes	..	−2.8 v.
HCl	108.6°	1.10	20.22	6.1	11.52	0.762	−1.359 v.
HBr	126°	1.49	47.	8.7	6.05	0.899	−1.065 v.
HI	127°	1.70	57.	7.6	4.46	0.901	−0.535 v.

23. Iodides

A few iodides are prepared by direct union; others are prepared by metatheses involving hydriodic acid. In general, they closely resemble the corresponding bromides and chlorides in appearance and behavior. The majority of iodides are fairly soluble, and some of them are more highly colored than are bromides, chlorides, and fluorides. Those of silver, mercurous mercury, and lead are the least soluble of the iodides, as might be expected. These salts are less soluble than the corresponding ones of either chlorine or bromine. Mercuric iodide, whose color is a brilliant yellowish-red, is only slightly soluble.

Electrode potentials given in the last column of the above table indicate that iodides are easily oxidized to free iodine. Chlorine and bromine are able to liberate iodine because of their strength as oxidizing agents, and the strength of sulfuric and nitric acids as oxidizing agents prevents their use in the preparation of HI from iodides.

SIMPLE GOITER INCIDENCE MAP OF THE UNITED STATES. The shaded area of the map indicates the region of highest incidence of simple goiter and of lowest concentration of iodine compounds. (Courtesy, *J.A.M.A.*, May 24, 1924.)

Silver iodide is used along with larger quantities of silver bromide in the preparation of photographic films, plates, and papers. The organic iodide, CHI_3, known as *iodoform*, is a yellow powder of strong odor which is used as a dusting antiseptic for open wounds. Some iodides, as well as free iodine, are used in the production of certain organic dyestuffs, and a number of inorganic iodides are used in the laboratory. Soluble iodides, including those of sodium and potassium, are used in the treatment of simple goiter.

Simple goiter (enlargement of the thyroid gland) results from a dietetic deficiency of iodine, though it may result from other causes too. The thyroid cannot manufacture thyroxine, the metabolism-controlling hormone, without iodine. When this is lacking in the diet, the gland becomes enlarged from overactivity as it attempts to make something out of nothing, so to speak. Iodine-deficient soils producing iodine-deficient foods are most common in inland and mountainous regions, hence simple goiter is also most common in such regions. In many of the towns and cities of such regions, iodides are added to public water supplies in an effort to reduce the incidence of the disease. Iodized salt containing one part of sodium iodide to 100,000 parts of sodium chloride is a common item at most grocery stores. Iodides and other iodine compounds should be taken only upon the advice of a physician, since too large an intake of iodine may be dangerous. A new drug used in treating goiter is thiouracil, whose use without medical advice and care is highly dangerous. Simple goiter is said to be six times more common among women than among men. The daily requirement of iodine to maintain health in a human adult is estimated to be 0.000002 g.

24. The Positive Oxidation States of Iodine

The action of solutions of strong bases on iodine to form a mixture of an iodide and a hypoiodite has already been mentioned in section 21. In solution, hypoiodites are hydrolyzed to free hypoiodous acid which is weak, unstable, and a good oxidizing agent, though inferior in this capacity to both hypochlorous and hypobromous acids. Solutions of the hypoiodites are also good oxidizing agents, but they are so easily reduced that they undergo autooxidation-reduction upon standing, especially if warmed:

$$3NaIO \rightarrow 2NaI + NaIO_3$$

The hydrolysis of iodine chloride first produces hypoiodous acid, which quickly decomposes into iodic acid and free iodine:

$$5ICl + 3HOH \rightarrow 5HCl + HIO_3 + \underline{2I_2}$$

Most important of the oxygen-containing compounds of iodine are iodic acid, HIO_3, and its salts, which are fairly stable, but which find use as oxidizing agents. The acid may be prepared by the electrolytic oxidation of iodine or by the oxidation of iodine with concentrated nitric acid, free chlorine, or chloric acid:

$$I_2 + 10HNO_3 \rightarrow 2HIO_3 + 10NO_2 + 4H_2O$$
$$I_2 + 5Cl_2 + 6H_2O \rightarrow 2HIO_3 + 10HCl$$

and

$$I_2 + 2HClO_3 \rightarrow 2HIO_3 + Cl_2$$

The last of these reactions illustrates the general principle that elementary iodine will displace chlorine from any of its oxygen-containing compounds forming the corresponding oxygen-containing iodine compound. The pure acid decomposes into its anhydride, iodine pentoxide, upon being heated strongly.

$$2HIO_3 \rightarrow H_2O + I_2O_5$$

The pentoxide is a white solid which readily redissolves to form the acid, but which itself decomposes into its elements if heated above 300° C. It readily absorbs carbon monoxide, and above 160° C. oxidizes this to the dioxide. Because of this ability, it is used in gas-mask canisters and in gas analysis.

Potassium and sodium iodates are used in medicine and in the laboratory. Iodic acid and its salts are more stable than chloric acid and its salts, nevertheless they are still strong oxidizing agents. Iodic acid will not oxidize hydrochloric acid, but it does oxidize hydriodic acid. Use is made of this reaction in iodometry. The addition of an acid to a mixture of an iodate and an iodide liberates the corresponding acids. These then react to liberate iodine which may be titrated in the usual manner:

$$NaIO_3 + 5NaI + 6HCl \rightarrow 6NaCl + HIO_3 + 5HI \rightarrow 6NaCl + 3H_2O + \underline{3I_2}$$

The quantity of acid employed may be calculated from the quantity of iodine liberated, since the equation shows that one atomic weight of iodine is liberated for each equivalent of H^+ ion present.

Concentrated sulfuric acid acts on iodic acid to yield iodine tetroxide, I_2O_4:

$$4HIO_3 \xrightarrow{H_2SO_4} 2I_2O_4 + O_2 \uparrow + 2H_2O$$

With water, the tetroxide reacts to form iodic acid and free iodine:

$$5I_2O_4 + 4H_2O \rightarrow 8HIO_3 + \underline{I_2}$$

The behavior of iodates upon being heated is not uniform; some yield iodides and oxygen; some give oxides, iodine, and oxygen; and others give periodates, iodine, and oxygen. For this reason, periodates are best prepared by the oxidation of iodates. Dry periodates are very stable to heat, but in solution they gradually decompose with an accompanying evolution of oxygen and ozone. Periodic acid and its salts are powerful oxidizing agents in acid solution.

A series of periodic acids having the formula $I_2O_7(H_2O)_n$, where n may be any number from 1 to 7, is known. The oxide I_2O_7 is not known. The fact that more OH groups may surround the iodine atom than surround the chlorine atom in perchloric acid probably is due to the larger size of the former. A majority of the commoner periodates appear to be salts of the acid H_5IO_6, which, upon dehydration, yields the meta acid HIO_4, the iodine analog of $HClO_4$.

25. Analytical Tests for the Halogens

The insolubility of the chlorides, bromides, and iodides of silver, mercurous mercury, and lead has been referred to. These halide ions usually are precipitated as their silver salts, which are white, cream, and yellow in color, respectively. Only the chloride of these silver salts is readily converted into a soluble ammino complex by the action of dilute ammonium hydroxide. The iodide is little affected even by concentrated ammonium hydroxide.

If the three ions are, or may be, present together, they are tested for in the order of their ease of oxidation to the free element. The solution is acidified and then treated with 1 ml. of carbon tetrachloride and a small volume of a fresh solution of potassium nitrite. Free iodine will be displaced if iodides are present, and will dissolve in the tetrachloride to give a pink to purple solution. After all of the iodide has been displaced, extracted with tetrachloride, and discarded, a fresh portion of tetrachloride and a few milliliters of a very dilute solution of potassium permanganate is added. If present, bromide ions will be oxidized to free bromine, which will dissolve in the tetrachloride layer, coloring it yellow to brownish-red. After the removal of all bromides, chloride ions may be precipitated as silver chloride by the addition of a few drops of a solution of silver nitrate.

Halogens of the oxygen-containing compounds are best identified by reduction to the free element.

Fluorides may be precipitated either as calcium fluoride or as lead chloro-fluoride, $PbClF$, or converted into silicon tetrafluoride, which is identified as described in the test for silicon (cf. section 18, Chapter 18).

(*See Appendix for Exercises*)

COLLATERAL READINGS

Badger and Baker: *Inorganic Chemical Technology*, New York, McGraw-Hill Book Co., 1941.

Emeleus: Fluorine, *J. Chem. Soc.*, 441 (1942).

Latimer and Hildebrand: *Reference Book of Inorganic Chemistry*, New York, The Macmillan Co., 1941.

Morgan and Burstall: *Inorganic Chemistry*, Cambridge, W. Heffer & Sons, Ltd., 1938.

Robertson: New American iodine industry, *Ind. and Eng. Chem.*, **26**, 374 (1934).

Stewart: Bromine from sea water, *Ind. and Eng. Chem.*, **26**, 361 (1934).

Weeks: *Discovery of the Elements*, 5th ed., Mack Printing Co., 1945.

Yost and Russell: *Systematic Inorganic Chemistry*, New York, Prentice-Hall, Inc., 1944.

Iodine supply and incidence of endemic goiter, *J. Am. Med. Assn.*, **96**, 20, 599 (1931).

ROBERT WILHELM BUNSEN

(1811–1899, German)

Upon mention of Bunsen, the average student thinks immediately of the laboratory burner which bears his name. It should be realized that he was also the inventor of many other pieces of laboratory equipment, a brilliant research worker, and a great teacher. After his graduation from the University of Göttingen in 1828, he held professorships in a number of universities before going to the University of Heidelburg where he taught and carried on his investigations from 1852 to 1889. With Kirchoff he invented the spectroscope, and by its use discovered the elements rubidium and cesium. His other studies include work on the reactions of the blast furnace and the analysis of gases, investigations of photochemical reactions, the discovery of cacodyl and the elucidation of its relationships, and a host of other problems. Many men who later attained fame in the field of chemistry were at one time or another students of Bunsen, and Tyndall has characterized him as the ideal university professor.

27

Carbon and Its Compounds

1. Introduction

In the periodic chart of the elements, carbon is to be found in the second period at the head of the IV A column. Thus situated, halfway between the elements which are active electron-losers and those which are active electron-gainers, its properties are intermediate between those of a metal and those of a nonmetal. One of its allotropes somewhat resembles a metal in physical appearance and behavior, while another has the definite physical characteristics of a nonmetal. Chemically, its behavior is also intermediate, for in most of its compounds it is linked to other atoms by shared pairs of electrons rather than by electrical attraction resulting from a gain or loss of electrons.

Carbon has the atomic number 6, and the distribution of its extranuclear electrons between the first two main energy levels is 2, 4, respectively. Since it shares its valence electrons in most of its compounds, its common valence is 4, but in various ones of its unions it exhibits oxidation numbers from -4 to $+4$. The four valence electrons are further divided between the first two sublevels of the second main level, 2 and 2; hence, there are formed a number of relatively unstable compounds in which only the two 2_1 electrons are involved, and in which the oxidation number is 2. With the exception of its formation of a few compounds of this latter type, carbon is best thought of as tending to react by forming four shared pairs of electrons. The element is an isotopic mixture of the atoms whose weights are 12 and 13; the former type predominates.

The members of the IV A family are carbon, silicon, germanium, tin, and lead. Carbon, having the lightest and smallest atoms of any of these elements, is naturally the most nonmetallic member of the family, yet is not pronouncedly nonmetallic; hence, metallic properties very shortly appear as one descends the column. Silicon is nonmetallic in character, but germanium, tin, and lead are metallic in physical appearance and properties though amphoteric in certain of their chemical properties. The chemistry of silicon was discussed at some length in Chapter 18; that of the remaining elements of the family will be considered in Chapter 31.

Carbon differs markedly from silicon in its chemical behavior, as antici-pated from its membership in the second period. For example, the silanes and other compounds in which silicon atoms are linked to each other are very unstable, yet compounds of carbon in which its atoms are linked together by shared electron pairs are quite stable. In fact, the ability of carbon atoms to form stable unions with each other is perhaps the most noteworthy and generally important chemical property of the element, for it is this ability which accounts for the existence of over 300,000 known carbon compounds and makes neces-sary a separate branch of chemistry for the study of the element and its deriva-tives. The origin and present significance of the term *organic chemistry* were discussed in section 12 of Chapter 1. This material should be reviewed at this time.

All compounds which contain carbon are, strictly speaking, organic com-pounds, but a number of them are of mineral origin, others contain metals, and still others because of their preparation or use, or both, are related to inorganic substances. The compounds which fall into one or more of the fore-going categories will be considered in this chapter; these will include prin-cipally binary compounds and derivatives of the oxides. Because of the space required to discuss them in a manner to give an adequate understanding, the great majority of the compounds of carbon must be neglected for the present. Organic chemistry is a somewhat involved subject, but it is a fascinating study, as well as one of paramount importance. The general principles set forth in this text apply to organic and all other branches of chemistry, and should be mastered thoroughly by all who would pursue further their study of any phase of the science.

A MODEL OF THE CRYSTAL LATTICE OF DIAMOND.

2. Physical Properties

Elementary carbon resembles the other solid nonmetals in that it exists in a variety of allotropic modifications. Notable among these are the poly-morphic varieties known, respectively, as diamond and graphite. Natural diamonds are found as octahedral crystals which are colorless when pure, though they are often discolored by the presence of traces of impurities. Diamond has a density of 3.5 g./ml., and a high index of refraction. It is a good conductor of heat but a poor conductor of electricity. Of special note is the fact that it is the hardest substance known to man. Be-cause of its hardness and high index of refraction, it is especially valued as a gem stone. The many facets of the gem stones are not those of the natural crystals, but have been produced by cutting and polishing the natural stones in order to increase the quantity of light which will be reflected, and hence the "brilliance" of the stone. Diamond dust must be used to grind and polish the facets.

The melting point of diamond is in excess of 3500° C. This high transition temperature and the properties of nonconductiveness, hardness, and resistance to cleavage are all related to the structure of the crystal of this allotrope. The illustration on p. 538 shows that each atom in the cubic diamond crystal is closely surrounded by four other carbon atoms. The bond between each pair of atoms is a shared pair of electrons; thus, there are no loosely held electrons to conduct a current. The atoms are so firmly bound to each other that much heat is required to disrupt (melt) the crystal lattice. Cleavage is made difficult by the peculiar interlocking pattern of the atoms. Planes of cleavage may be found only parallel to the natural faces of the stones, and the difficulty of splitting such valuable stones makes an expert splitter a highly paid technician. Hardness is undoubtedly due to the firmness of union of the atoms and to their interlocking pattern. It has been pointed out previously that the relative hardness of two substances is determined by rubbing them together; the one which remains unscratched is natu-

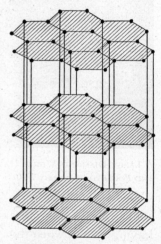

A MODEL OF THE CRYSTAL LATTICE OF GRAPHITE.

rally the harder. Usually Mohs' scale of hardness is used for purposes of comparison. It consists of 10 arbitrarily chosen minerals of varying hardness which were assigned numbers from 1 to 10. The scale is misleading, however, since the difference in hardness between successive minerals is not equal. The arbitrary and actual scales are shown graphically on p. 540.

Physically, graphite contrasts strongly with diamond. It is gray-black in color, and exists as soft, flaky crystals of the hexagonal system. Its density is 2.25 g./ml., and it is a fair conductor of both heat and electricity. It sublimes in the neighborhood of 3500° C. under standard pressure, and is highly resistant to oxidation. Examination of the diagram of the crystal lattice of graphite, shown above, reveals that in its structure each carbon atom is bonded to three other carbon atoms which are equidistant and which lie in the same plane. These carbon atoms form a pattern of interlocking, six-membered rings. Parallel to such a plane are similar planes which are attached to each other by the fourth valence electrons not used in forming the ring systems of the planes. The distance between these planes is more than twice that between atoms in a given layer, hence the binding between adjacent planes is weak and the crystal is readily split into thin, smooth flakes. Electrical conductivity is accounted for by the mobility of the electrons held loosely between the planes.

A LARGE DIAMOND WHICH HAS BEEN CUT AND POLISHED. (Courtesy, American Museum of Natural History.)

In addition to diamond and graphite, many other physical modifications of carbon are known. Collectively, these are generally known as *amorphous carbon*. Actually, these varieties are not amorphous but are made up of tiny crystals so small that their form is not apparent to the naked eye. Impurities, whose quantity varies, are usually present. Prominent members of this group are lampblack, carbon black, soot, charcoal, animal charcoal, coal, and coke, all of which demonstrate their impurity by leaving an ash when they are burned. The physical properties of these different varieties of carbon vary widely and are closely related to the state of subdivision of the sample. Certain specially prepared charcoals of high porosity possess the property of adsorbing gases, alkaloids, organic acids, and colloidally suspended coloring matters and metals. Such charcoal is usually described as *activated* and may serve as a catalyst in certain reactions.

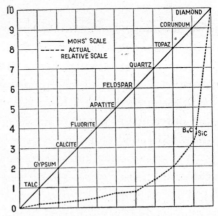

MOHS' SCALE OF HARDNESS AND THE ACTUAL SCALE.

None of the various forms of carbon is soluble in water nor in the other common liquid solvents. The so-called amorphous varieties and graphite will dissolve, however, in molten metals, especially iron.

3. *Occurrence*

Diamonds are found in a number of different places in the world, but their distribution is not wide nor are they too plentiful. The richest known source is in the Belgian Congo, but the Union of South Africa and Brazil also have important mines. Russia, India, Australia, Borneo, and the United States also produce a few stones. The only domestic diamond mines are located in southwestern Arkansas. The stones produced there are of good hardness and purity.

Important deposits of graphite are found on two islands of the Indian Ocean—Ceylon and Madagascar. Other deposits are to be found in the United States, Canada, Mexico, Italy, Russia, and Germany. Domestic production of this material (it is usually contaminated with impurities) is confined largely to the state of New York.

While coal contains many other substances, it also contains much free carbon. It is found widely distributed over the earth and was formed by the slow decomposition of vegetable matter which flourished in prehistoric eras. At first, peat was formed by the decomposition which occurred in the swamps and bogs where the plants had grown. Later, as the result of earthquakes and other telluric processes, the peat beds were buried and decomposition was continued underground in the absence of air. Successive products of decomposition are lignite (brown coal), bituminous coal (soft coal), and anthracite (hard coal).

Carbon in combination is widely distributed in many different compounds. Notable among its inorganic compounds are the slightly soluble carbonates of calcium, magnesium, zinc, and a number of other metals. As *limestone*, calcium carbonate, $CaCO_3$, it is found in every state in the Union and in most of the countries of the world. It also exists in the forms known as *marble*, and *calcite*, and mixed with magnesium carbonate in *dolomite*. Magnesium carbonate is the principal constituent of *magnesite*, while zinc carbonate is found as the mineral *smithsonite* which is an important ore of zinc. Natural gas and mineral oils contain various binary compounds of carbon and hydrogen (the hydrocarbons), and all plant and animal bodies and the products derived from them are compounds of carbon.

4. *Preparation*

No diamonds of any commercial value have ever been manufactured, though Moissan and later investigators are credited with having produced stones of microscopic size by dissolving carbon in molten iron, quickly chilling the mass, and then removing the iron by causing it to react with strong mineral acids.

Graphite is manufactured by a process developed by Acheson (cf. section 10, Chapter 18). When a powerful current is passed through a mixture of ground anthracite coal, or coke, mixed with tar, sand, and some iron oxide placed between the electrodes of an electric furnace, graphite is slowly formed. The sand, iron oxide, and natural impurities serve as a catalyst for the process. Synthetic graphite is gradually displacing the natural product in world markets.

Charcoal is in demand throughout the world for a great many purposes. For hundreds of years, its preparation and distribution have afforded employ-

THE MANUFACTURE OF WOOD CHARCOAL IN THE OLD-FASHIONED MANNER.

ment for many people in many countries. The old method of manufacture (which, incidentally, is still used in most countries which are not highly industrialized) consists of igniting a pile of hardwood which has been carefully stacked to leave a central vent and then covered with sod and dirt. The combustion of the volatile material driven from the wood supplies sufficient heat to complete the removal of the remaining volatile material. In modern plants, the stacks of hardwood which have been exposed for a number of weeks to sun and air are loaded on small iron cars which are run into a tunnel-like metallic retort that can be heated to a high temperature. The volatile matter driven off is led through a condenser in which a portion of the distillate is converted to an acidic, watery fluid known as *pyroligneous acid;* a second portion yields a black tar; and a third portion consists of gases which are not condensed and which are burned to heat the retort. From pyroligneous acid, acetic acid, $HC_2H_3O_2$, wood alcohol (methanol), CH_3OH, and acetone, $(CH_3)_2CO$, are obtained. The charcoal obtained amounts to about one-fourth of the weight of the original wood. The purest charcoal known is obtained by heating sugar in the absence of air and then in the presence of chlorine. Coconut shells, peach seeds, and certain kinds of sawdust are used to prepare *activated charcoal.*

Animal charcoal is formed by heating bones or dried blood in the absence of air. The charcoal made from bones (bone black) is very porous, highly adsorptive, and contains only about 10 per cent of carbon. It is widely used as an adsorbent, especially in the clarification of solutions of brown sugar. White sugar crystallizes from the decolorized solution. The distillate from bones is known as bone oil or Dippel's oil, and is a source of quinoline and other organic chemicals.

Coke is prepared by heating coal in the absence of air to drive off its volatile material. While not pure carbon, the product is important because of its high content of that element. Anthracite coal contains little volatile material, while bituminous coal contains a much larger, though variable, percentage. Originally, coke was made in the so-called beehive ovens, and the volatile material which issued through the vent hole in the top was either burned or permitted to escape, becoming a nuisance to all who lived in the vicinity. The wasted material was of greater value than the coke formed. Today, steel retorts known as by-product ovens are used. They give a better yield of coke than did the beehive ovens and from them are recovered the evolved

DIAGRAM OF THE CROSS-SECTION OF A BEEHIVE COKE OVEN.

tar and gases. The condensed tar yields benzene, naphthalene, phenol, and many other important industrial organic chemicals. The uncondensed gases are passed through sulfuric acid, which removes ammonia by uniting with it to form ammonium sulfate. About 50 per cent of the remaining gas is hydrogen and some 30 to 35 per cent is methane, CH_4. This mixture is used as fuel for heating the retorts, etc. By-product ovens were not common in the United States until after World War I, since, prior to that time, Germany had enjoyed a virtual world monopoly of coal tar and its derivatives. Coke ovens usually operate at temperatures between 900° to 1200° C., but lower temperatures (500° to 700° C.) are reported to yield larger quantities of tar.

When the flames of burning carboniferous material are cooled, small particles of unburned carbon are formed which collect in chimneys as flaky deposits known as soot. The chimneys of kerosene lamps often become smudged with deposits of a fine soot known as *lampblack*. Commercially, lampblack is produced in large quantities by rotating a water-cooled drum or disk through an oil flame. A very fine soot known as *carbon black* is produced by burning natural gas (mostly methane, CH_4) in an insufficient quantity of air. Both of these products are in great demand industrially.

5. *Chemical Properties*

All modifications of carbon show very little tendency to react at ordinary temperatures. As the temperature is raised, activity increases, and all forms are quite active at the temperature of the electric arc.

Most important of the reactions of the element is its union with oxygen to form either the monoxide or the dioxide, depending upon the relative quantities of oxygen available, and to liberate heat:

$$2C + O_2 \rightarrow 2CO + 53,360 \text{ cal.}$$
$$C + O_2 \rightarrow CO_2 + 94,380 \text{ cal.}$$

Because of the large quantities of heat liberated by the conversion of carbon to its dioxide, it and its combustible compounds find a wide use as fuels; in fact, they constitute almost our only fuels. The reaction is also of importance in the liberation of metals and other elements from their oxides. Many oxides when heated strongly with carbon relinquish their oxygen to it, hence it is widely used as a cheap, commercial reducing agent. Such use of coke and other forms of the element has been mentioned in preceding chapters, and will be mentioned again. The water-gas reaction may be cited as a single specific example:

$$C + H_2O \xrightarrow{\Delta} CO \uparrow + H_2 \uparrow$$

Diamond reacts with oxygen only when heated to redness, and graphite is even more stable, but the other forms of carbon, especially when finely divided, are rather easily ignited. The behavior of diamond and graphite with wet oxidizing agents reverses the above situation, for hot mixtures of nitric acid and potassium chlorate do not attack the former, but slowly convert the latter into a greenish-yellow solid, known as graphitic acid. Charcoal and other *amorphous* modifications are speedily attacked by these reagents which convert them to oxides.

At the temperature of the electric furnace, carbon unites with many metals and with some of the nonmetals to form carbides. Calcium carbide, which is usually made by heating calcium oxide and carbon, is prepared in great quantity for the manufacture of acetylene, C_2H_2, and the carbides of silicon and boron find wide use as abrasives. The carbides of the metals tungsten and tantalum are also of great hardness. The carbides of arsenic, antimony, tin, and lead are not known. A majority of the metallic carbides are easily hydrolyzed, and upon hydrolysis most of them yield methane. The behavior of the carbide of calcium in this respect is, therefore, unusual:

$$Al_4C_3 + 12HCl \rightarrow 4AlCl_3 + 3CH_4 \uparrow$$
$$CaC_2 + 2HCl \rightarrow CaCl_2 + C_2H_2 \uparrow$$

Even at elevated temperatures, hydrogen and carbon react but slightly, producing a mixture of various hydrocarbons. When hydrogen is passed through an electric arc struck between carbon rods, acetylene is the principal product. The yield of hydrocarbons from the union of the two elements is greatly increased by the use of pressure and a catalyst as well as heat. This, in essence, is the Bergius process which has been used commercially in Germany, where it was developed, and in England. A test plant using this method has been authorized by the United States Congress and is expected to be in operation by 1948. The oily mixture of hydrocarbons produced resembles natural petroleum in many respects.

Carbon does not unite directly with chlorine. Carbon tetrachloride is usually prepared from carbon disulfide, whose commercial preparation from the elements was referred to in section 5 of Chapter 21.

6. Carbon Disulfide

This compound is a colorless, very volatile, foul-smelling liquid whose boiling point is $46.3°$ C. and whose freezing point is $-108.6°$ C. The unpleasant odor is caused by the presence of traces of impurities. The liquid has an unusually high index of refraction, is insoluble in water, and is extremely inflammable. A dish of the liquid floating on hot water will shortly ignite, even in the absence of open flames. Products of combustion are the dioxides of the constituent elements:

$$CS_2 + 3O_2 \rightarrow CO_2 \uparrow + 2SO_2 \uparrow$$

Its instability is more clearly understood when it is known that its formation is highly endothermal:

$$C + 2S_r + 22,000 \text{ cal.} \rightarrow CS_2$$

Another peculiar property of the liquid is its ability to cause a violent and painful itching and burning of skin on which any hair grows. It is an excellent and widely used solvent for sulfur, phosphorus, iodine, and a wide variety of organic compounds, including fats, waxes, and rubber. Because of its volatility and the toxicity of its vapors, it is often used to exterminate rats, mice, prairie dogs, and other burrowing animals. It is also used to kill moths. Its major

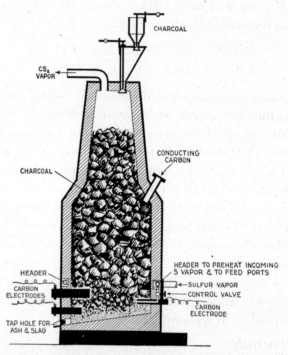

An Electric Furnace for the Manufacture of Carbon Disulfide. Sulfur vapor is admitted through ports near the bottom of the furnace. Resistance offered by the carbon to the passage of the current maintains the requisite temperature. Switches which control the electrodes in both pairs and groups make possible the regulation of the temperature. The lower electrodes near the tap hole are to prevent the freezing of the slag and ash and to foster their easy removal.

uses are in the preparation of carbon tetrachloride, in the vulcanizing of rubber, and in the manufacture of rayon by the viscose process.

7. Carbon Tetrachloride

Dry chlorine led into carbon disulfide to which a little iodine or antimony trichloride has been added reacts readily with it to form carbon tetrachloride and sulfur monochloride. The two liquid products are separated by fractional distillation:

$$CS_2 + 3Cl_2 \rightarrow CCl_4 + S_2Cl_2$$

The tetrachloride is a colorless, nonflammable liquid of pleasant odor and moderate volatility. Its boiling point is 76.8° C., its freezing point is − 23° C., and its density is 1.595 g./ml. at 20° C. It is an excellent solvent for the halogens and for a wide variety of organic compounds including oils, fats, waxes, and greases. This property, coupled with its nonflammability, makes it an especially effective and safe solvent for the dry cleaning of clothing. When so used, it leaves little residual odor. Large quantities of the fluid are used also in the small plunger type of hand fire extinguisher. It evaporates quickly in the presence of heat, forming a blanket of vapor which, being heavier than air, settles around the fire, smothering it. Its use in extinguishing fires can be dangerous, however, since its hot vapor reacts with water vapor to form carbonyl chloride (commonly called *phosgene*):

$$CCl_4 + H_2O \rightarrow 2HCl \uparrow + COCl_2 \uparrow$$

This substance, which is a colorless, almost odorless gas (b. p. 8.3° C.) at about 20° C., is extremely toxic.

8. Oxides of Carbon

Three oxides of carbon are known: the dioxide, CO_2; the monoxide, CO; and the suboxide, C_3O_2. Of these, the last is of little importance. At about 20° C., it is a colorless gas which is easily condensed to a colorless liquid whose boiling point is 7° C. It is prepared by the careful dehydration of malonic acid (propanedioic acid), whose anhydride it is:

$$H_2C_3H_2O_4 \rightleftarrows 2H_2O + C_3O_2$$

It reacts readily with either hot or cold water, to reform the acid. Every atom in its molecules apparently is sharing two electrons with every other atom to which it is united:

$$\overset{\circ\circ}{\underset{\circ\circ}{O}} \overset{\circ}{\underset{\circ}{C}} \overset{\bullet}{\underset{\bullet}{C}} \overset{\circ}{\underset{\circ}{C}} \overset{\circ\circ}{\underset{\circ\circ}{O}} \quad \text{or} \quad O{=}C{=}C{=}C{=}O$$

This is a very unusual combination. Such a structure, naturally, would be highly unstable because of the repulsion of the like electrical fields of the shared electron pairs.

9. Physical Properties of Carbon Monoxide

Under ordinary conditions, carbon monoxide is a gas of no color and almost no odor. Its density of 1.250 g./l. shows it to be just slightly lighter than air, and its solubility in water is slight, 2.5 ml. in 100 ml. of water at 19° C. That it is liquefied only with difficulty is shown by its critical temperature of −139.5° C. The liquid boils at −190° C. and freezes at −207° C.

10. *Preparation of Carbon Monoxide*

Whenever carbon or carbonaceous compounds are burned in a limited supply of air or oxygen, carbon monoxide is always one of the products, hence it is to be found in the exhaust gases of internal combustion engines and in the flue gases of "damped" stoves and furnaces. Industrially, it is usually manufactured by the water-gas reaction (*q.v.*) or by burning coke in a limited quantity

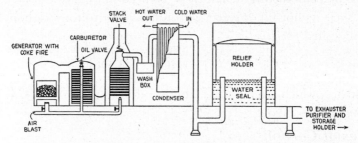

APPARATUS FOR THE MANUFACTURE OF CARBURETED WATER GAS. Coke is burned in the generator to preheat the carburetor and the superheater. When all have been heated, steam is admitted at the bottom of the generator and oil is admitted to the carburetor through the valve. The gas which emerges from the superheater is passed through the water of the wash box for purification, cooled in the condenser, and stored in the tank (Relief Holder), whence it is pumped by an exhaust pump through the purifier and the station meter to the mains for distribution. This is the apparatus as used originally.

of air. The product of the latter of these processes is essentially a mixture of nitrogen (from the air) and carbon monoxide, and is known generally as *producer gas*. The monoxide is best prepared in the laboratory by heating either formic acid (methanoic acid) or oxalic acid (ethanedioic acid) with a dehydrating agent such as concentrated sulfuric acid:

$$HCHO_2 \xrightarrow[H_2SO_4]{\Delta} H_2O + CO \uparrow$$

$$H_2C_2O_4 \xrightarrow[H_2SO_4]{\Delta} H_2O + CO \uparrow + CO_2 \uparrow$$

In the latter process, the carbon dioxide also formed may be removed by passing the evolved gases through a washbottle containing a strong solution of sodium hydroxide.

Carbon dioxide may be reduced to the monoxide by passing it over metals (all but the least active) which have been heated to high temperatures. Since the dioxide is prone to be stable even at advanced temperatures, yields obtained by this method are likely to be poor.

11. Chemical Properties of Carbon Monoxide

At ordinary temperatures, carbon monoxide is relatively inactive with respect to most substances, but when warmed or when a suitable catalyst is added, it manifests a rather high degree of activity. This activity is associated with the intermediate oxidation state of carbon in the compound. It would appear from the formula of the substance that in its molecules carbon is using only two of its four valence electrons, and hence might readily react with other substances which would assist it in attaining an inert gas structure. The behavior of the molecule is, in general, in accord with this idea, although no single electronic formula seems to be in agreement with all of the observed properties.

The gas burns readily in air with a pale blue flame, forming the dioxide and liberating much heat:

$$2CO + O_2 \rightarrow 2CO_2 + 135,400 \text{ cal.}$$

This is the basis of its use both as fuel and as a reducing agent. It is used industrially as a reducing agent in the refining of the oxides of iron, copper, and various other elements (cf. silicon):

$$Fe_2O_3 + 3CO \rightarrow 2Fe + 3CO_2 \uparrow$$

Although it may be prepared by the dehydration of formic acid, carbon monoxide does not react with water to form the acid, but under a pressure of several atmospheres and at a temperature of 200° C. it will react with strong bases to yield their formates:

$$CO + NaOH \xrightarrow[6 \text{ atm.}]{200° C} HCOONa(\text{or } NaCHO_2)$$

The gas combines directly with a number of metals to form compounds known as *carbonyls*. Iron, cobalt, and nickel are especially active in this respect. Iron pentacarbonyl, $Fe(CO)_5$, is a yellow liquid; cobalt tricarbonyl, $Co_2(CO)_6$, is a black solid; cobalt tetracarbonyl, $Co_2(CO)_8$, is an orange-colored crystalline solid; and nickel carbonyl is a colorless, volatile, inflammable liquid whose boiling point is 43° C. The formation of such compounds is favored by a high pressure of the gas. Nickel carbonyl is formed when carbon monoxide is passed over the finely divided metal maintained at 30° C. and is of considerable importance in the refining of the metal by the Mond process.

The absorption of carbon monoxide by either ammoniacal or HCl solutions of cuprous chloride, CuCl, is accounted for by the fact that with these solutions it forms the rather unstable complexes $[Cu(CO)NH_3]^+$ and $[Cu(CO)Cl_2]^-$ respectively. These solutions are used in gas analysis for the removal of carbon monoxide from gaseous mixtures.

The action of the gas on iodine pentoxide has been referred to (cf. section 24, Chapter 26):

$$5CO + I_2O_5 \rightarrow 5CO_2 + \underline{I_2}$$

The iodine liberated may be titrated with standard thiosulfate and the quantity of carbon monoxide calculated from the data thus obtained.

Also referred to in a preceding chapter is the union of carbon monoxide and hydrogen under the influence of pressure and a catalyst to form methanol (wood alcohol):

$$2H_2 + CO \rightleftarrows CH_3OH$$

Another catalytic process which employs the same starting materials is the Fischer-Tropsch process by which a mixture of hydrocarbons somewhat resembling petroleum is prepared. The process has been used in Germany and other countries for the manufacture of gasoline and other hydrocarbon products, and the future construction in the United States of a test plant utilizing the method has been authorized by Congress.

The gas unites directly with chlorine in the presence of either ultraviolet light or a suitable catalyst to form carbonyl chloride (phosgene):

$$CO + Cl_2 \rightarrow COCl_2$$

Common practice is to pass a mixture of the reacting gases heated to about 200° C. over a bed of activated charcoal. As previously stated, carbonyl chloride is an extremely toxic gas. It was used extensively in World War I, though not too satisfactorily, as a poison gas. It is only slightly soluble in water, but is gradually hydrolyzed to carbon dioxide and hydrochloric acid:

$$COCl_2 + H_2O \rightarrow CO_2 \uparrow + 2HCl$$

It finds considerable use in the preparation of dyes.

The toxicity of carbon monoxide results from its ability to form a rather stable compound with the hemoglobin of the blood. Having combined with the monoxide, the hemoglobin can no longer combine with oxygen, whose distribution is its normal function. Victims of monoxide poisoning therefore die of a kind of internal suffocation. The poison is especially insidious since it has no color, no taste, and almost no odor. Early symptoms of such poisoning are headache and nausea. One volume of the gas in 500 of air will produce unconsciousness in about an hour, and one part in 100 parts of air is reported to be rapidly fatal. Inhalation of oxygen containing about 5 per cent of carbon dioxide is the best antidote.

Gas masks containing activated charcoal are of little value for use in an atmosphere of carbon monoxide. Because of its low critical temperature, little of the gas is absorbed. A catalyst developed by chemists of the Johns Hopkins University and the University of California and known as *hopcalite* is used in carbon monoxide gas masks. The catalyst contains manganese dioxide with smaller quantities of the oxides of copper and cobalt, and brings about the conversion of CO to CO_2. Considerable investigational work has been done on the problem of attaching catalytic chambers to the exhaust systems of automobile engines for the purpose of eliminating the evolution of the monoxide, and it now appears entirely likely that within a relatively short time many cars will be so equipped by their manufacturers. Canary birds are especially susceptible to monoxide poisoning, so they are often used in mines and elsewhere to indicate dangerous concentrations of the gas. Filter paper soaked in a solution of palladous chloride quickly becomes black in the presence of an appreciable concentration of the gas.

12. *Physical Properties of Carbon Dioxide*

Carbon dioxide is a colorless, odorless gas whose taste, due to its dissolving in water to form a weak acid, is slightly sour. Its density of 1.977 g./l., or 44.28 g./22.4 l., indicates that it is approximately 1.5 times as dense as air. It is fairly soluble in water, 90 ml. dissolving in 100 ml. of water at 20° C. The critical temperature of the gas is 31.1° C., hence it is fairly easily liquefied. Cylinders of the liquid are a common article of commerce. The liquid freezes at −56.6° C. under a pressure of 5.2 atmospheres to a snowy white solid which, because of its high vapor pressure and consequent ability to sublime, is commonly known as *dry ice*. The sublimation temperature of the solid under standard pressure is −78.5° C.

13. *Preparation of Carbon Dioxide*

The principal industrial sources of carbon dioxide are the complete combustion of carbon and carbonaceous fuels, the fermentation of various sugars and starches, and the calcining of limestone. Carbon dioxide is a by-product of each of these processes. In the first case, the heat evolved is the primary consideration; in the second, alcohol is the principal product; and in the third, lime is the more valuable resultant:

$$C + O_2 \rightarrow CO_2 \uparrow + \text{heat}$$
$$C_6H_{12}O_6 \rightarrow 2C_2H_5OH + 2CO_2 \uparrow$$

and

$$CaCO_3 \rightleftarrows \underline{CaO} + CO_2 \uparrow$$

The gas is most easily prepared in the laboratory by the action of an acid upon the carbonate of calcium or upon other carbonates or bicarbonates. Fairly large quantities are easily prepared by the action of hydrochloric acid on marble or limestone chips contained in a Kipp generator. The unstable carbonic acid first formed rapidly decomposes into the gas and water:

$$CaCO_3 + 2HCl \rightarrow CaCl_2 + H_2CO_3 \rightarrow CaCl_2 + H_2O + CO_2 \uparrow$$

Carbon dioxide is exhaled by all of the higher animals, and during the hours of darkness is given off by green plants. The decay and fermentation of all organic matter forms varying quantities of the gas. It may be obtained also by heating a wide variety of metallic carbonates and bicarbonates:

$$2NaHCO_3 \xrightarrow{\Delta} Na_2CO_3 + H_2O + CO_2 \uparrow$$

Many natural spring waters contain dissolved carbon dioxide, and natural wells yielding the gas are found in Colorado, California, New Mexico, and other states, and also in Mexico, Italy, and a number of other countries. The solid may be prepared by tying a canvas bag over the valve of a cylinder of the liquid, inverting the cylinder, and opening the valve. Evaporation of some of the liquid sufficiently reduces the temperature of the remainder to cause it to freeze.

14. *Chemical Properties of Carbon Dioxide*

Carbon dioxide, being highly exothermal in its formation, is quite stable with respect to heat. Even at 2000° C., it is only 1.8 per cent dissociated into oxygen and the monoxide:

$$2CO_2 \overset{\Delta}{\rightleftharpoons} 2CO \uparrow + O_2 \uparrow$$

If some active substance which will combine with the oxygen evolved is present, the equilibrium is displaced and the reaction may proceed to completion. The most active metals may remove all of the oxygen, leaving only carbon. Carbon dioxide thus may act as an oxidizing agent with active reducing agents at high temperatures. With zinc or carbon, the product is carbon monoxide; with magnesium, it is free carbon; and with sodium or potassium, the metallic carbonate and free carbon are apt to be formed:

$$Zn + CO_2 \rightarrow \underline{ZnO} + CO \uparrow$$
$$C + CO_2 \rightarrow 2CO \uparrow$$
$$2Mg + CO_2 \rightarrow \underline{2MgO} + \underline{C}$$

and

$$4Na + 3CO_2 \rightarrow \underline{2Na_2CO_3} + \underline{C}$$

The preceding section showed the pyrolytic decomposition of calcium carbonate to be reversible. The same is true of many other carbonates, hence it may be said that carbon dioxide unites with metallic oxides to form the corresponding carbonates.

When the dioxide dissolves in water, it forms the weak and very slightly stable carbonic acid:

$$CO_2 + H_2O \rightleftharpoons H_2CO_3$$

It unites with strong bases to form carbonates and bicarbonates:

$$CO_2 + NaOH \rightarrow NaHCO_3$$

and

$$CO_2 + 2NaOH \rightarrow Na_2CO_3 + H_2O$$

It has been stated that green plants may convert carbon dioxide and water to a variety of starches and sugars. Ultraviolet light and chlorophyll, the green coloring matter of the plant, are necessary for the functioning of the process. The gas is not a poison to human beings and other of the higher animals, though it will not sustain life and in the absence of sufficient oxygen may cause suffocation. It has been mentioned that about 5 per cent of the gas when mixed with oxygen seems to serve as a slight stimulant to respiration.

15. Carbonic Acid

Carbonic acid is very weak—in fact, it is so weak that its aqueous solutions, known popularly as *soda water*, may be and are drunk with impunity in a great variety of carbonated beverages. In the second place, it is a hypothetical acid. Its stability is so slight that all attempts to concentrate its solutions are unsuccessful, yet when these are treated with strong bases carbonates or bicarbonates are formed. This behavior indicates that, despite being weak, the acid is, nevertheless, dibasic. As might be anticipated, the second degree of ionization is extremely slight. The primary and secondary ionization constants are 4.3×10^{-7} and 4.7×10^{-11}, respectively. At normal pressure, the saturated aqueous solution of the dioxide has an H^+ ion concentration of about $0.0001\ M$. It is this manifestly acidic character of the dioxide which permits it to react with basic oxides and hydroxides to form salts. In the analysis of gaseous mixtures, carbon dioxide is usually absorbed in solutions of strong bases or by solids such as sodium hydroxide or soda-lime (a mixture of NaOH and CaO).

16. Carbonates and Bicarbonates

Since carbonic acid is so weak, one would expect the existence of only the carbonates and bicarbonates of the strong bases, but because so many of the metallic carbonates are but slightly soluble, a wide variety of them is known. It will be recalled that the formation of an insoluble substance shifts the equilibrium to the right, thus permitting the metathesis to go to completion. The most readily soluble carbonates are those of ammonium and the metals of the I A family. All carbonates are soluble in acid because of the instability of carbonic acid with respect to decomposition into gaseous CO_2 (cf. the action of HCl on $CaCO_3$). The bicarbonates of only ammonium and the metals of the I A family are stable in the dry condition.

The bicarbonates of all the I A metals, save lithium, are less soluble than the corresponding normal carbonates; the opposite is true of the carbonates and bicarbonates of lithium and the metals of the II A family. The insolubility of calcium carbonate furnishes the basis for the common qualitative test for carbon dioxide, which consists of passing the gas into a saturated solution of calcium hydroxide, whereupon a milky precipitate forms:

$$Ca(OH)_2 + CO_2 \rightarrow \underline{CaCO_3} + H_2O$$

If an excess of the gas is used, the precipitate may redissolve as a result of the conversion of the calcium carbonate into its more soluble bicarbonate:

$$CaCO_3 + CO_2 + H_2O \rightleftarrows Ca(HCO_3)_2$$

The latter reaction occurs when natural waters containing dissolved carbon dioxide come in contact with limestone and other natural carbonates, and is accountable for the presence in those waters of some of the dissolved salts which constitute *hardness*. The reversal of the reaction accounts for the formation of mineral deposits in teakettles and boilers and for the formation of stalactites and stalagmites in caverns where such waters drip.

Calcium and magnesium carbonates are among the most important of the natural carbonates, not only because they occur in large quantity, but also because they find a wide variety of uses. Calcium carbonate is of special importance as the principal source of lime, CaO, and in the form of marble it is widely used as an ornamental building stone. Although deposits of sodium carbonate are to be found in certain of the desert regions of the earth, it and sodium bicarbonate are usually manufactured, as are the other soluble carbonates, notably those of potassium and ammonium.

Being salts of strong bases and a weak acid, the carbonates and bicarbonates of sodium and potassium hydrolyze readily, yielding solutions which react alkaline. Solutions of the carbonates are strongly alkaline, while those of the bicarbonates are less strongly so. The latter afford excellent examples of solutions of an acid salt whose reaction is basic.

$$Na^+HCO_3^- + HOH \rightarrow Na^+ + OH^- + H_2CO_3$$

Behavior similar to the pyrolytic decomposition of calcium carbonate is characteristic of carbonates in general. The ease of decomposition increases as the strength of the parent base decreases. Sodium and potassium carbonates are, therefore, relatively stable to heat, though not completely so. Bicarbonates are much less stable to pyrolysis, decomposing first into carbonates, water, and carbon dioxide as they are heated.

17. The Manufacture and Use of Sodium Carbonate

The scantiness and inaccessibility of the natural supply of sodium carbonate and its wide usefulness caused a prize to be offered in France late in the eighteenth century for the development of a practical process for its manufacture on an industrial scale. The competition was won in 1787 by Nicolas Leblanc, but the prize was never awarded him. His method is outlined in the following equations:

$$2NaCl + H_2SO_4 \xrightarrow{\Delta} Na_2SO_4 + 2HCl \uparrow$$

$$Na_2SO_4 + 4C \xrightarrow{\Delta} Na_2S + 4CO \uparrow$$

and

$$Na_2S + CaCO_3 \xrightarrow{\Delta} Na_2CO_3 + CaS$$

For several decades following its discovery, the Leblanc process was of inestimable value, but in 1864 Ernest Solvay, a Belgian, developed a process which has now largely displaced it for manufacture of sodium carbonate.

By the Solvay process brine is saturated with ammonia, a treatment which, incidentally, serves to precipitate as hydroxides any iron and some of the magnesium which may be present. The solution, which has been clarified and warmed to about 30° C., is allowed to descend over the perforated plates of a tower similar to that illustrated herewith. The descending fluid encounters an ascending stream of carbon dioxide, with which it reacts thus:

$$NH_4OH + CO_2 \rightarrow NH_4HCO_3$$

and

$$NH_4HCO_3 + NaCl \rightarrow NaHCO_3 + NH_4Cl$$

So long as the carbon dioxide is supplied in excess of the ammonia, the bicarbonate will form and will be partially precipitated as a result of the operation of the common-ion effect brought into play by the excess sodium chloride employed. The base of the tower is cooled to foster precipitation. After being washed and dried, the product is heated to form the normal carbonate:

$$2NaHCO_3 \xrightarrow{\Delta} Na_2CO_3 + H_2O + CO_2 \uparrow$$

The carbon dioxide evolved is returned to the process, as is the ammonia obtained by the decomposition of the ammonium chloride obtained above:

$$2NH_4Cl + Ca(OH)_2 \xrightarrow{\Delta} CaCl_2 + 2NH_3 \uparrow + 2H_2O$$

Calcium hydroxide for this last step is obtained by slaking (treating with water) the calcium oxide obtained as a by-product in the preparation of the carbon dioxide to be used in the carbonating tower:

$$CaCO_3 \overset{\Delta}{\rightarrow} CaO + CO_2 \uparrow$$

Some of the calcium chloride produced in the recycling of the ammonia is collected and marketed, but much of it is a waste product.

Much of the anhydrous sodium carbonate produced by the Solvay process is sold directly as *soda ash;* some of it is recrystallized as the decahydrate, Na_2-

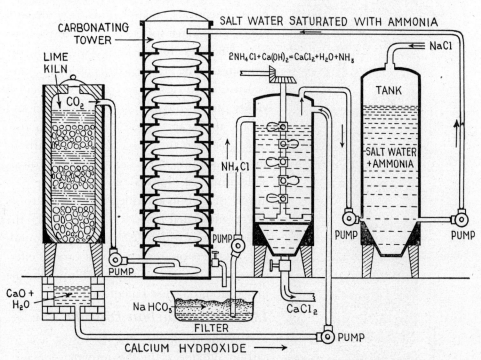

DIAGRAMMATIC REPRESENTATION OF A PLANT FOR THE MANUFACTURE OF SODIUM BICARBON-
ATE BY THE SOLVAY PROCESS.

$CO_3.10H_2O$, and sold as *washing soda* or *sal soda;* and a last portion is dissolved and treated with more CO_2, being converted thereby to a very pure grade of the bicarbonate which is sold as *baking soda* or for medicinal purposes.

The Solvay process is not used for the manufacture of potassium carbonate, because potassium bicarbonate is too soluble to precipitate under the same conditions as does sodium bicarbonate.

The carbonate and bicarbonate of sodium may also be prepared by treating with carbon dioxide the solutions of sodium hydroxide obtained by the electrolysis of brine. Carbon dioxide for the process is usually obtained by the calcining of limestone and the resultant lime is utilized in the manufacture of bleaching powder. Considerable quantities of the carbonate and bicarbonate of soda are now manufactured by this process, whose use will increase as the cost of electric power decreases.

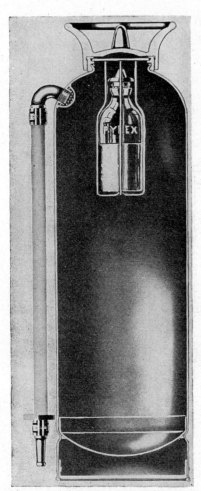

Uses of sodium carbonate in order of diminishing quantity are the manufacture of glass, chemicals, soap, cleansers, pulp and paper, and water softeners, and the processing of textiles. It also finds wide use in the laboratory. The bicarbonate is used in baking because when heated or treated with acid it yields carbon dioxide whose expansion and efforts to escape cause the bread to rise. *Baking powders* are a mixture of the bicarbonate and some solid which upon hydrolysis will furnish H^+ ions to bring about the evolution of carbon dioxide. In addition to its direct medicinal use, as an antacid, the bicarbonate is widely used in the compounding of tablets of all sorts and of various effervescents. The carbonate is much too alkaline in solution to be used medicinally.

18. Uses of Carbon Dioxide

Without doubt, the foremost use of carbon dioxide is in the growth of plants. Also of importance is its use in the manufacture of sodium carbonate, in the manufacture of carbonated beverages, and in the manufacture of the pigment known as white lead, a basic lead carbonate. The gas is also

CROSS-SECTION OF A SODA-ACID TYPE FIRE EXTINGUISHER. (Courtesy, American-LaFrance-Foamite Corp.)

a good fire extinguisher, since it is heavier than air and nonflammable. Only a few per cent of it in air will render the latter incapable of supporting combustion. There are several types of fire extinguisher which make use of it. One type contains the liquid dioxide; another contains a solution of baking soda and a bottle of sulfuric acid so situated that when the extinguisher is inverted the two mix and react to liberate the gas, which exerts pressure on the liquid, thus expelling it; and a third, built on the same general principle as the second,

THE PRESSING OF DRY ICE (CARBON DIOXIDE SNOW) INTO BLOCKS. (Courtesy, Mathieson Alkali Works.)

contains sulfuric acid which reacts upon a solution containing both baking soda and aluminum sulfate and throws a stream of a foamy suspension of aluminum hydroxide which is highly effective in blanketing oil fires.

Liquid carbon dioxide is used in some refrigerating machines, and the solid is used in the packing of frozen foods and in various types of coolers.

The rising of bread is always brought about by the expansion of gaseous carbon dioxide, which may be produced by the use of baking soda, baking powders, or the fermentation of sugar catalyzed by the zymase produced by yeast incorporated in the dough.

19. Percarbonates

Permonocarbonates and perdicarbonates of the alkali metals are known. Examples of these salts are Na_2CO_4 and $K_2C_2O_6$. Like other peroxy compounds, they are good oxidizing agents, and are of fair stability when dry, but their corresponding acids are too unstable to be of any importance.

20. Other Acids of Carbon

Hundreds of acids containing carbon are known to the organic chemist. Many of these are so closely related to each other in chemical behavior as to form groups or families. One of the most important of these families is that of the *fatty acids*, so called because their derivatives make up a large part of our plant and animal fats. These acids are represented by the type formula C_nH_{2n+1}-COOH, where n may be any number from 0 on up. The hydrogen of the —C=O group (the carboxyl group) is weakly ionizable, but the hydrogens
$\diagdown$
    OH
of the $-C_nH_{2n+1}$ group are not ionized at all. Formic acid is the simplest member of the family (n = 0) and acetic acid is the next simplest member (n = 1). Both of these substances are liquids at about 20° C. They are included here because they and their metallic salts are frequently used in the general laboratory. Acetic acid is found in vinegar (prepared by the oxidation of alcohol) and in the distillate of wood, and is prepared commercially by the oxidation of the product obtained when acetylene adds to water in the presence of a catalyst of mercuric sulfate.

COOH
Oxalic acid, $H_2C_2O_4$, or | , and its salts are common laboratory re-
COOH

agents. Since it contains two carboxyl groups, it is a dibasic acid and is of necessity the simplest of the organic dibasic acids. It is a colorless solid, can be easily purified, and is one of the strongest of the organic acids. It is easily obtained by treating with a mineral acid the sodium oxalate prepared by heating sodium formate to about 200° C.:

$$2HCOONa \xrightarrow{\Delta} \begin{matrix} COONa \\ | \\ COONa \end{matrix} + H_2 \uparrow$$

Malonic acid is the second member of the oxalic acid family, the type formula of whose members is $(CH_2)_n(COOH)_2$, where n may be 0 or any number above.

Hydrocyanic acid, HCN, is a very weak acid of extreme toxicity whose odor is reminiscent of oil of bitter almonds. Its salts of the alkali metals find considerable use as sources of the acid for fumigation and pest eradication. Sodium cyanide is prepared by heating carbon with sodamide,

$$C + NaNH_2 \rightarrow NaCN + H_2 \uparrow$$

and by fusing calcium cyanamide (cf. Chapter 24) with carbon and sodium carbonate:

$$CaCN_2 + C + Na_2CO_3 \rightarrow 2NaCN + CaCO_3$$

Because of hydrolysis, its solutions are strongly alkaline and evolve HCN fumes. The acid is weaker than carbonic acid, as is shown by the displacement of cyanides by carbon dioxide. The cyanides resemble the halides in many of their properties, and from them may be obtained cyanogen, $(CN)_2$, a toxic gas:

$$Hg(CN)_2 \xrightarrow{\Delta} Hg + (CN)_2 \uparrow$$

A wide variety of complex cyanides such as potassium ferrocyanide, $K_4Fe(CN)_6$, and potassium argenticyanide, $KAg(CN)_2$, may be derived from the simple cyanides.

Many cyanides, when carefully oxidized with mild agents, are converted to cyanates, which may be thought of as salts of the unstable cyanic acid, HOCN. Several metallic cyanates find rather general use in the laboratory. Isomeric with cyanic acid are isocyanic acid, HNCO, and fulminic acid, HONC. These acids are of little importance, but a number of their derivatives find various employments; for example, mercuric fulminate, $Hg(ONC)_2$, because of its instability is widely used in detonating caps.

When alkali cyanides are fused with sulfur, thiocyanates are formed:

$$NaCN + S \xrightarrow{\Delta} NaSCN$$

These may be thought of as salts of thiocyanic acid, HSCN, a compound of little importance in itself. The thiocyanates of sodium, potassium, and ammonium are common and important laboratory reagents. In further analogy to the oxygen compounds there are also isothiocyanates which may be considered to be derivatives of isothiocyanic acid HNCS.

21. Other Carbon Compounds

Among the many compounds of carbon whose discussion space will not permit, there are a number which deserve at least passing mention. Notable among these are: the many hydrocarbons found in petroleum, coal tar, and elsewhere; the all-important carbohydrates which contain carbon, hydrogen, and oxygen, and of which our starches, sugars, and celluloses are prime examples; the alcohols; the synthetic plastics whose applications are legion; the natural and synthetic rubbers; our industrial explosives; fats and oils; dyes; drugs; perfumes and extracts; vitamins; urea; and all the host of organic compounds which make up the structure of plants and animals. The student who is interested in these materials is directed to some of the popular writings concerning them. Titles of a number of such books are listed at the end of this chapter.

22. Fuels

Fuels are those materials whose oxidation is carried on for the sake of the energy liberated by the reaction. The common fuels are all either some form of

Table 27

HEATS OF COMBUSTION OF FUELS

Material	B.t.u./lb.	Material	B.t.u./lb.	Material	B.t.u./cu. ft.
Coal, bituminous	13,100	Alcohol	11,500	Acetylene	1,483
Coal, anthracite	13,740	Gasoline	20,750	Coal gas	634
Coke	14,700	Kerosene	19,810	Natural gas	2,000 ca.
Charcoal	12,200	Benzene	17,500	Producer gas	136
Wood, air dried	5,800	..	..	Water gas	310
Peat, air dried	7,400	..	..	..	..

carbon, usually impure, or some compound of carbon, and are generally classified upon the basis of their physical state—thus we have solid, liquid, and gaseous fuels. As has been noted previously, however, all substances must be vaporized before they inflame.

Most important of the solid fuels are coal, coke, wood, and charcoal, with peat finding considerable use in some countries. Heats of combustion of these materials are given in Table 27. It must be remembered that these figures are averages, since the materials listed are not pure substances. Much of the greatness of the United States and others of the world's industrial nations has been built on coal. The principal producers of this commodity are the United States,

A MODERN PETROLEUM REFINERY. (Courtesy, Phillips Petroleum Company, Bartlesville, Okla.)

Great Britain, and Germany. At present, it is calculated that known deposits of coal will be sufficient for another 5,000 years at the average rate of consumption common to the present century.

Among the liquid fuels, gasoline, kerosene, and the other derivatives of petroleum are of the greatest importance, though benzene, C_6H_6, and ethyl alcohol (grain alcohol), C_2H_5OH, are also widely used. Ethyl alcohol is of special importance in countries whose supply of petroleum is scant but whose production of sugars and starches from which alcohol may be made is good. Petroleum is, in essence, a mixture of hydrocarbons, principally those of the paraffin series whose general formula is C_nH_{2n+2}, although other compounds may be present also. From the type formula it will be seen that methane, CH_4, is the simplest member of the paraffin series and its association with petroleum is thus emphasized. The first oil well in the United States was drilled in Pennsylvania in 1859, but the great expansion of the oil industry came only with the development and wide distribution of the automobile. At present our principal domestic oil fields are those of the Pennsylvania region, the mid-continent region (Texas, Oklahoma, Kansas, Arkansas, and Louisiana) and the southern California region, while the principal oil-producing countries are the United States, Russia, Venezuela, Mexico, Iran, and Rumania. In the earlier days of oil technology, the refining of petroleum consisted principally of the fractional distillation of the crude oil into liquids of varying degrees of volatility and oiliness. Gasoline, which is one of the more volatile fractions, was further

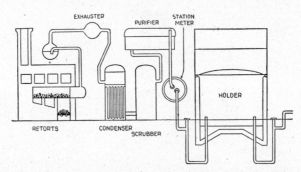

DIAGRAM OF A PLANT FOR THE MANUFACTURE OF COAL GAS.
Coal is heated in the retorts and the evolved gas is pumped away by the exhauster. In the condenser tar, water, and oils are removed from the gas and in the scrubber ammonia is dissolved in a descending stream of water. Sulfurous impurities are removed by passage of the gas over iron oxide in the purifier from which it is measured by the station meter into storage tanks or holders.

purified to remove traces of objectionable sulfur and nitrogen compounds, and the higher boiling motor oils were desludged. Today, with its *cracking* processes to break long-chain carbon compounds into shorter, more volatile ones, and its *polymerization* processes to convert short unsaturated molecules resulting from cracking into bigger ones of higher carbon content, petroleum refining is a very complex and highly specialized industry whose by-products are an important source of raw materials for the organic chemical industry. Known world supplies of crude oil are far inferior to those of coal, and have suffered a heavy drain as a result of World War II.

Gaseous fuels of note are natural gas, water gas, producer gas, coal gas, and acetylene. The production of these gases has already been referred to. Acetylene, C_2H_2, is generally produced by the action of water on calcium carbide and is used principally for the cutting and welding of metals and in the manufacture of the synthetic rubber-like substance known both as Neoprene and as Duprene, though it formerly was used quite a bit for lighting. Because $24/26$ of the mass of the acetylene molecule is carbon, the gas gives an unusually hot flame when burned in sufficient oxygen for its complete combustion. The carbon of all carbonaceous fuels is converted upon complete combustion to carbon dioxide, while any hydrogen present is at the same time oxidized to water.

Table 28

COMPOSITION OF GASEOUS FUELS

Fuel	% CH_4 and Other Hydrocarbons	% H_2	% CO	% CO_2	% N_2
Coal gas...............	42	49	6	0.5	2.5
Natural gas.............	98.5	..	..	..	1.5
Producer gas...........	3	12	27	2.5	55.
Water gas.............	..	51	41	4.0	4

23. *Uses of Carbon*

All are familiar with the use of diamonds as gem stones, but it should be realized that ordinarily less than one-fourth of the total production is so used, with the remainder finding many industrial applications. Many are used in the manufacture of diamond drills for cutting rock; others are used in the cutting and polishing of gem stones, including other diamonds; and still others are used as nozzles to withstand the wear of flowing liquid or solid particles.

Because of its thin slick plates, graphite finds wide use as a lubricant, either alone or in mixtures. Mixed with clay and baked into rods, it forms the "lead" of "lead pencils." Also, when mixed with a little clay, it is used to manufacture crucibles and other pieces of laboratory ware which must withstand high temperatures. It is also used for the manufacture of electrodes which must withstand the action of chemicals maintained at a high temperature. Because of its stability to heat, it finds further use as an ingredient of stove polishes.

Charcoal is used principally as a fuel, as a reducing agent, and as an adsorbent, when activated. Coke is an important industrial fuel, an important reducing agent, and a prime source of carbon monoxide and other carbonaceous compounds. Lampblack is used as a black pigment in the manufacture of paints, lacquers, India ink, printer's ink, carbon paper, typewriter ribbons, phonograph records, and other similar black products. Carbon black is used principally as a filler and pigment in the manufacture of tires and other black rubber goods. Pure rubber has very little resistance to wear, hence if carbon black were not present in close admixture with it, the life of an automobile tire would be very short. In general, lampblack and carbon black are interchangeable in their uses.

Coal is used principally as a fuel and as a source of coal tar, and bone black is used principally as an adsorbent.

(See Appendix for Exercises)

COLLATERAL READINGS

Clarke: *Marvels of Modern Chemistry*, New York, Harper and Brothers, 1932.
Deming: *In the Realm of Carbon*, New York, John Wiley & Sons, Inc., 1930.
Ellis and Kirkby: *Flame*, New York, Chemical Publishing Co., 1945.
Haynes: *This Chemical Age*, New York, Alfred A. Knopf, Inc., 1942.
Helbig: Activated carbon, *J. Chem. Education*, **23,** 98 (1946).
Holmes: *Out of the Test Tube*, New York, Emerson Books, Inc., 1937.
Jones: Carbon dioxide in industry, *Chem. and Met. Eng.*, **40,** 76 (1933).
Killefer: Dry ice, *Ind. Eng. Chem.*, **22,** 1086 (1930).
Kraus: *Gems and Gem Materials*, New York, McGraw-Hill Book Co., 1931.
Latimer and Hildebrand: *Reference Book of Inorganic Chemistry*, New York, The Macmillan Co., 1941.
Levin: Synthesis of precious stones, *Ind. Eng. Chem.*, **5,** 495 (1913).
Little: The romance of carbon, *Ind. Eng. Chem.*, **18,** 444 (1926).
Moissan: *The Electric Furnace*, New York, Chemical Publishing Co., 1920.
Morrison: *Man in a Chemical World*, New York, Charles Scribner's Sons, 1937.
Oesper: Nicolas Leblanc, *J. Chem. Education*, **19,** 567 (1942); **20,** 11 (1943).
Quinn: Carbon dioxide, *J. Chem. Education*, **7,** 151, 403, 637 (1930).
Silverman: *Magic in a Bottle*, New York, The Macmillan Co., 1941.
Slosson: *Creative Chemistry*, New York, Century Co., 1923.
Weeks: *Discovery of the Elements*, 5th ed., Mack Printing Co., 1945.
Wertheim: *Textbook of Organic Chemistry*, 2d ed., Philadelphia, The Blakiston Company, 1945.
Diamonds, *Fortune*, **11,** No. 5, 66 (1935).
Diamond deposits of Arkansas, *Eng. Min. Journ. Press*, **116,** 285 (1923).

28

Boron, Its Compounds, and Other Elements of the III A Family

1. Introduction

Boron, aluminum, gallium, indium, and thallium are the elements which constitute the III A family of the periodic system. The latter three of these elements are very rare metals which find but scant industrial application either in the free or combined condition, hence boron and aluminum are the only commonly important members of the family. Since aluminum has already been discussed at length in Chapter 15, this chapter will be devoted largely to a consideration of boron.

The maximum and common oxidation state of the members of the III A family is +3; in addition, however, gallium, indium, and thallium also exhibit lower positive valences, as will be noted later. Like the last three elements of the IV A, V A, VI A, and VII A families, these three elements contain 18 electrons in the energy level immediately below the energy level containing the valence electrons, while boron and aluminum, like the first two elements of the families listed, contain eight electrons in the underlying level.

Boron is the only distinctly nonmetallic member of the III A family, and being so, it much more closely resembles silicon in all properties, save valence, than it does the members of its own family.

2. The Diagonal Relationship

At this juncture, it is well for the student to become acquainted with that feature of the periodic classification of the elements which is generally known as the *diagonal relationship*. Attention has already been called to the fact that because the radii of the atoms and ions of the elements of the second period are much smaller than those of corresponding elements in succeeding periods, the properties of the second period elements differ considerably from those of the other members of their respective families. This difference is even more marked in the case of the first three elements of the second period than in the case of the remaining members of that period.

The foregoing is perhaps more clear when one considers the ionic potentials of these second period elements. The ionic potential (cf. section 12, Chapter 6) has been defined as the quotient obtained by dividing valence by the ionic radius expressed in Ångström units, and to the square root of this quotient the relationship of certain properties has been noted. For example, as $\sqrt{\phi}$ increases, the oxides become more acidic in nature. It is evident that a small value for the magnitude of the radius will make both ϕ and $\sqrt{\phi}$ larger, and that $\sqrt{\phi}$ will increase in value more markedly in the case of the smaller valences than in the case of the larger ones. These more markedly varying values of $\sqrt{\phi}$ reflect a similar rapid variation in properties, hence three elements of the second period represent a variation as great as that achieved by four elements of the third period. The elements which show a diagonal relationship are, then, the first three of the second period. In all points save valence, lithium resembles magnesium; beryllium resembles aluminum; and boron resembles silicon.

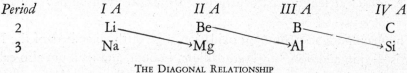

Period	I A	II A	III A	IV A
2	Li	Be	B	C
3	Na	Mg	Al	Si

THE DIAGONAL RELATIONSHIP

As the physical and chemical properties of boron are discussed, they should be compared with the corresponding ones of silicon and contrasted with those of aluminum.

I. BORON

3. Physical Properties

It is very difficult to obtain pure boron because, under the conditions of its preparation, it shows a marked tendency to combine with the reducing agents employed. Because of this difficulty, not too much is known with authority concerning its physical properties. As usually prepared, it is a somewhat impure brownish powder known as *amorphous* boron. In actuality, however, this powder is finely crystalline. Crystalline boron is said to be colorless and to resemble diamond in both brilliance and hardness, but little is known of its crystalline form. Both modifications of the element are poor conductors of electricity at ordinary temperatures, but, unlike most metals, the conductivity of the crystals increases as the temperature is raised. The density of the brown powder is reported to be 1.73 g./ml., while that of the crystals is reported as about 2.45 g./ml. It is reported to melt at 2300° C., to sublime at 2550° C., and to have a considerable vapor pressure at temperatures well below its melting point. The specific heat of boron, when measured at moderate temperatures, is abnormally low as compared with the values calculated by the law of Dulong and Petit. When measured at temperatures near the melting point, it agrees

MINERALS OF BORON. *Upper left:* Kramerite (proberite), $NaCaB_5O_9.5H_2O$. *Upper right:* Ulexite, $NaCaB_5O_9.8H_2O$. *Lower left:* Colemanite, $Ca_2B_6O_{11}.5H_2O$. *Lower right:* Priceite (pandermite), $Ca_5B_{12}O_{23}.9H_2O$. (Courtesy, Pacific Coast Borax Co.)

very well with the calculated value. In this respect, carbon and silicon exhibit a similar behavior, which is associated with their low molecular weights and high melting points.

4. Occurrence

Boron occurs principally as boric acid and as salts of various polyboric acids—never in the free condition. Despite the fact that the element makes up only about 0.001 per cent of the earth's crust, rather extensive deposits of its compounds are found in a number of places—principally where the salt-laden waters of lakes and inland seas have dried up. A major portion of the world's supply of boron compounds is produced by the United States. Domestic production stems largely from the "dry" lakes of the Death Valley and Mojave Desert regions of southern California and from adjacent areas in Nevada. The principal boron mineral of this region is *kernite*, or *rasorite*, $Na_2B_4O_7.4H_2O$, but considerable quantities of *borax*, $Na_2B_4O_7.10H_2O$, *cole-manite*, $Ca_2B_6O_{11}.5H_2O$, and *ulexite*, $CaNaB_5O_9.8H_2O$ are also found there. Second in production is Italy, in whose volcanic regions the hot springs contain dissolved boric acid from which considerable deposits of this substance have formed. The Stassfurt salt deposits of Germany contain some borates, principally those of magnesium, such as *boracite*, $Mg_7Cl_2B_{16}O_{30}$.

5. Preparation

Although borax has been known for hundreds of years, the free element was not known until 1808 when Davy, Gay-Lussac, and Thenard all succeeded in preparing it in impure form by reduction of its oxide, B_2O_3. At the present time, the impure *amorphous* form of the element is prepared by reduction of the oxide with magnesium:

$$B_2O_3 + 3Mg \rightarrow 3MgO + 2B$$

As in the preparation of silicon, an excess of magnesium must be avoided, since it will combine with the freed element to form, in this case, a boride. The magnesium oxide is removed by treatment with hydrochloric acid. The substitution of aluminum for magnesium yields a more crystalline, but no less impure, product. Pure boron was finally prepared in 1909 by Weintraub, who subjected a mixture of hydrogen and boron trichloride to the action of the electric arc:

$$2BCl_3 + 3H_2 \xrightarrow{\Delta} 2B + 6HCl \uparrow$$

The element has also been prepared by the reduction of potassium borofluoride, KBF_4, with sodium in a magnesia-lined crucible. Only the most active elements serve to liberate the element from its compounds.

6. Chemical Properties

Because of its small size and its three valence electrons, the boron atom has principally the properties of a nonmetal; however, it does have a few properties which relate it to the metals. In general, its chemical behavior is very much like that of silicon. It is stable at about 20° C. with respect to its combination with oxygen, but at 100° C. it oxidizes slowly and at 700° C. it ignites in oxygen to burn with a green flame. The reaction is highly exothermic:

$$4B + 3O_2 \rightarrow 2B_2O_3$$

Aqueous solutions of nitric acid, sulfuric acid, ferric ions, and other strong

ELECTRIC FURNACES IN WHICH BORON CARBIDE IS MANUFACTURED. (Courtesy, Norton Co.)

oxidizing agents will also oxidize the element, converting it to orthoboric acid, H_3BO_3.

In an atmosphere of fluorine, boron ignites spontaneously even at about 20° C. The product of this combustion is the trifluoride, BF_3. It behaves in an analogous manner with chlorine and bromine, though higher temperatures (410° C. for chlorine and 700° C. for bromine) are required for initiation of the reactions. It does not combine directly with iodine; however, the triiodide may be prepared by indirect methods.

When heated with sulfur, boron forms the trisulfide (sesquisulfide), B_2S_3. Also worthy of note is the fact that boron is one of the few elements which combines directly with nitrogen. The nitride is formed whenever the element is heated in an atmosphere of pure nitrogen, air, ammonia, or nitric oxide:

$$2B + N_2 \rightarrow 2BN \qquad \text{and} \qquad 3NO + 5B \rightarrow 3BN + B_2O_3$$

Boron and carbon unite at the temperature of the electric arc to form the carbide B_6C, which may be an impure form of B_4C, and which is second only to diamond in hardness. At elevated temperatures, the element will unite with a wide variety of metals to form the corresponding metallic borides. It will not

A MASS OF BORON CARBIDE CRYSTALS. (Courtesy, Norton Co.)

combine directly with hydrogen. All of the foregoing binary compounds of the element save the oxide and the carbide are readily hydrolyzed, especially by acidified water.

Boron is a strong reducing agent. Not only does it combine with the oxygen of the air and that furnished by strong oxidizing agents in aqueous solution, but it unites directly with the oxygen of sulfur dioxide, carbon dioxide, the oxides of nitrogen, water, and many other oxides when it is heated with them. Because of this behavior, it is often used as a deoxidant, especially in the casting of copper and copper alloys.

Elementary boron dissolves in fused alkalies to form borates:

$$2B + 6NaOH \rightarrow 2Na_3BO_3 + 3H_2 \uparrow$$

As a result of its slight metallic tendencies, boron forms the phosphate, BPO_4, and the bisulfate, $B(HSO_4)_3$. Boron phosphate is relatively stable, but the bisulfate is unstable to both heat and water. Neither compound is of practical importance.

7. Oxides

Several oxides of boron are known, but of these the regular trioxide (sesquioxide), B_2O_3, is the most common and the most important. Although it can be prepared by the direct union of its elements, it is more cheaply and more conveniently obtained by the decomposition of boric acid at red heat:

$$2H_3BO_3 \xrightarrow{\Delta} B_2O_3 + 3H_2O \uparrow$$

When so prepared, it is a very brittle, colorless, glasslike solid.

Boric oxide and its derivatives are the most important compounds of the element. It unites with water in varying quantities to form a series of boric and polyboric acids which are the parents of a number of important salts. The oxide is sometimes employed as a drying or dehydrating agent because of its affinity for water. When heated with metallic oxides, it forms a series of glassy borates which are colorless save when the metallic ions bring color to the compound. The oxide is used in large quantities in the manufacture of heat-resistant glasses. The well-known *Pyrex* laboratory ware is made from a mixture which contains about 12 to 15 per cent of B_2O_3 and about 80 per cent of sand.

Sub-oxides of the formulas BO and B_4O_5 have been reported. They are prepared by the dehydration of the acids $H_2B_4O_5$ and $H_2B_4O_6$, respectively, and are of little importance. A sub-oxide prepared by the partial reduction of the sesquioxide is occasionally used as a scavenger in the casting of metals.

8. Acids

The boric acid which occurs naturally in the hot springs of Italy's volcanic region has the formula H_3BO_3. This acid, known commonly as boric acid and sometimes by the older name boracic acid, is the regular ortho acid of boron whose existence might be expected in the light of the common valence of the element. It is so slightly soluble that at 20° C. 100 g. of water will dissolve only 4.96 g. of it. When its hot solutions are cooled, it precipitates as thin, shiny plates which are soft and waxy to the touch; it is, therefore, easily purified by recrystallization. The ability of boric acid to crystallize is in marked contrast to silicic acid, which is gelatinous. When its solutions are boiled, some of the acid is also volatilized. This behavior accounts for its presence in the steam which escapes from volcanic fumaroles. As an acid, it is weaker than carbonic acid or hydrogen sulfide, and is so weakly ionized that its solutions barely affect blue litmus paper. Its primary ionization constant is 6.4×10^{-10} at 25° C. Naturally, its second and third degree of ionization are even weaker.

Because the acid is a mild antiseptic, its solutions are used as washes for the eyes and nose and as dressings for open wounds. It is also a good food preservative, but because its continued ingestion is harmful, its use in this capacity is generally prohibited by law. The acid may be prepared by the action of strong mineral acids on naturally occurring borates.

When orthoboric acid is heated to 100° C., it loses water to form the meta acid,

$$H_3BO_3 \xrightarrow[100° C.]{\Delta} HBO_2 + H_2O \uparrow$$

and at 140° C., the meta acid is further dehydrated to yield tetraboric acid,

$$4HBO_2 \xrightarrow[140° C.]{\Delta} H_2B_4O_7 + H_2O \uparrow$$

Both of these acids are white solids. A wide variety of polyborates are known and may be looked upon as being salts of polyboric acids of the general type formula $(H_2O)_a(B_2O_3)_b$, where a is usually one, two, or three and b may be any number from one to six. Examples of these acids are:

$H_2B_2O_4 (H_2O + B_2O_3)$ $H_2B_8O_{13} (H_2O + 4B_2O_3)$
$H_2B_4O_7 (H_2O + 2B_2O_3)$ $H_6B_8O_{15} (3H_2O + 4B_2O_3)$
$H_6B_4O_9 (3H_2O + 2B_2O_3)$ $H_6B_{10}O_{18} (3H_2O + 5B_2O_3)$
$H_2B_6O_{10} (H_2O + 3B_2O_3)$ $H_2B_{12}O_{19} (H_2O + 6B_2O_3)$
$H_4B_6O_{11} (2H_2O + 3B_2O_3)$

All of these acids are looked upon as being hydration products of boron trioxide, though in actuality many of them are known only as their salts. The polyboric acids are of no practical importance.

The metals of the I A and II A families form hypoborates which appear to be salts of hypoboric acid, $HOBH_3$, a very unstable compound which readily hydrolyzes thus:

$$2HOBH_3 + 2H_2O \rightarrow 2HBO_2 + 5H_2 \uparrow$$

The acid and its salts are powerful reducing agents.

9. Borates

Metallic orthoborates are so unstable that few of them are known, and the metallic metaborates are almost never found in nature though they may be prepared in the laboratory, as hereinafter described. For the most part, the naturally occurring metallic borates are salts of various ones of the polyboric acids mentioned in the preceding section.

Most important of the metallic polyborates is *borax*, sodium tetraborate decahydrate, $Na_2B_4O_7.10H_2O$. Formerly, most of the domestic supply of borax was prepared by boiling pulverized colemanite with sodium carbonate,

$$2(Ca_2B_6O_{11}.5H_2O) + 4Na_2CO_3 + 21H_2O \rightarrow \underline{4CaCO_3} + 3(Na_2B_4O_7.10H_2O) + 2NaOH$$

CRYSTALS OF KERNITE. These crystals have the formula $Na_2B_4O_7.4H_2O$. (Courtesy, Pacific Coast Borax Co.)

but at present most of it is prepared from kernite, $Na_2B_4O_7.4H_2O$, with a portion being obtained directly from the "dry" lakes of southern California. When crystallized from solution, borax forms large, colorless, prismatic crystals which effloresce readily. The solubility of the salt in water increases from 1.3 g. per 100 g. of water at 0° C. to 201 g. in a like volume of solvent at 100° C.

Crystals of the formula $Na_2B_4O_7.5H_2O$ separate from supersaturated solutions at temperatures above 60° C.

Being the salt of a strong base and a weak acid, borax readily hydrolyzes to give a solution which is distinctly alkaline. Its dilute solutions act as if they contained sodium metaborate, a little sodium hydroxide, and some free boric acid,

$$Na_2B_4O_7 + 3H_2O \rightleftarrows 2NaBO_2 + 2H_3BO_3$$

and

$$NaBO_2 + 2H_2O \rightleftarrows NaOH + H_3BO_3$$

THE WORKING OF A PIECE OF BOROSILICATE GLASS. (Courtesy, Corning Glass Works.)

and hence serve some of the same purposes as do solutions of the acid. Strong solutions of the salt contain principally the tetraborate ion, which upon addition of sodium hydroxide is converted to the metaborate ion.

Upon being heated, borax crystals swell to form a porous, opaque mass which upon further heating melts to a clear, glasslike consistency. Since this glassy anhydrous tetraborate contains boron trioxide in excess of the quantity required to form sodium metaborate, it will readily react with metallic oxides when heated with them. Metallic metaborates are formed:

$$Na_2B_4O_7(\text{or } Na_2O.2B_2O_3) + NiO \rightarrow 2NaBO_2 + Ni(BO_2)_2$$

Three uses are made of this behavior of borax: (1) It is used as a flux to remove metallic oxide scales from metal surfaces on which welding or soldering is to be done; (2) it is used to test analytically for the presence of metals whose glassy metaborates have characteristic colors; (3) it is used to produce colored enamels which may be fused on iron or ceramic ware or which may be pulverized for use as pigments in paints. Borax bead tests are made with the aid of a platinum wire in the same fashion that phosphate bead tests (*q.v.*) are made. Some elements give beads of one color in the reducing flame and of another in the oxidizing flame. Characteristic bead colors are: for chromium, green in both flames; for manganese, violet in the oxidizing flame and colorless in the reducing flame; for iron, yellow in the oxidizing flame and green in the reducing flame; and for cobalt, blue in both flames.

Some uses of borax, in addition to those mentioned above, are: in the manufacture of glass to lower the coefficient of expansion, raise the index of refraction, and decrease the tendency toward crystallization; in the cleaning of hides; in the degumming of raw silk; in the mordanting of textiles and leather; in the softening of water; in the manufacture of cleaning agents; in the preparation of certain antiseptic solutions; in the preserving of wood; in the manufacture of artificial gem stones; and in the manufacture of glazed papers and cardboards.

10. Sodium Perborate

By treating an aqueous solution of borax with sodium peroxide, or with sodium hydroxide and hydrogen peroxide, one obtains a precipitate of sodium perborate. The salt may also be prepared by the action of sodium percarbonate on sodium metaborate. Commercially, it is usually prepared by the electrolysis of a borax solution to which sodium hydroxide has been added. Sodium perborate is colorless, forms monoclinic crystals, is but slightly soluble in cold water, and has the formula $NaBO_2.H_2O_2.3H_2O$. One can see from the formula that the salt is not a true perborate, but is rather a metaborate which contains both water and hydrogen peroxide of crystallization, or hydration. A few true perborates, such as $2KBO_3.H_2O$, are known, but are of scant importance. The potassium perborate hemihydrate is precipitated when hydrogen peroxide is added to an alcoholic solution of potassium metaborate.

Aqueous solutions of $NaBO_2.H_2O_2.3H_2O$ exhibit the characteristic properties of hydrogen peroxide and are hence good oxidizing and bleaching agents. Cold solutions slowly liberate oxygen, and hot ones or ones to which suitable catalysts have been added evolve the gas much more rapidly. The dry powder is an ingredient of a number of tooth powders. The theory is that the oxygen liberated when the powder is moistened in the mouth will oxidize bacteria and food particles held between the teeth beyond the reach of the brush. Continuous use of such powders has a tendency to loosen metallic fillings. The dry salt is fairly stable, but is rendered much more so by the removal of the three molecules of water of hydration. This is accomplished commercially by heating the hydrated salt to 100° C. *in vacuo* or by treating it with anhydrous alcohol.

11. Analytical Tests for Borates

When boric acid or borates are warmed with methanol, CH_3OH, in the presence of a small quantity of concentrated sulfuric acid, there is formed a volatile methyl orthoborate which when ignited burns with a green flame:

$$H_3BO_3 + 3CH_3OH \xrightarrow{H_2SO_4} (CH_3)_3BO_3 + 3H_2O$$

A second test consists of acidifying the fairly concentrated aqueous solution with hydrochloric acid and using it to moisten a strip of turmeric paper. If borates are present, the paper should turn a dull red as it dries, and then should turn dark green, dark blue, or black when moistened with a drop of ammonium hydroxide or sodium hydroxide.

12. Halides

Mention has already been made of the fact that boron combines spontaneously with fluorine, directly with chlorine and bromine, and only indirectly with iodine. In practice, however, the boron halides are usually prepared from boron trioxide. The fluoride is made by the action of hydrofluoric acid on the oxide, while the other three halides are prepared by heating a mixture of the oxide and carbon with the proper halogen:

$$B_2O_3 + 6HF \rightarrow 2BF_3 + 3H_2O$$

and

$$B_2O_3 + 3C + 3Cl_2 \xrightarrow{\Delta} 2BCl_3 \uparrow + 3CO \uparrow$$

The iodide is also prepared by heating a mixture of boron trichloride and hydriodic acid.

All four of the halides are colorless. The fluoride and chloride are gases, the bromide is a liquid, and the iodide is a solid. All fume in moist air, and all undergo hydrolysis. The chloride, bromide, and iodide are completely hydrolyzed to boric acid and the corresponding hydrohalic acid, while the fluoride, in analogy to silicon fluoride, yields boric acid and fluoboric acid:

$$BCl_3 + 3H_2O \rightarrow H_3BO_3 + 3HCl \uparrow$$

and

$$4BF_3 + 3H_2O \rightarrow H_3BO_3 + 3HBF_4$$

Boron trifluoride finds commercial application as a catalyst.

13. Fluoboric Acid

This acid may also be prepared by the direct union of hydrofluoric acid and boron trifluoride:

$$HF + BF_3 \rightarrow HBF_4$$

Its structure is believed to be

$$
\begin{array}{c}
\ddot{} \\
:F: \\
\ddot{} \cdot o \cdot \ddot{} \\
H \times F : B \stackrel{o}{:} F : \\
\ddot{} \; o \; \ddot{} \\
:F: \\
\ddot{}
\end{array}
$$

The pure acid is unstable, but its cold aqueous solutions are stable. The acid is strong and a number of its salts are known. Its potassium salt is of only slight solubility.

14. Hydrides

Like silicon and unlike the members of its own family, boron forms a number of unstable hydrides, usually referred to as *boranes*. These compounds are of no practical importance, but they are of theoretical interest because of the problems they present. It would be anticipated that BH_3 would be the simplest of the boranes; in actuality, however, this compound is unknown, probably because it is very unstable with respect to polymerization into more complex structures. The simplest of these compounds which has been isolated is diborane, or boroethane, B_2H_6. When magnesium boride is treated with dilute hydrochloric acid, the principal product is hydrogen, but appreciable quantities of tetraborane, borobutane, B_4H_{10}, and lesser amounts of B_5H_9, B_6H_{10}, and B_6H_{12} are also produced. Tetraborane is a foul-smelling gas which is toxic, ignites spontaneously in air, and is unstable with respect to decomposition into diborane and a number of complex liquids and solids. Both the di-

and tetraboranes react with solid potassium and sodium hydroxides to form the corresponding metallic hypoborates, which are quite stable when dry:

$$B_4H_{10} + 4NaOH \rightarrow 4NaOBH_3 + H_2 \uparrow$$

The structure of the boranes has been a problem which has attracted much interest, and for which a number of solutions have been proposed.

II. GALLIUM, INDIUM, AND THALLIUM

15. *General Relationships*

Like boron and aluminum, the three remaining elements of the family possess three valence electrons, and therefore show a characteristic valence of $+3$. Because the first of these valence electrons is in the one sub-level, it is

Table 29

PHYSICAL PROPERTIES OF THE ELEMENTS OF THE III A FAMILY

Property	Boron (B)	Aluminum (Al)	Gallium (Ga)	Indium (In)	Thallium (Tl)
Atomic weight............	10.82	26.97	69.72	114.76	204.39
Isotopes.................	10, 11	none	69, 71	113, 115	203, 205
Atomic number...........	5	13	31	49	81
Electronic distribution.......	2, 3	2, 8, 3	2, 8, 18, 3	2, 8, 18, 18, 3	2, 8, 18, 32, 18, 3
Ionization potential of gaseous atoms in volts					
1st valence electron.....	8.26	5.96	5.97	5.76	6.07
2d valence electron......	25.00	18.74	20.43	18.79	20.32
3d valence electron......	37.75	28.31	30.6	27.9	29.7
Density, g./ml............	2.45	2.699	5.91	7.3	11.85
Melting point, ° C.........	2300	660	29.75	155	303.5
Boiling point, ° C.........	2550(subl.)	1800	>1600	1450	1650
Specific heat in cal./g.......	0.510 (900°)	0.214 (20°)	0.079 (12° to 23°)	0.057 (0° to 100°)	0.0326 (20° to 100°)

more easily removed than are the other two, which, in each case, are in the zero sub-level. In fact, the first of the valence electrons of each of these elements is so easily removed that salts of these elements impart characteristic colors to the gas flame. Also, because of the ease of removal of this first electron, thallium regularly shows a valence of $+1$ while indium exhibits a $+1$ valence in a few of its compounds. In a very few of its compounds, gallium has been observed to exhibit a valence of $+2$. Physical constants and data relating to the elements of the III A family are given in Table 29.

Because gallium, indium, and thallium occur in such small quantities in the ores of other metals, their separation is rather expensive and hence their commercial uses are few.

The hydroxides of the metals are more strongly basic than is the hydroxide of aluminum, and they increase in strength from gallium to thallium; nevertheless, all are weak bases. The sulfates of the trivalent ions of all three resemble aluminum sulfate in their ability to form alums with the sulfates of monovalent cations.

16. Gallium

The existence of gallium was predicted by Mendelejeff as a result of his periodic classification of the elements. He also foretold very accurately what the properties of the element should be. Its discovery came in 1875 when Lecoq de Boisbaudran detected the spectral lines of a new element while he was examining spectroscopically a sample of zinc ore from southern France. For the new element he chose the name *gallium* in honor of France, his native country, whose old Latin name was *Gallia*.

The metal occurs as its salts in the ores of zinc, aluminum, chromium, and iron, but is usually present in quantities of less than 0.01 per cent. Its separation is, therefore, both tedious and expensive. The free metal is gray, and, in contrast to aluminum, it is both hard and brittle. It melts at 29.75° C., and readily remains in a supercooled condition at average room temperature (about 20° C.), a property which accounts for its often being referred to as a liquid metal. Its low melting point, low vapor pressure at temperatures below 1500° C., and uniform coefficient of linear expansion at temperatures below 1000° C. make it suitable for use in high-temperature thermometers whose tubes are of fused quartz.

Even at red heat, gallium is only slightly oxidized, presumably because of the protective coating of gallic oxide, Ga_2O_3, which is formed. Gallous oxide, Ga_2O, is known, but it is unstable, decomposing readily into gallic oxide and the free metal:

$$3Ga_2O \rightarrow Ga_2O_3 + 4Ga$$

The free metal liberates hydrogen from strongly acidic solutions, combines directly with many less positive elements when heated with them, and is easily oxidized by a wide variety of oxidizing agents.

The gallic ion is colorless, and its compounds behave very much like the corresponding ones of aluminum. Gallic hydroxide is more basic than aluminum hydroxide, but is still amphoteric; it is precipitated by the addition of

EDWARD GOODRICH ACHESON

(1856–1931, American)

As a young man, Acheson worked with a civil engineer crew; later he did research work at the Edison laboratories; and later still, but while still a young man, he set out on his own as research scientist and inventor. By industrial application of his inventions, in time he became a powerful industrialist. His contributions include the invention of an anti-inductive telephone wire, the development of methods of preparing carborundum and other abrasives by use of the electric furnace, the origination of methods of preparing synthetic graphite and of using it as a lubricant, and the treatment of clays to increase their strength and plasticity. He received many honors, among which were the Scott Medal (1899 and 1901), the Rumford Medal (1907), and the Perkin Medal (1909). (Underwood and Underwood.)

strong bases to solutions of gallic ions, and will redissolve in excess of caustic to form metallic gallates. White gallium ferrocyanide is easily precipitated, and is one of the least soluble salts of the element.

17. *Indium*

Indium was also discovered spectroscopically, but at an earlier date than gallium. Reich and Richter first noted its spectral lines in 1863. It was christened *indium* in token of its indigo spectral lines, and the deep blue color which it imparts to a gas flame. The metal occurs as its compounds in zinc sulfide ores and in the ores of both tungsten and tin, and is separated from zinc ores a bit more readily than is gallium. Indium is a bright silvery metal whose softness approaches that of lead. It tarnishes very little even in moist air, and forms a nontarnishing silver alloy. When heated in air, however, it burns with the characteristic blue flame forming the oxide In_2O_3. Other reactions of the free element are similar to those of gallium.

When the oxide In_2O_3 is strongly heated, the oxide In_3O_4 is formed, and, when it is heated to a temperature of 300° C. in an atmosphere of hydrogen, the oxide In_2O_2 is formed.

The indic ion, In^{+3}, is colorless and is readily precipitated as its colorless hydroxide, $In(OH)_3$, which is less amphoteric than gallic hydroxide and is, therefore, attacked only by the strongest bases. Also reflecting the increased basicity of the hydroxide is the relative stability of indic carbonate in solution; it is only slightly hydrolyzed. The indic ion is readily precipitated in feebly acidic solution as the yellow sulfide In_2S_3, and it may also be precipitated as a chromate, a cyanide, or a ferrocyanide.

In addition to indic chloride, $InCl_3$, the mono- and dichlorides of indium are also known. These latter chlorides, when in aqueous solution, are unstable with respect to their conversion to the indic salt. Contrary to the general behavior of salts, the chlorides of indium are but slightly ionized in solution.

18. *Thallium*

Of the three elements under discussion, thallium is the most plentiful and was the first to be discovered. Its characteristic green spectral line was first observed in 1861 by Crookes, who gave it the name *thallium* which he derived from the Greek word meaning *a green twig*. The element is never found free. Its compounds are sometimes found along with those of the alkali metals, but more frequently its sulfide is found associated with the sulfides of iron, lead, zinc, and others of the heavy metals. It is most commonly obtained by the processing of the flue dusts of pyrite burners to be found in certain sulfuric acid plants. Thallium is a soft, silvery metal with a distinct bluish cast. It closely resembles lead in appearance and in other physical properties. It is easily cut with a knife, has low tensile strength, is malleable, has a low melting point, and once melted is easily supercooled. Two distinct crystalline forms of the metal are known, and their transition temperature is recorded as 226° C. The metal oxidizes slowly in moist air, and when heated in either air or oxygen. It combines directly with many of the nonmetals when mixtures of the two are heated.

Two series of thallium compounds are known; in the thallous compounds the element has a valence of $+1$, while in the thallic compounds it has a valence of $+3$. In their solubilities, most of the thallous salts resemble those of plumbous lead, but in strength of hydroxide, inability to form complexes, and other chemical properties, they resemble the compounds of potassium. Thallous hydroxide, $TlOH$, is a strong base which, upon being heated in the absence of air, loses water to form its anhydride, Tl_2O, which is obtained as a black solid. Thallous sulfide, Tl_2S, is precipitated from either neutral or alkaline solution. Also of slight solubility are the iodide, chromate, phosphate, and cobaltinitrite of this ion. Thallous chloride is only slightly soluble in cold water. Because of the formation of an adhering coat of this salt, the free metal soon ceases to be attacked by hydrochloric acid.

Strong oxidizing agents such as acidified permanganate will oxidize the thallous ion to the thallic condition. Under ordinary circumstances, however, thallic ions are easily reduced to the thallous condition, and hence solutions of thallic salts act as good oxidizing agents. Thallic hydroxide, $Tl(OH)_3$, is of a rusty brown color and is of very slight solubility. In general, its behavior is much like that of aluminum hydroxide, though, due to the larger size of the thallic ion, it is less acidic; nevertheless, it will dissolve in concentrated solutions of sodium hydroxide and other strong bases. Upon being dehydrated, the hydroxide yields the reddish-brown thallic oxide, Tl_2O_3. Because of the weakness of $Tl(OH)_3$ as a base, soluble thallic salts are highly hydrolyzed in solution. Unlike thallous salts, those containing the thallic ion readily form complexes. Thallic sulfide is very unstable with respect to its decomposition into thallous sulfide and sulfur.

Quantitatively, thallium is usually precipitated as thallous iodide, although solutions of thallous salts may be titrated with standard permanganate solutions.

Soluble thallium salts are used for poisoning prairie dogs and other rodents. Other compounds of the element are used in the preparation of optical glass of high refractive power, and the element is used in the preparation of certain alloys. Care should be exercised in the handling of soluble thallium compounds, for, like those of lead, they are poisonous to human beings.

(See Appendix for Exercises)

COLLATERAL READINGS

Dingley: The borax industry in southern California, *J. Chem. Education*, **8,** 2112 (1931).

Emeleus and Anderson: *Modern Aspects of Inorganic Chemistry*, London, Routledge, George, & Sons, Ltd., 1938.

Geckler and Marchi: Indium, *J. Chem. Education*, **21,** 407 (1944).

Johnston: Boron: its importance in plant growth, *J. Chem. Education*, **5,** 1235 (1928).

Latimer and Hildebrand: *Reference Book of Inorganic Chemistry*, New York, The Macmillan Co., 1941.

Laubengayer, *et al.:* Preparation and properties of pure crystalline boron, *J. Am. Chem. Soc.*, **65,** 1924 (1943).

Morgan and Burstall: *Inorganic Chemistry*, Cambridge, W. Heffer & Sons, Ltd., 1938.

Stock: *The Hydrides of Boron and Silicon*, Ithaca, Cornell University Press, 1933.

Turril: Mineral and chemical resources of the Mojave Desert, *J. Chem. Education*, **9,** 1318, 1530 (1932).

Weeks: *Discovery of the Elements*, 5th ed., Mack Printing Co., 1945.

LISE MEITNER
(1878–   , *Austrian*)

Dr. Meitner is an atomic physicist who was a student in Berlin of the famous German physicist, Max Planck. Her schooling completed, she remained in Berlin to work with Dr. Otto Hahn on radioactivity. Later she served as professor at the Kaiser Wilhelm Institute, and, until she left Germany in 1938 because of her antifascist beliefs, she continued to work on various scientific projects with Hahn. In 1918 they reported the discovery of the element protoactinium. After leaving Germany, in reviewing the results obtained when she and Hahn had repeated Fermi's experiment of bombarding uranium with neutrons, Dr. Meitner concluded that they had split the uranium atom. Upon this conclusion, which she transmitted to Niels Bohr, was based the work which led to the production of the atomic bomb. (Courtesy, Press Association, Incorporated.)

29

The Alkali Metals and Their Compounds

1. Introduction

Lithium, sodium, potassium, rubidium, and cesium are the elements which constitute the I A family of the periodic chart. In this family there should be one other element, number 87, which has been christened *virginium* by Allison. Although evidence of the existence of this element has been found by several investigators, neither the element nor any of its compounds has ever been isolated from naturally occurring material. Because all of the members of the I A family are metals, and because their hydroxides are all soluble and strongly ionized as bases, they are known collectively as the *alkali metals*.

The atoms of each of the alkali metals possess only one valence electron which, as is shown by the ionizing potentials listed in Table 30, is rather easily removed. These metals are, therefore, highly reactive, and, as a consequence of their activity, never occur naturally in the elementary condition. Because of the ease with which the single valence electron is removed, the I A metals are liberated from their compounds only at the expense of considerable energy, and in their compounds they exhibit only a valence of $+1$, which is, of course, a true electrovalence. The difficulty of liberating the elements accounts for the fact that no member of the family was obtained in the free condition until 1807, when Davy isolated sodium and potassium by electrolyzing their respective molten hydroxides.

The ions of the alkali metals are colorless; their salts are, in general, highly soluble; and they show little tendency to form complex compounds. Here, as in other regular families, the ions increase in size with increasing atomic weight, and their hydroxides consequently increase in strength as bases in the same order. The free elements all displace hydrogen from cold water, with that of largest atomic radius, cesium, acting most violently in this respect. All form saltlike hydrides when heated with hydrogen, and all react spontaneously with the moisture, oxygen, and carbon dioxide of the air. Because of their reactivity, they must all be preserved in an inert atmosphere or under oil (cf. sodium).

Sodium and its compounds have been discussed at some length in Chapter 7. At this juncture the student should review this material, for the chemistry of the other members of the family is very similar to that of sodium.

Since the compound cation ammonium, NH_4^+, exhibits the same valence and many of the characteristic properties of the ions of the I A family, it is customary to discuss it along with them.

2. General Physical Properties

A number of the atomic and physical properties of the alkali metals are presented in Table 30.

Table 30

PHYSICAL PROPERTIES OF THE ALKALI METALS

Property	Lithium (Li)	Sodium (Na)	Potassium (K)	Rubidium (Rb)	Cesium (Cs)
Atomic weight...........	6.940	22.997	39.096	85.48	132.91
Mass of isotopes.........	6, 7	23	39, (40), 41	85, (87)	133
Atomic number.........	3	11	19	37	55
Distribution of planetary electrons.............	2, 1	2, 8, 1	2, 8, 8, 1	2, 8, 18, 8, 1	2, 8, 18, 18, 8, 1
Melting point, ° C.......	186	97.5	62.3	38.5	28.5
Boiling point, ° C.......	1609	880	760	700	670
Density, g./ml. at 20° C.	0.534	0.971	0.87	1.53	1.90
Ionizing potential, volts..	5.36	5.12	4.32	4.16	3.87
Electrode potentials, volts	2.96	2.71	2.924	2.926	3.02(?)
Ionic radius, Angström units................	0.60	0.95	1.33	1.48	1.69
Heat of hydration, cal.....	123,000	97,000	77,000	70,000	63,000
Specific heat, cal./g.......	0.079(0° C.)	0.295(20° C.)	0.18(14° C.)	0.08(0° C.)	0.052(20° C.)
Flame colors............	Crimson	Yellow	Lavender	Bluish-red	Purplish-blue

All of these elements are good conductors of electricity, a property which they owe to the looseness with which their valence electrons are bound to their atoms. The characteristic spectral lines of these elements and the characteristic colors which they impart to the gas flame are also associated with the weak binding of the valence electrons. Even a gas flame supplies sufficient energy to excite these atoms; the return of the excited electrons to lower energy levels is accompanied by an emission of energy.

The elements are all silvery-white metals which tarnish quickly upon exposure to air. Their melting points decrease and they become increasingly soft as the atoms increase in size. These two properties are accounted for by the fact that the atoms which make up samples of the massive elements do not possess sufficient valence electrons to bind their atoms securely to all of the other surrounding atoms. Lithium, whose hardness is comparable to that of lead, is the hardest of the metals. Sodium, potassium, and rubidium are soft enough to be molded with the fingers (a dangerous practice) or to be cut easily with a knife. Cesium, as a result of supercooling, is often a liquid at about 20° C. The ability of these metals to dissolve in ammonia (cf. section 24 of Chapter 24) is associated with this lack of binding between atoms. The attractive forces of the solvent dipoles are sufficiently strong to tear down the solid structure.

The nuclei of potassium and rubidium exhibit a slight radioactivity.

I. LITHIUM

3. Occurrence

Although the existence of compounds of lithium was discovered as early as 1817, the free element was not isolated until 1855. Credit for its liberation goes to Bunsen and Mathiessen. The name *lithium* is derived from the Greek word for *stone*, and was applied to the element because it was then believed that its compounds were never present in plant and animal matter. At present, its salts are known to occur in minute quantities in tobacco, the sugar beet, and a few other plants. Minerals which contain lithium in appreciable quantities are relatively rare. The best domestic deposits are found in the states of South Dakota, California, and Maine. Its principal minerals are *spodumene*, $LiAl(SiO_3)_2$; *amblygonite*, $LiAlFPO_4$; and *lithium mica*, or *lepidolite*. Spodumene, in addition to being found in South Dakota, is also found in the Canadian provinces of Quebec and Manitoba. The other two minerals mentioned above are also found in these same general areas and in parts of southwest Africa. One of the by-products obtained in the refining of the Searles Lake brines in California is lithium phosphate.

4. Preparation

Lithium is prepared by the electrolysis of its fused chloride or by the electrolysis of a fused mixture of its chloride and that of potassium. Since the hot metal combines with both oxygen and nitrogen, it must be protected from exposure to the air. At present, the production of lithium is not large.

5. Chemical Properties

When heated in an atmosphere of oxygen, lithium forms the simple oxide, Li_2O, contaminated by traces of the peroxide, Li_2O_2. The normal oxide unites with water to form the soluble and very strong base, LiOH, while the peroxide unites with water to form the base and to liberate oxygen. When heated with hydrogen, the element forms the crystalline, saltlike hydride, LiH, which is readily hydrolyzed to yield the hydroxide and hydrogen. Lithium alone of the alkali metals will combine directly with nitrogen; the nitride, Li_3N, like other metallic nitrides, is readily hydrolyzed to the hydroxide and ammonia. In the formation of a nitride, lithium shows its diagonal relationship with magnesium of the II A family, a relationship further emphasized by the slight solubility of the fluoride, carbonate, and phosphate of the element and the pronounced solubility of the bicarbonate. Like magnesium chloride, lithium chloride crystallizes from solution as a hydrate and is highly soluble; it is also soluble in amyl alcohol. The nitrate and sulfate are also readily soluble in water.

Most important of the compounds of lithium is its carbonate, which is insoluble enough to be easily precipitated from solution and which finds use in the preparation of other lithium compounds, in medicine, in the manufacture of ceramic glazes, and in the manufacture of glass. Lithium salts are used in this last capacity to increase the fluidity of molten glass and to decrease the coefficient of expansion, to increase the electrical resistance, and to increase the transmission of ultraviolet light of the finished product. Lithium bromide finds some use in medicine as a component of nerve sedatives, and synthetic crystals of the fluoride are employed in place of natural crystals of calcium fluoride in certain optical devices.

The abnormally high electrode potential recorded for lithium in Table 30 is accounted for by the fact that the smallness of the lithium ion gives it the ability to attract water dipoles more strongly than do the ions of the other alkali metals. Ions which are firmly bound to water dipoles are less readily liberated than are those which are less firmly bound.

Lithium salts color the gas flame a brilliant crimson red. Because of this ability, these salts find some use in the manufacture of fireworks and signal flares.

6. Uses

Elementary lithium is too reactive to be of much use save in a few syntheses and when alloyed with less active metals. An alloy of less than 1 per cent of it with aluminum is said to have the tensile strength and elasticity of mild steel. Its incorporation into other light-weight alloys seems highly probable, since it is the lightest of the metals.

II. POTASSIUM

7. Occurrence

Potassium compounds have been known since prehistoric times, but the element, as stated previously, was not isolated until 1807. The name *potassium* was derived by Davy from *potash*, the common term used in that day to designate the carbonate of the element. *Potash*, in turn, derived from the concentration in large iron pots of the aqueous extract of wood ashes. The symbol *K* derives from *kalium*, the Latin name for the element.

Like the other members of its family, potassium is never found free in nature. Among the members of its family it is second only to sodium in the order of abundance, and is therefore rather plentiful and rather widely distributed in nature. Despite the fact that potassium salts as a whole are quite soluble in water, they are in general less highly hydrated and less soluble than are the corresponding salts of sodium. Because of this difference in solubility, and because of the slightly greater occurrence of sodium compounds, they are 30 to 35 times more plentiful in sea water than are those of potassium, while those of the latter are more plentiful in the soil. Land and sea plants have adapted themselves to this situation so that potassium salts are now essential to the economy

THE EFFECT OF POTASH DEFICIENCY ON PLANT GROWTH. The plants pictured are of the same age and type and were grown under conditions which were identical save for available potassium salts. (Courtesy, U.S. Department of Agriculture.)

of the former, while sodium salts are necessary in most cases to the economy of the latter. It is as a result of this state of affairs that intensively farmed areas ultimately require the addition of fertilizers which contain potassium salts. The removal of these salts by land plants explains the presence of potassium salts in wood ashes and in the ashes of other plants. The necessary potassium salts are gradually made available for plant use by the slow weathering of the insoluble igneous rocks, principally the feldspars and micas (cf. section 3 of Chapter 15).

The feldspars and micas, though plentiful and widely distributed in nature, do not constitute the primary commercial sources of potassium compounds. Prior to World War I, most of the world's supply of these salts came from the Stassfurt deposits in Germany. Among the minerals found there are

THE SALT SURFACE OF CALIFORNIA'S SEARLES LAKE. (Courtesy, American Potash & Chemical Corp.)

sylvite, KCl; *carnallite*, $KCl.MgCl_2.6H_2O$; and *kainite*, $KCl.MgSO_4.3H_2O$. From these, potassium chloride was recovered for sale. The stoppage of the flow of this substance to the United States was a severe blow to our agriculturists. Since that time, a considerable domestic potash industry has been developed.

New Mexico and California lead in the domestic production of these essential salts. In the former state, the salts are found in deep sub-surface strata underlying the plains east of Carlsbad, while in California they are obtained by surface workings at Searles Lake. Other important potassium minerals include *silvinite*, which contains the chlorides of both potassium and sodium, *polyhalite*, whose composition is $K_2SO_4.MgSO_4.2CaSO_4.2H_2O$, and *hanksite*, $KCl.2Na_2CO_3.9Na_2SO_4$. Domestic production is about equal to the national demand, provided there is no exportation; in consequence, World War II did not precipitate a potash crisis similar to that caused by its predecessor. Agriculture utilizes about 90 per cent of the total production.

8. Preparation

Although potassium was first prepared electrolytically, for many years it was obtained principally by the reduction of the carbonate of the metal with charcoal:

$$K_2CO_3 + 2C \rightarrow 3CO \uparrow + 2K$$

A disadvantage of the method was the tendency of the potassium and the carbon monoxide to interact to form the potassium salt of hexahydroxybenzene, $C_6O_6K_6$, which is highly explosive. At the present time, most of the elementary potassium produced in this country is prepared by the electrolysis of the molten hydroxide, though some is prepared by the electrolysis of the molten chloride. The latter method offers the greater number of technical difficulties. (Cf. the production of metallic sodium.)

9. Chemical Properties

In general, the chemical properties of potassium closely resemble those of sodium (q.v.); however, since the potassium atom is the larger of the two, its valence electron is held less securely and it is a bit more reactive with the electron-accepting elements, the nonmetals. It will combine directly with all of the nonmetals

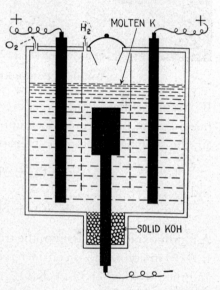

DIAGRAM OF THE CASTNER CELL FOR THE ELECTROLYTIC PRODUCTION OF POTASSIUM FROM ITS HYDROXIDE.

save nitrogen and the inert gases. As has been noted already, corresponding compounds of the two elements do not exhibit the same degrees of hydration or of solubility. The two elements also differ somewhat in their reactions with oxygen.

10. Oxides and Hydroxide

When potassium is heated in an excess of air or oxygen, the superoxide KO_2 (or K_2O_4) is formed. This compound is of an orange-yellow color, and melts in the neighborhood of 400° C. to a black oil. By heating the metal in the calculated quantity of air or oxygen, the peroxide K_2O_2 is formed. In its behavior with water and as an oxidizing agent, this substance is very similar to Na_2O_2, though much less widely used:

$$2K_2O_2 + 4H_2O \rightarrow 4KOH + 2H_2O_2 \rightarrow 4KOH + 2H_2O + O_2 \uparrow$$

AN AMERICAN POTASH REFINERY. (Courtesy, U.S. Potash Co.)

By heating either of the foregoing oxides with the calculated quantity of the free metal, or by heating potassium nitrite with the free metal in the absence of air, the simple oxide may be prepared:

$$KO_2 + 3K \rightarrow 2K_2O$$

and

$$2KNO_2 + 6K \rightarrow 4K_2O + N_2 \uparrow$$

A fourth oxide of potassium, the trioxide or sesquioxide, K_2O_3, is also known. It is red in color, and is considered by some to be formed from the super oxide and the peroxide, $2KO_2 + K_2O_2$.

The oxides of the metal react with water to form the hydroxide, KOH, and to evolve oxygen save in the case of the simple oxide. Commercially, however, the hydroxide is prepared in manners similar to those used for the preparation of sodium hydroxide. The principal method of preparation is the electrolysis of aqueous solutions of potassium chloride. Second in importance is the treatment of potassium carbonate with calcium hydroxide:

$$2KCl + 2H_2O \xrightarrow{elec.} 2KOH + H_2 \uparrow + Cl_2 \uparrow$$

and

$$K_2CO_3 + Ca(OH)_2 \rightarrow 2KOH + \underline{CaCO_3}$$

Potassium hydroxide is a white solid which is sold in the form of pellets, sticks, and flakes. It is extremely deliquescent, and very soluble in water. When moistened, it reacts readily with carbon dioxide to form potassium carbonate. Its solutions attack glass less readily than do those of sodium hydroxide. As a base, it is slightly stronger than sodium hydroxide, but the reactions of the two alkalies are very similar.

11. Carbonates

Potassium carbonate is a white, somewhat lustrous substance which is known both as *pearlash* and *potash*. The derivation of the latter name from the old method of extracting the salt from wood ashes has already been mentioned. The compound is known in the anhydrous form and as the mono-, di-, and trihydrates. Because potassium bicarbonate is nearly three times as soluble as sodium bicarbonate, it cannot be manufactured by the Solvay process, and, therefore, other processes must be used for the production of the normal carbonate. By substituting potassium chloride for sodium chloride, the Leblanc process will serve for the production of K_2CO_3. The Stassfurt process, by which carbon dioxide is passed into a solution of potassium chloride containing a suspension of finely divided magnesium carbonate, also finds wide application. A precipitate of the slightly soluble double salt, $KHCO_3.MgCO_3.4H_2O$, forms, is collected, and is then decomposed by treatment with hot water. This latter treatment precipitates magnesium carbonate, which may be used again; causes the evolution of carbon dioxide, which also may be used again; and leaves the potassium carbonate in solution to be recovered by evaporation. Equations for the Stassfurt process are:

$$2KCl + 3MgCO_3 + CO_2 + 9H_2O \rightarrow MgCl_2 + \underline{2(KHCO_3.MgCO_3.4H_2O)}$$

and

$$2(KHCO_3.MgCO_3.4H_2O) \xrightarrow[\text{aq.}]{\Delta} K_2CO_3 + \underline{2MgCO_3} + 9H_2O + CO_2 \uparrow$$

Smaller quantities of the normal carbonate are obtained by heating the potassium salts of organic acids which are obtained from the mother liquors remaining after the crystallization of beet sugar, from wine lees, and from the washing of wool.

Potassium bicarbonate, $KHCO_3$, which is less soluble than the normal carbonate, is usually prepared by passing carbon dioxide into a saturated solution of the normal salt:

$$K_2CO_3 + H_2O + CO_2 \rightarrow 2KHCO_3$$

The normal carbonate is the more important of the two, and is manufactured in considerable quantities for the preparation of hard glass, soft soaps, and other compounds of potassium. The treatment of the carbonate with the proper acid yields the desired salt uncontaminated by by-products:

$$K_2CO_3 + 2HNO_3 \rightarrow 2KNO_3 + H_2O + CO_2 \uparrow$$

12. Soaps

Soaps are the metallic salts of the fatty acids and of the closely related, unsaturated organic acids. Fatty acids have the type formula $C_nH_{2n+1}COOH$. The soaps of the heavy metals, while they have their uses, are not soluble, and are, therefore, not suitable for use as cleaning agents. The common cleaning agents, for the most part, are the sodium and potassium salts of palmitic acid ($C_{15}H_{31}COOH$) and stearic acid ($C_{17}H_{35}COOH$). Sodium soaps are hard, while potassium soaps are soft and more soluble than their sodium counterparts. Soaps made by the pioneers from ash leachings were, therefore, soft.

The most common method of preparing soap is the cooking of fats with a solution of a strong base. Fats and oils from plant and animal sources are mixtures of the glyceryl esters of the organic acids mentioned above, hence glycerol (glycerin) is a by-product of soap manufacture. The following equation represents the manufacture of sodium stearate from glyceryl stearate:

$$C_3H_5(OOCC_{17}H_{35})_3 + 3NaOH \rightarrow 3C_{17}H_{35}COONa + C_3H_5(OH)_3$$

The solubility of the soap in the preparation mixture may be decreased by the addition of salt, NaCl. This process is known as *salting-out*.

13. Halides

All four of the halides of potassium are known, and in addition the acid fluoride, KHF_2, is also known. The metal will combine directly with all of the halogens, but its halides are usually prepared by indirect methods. The neutralization of solutions of either the hydroxide or carbonate of the metal with the proper hydrohalic acid will yield the salts. Natural sources account for most of the chloride, while the bromide and iodide are most commonly prepared by treating a hot solution of potassium hydroxide with the free halogen. The halates, simultaneously formed, are decomposed into the halides by heating. The iodide is also prepared commercially by treating Fe_3I_8, obtained by the action of iodine on wet iron filings, with potassium carbonate:

$$Fe_3I_8 + 4H_2O + 4K_2CO_3 \rightarrow Fe_3O_4.4H_2O + 8KI + 4CO_2 \uparrow$$

The solubility of the halides increases from chloride to bromide to iodide. The bromide is used in medicine, in the laboratory, in the preparation of silver bromide, and in photographic chemistry as a retardant to the process of development. The iodide is used in medicine and in the laboratory as a reagent and source of the iodide ion.

14. Cyanide, Cyanate, and Thiocyanate

Sodium cyanide, because of its cheaper price, is much more widely used than is the corresponding potassium salt. Considerable quantities of the latter salt are still used, however. It may be manufactured by heating the carbonate with carbon and either ammonia or nitrogen:

$$K_2CO_3 + 4C + 2NH_3 \rightarrow 2KCN + 3CO \uparrow + 3H_2 \uparrow$$

The salt is very soluble in water, is strongly hydrolyzed in solution, and is very poisonous. Its principal uses are in the recovery of gold and silver and in the plating of metal objects with silver, gold, and platinum. These uses depend upon its ability to form soluble complex cyanides with these metals. It finds some use in analytical work, as a laboratory reagent, and as a source of HCN for fumigating.

Potassium cyanate, KOCN, is readily prepared by heating the cyanide with lead monoxide or other suitable oxidizing agents:

$$KCN + PbO \rightarrow KOCN + Pb$$

The sulfur analog of this salt, potassium thiocyanate, KSCN, is readily prepared by heating the cyanide with sulfur. In solution, the thiocyanate is readily prepared by treating the cyanide with either an alkaline polysulfide or an alkaline thiosulfate:

$$KCN + (NH_4)_2S_x \rightarrow (NH_4)_2S_{x-1} + KSCN$$

and

$$KCN + Na_2S_2O_3 \rightarrow Na_2SO_3 + KSCN$$

Both the cyanate and the thiocyanate find use as laboratory reagents. The thiocyanates of both potassium and sodium are used medicinally in the treatment of hypertension.

15. Nitrate

As a constituent of black gunpowder, potassium nitrate has played an important part in world history. It has been known at least since the alchemical era and takes its common name, *saltpeter*, from *sal petrae*, the name given it by the alchemist Geber. It is a colorless salt of high solubility and is, therefore, seldom found in any quantity in nature, although it is formed by the decay of organic matter which contains potassium salts. Incrustations of the salt are found in cesspools, in barnyards, and in other deposits of excretory matter. During the War of 1812, saltpeter to be used in the manufacture of gunpowder was extracted from the bat guano deposits of Mammoth Cave in Kentucky.

At the present time, potassium nitrate is manufactured by the metathetical reaction of sodium nitrate and potassium chloride, both of which occur naturally in quantity:

$$KCl + NaNO_3 \rightleftarrows KNO_3 + NaCl$$

With the exception of that of sodium chloride, the solubilities of all of the salts involved increase rapidly with temperature. When hot saturated solutions of the two reactants are mixed, a precipitate of sodium chloride is formed. After the removal of this precipitate, the solution is cooled, whereupon saltpeter crystals form. These crystals, which are contaminated with small quantities of sodium chloride, may be purified by recrystallization. In addition to its use in the manufacture of gunpowder, the salt finds use as a component of solutions used to preserve meats, as a fertilizer, and as a dry oxidizing agent. The behavior of the salt when heated is discussed in section 8 of Chapter 24.

16. Gunpowder

The exact origin of black gunpowder is lost in antiquity, but its discovery and subsequent application have had a marked influence upon the course of world history. As a military explosive it has slowly given way since the turn of the century to more powerful agents. Gunpowder is not a compound, but an intimate mixture of about 75 per cent potassium nitrate, 13 per cent charcoal, and 12 per cent sulfur. It is the function of the nitrate to supply oxygen for the combustion of the two other ingredients. The expansion of the gaseous non-metallic products formed by combustion supplies the propelling power for the bullet or other missile to be hurled. Although the course of the reaction is a bit different when it occurs in a confined space, its course when the powder is burned in the open air is given by the equation:

$$4KNO_3 + 3S + 2C \rightarrow 2K_2CO_3 + 3SO_2 \uparrow + 2N_2 \uparrow$$

The solid produced accounts for the visible smoke and for the fouling of gunbarrels. Black powder is used at the present time principally for blasting and for the production of fireworks.

17. Sulfates

Several different minerals which contain potassium sulfate along with salts of magnesium are found in the Stassfurt deposits. Notable among these is *kainite*, $K_2SO_4.MgSO_4.MgCl_2.6H_2O$. In Germany, the sulfate is refined from these minerals, but, in the United States, it is obtained principally by the action of sulfuric acid on potassium chloride. The salt is a colorless substance whose crystals are anhydrous. It is used in the preparation of alums, as a fertilizer, and in the manufacture of glass.

The acid sulfate, potassium bisulfate, $KHSO_4$, is prepared by heating the normal sulfate with an equimolar quantity of sulfuric acid. It is a colorless compound which is used as a laboratory reagent and for the preparation of the pyrosulfate:

$$2KHSO_4 \xrightarrow{\Delta} K_2S_2O_7 + H_2O \uparrow$$

The properties of the pyrosulfate have been discussed (cf. section 26, Chapter 21), and the perdisulfate of potassium, $K_2S_2O_8$, has already been treated in section 32 of Chapter 21.

18. Salts of the Oxygen Acids of the Halogens

Most important of the potassium salts of these acids are the chlorate and perchlorate. The preparation, properties, and uses of these salts, as well as of others of the family, are discussed at some length in Chapter 22. The material concerning them should be reviewed at this time.

19. Analytical Tests

Soluble, volatile potassium salts are most easily identified by the delicate lavender color which they impart to the colorless gas flame. The chloride gives this test most satisfactorily because of its ready volatility. Since sodium salts color the flame much more readily than do those of potassium, and since the flame color is deeper and more intense, it is necessary when both substances are present to use one or more thick blue glasses to filter out the yellow radiations so that the delicate potassium flame may be detected.

Precipitation tests for potassium are none too satisfactory, because of the general solubility of its salts. Least soluble of these is $K_2NaCo(NO_2)_6$, which appears as a yellow precipitate when de Konink's reagent (a solution of sodium cobaltinitrite) is added to a solution containing a fair concentration of potassium ions. Rubidium, cesium, and ammonium ions behave similarly. With basic solutions of paradipicrylamine, potassium ions in slightly basic solution yield an orange-red precipitate. The ions of the I A and II A families do not interfere with this test nor does the ammonium ion, save when it is present in high concentration. Other potassium salts of low solubility are the fluosilicate, K_2SiF_6; the perchlorate, $KClO_4$; the acid tartrate, $KHC_4H_4O_6$; the picrate, $KOC_6H_2(NO_2)_3$; and the chloroplatinate, K_2PtCl_6.

III. RUBIDIUM AND CESIUM

20. Occurrence

Rubidium and cesium, like the other alkali metals, never occur free in nature. Their percentages in the earth's crust are calculated to be 10^{-6} and 10^{-7}, respectively; hence, only minute quantities of their salts are to be found, and these are usually found associated with *lepidolite*, *carnallite*, and others of the minerals of the more plentiful elements of the family. Cesium is a constituent of the rare mineral *pollucite*, $CsAlSi_2O_6.xH_2O$, which was discovered on the island of Elba and later found to exist in Maine. Minute traces of both elements are found in the ashes of tea, tobacco, and a few other plants.

Both elements were discovered spectroscopically by Bunsen in 1860 shortly after his invention with Kirchoff of the spectroscope. In fact, cesium was the first element discovered by use of this instrument. It takes its name from the Latin word for *grayish-blue*, because of the blue lines in its spectrum, while rubidium takes its name similarly from the Latin word for *red*, because of the intense red lines in its spectrum.

21. Preparation

The principal source of these elements is the mother liquors which remain after the extraction of potassium chloride from carnallite. They are removed usually as their slightly soluble alums. The metals usually are prepared by displacement by calcium from their molten chlorides. This is possible despite the lower activity of calcium, because of the volatility of cesium and rubidium. Other metals and other compounds of the elements may also be used. Because the elements occur together and because their chemical properties are so nearly identical, usually no effort is made to separate them, and their alloy is sold as "cesium."

22. Chemical Properties

When burned in an excess of air, rubidium and cesium, like potassium, form superoxides whose formulas are $RbO_2(\text{or } Rb_2O_4)$ and $CsO_2(\text{or } Cs_2O_4)$, respectively. Of all of the oxides of the alkali metals, only CsO_2 shows any tendency to decompose when heated; at elevated temperatures it is partly decomposed into oxygen and Cs_2O_3. Each element also forms the three other oxides analogous to those of potassium. They form the hydroxides, RbOH and CsOH, respectively. These are dense colorless compounds of high hygroscopicity which are extremely soluble and of strong basicity. In fact, cesium hydroxide is the strongest of the basic hydroxides, just as its parent metal is the most active of all metals. In general, the compounds of these elements are analogous to those of potassium in formula, solubility, and other properties, though they show a marked tendency to form double salts such as CsI_3 and $CsCl_2I$. This tendency is associated with the increased radii of their respective ions. Double salts involving the ions of other metals are also known.

Compounds of the elements are largely laboratory curiosities, but the mixed metals are used in the manufacture of light-sensitive surfaces in photoelectric cells and in the manufacture of other electronic devices.

IV. AMMONIUM SALTS

23. General

The preparation and properties of ammonia and its aqueous solutions were discussed at some length in Chapter 24, where the basic nature of the aqueous solution (ammonium hydroxide) was pointed out, and its ability to react with acids to form ammonium salts was cited. These salts are, for the most part, soluble, and in solution they give rise to the ammonium ion, NH_4^+. The method of formation of the ion was also discussed in Chapter 24. All efforts to isolate NH_4 as a neutral entity have failed, but that the NH_4^+ ion is somewhat metallic in nature is shown by the formation of an unstable ammonium amalgam when mercury is shaken with a solution of ammonium chloride. At this juncture, the sections of Chapter 24 which deal with ammonia and its compounds should be reviewed.

The purpose of considering the ammonium ion again is to emphasize the similarity of its properties to those of the ions of the I A family, particularly potassium, and to note some of the important ammonium salts and their similarity to the analogous compounds of potassium. Corresponding ammonium and potassium salts are usually isomorphic, and possessed of solubilities of like degree (cf. section 19). The chief point of difference is the volatility and instability of ammonium salts to heat, and their decomposition into ammonia when warmed with a strong base.

24. *Important Salts*

From time to time in previous chapters, the preparation, properties, and uses of various ammonium salts have been mentioned. Ammonium salts of all of the common acids are manufactured and find a wide use. Their solubility and their general cheapness account in a large measure for their wide use, though in the laboratory the fact that they introduce no metallic ion is of importance. The majority of the ammonium salts are manufactured by the action of acids on aqueous solutions of ammonia or by the introduction of gaseous ammonia into solutions of the proper acids.

Most widely used of the ammonium salts are the chloride, NH_4Cl, the nitrate, NH_4NO_3, and the sulfate, $(NH_4)_2SO_4$. The first of these salts is sometimes known as *sal ammoniac*, and finds use in the manufacture of dry-cell batteries, as a cleaning agent, in soldering and galvanizing, in dyeing, and to a slight degree in medicine. The two other salts both find use as fertilizers, and the nitrate, because of its instability to heat, is often mixed with explosives to serve as an oxidizing agent. The sulfate finds some use in the preparation of alums.

Ammonium carbonate, $(NH_4)_2CO_3$, and ammonium bicarbonate, NH_4HCO_3, are both known. Both are fairly stable when dry, though they decompose upon being heated. The ammonium carbonate of commerce, usually sold in the form of small white cubes, is in reality a mixture of the bicarbonate and

$$\text{ammonium carbamate, } NH_4O-\overset{\displaystyle O}{\overset{\|}{C}}-NH_2,$$

which is obtained as a sublimate by heating together in an iron vessel a mixture of ammonium sulfate and calcium carbonate. This product is used in the manufacture of smelling salts, rubber accelerators, fire-extinguishing compounds, and other ammonium compounds. It also finds use as a laboratory reagent. Ammonium bicarbonate is sometimes used instead of $NaHCO_3$ in the production of baked goods, notably soda crackers.

Ammonium thiocyanate, NH_4SCN, is used as a laboratory reagent and in dyeing to prevent the injurious action of iron salts. It may be prepared by the action of a solution of ammonia in a 50-50 mixture of alcohol and water upon carbon disulfide. The thiocarbamate first formed is decomposed as its solution is evaporated:

$$2NH_3 + CS_2 \rightarrow NH_4-\overset{\displaystyle S}{\overset{\|}{S-C}}-NH_2 \overset{\Delta}{\rightarrow} NH_4SCN + H_2S \uparrow$$

The phosphates, perdisulfate, chlorate, and perchlorate of ammonium have been discussed in earlier chapters (*q.v.*). Other salts of some importance are the fluoride, bromide, iodide, acetate, sulfide, cyanate, and molybdate.

The ammonium salts of least solubility are those which are analogous to the least soluble compounds of potassium; the ammonium ion is usually tested for, however, not by its precipitation, but by the decomposition of its salts with a strong base and heat. The odor of the free ammonia evolved by this treatment is unmistakable, as is its effect upon moistened litmus paper or other suitable test papers.

(*See Appendix for Exercises*)

COLLATERAL READINGS

Badger and Baker: *Inorganic Chemical Technology*, New York, McGraw-Hill Book Co., 1941.

Browne: Domestic potash industry in early Colonial and later times, *J. Chem. Education*, **3**, 749 (1926).

Cramer: Production of potassium chloride in New Mexico, *Ind. Eng. Chem.*, **30**, 865 (1938).

Creighton and Koehler: *Electrochemistry*, Vols. I & II, New York, John Wiley & Sons, Inc., 1943, 1944.

Ephraim: *Inorganic Chemistry*, 3d Eng. ed., London, Gurney and Jackson, 1939.

Finn: Potash in the glass industry, *Ind. Eng. Chem.*, **30**, 891 (1938).

Hoffer: Potash in plant metabolism, *Ind. Eng. Chem.*, **30**, 885 (1938).

Latimer and Hildebrand: *Reference Book of Inorganic Chemistry*, New York, The Macmillan Co., 1941.

Lodge: Potash in the fertilizer industry, *Ind. Eng. Chem.*, **30**, 878 (1938).

Mansfield: American potash reserves, *Ind. Eng. Chem.*, **34**, 1417 (1942).

Mumford: Potassium chloride from the brine of Searles Lake, *Ind. Eng. Chem.*, **30**, 877 (1938).

Turrentine: Wartime contribution of the American potash industry, *Ind. Eng. Chem.*, **34**, 1422 (1942).

Weeks: *Discovery of the Elements*, 5th ed., Mack Printing Co., 1945.

SIR HUMPHRY DAVY
(1778–1829, English)

Davy was a skilled experimentalist who for many years held the professorship at the Royal Institution in London. Perhaps his most important work was the preparation of the alkali and alkaline earth metals by electrolysis, thereby clearing up the confusion which then existed as to the classification of various substances as elements or compounds. He established that chlorine is an element, and not a compound as Lavoisier had supposed, and he discovered the peculiar physiological action of nitrous oxide which accounts for its pseudonym of "laughing gas." Also to Davy goes credit for the association of chemical activity of matter with electrical charges.

30

The Alkaline Earth Metals and Their Compounds

1. Introduction

In the order of their increasing atomic numbers, the members of the II A family of the periodic classification of the elements are beryllium, magnesium, calcium, strontium, barium, and radium. As a family, these elements are sometimes referred to as the *alkaline earth metals*. The term *alkaline earth* was used by the early chemists to describe the oxides of calcium, strontium, and barium, which were basic in nature yet nevertheless resembled the oxides of the trivalent elements, which because of their natural occurrence were known as *earths*. As the family name indicates, each member of the group is a metal, although beryllium, because of the smallness of its ion, is amphoteric in its behavior and thus bears a diagonal relationship to aluminum of the III A family. In their outermost energy level, the atoms of each of the alkaline earth metals contain two electrons which, when removed, leave a kernel whose structure corresponds to that of the atom of the preceding inert gas. Having, thus, two valence electrons, these metals all exhibit an oxidation number of $+2$ in their compounds. Since most of these compounds are formed by the loss of the two valence electrons, it may be said that, in most instances, the elements show an electrovalence of $+2$.

Within the family, the four heavier elements resemble each other closely in their chemical behavior, but beryllium and magnesium resemble neither the heavier elements nor each other too closely. These differences are associated with the smaller sizes of their ions. Beryllium shows this difference most markedly, and therefore more closely resembles the aluminum ion in its properties.

Because they have but two valence electrons, the metals of the II A family are second only to the metals of the I A family in their activity as electron-losers. In fact, as shown by electrode potentials, calcium, strontium, and barium are less readily displaced from solutions of their ions than is sodium; hence, comparison is better made with corresponding members of both families. The hydroxides of the four heavier members of the II A family are all strong bases. All members of the family will form nitrides by direct union, but only the four heavier members form saltlike hydrides. The solubility of many of the II A compounds and the heat stability of some of them, such as the carbonate and nitrate, are less than that of corresponding compounds of the I A family.

The chemistry of magnesium has already been discussed at some length in Chapter 13, and, since radium behaves chemically much like barium, and is of more importance from the standpoint of its radioactivity than from the standpoint of its reactions, it is better discussed in Chapter 35, which deals with radioactive changes.

2. General Physical Properties

All of the alkaline earth elements exhibit a bright, silvery luster when a fresh surface is exposed, but this surface tarnishes quickly in air, with the

Table 31

PHYSICAL PROPERTIES OF THE ALKALINE EARTH METALS

Property	Beryllium (Be)	Magnesium (Mg)	Calcium (Ca)	Strontium (Sr)	Barium (Ba)	Radium (Ra)
Atomic weight.............	9.02	24.32	40.08	87.63	137.36	226.05
Mass of isotopes..........	9	24, 25, 26	40, 42, 43, 44, 46, 48	84, 86, 87, 88	130, 132, 134, 135, 136, 137, 138	224, 226
Atomic number............	4	12	20	38	56	88
Distribution of planetary electrons.	2, 2	2, 8, 2	2, 8, 8, 2	2, 8, 18, 8, 2	2, 8, 18, 18, 8, 2	2, 8, 18, 32, 18, 8, 2
Melting point, °C.........	1350	651	810	800(?)	850	960(?)
Boiling point, °C.........	1530 at 5 mm.	1110	1170	1150	1140	1140(?)
Density, g./ml. 20° C......	1.85	1.74	1.55	2.54	3.5	5.0(*ca.*)
Ionizing potential, volts.						
1st electron..............	9.28	7.61	6.09	5.67	5.19	5.25
2nd electron.............	18.12	14.96	11.82	10.98	9.95	10.10
Electrode potential........	+1.69(?)	+2.40(?)	+2.87(?)	+2.92(?)	+2.90(?)	..
Ionic radius, Ångström units...................	0.31	0.65	0.99	1.13	1.35	..
Heat of hydration, cals......		460,000	395,000	355,000	305,000	..
Specific heat, cal./g.........	0.425(0° to 100° C.)	0.246(20° C.)	0.168(24° C.)	..	0.068(−185 to 20° C.)	..
Flame colors..............	None	None	Brick red	Carmine	Yellow-green	Crimson

heavier, more positive members of the family showing this property to a much higher degree than do the two lighter members which do not displace hydrogen from cold water. Like the members of the I A family, these elements become softer as one proceeds from lower to higher atomic numbers. All are fair conductors of electricity. Calcium, strontium, and barium have oxalates, sulfates, carbonates, silicates, phosphates, chromates, borates, and fluorides which are of slight solubility in water.

Beryllium and magnesium compounds impart no characteristic colors to the gas flame, but the more loosely held, and therefore more easily excited, electrons of calcium, barium, and strontium permit the volatile compounds of those elements to color the flame. The characteristic colors imparted by these elements and other physical and atomic properties of the II A elements are presented in Table 31.

I. BERYLLIUM

3. Occurrence

Like the other members of its family, beryllium is never found free in nature. It makes up but a tiny fraction of the earth's crust, hence large deposits of its compounds are seldom found. It occurs principally in the form of its silicates, which are widely distributed among the granitic rocks.

The element was discovered in 1789 by Vauquelin, who isolated it from the mineral *beryl*, from whose name the present name of the element derives. An earlier name for the element is *glucinium*, derived from the Greek word meaning *sweet*, and applied because of the sweetish taste of solutions of the compounds of the element.

Beryl is still the chief source of the element. Its formula is $Be_3Al_2Si_6O_{18}$.

EMERALD AS IT OCCURS NATURALLY. (Courtesy, American Museum of Natural History.)

Deposits of it have been located in Alaska, Colombia, and other countries of the various continents. Known deposits within the continental United States are small. When colored dark green by the presence of traces of chromic salts, beryl is known as *emerald*, and when colored a pale greenish-blue it is known as *aquamarine*.

4. Preparation

Beryllium may be obtained from its salts in a number of ways. It is perhaps most conveniently prepared by the electrolysis of a fused mixture of its chloride and that of sodium. Other methods consist of electrolyzing a fused mixture of the oxide and fluoride of the element and the fluoride of sodium, the electrolysis of fused potassium beryllofluoride, $KBeF_3$, the electrolysis of a solution of beryllium chloride in liquid ammonia, and the reduction of the oxide with carbon in an electric furnace.

5. Uses

Because of its scarcity, cost, and brittleness, beryllium had few uses until studies made several years ago revealed that a number of its alloys have properties which make them especially useful. One of the most interesting of these alloys is that obtained by adding 2 to 3 per cent of the element to copper. The

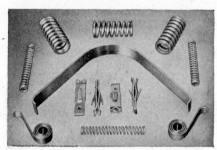

SPRINGS AND OTHER ARTICLES MADE OF A BERYLLIUM-COPPER ALLOY. (Courtesy, The American Brass Co.)

product thus obtained may be heat tempered after the fashion of steel, and when used as a material for springs shows little of the "fatigue" exhibited by steel under similar conditions. Its properties vary little with use or with changes of temperature. In general, beryllium alloys show good electrical and heat conductivity and are nonsparking and nonmagnetic. Certain of its alloys with cobalt and copper are especially hard, and others with nickel have great tensile strength. Its nontarnishing silver alloy has received previous mention.

The free metal is hard enough to scratch glass (contrast this with the behavior of the heavier metals of the family), and takes a high polish which tarnishes but slowly. It is so easily penetrated by x-rays that windows of it are often incorporated into x-ray tubes. One of its most unusual properties is the especially high speed with which sound waves travel through it. Future uses may be based upon this property.

6. Chemical Properties

Beryllium compounds find little use either industrially or in the laboratory. This situation is due both to the relative scarcity of the parent element and to its amphoteric nature, which fosters a ready hydrolysis of its salts in solution. The oxide, with a melting point of 2570° C., finds some use as a refractory, and when thoroughly purified is used in the preparation of fluorescent lamps and screens. Neither the oxide nor the hydroxide is soluble in water. From solution, the compound $Be_2O(OH)_2$ precipitates, but gradually forms the compound $Be(OH)_2$. Upon being heated, the hydroxide loses water to yield the oxide, BeO, which will sinter to a solid as hard as corundum (sintered aluminum oxide). The oxide and hydroxide dissolve in strong acids to form the corresponding salts, but the normal salts can be crystallized from such solutions only in the presence of a considerable excess of acid, so great is the tendency to hydrolysis. Strong bases also dissolve the oxide and hydroxide to form metallic beryllates of the type K_2BeO_2. These may be made also by the dry fusion of the oxides of beryllium and an active metal. When solutions of the beryllates are either diluted or boiled, $Be(OH)_2$ is reprecipitated.

Unlike most metallic halides, those of beryllium when molten are poor conductors of electricity (cf. anhydrous aluminum chloride).

The normal carbonate of the element is not known, but a basic carbonate may be precipitated by the addition of a solution of sodium or ammonium carbonate to solutions of its salts. The element may be distinguished from aluminum by this behavior. The precipitate is soluble in an excess of the precipitating reagent.

II. CALCIUM

7. Occurrence

In the order of their abundance in the earth's crust, calcium stands fifth among the elements and third among the metals. Like the other members of its family, it is too active ever to be found free, but its compounds are widely distributed over the earth and occur in large deposits in many places. Most plentiful of its compounds is the slightly soluble carbonate which is the principal constituent of *limestone*. A slightly more pure and much more compact variety of the naturally occurring carbonate is known as *marble*, and, because it may

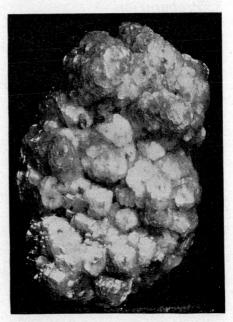

A MASS OF CALCITE CRYSTALS. (Courtesy, American Museum of Natural History.)

be given a high polish, is in considerable demand as a stone for the construction of buildings and monuments. Naturally occurring colorless crystals of calcium carbonate are known as *calcite* when they are of the hexagonal system, and *aragonite* when of the rhombic. This compound is also the principal constituent of chalk, marl, coral, sea shells, and eggshells. *Dolomite*, the mixed carbonate of calcium and magnesium, has already been referred to (section 3, Chapter 13) as being widely distributed in nature.

Much calcium sulfate also occurs naturally. It is found as the mineral *anhydrite*, $CaSO_4$, but even more commonly as *gypsum*, $CaSO_4.2H_2O$. Other important calcium-containing minerals already referred to in preceding chapters are *phosphorite* or *phosphate rock*, *apatite*, *chlorapatite* (Chapter 20), and *fluorite* or *fluorspar*, CaF_2 (Chapter 26). Calcium is also a constituent of many naturally occurring silicates. The importance of calcium phosphate in the bony structures of animals has been mentioned previously. Calcium salts are to be found in small quantities in the blood of human beings and other animals. There it plays an important role in the clotting of the blood when exposed, in the maintenance of the proper pH of the fluid, and in the health of the nerves.

8. Preparation

Although calcium compounds have been known to man since he first roamed over limestone hills and took refuge in limestone caves, the free element was not known until 1808, when Davy, the discoverer of many of the other alkali and alkaline earth metals, obtained it by electrolysis. To him it also owes the name *calcium*, which he derived from *calx*, the Latin word for *lime*. At the present time, the metal is obtained in essentially the same manner. The anhydrous chloride, $CaCl_2$, is melted in a graphite crucible which serves as the anode of the cell. The cathode is usually a copper rod tipped with iron. As metallic calcium is deposited on the rod, it is raised so that shortly the cathode is in essence a rod of calcium. The cathode must be raised as more of the metal is deposited, for, if left in contact with the molten chloride, it tends both to react and to dissolve. The deposit must be raised from the bath so that it retains a coating of the solidified electrolyte to protect it from the air. The irregular deposit of the metal obtained is usually referred to as a "carrot."

9. Uses of the Metal

Prior to 1939, practically all of the calcium used in the United States was imported from France. The maximum quantity imported in any one year was 40,000 lb. Domestic production was begun during the summer of 1939, and in the succeeding years use of the metal far exceeded that of the prewar years. The metal is used in the manufacture of alloys, as a deoxidizer, as a reducing agent, and in the manufacture of organic compounds used as pharmaceuticals.

Calcium-lead alloys are used as bearing metals, as cable sheathings, as battery grids, and for a number of other purposes. As a deoxidant, the metal is used in the casting of copper, stainless steel, and ordnance and other alloy steels. It is also used to remove oxygen and nitrogen from radio tubes and other

AN ELECTROLYTIC CELL FOR THE PRODUCTION OF CALCIUM. (Courtesy, Union Carbide & Carbon Research Lab., Inc.)

vacuum equipment, and to dry alcohol and other organic liquids. As a reducing agent, it is used in the preparation of cesium, chromium, thorium, uranium, and other very active metals from their ores. Uses for calcium increase as research progresses and as its price decreases.

10. *Chemical Properties*

Freshly exposed calcium surfaces have a bright silvery luster which slowly tarnishes upon exposure to water vapor. At about $20°$ C., the metal reacts readily with solutions of hydrochloric acid and with dilute solutions of various acids and bases. Reaction is much slower with concentrated solutions of the oxidizing acids and the strong bases.

At ordinary temperatures, the dry metal shows little tendency toward combination, even with oxygen or the halogens. At bright red heat, it burns in air to form a mixture of the colorless oxide and nitride, CaO and Ca_3N_2. It will combine under similar conditions with the halogens, hydrogen, phosphorus, sulfur, carbon, and silicon. The hydride is of the saltlike variety and is easily hydrolyzed to yield the hydroxide of calcium and hydrogen. The nitride, phosphide, sulfide, carbide, and silicide are also easily hydrolyzed. The student should write an equation to represent each of these reactions, and should name the products formed.

11. Oxide and Hydroxide

Calcium oxide, CaO, is known both as *quicklime* and as *unslaked lime*, and, although it may be made by direct union of its elements, it is most cheaply prepared by heating the naturally occurring carbonate to 800° to 1000° C.:

$$CaCO_3 \rightleftharpoons CaO + CO_2 \uparrow$$

It will be observed from the equation that the reaction is reversible; however, if the carbon dioxide formed is allowed to escape, the reaction will proceed to completion. In some instances, the escaping gas is collected, purified, and sold; in others, it is allowed to enter the air. Both vertical furnaces (lime kilns) and more or less horizontal rotary kilns are used. If the temperature is allowed to rise above 1200° C., the siliceous material usually present in limestone forms a glassy slag which coats the lime and thus slows its reaction. Such a product is described as *dead-burnt*, and is practically valueless. The oxide has a strong affinity for water and is, therefore, a good drying agent.

When water is added to quicklime, a vigorous reaction which is strongly exothermic occurs:

$$CaO + H_2O \rightarrow Ca(OH)_2 + 15,540 \text{ cal.}$$

The product is the hydroxide, *slaked lime*, or *hydrated lime*, which may be reconverted to the oxide by being heated to 450° C. The hydroxide is a white powder of low solubility in water, notable for the fact that it is more soluble in cold water than in hot. Its saturated solution is known as *lime water* and at 20° C. contains 0.161 g. of solute per 100 g. of water. Because it is both a strong base and cheap, calcium hydroxide finds a wider industrial use than any of the other strong bases.

Both the oxide and hydroxide react readily with a wide variety of acids to form the corresponding salts. Both slaked lime and quicklime react with chlorine to form bleaching powder, CaCl(OCl) (cf. section 6, Chapter 22), and with carbon dioxide to form calcium carbonate. To prevent this last reaction, both limes should be packed in moisture-proof containers. At high temperatures, quicklime combines with sand and other siliceous materials to form fusible slags, hence is used in the refining of metals whose ores contain such siliceous substances. The pure calcium oxide has a melting point of 2572° C., is little affected by heat, and can be reduced only by sodium and the other very active metals. When heated strongly, it glows with a brilliant white light (lime light)—a property which made it useful in theaters before the day of high-power electric lamps.

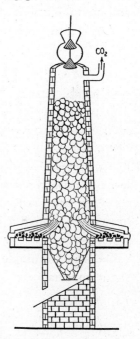

Slaked lime finds its biggest use in the building trades as a constituent of mortars, plasters, and cements. Other large uses are in the refining of metals, the manufacture of paper, the practice of agriculture (as a fertilizer, as a soil conditioner, and as a component of various insecticidal and fungicidal spray mixtures and whitewashes), the refining of water, the manufacture of glass, and the dehairing of hides. The list of lesser uses is almost interminable.

12. Halides

Naturally occurring calcium fluoride finds wide use as a source of fluorine and fluorine compounds, as a flux in metallurgical processes, and as a component of certain enamels, glazes, and glasses. Transparent crystals

A VERTICAL LIME KILN.

of the substance are used in various optical devices, but, because of their increasing scarcity, they are being replaced in this use by synthetic lithium fluoride crystals. The production of fluorspar is discussed in section 3 of Chapter 26. Some calcium fluoride is also obtained from apatite.

Calcium chloride is a constituent of *chlorapatite*, of *tachydrite*, $2MgCl_2.$-$CaCl_2.12H_2O$, and of a number of other minerals. It is also found to the extent of about 0.15 per cent in ocean water and in varying percentages in the brines of various salt wells. Its production in superabundance as a by-product of the Solvay process has already been mentioned (cf. section 17 of Chapter 27). It crystallizes from solution as the hexahydrate, but the mono-, di-, and tetra-hydrates are also known. When partially or totally dehydrated, the salt is an excellent drying agent, and as such finds wide application both industrially and in the laboratory. This property, coupled with its cheapness, permits its use on clay tennis courts, in mines, and in other dusty places to lay the dust. The equilibrium pressure for the reaction $H_2O + CaCl_2 \rightleftarrows CaCl_2.H_2O$ is 0.34 mm. of mercury at 25° C., hence the anhydrous salt does not absolutely dry the air but will reduce its water vapor content to a low value. The anhydrous salt also will combine in a similar fashion with molecules of the lower alcohols and with molecules of ammonia.

When the hydrated salt is heated there ensues partial hydrolysis:

$$CaCl_2 + H_2O \xrightarrow{\Delta} CaO + 2HCl \uparrow$$

This is accounted for in part by the volatility of the HCl formed. The salt so prepared is not suitable for use in the production of calcium metal. Like other deliquescent salts, calcium chloride is highly soluble in water, even at low temperatures. Its solutions are therefore well suited to the preparation of brines for use in refrigerating and cold-storage plants. The eutectic temperature for water and $CaCl_2.6H_2O$ is −54.9° C., hence ice cream may be frozen much harder with a mixture of ice and this salt than with a mixture of ice and sodium chloride.

Calcium bromide finds some use in medicine, but it and the iodide are of slight importance.

13. *Sulfates*

Attention has already been directed to the natural occurrence of calcium sulfate as the minerals gypsum and anhydrite. Of the two, gypsum is the much more important and the much more common. It is widely distributed in nature in its massive form. Its crystalline forms, known as *alabaster, selenite,* and *satin spar,* are less common. States which lead in the production of gypsum are New York, Michigan, Iowa, Texas, and Ohio. The compound is but slightly soluble in water (0.222 g./100 g. of water at 100° C.), and, when calcium sulfate is precipitated from solution, the deposit consists of crystals of the dihydrate. Untreated gypsum is used in large quantities for addition to agricultural lands to reduce alkalinity, and for addition to Portland cement to reduce its rate of setting. Much partially dehydrated gypsum is also used industrially.

When gypsum is heated for about an hour at about 175° C., it loses three-fourths of its water, forming the hemihydrate:

$$2(CaSO_4.2H_2O) \xrightarrow{\Delta} (CaSO_4)_2.H_2O + 3H_2O \uparrow$$

When mixed with a proper quantity of water, the product, known commonly as *plaster of Paris*, readily reforms gypsum and sets to a hard mass of small, interlocking crystals. During the process, there is an evolution of heat and a slight expansion which permits the plaster to give a sharp and very accurate reproduction of the vessel or mold in which it set. Gypsum which has been heated too long or above 200° C., so that it has become completely dehydrated, gives dead-burned plaster of Paris, which shows little tendency to set. Plaster of Paris is used in making surgical and dental casts, molds, patterns, and reproductions of art objects. It and other partially calcined gypsums are used in making stucco, wallboard, and a variety of building plasters, and in the manufacture of glass, pottery, terra cotta, and blackboard crayon (popularly and erroneously known as chalk).

Alabaster finds some use in the manufacture of art objects and as an ornamental building stone.

14. Sulfites

When solutions of calcium salts and of sulfites are mixed, a precipitate of the formula $CaSO_3.2H_2O$ readily forms. If sulfur dioxide is now passed into the solution containing the precipitate, it gradually dissolves as the more soluble bisulfite, $Ca(HSO_3)_2$, is formed. On an industrial scale, this latter substance is usually prepared by passing an excess of sulfur dioxide into solutions of calcium chloride obtained from the Solvay process. The bisulfite solution will dissolve the lignin of wood without dissolving the cellulose, hence is important in the manufacture of wood-pulp paper. Vanillin and other useful products may be obtained and alcohol may be manufactured from the waste liquors. The sulfite and bisulfite are used in the bleaching of wood pulp, in the extraction of protein from cereal grains, and to prevent souring in the fermentation industries.

15. Sulfide

Because of its solubility and ready hydrolysis, the sulfide of calcium cannot be prepared in aqueous solution. It is best prepared by reduction of the dry sulfate with carbon, and is obtained in quantity as a by-product of the Leblanc process (*q.v.*). A paste of the salt prepared with water slowly hydrolyzes, with the evolution of hydrogen sulfide, and is an effective solvent of hair. As a depilatory it is used as a toilet article and for the commercial dehairing of hides.

Impure calcium sulfide which has been irradiated glows in the dark and is used in the preparation of luminous paints. Impure barium sulfide behaves similarly.

16. Nitrate

Calcium nitrate crystallizes from solution as large, colorless, monoclinic crystals of the formula $Ca(NO_3)_2.4H_2O$. They are deliquescent and so soluble that the salt is found in nature only in traces in fertile soils. The salt is prepared from the carbonate, usually, and is sometimes sold as a fertilizer. The anhydrous salt and the trihydrate are also known.

17. Phosphate

Mention has already been made of the natural occurrence of large deposits of phosphorite and other minerals which contain tertiary calcium phosphate, and of the importance of both calcium and phosphorus in the economy of plants and animals. The manufacture of superphosphate fertilizers containing both elements is discussed in section 25 of Chapter 20. For the human organism, milk is a good source of both. Vitamin D is essential to their proper assimilation.

18. Carbonates

In section 7, mention was made of the abundance and of the forms in which calcium carbonate occurs. It may be pointed out further that pearls are also composed of this material and are formed by certain mollusks, such as the oyster, as a result of injury or of irritation caused by the presence of a foreign particle. Oyster shell is fed to chickens and other fowls to supply them with sufficient calcium to manufacture the shells of their eggs. Calcite is known by various names, such as *Iceland spar*, *onyx*, and *oriental alabaster*, and finds a variety of uses. From the standpoint of quantity used, limestone is the most important of the calcium carbonate minerals. It is a massive form of the compound, is a dull, pale gray in color, and is nearly insoluble in water. Large quantities of it are used as building stones, further quantities of it are used as a source of lime as discussed in section 11, and still further quantities of it are used in the refining of siliceous ores as a slagging agent. When used in this latter capacity, the carbonate is, of course, converted by the heat of the furnace to quicklime, which is the actual slagging agent (cf. section 11). Other uses include the manufacture of cement, calcium carbide, and calcium cyanamide.

A Travertine Formation in Yellowstone National Park. (Courtesy, U.S. National Park Service.)

Calcium carbonate in all of its various forms is very nearly insoluble in pure water. Its ability to dissolve in water containing dissolved carbon dioxide, however, was pointed out and discussed in section 16 of Chapter 27. Many of the caves which are characteristic of limestone formations have been formed by such solutions gradually dissolving away the solid matter which once filled the void. After the formation of such caverns, other calcium-bicarbonate-laden waters entering through their ceilings form the stalactites, stalagmites, and columns which adorn many of them. Water seeping through the rocky formation is under more or less pressure, but the pressure is somewhat relieved when it enters the cave so that carbon dioxide is permitted to escape and the soluble bicarbonate contained by the solution becomes an insoluble carbonate. Since some of the water has dripped to the cavern floor, deposits are built up on both the ceiling and the floor as evaporation occurs. Stalactites build from the ceiling, stalagmites from the floor. In time, two such matching formations may unite into a column, but their growth is usually infinitely slow. Deposits of calcium carbonate formed in a similar way around springs are known as *travertine*. Sometimes travertine is used as a building stone.

19. Hardness in Water

The *hardness* of water is due largely to the presence of certain ions, among which are the calcium and bicarbonate ions referred to in the preceding section. The other ions most commonly present in hard waters are magnesium, iron,

and manganese, along with sulfates and chlorides. Colloidal particles of siliceous material may also cause some hardness. It is thus apparent that hard
waters seldom have exactly the same composition.

The most noticeable effects of hardness are two: (a) with soap it causes
the formation of a sticky, curdy precipitate, and (b) in steam boilers, teakettles,
and water pipes it causes the formation of a hard scaly deposit. Commercial
soaps, as has been shown in section 12 of Chapter 29, for the most part are
the sodium salts of a mixture of organic acids. When such compounds are
added to hard waters, there ensue metatheses by which insoluble soaps of the
metallic ions mentioned above are formed. Before any lather will develop,

CROSS-SECTIONS OF PIPES CLOGGED WITH DEPOSITS OF BOILER
SCALE. (Courtesy, The Permutit Co.)

sufficient soap to precipitate those cations must be added. The sticky curds
formed have a pronounced tendency to adhere to skin, hair, cloth, or almost
anything else with which they come in contact. If an iron curd stuck to cloth
is pressed with a hot iron, a brown stain of ferric oxide is left on the cloth; if a
manganous curd is so pressed, a black stain of manganese dioxide is left. The
former stain may be removed from white cloth by treatment with a solution of
oxalic acid, while the latter may be removed by treatment with a solution of
sodium bisulfite.

When hard waters are heated, the water is removed as steam, but its nonvolatile solutes are left behind in the boiler, and in due course a considerable
deposit of solids collects on the walls of the vessel. These solids are poor
conductors of heat and thus insulate the water from the fire, thereby causing
more fuel to be used to bring the water to the requisite temperature. Since

more heat must be applied, the iron of the boiler may become red hot and may react with water, thereby becoming weakened to the point of ultimately permitting an explosion.

It is common practice in the United States to express the hardness of water in terms of parts per million (p.p.m.) of calcium carbonate or its equivalent, or in terms of grains of that salt, or its equivalent, per gallon (58,333 grains). One grain per gallon is equivalent to 17 p.p.m.

20. The Softening of Hard Waters

It will be seen from the preceding paragraphs that the softening of hard waters is of importance from the practical and economical standpoints as well as from the theoretical.

Hard waters are of two generally recognized categories: temporary and permanent. Waters of the first class contain only the bicarbonates of the metals whose carbonates are insoluble. By boiling such waters, the insoluble carbonates are formed as a scale which adheres to the walls of the containing vessel:

$$Mg(HCO_3)_2 \xrightarrow{boil} \underline{MgCO_3} + H_2O + CO_2 \uparrow$$

The scale may be removed by treatment with dilute hydrochloric acid. Usually, however, it is not convenient to remove temporary hardness by boiling, but when it is, protective colloids (q.v.) are often added so that the particles of precipitated carbonate may not adhere to each other and to the walls of the boiler. No scale forms in such a case, and the boiler may be readily cleaned by flushing. Temporarily hard water most commonly is softened chemically by treatment with the proper quantity of slaked lime,

$$Ca(HCO_3)_2 + Ca(OH)_2 \rightarrow \underline{2CaCO_3} + 2H_2O$$

followed by filtration to remove the precipitate formed.

Permanently hard waters contain the usual cations, and anions other than bicarbonates, and may be softened only by chemical treatment. Especially well suited for the softening of such waters is sodium carbonate. It will precipitate the undesired cations as their insoluble carbonates, and in exchange will leave only the sodium ion, which is not a source of hardness:

$$Ca^{++} + SO_4^{--} + 2Na^+ + CO_3^{--} \rightarrow \underline{CaCO_3} + 2Na^+ + SO_4^{--}$$

Waters which contain both types of hardness are softened commercially by treatment with sodium hydroxide. It converts the soluble bicarbonates to

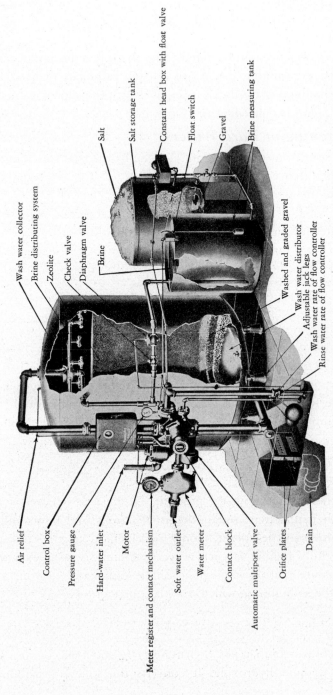

EQUIPMENT FOR THE SOFTENING OF WATER BY THE PERMUTIT PROCESS. The Permutit process utilizes synthetic sodium aluminosilicates. (Courtesy, The Permutit Co.)

insoluble carbonates, and the sodium carbonate formed as a by-product then acts as described above to remove permanent hardness.

Other softening agents are borax, $Na_2B_4O_7.10H_2O$; trisodium phosphate, $Na_3PO_4.12H_2O$; sodium hexametaphosphate, $Na_6P_6O_{18}$; and sodium meta-silicate, $Na_2SiO_3.5H_2O$. Like sodium carbonate, these reagents are all well suited to household water softening, since their use in slight excess causes no difficulties. In general, their solutions are mildly alkaline, as a result of hydrolysis. Soaps should not be used until the softening agent has had time to react, and it is cheaper, in general, to use a softening agent and a soap than it is to buy a soap in which a softener has been incorporated.

Large quantities of water are also softened by the use of ion-exchange reactions. The active chemical agent in these exchanges is usually a granular, synthetic sodium aluminosilicate which is closely related chemically to the naturally occurring *zeolites*. As the water to be treated flows through a tank containing this material, calcium and other cations which cause hardness displace sodium ions from it. When the softening cartridge has been exhausted, it may be regenerated by being soaked for a time in a concentrated solution of sodium chloride. If the formula for the sodium aluminosilicate is taken as Na_2Z, the reactions involved are:

$$Na_2Z + Ca^{++} \rightarrow \underline{CaZ} + 2Na^+$$

and

$$CaZ + 2NaCl \rightarrow \underline{Na_2Z} + CaCl_2$$

The reversal of a reaction by a change in concentration is well illustrated by this process.

By similar ion-exchange methods, it is now possible to demineralize waters completely, thus making possible the use of sea water for drinking purposes. In most of these processes, metallic ions are exchanged for hydrogen, or hydronium, ions, which in turn are removed in a deacidizing unit which also effects the removal of anions. In this process, synthetic resins serve as the source of hydrogen ions, and when spent they may be regenerated for further use by treatment with dilute sulfuric acid.

21. Mortar and Plaster

Mortar is the binding agent commonly employed in the erection of brick walls. It is made by mixing one part of slaked lime and three or four parts of sand with sufficient water to make a paste of the proper consistency. Upon exposure to the air, the mixture "sets" by losing water and by reacting with carbon dioxide to form interlocking crystals of calcium carbonate:

$$Ca(OH)_2 + CO_2 \rightarrow \underline{CaCO_3} + H_2O \uparrow$$

The reaction is rapid at first, but slows as the crystals formed offer protection to the internal material, and may not be completed for many years.

Ordinary plaster is very similar to mortar save that it usually contains hair or other fibers to help hold it in place. Special plasters contain plaster of Paris and other ingredients which vary with the demands of the use to which they are to be put.

22. Portland Cement

Portland cement is manufactured in large quantities for use in the building trades. Its use was known to the early Romans, and it takes its name from

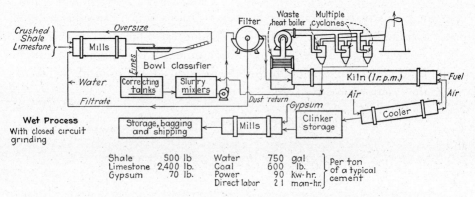

Shale 500 lb.   Water 750 gal.
Limestone 2,400 lb.   Coal 600 lb.
Gypsum 70 lb.   Power 90 kw-hr.   Per ton of a typical cement
Direct labor 21 man-hr.

DIAGRAMMATIC REPRESENTATION OF A PLANT FOR THE MANUFACTURE OF PORTLAND CEMENT. (Courtesy, "Chemical and Metallurgical Engineering," 4th ed., New York, McGraw-Hill Book Co.)

Portland, England, whose famous building stone it closely resembles in composition. In essence, it is a mixture of calcium aluminates and silicates which set to a hard, stonelike mass after being mixed with water. It is manufactured by grinding together clay, limestone, and water to form a thin mud, or "slurry." This mixture is heated in a rotary kiln until fusion just begins (to about 1420° C.). The cooled clinkers are then ground, and about 3 per cent of gypsum is added to slow the rate of setting. The grinding must be effective enough to yield a product 90 per cent of which will pass through a screen containing 40,000 perforations to the square inch.

Because it will set under water, Portland cement is sometimes known as *hydraulic cement*. It sets and hardens by the hydration of the compounds it contains. A mass of interlocking crystals is formed which at first gives form to the mass and then strength as the crystal growth progresses. A good cement should have a composition which falls within the following limits: CaO, 60.0 to 64.5 per cent; SiO_2, 20 to 24 per cent; Al_2O_3, 5 to 9 per cent; Fe_2O_3, 2 to 4 per cent; MgO, 1 to 4 per cent; and SO_3, 1.0 to 1.75 per cent.

Concrete is a hardened mixture of cement, sand, gravel or crushed rock, and water.

23. Calcium Carbide

Pure calcium carbide may be made by heating calcium hydride in an atmosphere of acetylene:

$$CaH_2 + C_2H_2 \rightarrow CaC_2 + 2H_2 \uparrow$$

When so prepared, it is a colorless, crystalline mass whose reactivity closely parallels that of the gray, massive, commercial product. This latter is made in large quantities by heating together lime and carbon in the electric furnace:

$$CaO + 3C \rightarrow CaC_2 + CO \uparrow$$

FURNACES USED FOR THE COMMERCIAL PREPARATION OF CALCIUM CARBIDE. (Courtesy, Tennessee Valley Authority.)

It is used principally as a source of acetylene,

$$CaC_2 + 2HOH \rightarrow \underline{Ca(OH)_2} + C_2H_2 \uparrow$$

and in the manufacture of calcium cyanamide, $CaCN_2$ (cf. §21, Chapter 24).

24. *Analytical Reactions*

The characteristic color imparted to the gas flame by volatile calcium salts is a brick red. Calcium ion is precipitated as a sulfide neither in acidic nor basic solution, but it is readily precipitated as the carbonate. Least soluble of its salts is the oxalate, which precipitates readily from solution as colorless cubes. Quantitatively, calcium is usually determined by the precipitation of this latter substance which is then ignited to the oxide and weighed:

$$2CaC_2O_4 + O_2 \xrightarrow{\Delta} 2CaO + 4CO_2 \uparrow$$

III. STRONTIUM AND BARIUM

25. *Occurrence*

Although compounds of both strontium and barium had been known for some years, the free elements were not known until 1808, when Sir Humphry Davy prepared both electrolytically. Strontium takes its name from the Scotch village of Strontian, from which came the ore in which Crawford discovered compounds of the element. Barium takes its name from the Greek word for *heavy*, in token of the high density of some of its compounds.

Neither strontium nor barium is found free in nature, and neither occurs naturally in the great quantities characteristic of the calcium compounds. Of the two, barium is the more plentiful. Both occur as their insoluble sulfates and carbonates. The sulfate of strontium is known mineralogically as *celestite*, while that of barium is known as *barite;* the carbonates are known as *strontianite* and *witherite*, respectively. In each case, the sulfate ore is the more plentiful but the more difficult to handle chemically. Because of the instability and volatility of the by-products formed when the carbonates are treated with acids, they are easily converted into other salts, but the sulfates are so slightly soluble that they are not attacked by the same acids. In general practice, the sulfates are either reduced to sulfides by fusion with carbon or are converted to carbonates by fusion with sodium carbonate; they are then treated with mineral acids to yield the desired salts:

$$SrCO_3 + 2HNO_3 \rightarrow Sr(NO_3)_2 + H_2O + CO_2 \uparrow$$

and

$$BaS + 2HCl \rightarrow BaCl_2 + H_2S \uparrow$$

Deposits of barium salts are found in the states of Georgia, Missouri, Arkansas, California, and Tennessee, and in Germany. Strontium salts are found in Scotland, Arkansas, Arizona, and in a number of other widely scattered localities.

26. Preparation

Both metals may be obtained in the elementary form by electrolysis of their molten chlorides. Because of the activity of the free metals, a cathode of mercury is frequently employed, and the amalgam formed is resolved by vacuum distillation. Some elementary barium is prepared by reduction of its oxide with either aluminum or silicon. Strontium is a silvery metal with a yellowish cast for which few uses have been found. Barium is silvery-white and of a high degree of activity. It is used as a degassing agent in the manufacture of vacuum tubes and in the preparation of a few alloys, but its uses are not yet numerous.

27. Chemical Properties

Both strontium and barium are metals of high activity, with the latter being the more active of the two. It inflames in moist air, reacts readily with cold water, and tarnishes quickly in an atmosphere of carbon dioxide. Both metals are active enough to enter into a wide variety of displacement reactions, and both are sufficiently active to enter into combination with a majority of the nonmetallic elements. As has been pointed out, however, most of their compounds are prepared by the action of acids on the sulfates and carbonates or their derivatives. In both chemical and physical properties, the compounds of the two elements closely resemble the corresponding compounds of calcium.

28. Oxides and Hydroxides

Although the oxides of both elements may be prepared by direct union of the elements, they are most easily prepared by the pyrolytic decompositions of their respective nitrates. The carbonates also decompose in a fashion analogous to that of limestone to yield the oxides, but their rates of decomposition are too slow for convenience. Like calcium oxide, the oxides of both of these elements react with water to form the corresponding hydroxides, both of which are rather strong bases. The hydroxides are more conveniently prepared by the decomposition of the carbonates with superheated steam:

$$BaCO_3 + H_2O \overset{\Delta}{\rightarrow} Ba(OH)_2 + CO_2 \uparrow$$

Both elements form a peroxide of the type MO_2. The formation of barium peroxide at a temperature in the neighborhood of 500° C. has already been discussed, as has its decomposition at higher temperatures and its use in the manufacture of hydrogen peroxide (cf. section 19 of Chapter 23). Strontium peroxide is said to be formed when the normal oxide is heated to a temperature of 400° C. with oxygen under a partial pressure of 90 atm. Both peroxides form hydrates to the type $MO_2.8H_2O$.

29. Important Compounds and Their Uses

Most important of the compounds of strontium are the halides, the nitrate, the chlorate, the carbonate, and the hydroxide. The bromide and the iodide find some use in medicine, as do the lactate and salicylate; the nitrate and the chlorate are used in the manufacture of fireworks which burn with a bright carmine flame; the carbonate is a source of other compounds and is used in the manufacture of iridescent glass; and the hydroxide is sometimes used as are the hydroxides of calcium and barium for the extraction of table sugar from molasses.

Among the compounds of barium, the insoluble sulfate is one of the most important. Large quantities of crude barite are used in the preparation of thixotropic muds used in the drilling of oil wells. It is also used as a filler in the making of paper, linoleum, oilcloth, rubber goods, etc. *Lithopone*, which is used as a filler and as a fume-proof white pigment, is a mixture of the white insoluble salts barium sulfate and zinc sulfide which are precipitated simultaneously by the reaction

$$BaS + ZnSO_4 \rightarrow \underline{BaSO_4} + \underline{ZnS}$$

Previous mention has been made of the use of a mush of barium sulfate in the taking of x-ray photographs of the alimentary tract. Because of the very slight solubility of the sulfate, this is possible despite the extreme toxicity of barium ion.

The salts of barium most commonly employed in the laboratory are the chloride, the nitrate, and the acetate. The chloride readily crystallizes from solution as the dihydrate $BaCl_2.2H_2O$.

Barium carbonate is a good source of the other compounds of the element. It is more stable to heat than is calcium carbonate, and finds use in the manufacture of glass and enamels, in the removing of sulfate ions from solution, and in the precipitation of sulfates in clay to be used in the manufacture of brick and tile. The nitrate and the chlorate are used in the manufacture of fireworks which will burn with a green flame. The perchlorate, $Ba(ClO_4)_2$, is used as a drying agent; the carbonate is occasionally used as a rat poison; the fluosilicate, $BaSiF_6$, is employed as an insecticide; and the fluoride is used in the manufacture of enamels and glazes.

30. Analytical Tests

The characteristic colors imparted to the gas flame by the volatile compounds of strontium and barium easily serve to identify the respective elements. Like calcium, neither of these elements forms an insoluble sulfide, but, also like calcium, both are readily precipitated in slightly basic solutions as carbonates. Both elements form slightly soluble colorless sulfates, and in weakly alkaline solution both form insoluble yellow chromates. The chromate of strontium is soluble in very weakly acidic solutions, while that of barium is soluble only in solutions of a fair degree of acidity. The least soluble salt of barium is its sulfate, hence the element is usually determined quantitatively by precipitating it as the sulfate which is then collected, dried, and weighed. Volumetrically, solutions of barium ion may be determined quantitatively by titration with standard sulfate solutions, with the use of tetrahydroxyquinone as an indicator. With this reagent, barium ions cause a pink color to develop. Sulfates may be determined by the reverse of these processes (cf. section 27 of Chapter 21).

(See Appendix for Exercises)

COLLATERAL READINGS

Bagley: Calcium and magnesium, *Chem. and Eng. News*, **22**, 921 (1944).

Bogue: Portland cement and plastic concrete, *J. Chem. Education*, **19**, 36 (1942).

Creighton and Koehler, *Electrochemistry*, Vol. II, New York, John Wiley & Sons, Inc., 1944.

Ephraim: *Inorganic Chemistry*, 3d Eng. ed., London, Gurney and Jackson, 1939.

Felsing: Gypsum and gypsum products, *J. Chem. Education*, **7**, 2788 (1930).

Larson and Buswell: Water softening, *Ind. Eng. Chem.*, **32**, 132 (1940).

Latimer and Hildebrand: *Reference Book of Inorganic Chemistry*, New York, The Macmillan Co., 1941.

Mantell and Hardy: *Calcium Metallurgy and Technology*, New York, Reinhold Publishing Corp., 1945.

Meyers: Ion exchange resins, *Ind. Eng. Chem.*, **35**, 858 (1943).

Ryan: The story of Portland cement, *J. Chem. Education*, **6**, 1854 (1929).

Sawyer and Kjellgren: Newer developments in beryllium, *Ind. Eng. Chem.*, **30**, 501 (1938).

Weeks: *Discovery of the Elements*, 5th ed., Mack Printing Co., 1945.

Hardwater, *Life*, 53 (March 18, 1946).

IRÈNE AND FRÉDÉRIC JOLIOT
(1897–　, 1900–　, French)

Much of the valuable scientific work of the Joliots has been done jointly. In 1932 they discovered that neutrons may be ejected from atomic nuclei; the next year they studied the production of protons by gamma-ray radiation; and in 1934 they announced the preparation of artificially radioactive elements. A number of the elements so produced were isotopes of the lighter, naturally occurring elements. This discovery has inspired much work on the preparation of similar isotopes and on their chemical, physical, and radioactive properties, as well as studies of their uses in the solution of a host of perplexing problems of chemical, physical, and biological natures. Mme. Joliot is the elder daughter of the Curies of radium fame. Both she and her husband are Parisians by birth. In 1935 they were awarded jointly the Nobel Prize for their work on elementary transmutations. (Courtesy, Weeks: "Discovery of the Elements," *Journal of Chemical Education.*)

Metallurgy—Germanium, Tin, Lead, and Their Compounds

I. METALLURGY

1. Introduction

Metallurgy is sometimes defined as the art of extracting metals from their ores. As a definition, however, such a statement is too limited, for metallurgy is no longer entirely an art, and it deals with metals in connections other than their production. At present, the field of metallurgy includes the production and refining of metals, the study of their properties, the preparation of products of a metallic nature, the finding of uses for metals and metallic products, and the study of the principles involved in such work. By applying the principles of physics and chemistry to metallurgy, workers in the field have done much to convert it from an *art* to a *science*. Thanks to the efforts of these investigators, the price of many metals has decreased, the purity of many metallic products has been greatly increased, and the development of special-purpose alloys has gone forward rapidly.

Alloys and the refining and purification of a number of specific metals have been referred to in preceding chapters, and in succeeding chapters the extraction and purification of still other individual metals will be treated, but at this juncture it seems advisable to discuss briefly and in a general way a few of the principles which apply to the field as a whole. Such a discussion seems particularly desirable, when it is considered that the majority of the metals whose extraction and refinement have been considered thus far are the highly active light metals, while those whose production remains to be discussed are, for the most part, the heavy metals of the lower, central portion of the periodic table.

2. Ores and Their Concentration

A *mineral* is any naturally occurring compound of the element in question, but an *ore* is a mineral which contains that element in a quantity sufficient to make its extraction profitable. In addition, it is only rarely that an ore consists of a pure mineral; usually varying quantities of rocky or earthy material of little value are mixed with the desired material. This worthless material is known as *gangue*.

Gold, the platinum metals, and a very few of the metals of low reactivity occur free in nature. The ores of such metals are known as *native ores*. A majority of the metals, however, are sufficiently active to occur in combination, and their ores are referred to, therefore, as *compound*. The silicates are the most abundant of the minerals, but, because of the strength of the unions in these compounds and because of their general refractoriness, they do not make good sources of the metals (cf. section 3, Chapter 18). Of prime importance among the compound ores are the oxides, sulfides, and carbonates; of secondary importance are the sulfates and chlorides.

If the ratio of gangue to mineral in an ore is high, it is usually desirable to use purely mechanical means to extract as much of the worthless material as possible. Such treatment is known as *concentration* and usually consists of crushing, followed by grinding to a fine mesh in a ball-mill, and subsequent washing in a stream of water which carries away much of the lighter rocky waste. The sulfide ores of copper and of a number of other metals and even a few ores of other types are best concentrated by the froth-flotation process described in section 8 of Chapter 19. With certain ores a "reverse"-flotation process is used; that is, the gangue particles are wet by the froth while the mineral particles remain in the water. The froth-flotation method of concentrating ores makes possible the working of low-grade material whose treatment by other methods would be unprofitable.

3. The Treatment of Native Ores

Sometimes metals which occur in the native state are in such condition that they may be recovered by methods which are wholly mechanical: for example, gold or platinum nuggets and dust are often found in stream beds and need only be picked up or washed out of the sand. More often, though, the free metals are distributed in fine particles through a matrix of valueless material. Methods of treating the concentrates of such ores depend largely upon the nature of the metal involved. For gold and silver, the amalgamation and cyanide processes (cf. Chapter 33) are used. Mercury and bismuth have sufficiently low melting points to be melted out of their ores, and native copper is recovered from its ores by fusing them with some substance that will cause the earthy material present to form a glassy slag which will float on the molten metal. Copper may also be extracted by dissolution in a solution containing the cupric tetrammino ion, $Cu(NH_3)_4^{++}$.

4. *The Treatment of Compound Ores—Smelting*

Concentration of an ore while removing much of the gangue does not remove all of it by any means. After concentration, compound ores still require to be treated in such a manner that the metal will be liberated from combination and separated from any gangue which may be present. These last two aims are usually best accomplished for most metals by a suitable heat treatment—that is, by *smelting*, generally defined as any process of metal recovery and refinement in which heat is applied and the metal melted as a result of its application. Generally, there is added to the concentrate to be smelted a suitable quantity of reducing agent to liberate the metal and a suitable quantity of a *flux* whose purpose it is to unite with the gangue to form an easily fused glassy material, usually referred to as a *slag*. If the gangue is siliceous in nature, as is usually the case, a basic flux such as calcium carbonate or magnesium carbonate is added and the slag formed is a calcium or magnesium silicate. If, on the other hand, the gangue is of a basic nature, say limestone, then an acidic flux such as sand is added and again the slag is a metallic silicate. Specific examples of such procedures will be encountered in succeeding chapters.

5. *The Treatment of Oxide Ores*

The treatment of oxide ores is of special importance because sulfide and carbonate ores are frequently converted into oxides by their initial heat treatment. To obtain a metal from its oxide, a reduction must occur. Again the exact reducing agent and the exact procedure to be followed depend upon the specific nature of the oxide to be treated and upon the melting or boiling point of the metal to be liberated, and also, as pointed out in the preceding section, to some extent upon the nature of the gangue.

In general, the lower a metal stands in the activity series, the more easily is it liberated from its ores. The commonest method of reduction is treatment with coke, which is cheap and which serves as a source of heat and also as a source of carbon monoxide. Reduction is brought about by both the hot coke and the hot monoxide gas. More active metals, and those which tend to form carbides, are displaced from their oxides by aluminum (cf. the Goldschmidt process). Sometimes silicon, magnesium, iron, and other metals are employed as reducing agents. As will be seen in the discussion of the recovery of lead (cf. section 26), sulfides are sometimes used to reduce oxides. The oxides of the most active elements, such as that of aluminum (cf. section 4, Chapter 15), are usually reduced by electrolysis.

The oxide ore which is refined in greatest quantity is that of iron. Special attention will be given to the process in Chapter 33.

6. The Treatment of Sulfide Ores

Many of our most important metals occur naturally as sulfides. Among metals which so occur may be listed copper, lead, zinc, silver, cadmium, mercury, and antimony. Such ores usually require considerable concentration, and again their smelting varies considerably with the stability of the compound in question. Mercuric sulfide is so unstable that mercury distils from the dry ore when it is heated in air. Similarly, arsenic is driven from arsenopyrite, FeAsS, when it is heated, and the sulfides of bismuth and antimony are easily reduced by heating them with iron filings:

$$Sb_2S_3 + 3Fe \xrightarrow{\Delta} 2Sb + 3FeS$$

The commonest treatment of sulfide ores is roasting—that is, they are heated in the air, being thereby totally or partially converted to oxides whose further treatment follows one of the plans mentioned in section 5. The discussions of the metallurgy of lead, copper, and zinc will serve to clarify the various aspects of this treatment.

7. The Treatment of Carbonate Ores

Upon being heated, the majority of the carbonates of the heavier metals readily decompose into the corresponding oxides (cf. section 16, Chapter 27). Further treatment is naturally that of the regular oxide ores. The refining of magnesium carbonate has already been dealt with in Chapter 13, and the recovery of zinc from its carbonate will be treated in Chapter 34. Some copper is recovered from the basic carbonate ores, which occur principally in the state of Nevada. The oxide obtained by roasting is then smelted with coke and a flux.

8. The Refining of Metals

Even when the methods described in the preceding sections of this chapter are carried out with great care, the metals produced by them are far from pure. The impurities consist of varying quantities of other metals whose minerals were present in the crude ore, of streaks of admixed slag, of dissolved gases formed during the heat treatment, of dissolved bits of the reducing agent, and of compounds formed by the hot metal and the reducing agent or other active

An Electrolytic Plant for the Refining of Copper. (Courtesy, International Smelting & Refining Co.)

nonmetallic substances present during the smelting. Sometimes the impurities are of such a nature that their presence improves the properties of the metal; for instance, carbon and manganese make iron tougher and harder. More often, however, the impurities have an opposite effect upon the properties of the metal and must be removed to increase the value of the product; for example, the conductivity of copper is greatly increased by the removal of traces of arsenic. In other instances, impurities are removed because their value is sufficiently high to make their separation profitable; silver and gold fall into this class of impurities.

The methods chosen for the purification of a given metal must naturally take into account the differences in properties of the metal and the impurities, the relative quantity of the impurities, the degree of purity required, and the economic aspects of the problem. A number of methods of refinement are in use—some are highly specialized and will be mentioned in the proper connection, while others are more or less general. Among the general methods are *distillation, liquation,* and *electrolysis.* Distillation, naturally, is suitable for use only in those cases in which there is a large difference in volatility between the metal and the impurities. It is especially suitable for mixtures which contain mercury. The use of distillation has been extended by the introduction of vacuum distillation (cf. section 8, Chapter 13). Liquation is applicable generally to the refining of metals whose melting points are considerably lower than those of the impurities. By this method, the mixture usually is heated in a furnace whose hearth slopes gently, whereupon the molten metal collects at the bottom of the hearth while the solid impurities remain above. Electrolysis is a relatively modern method whose use has steadily increased as the cost of electricity has decreased. In the electrolytic process, sheets of the crude metal serve as the anode, a solution of a suitable salt of the metal is the electrolyte, and thin sheets of the pure metal usually serve as the cathode, though some relatively inert material may be used. Large quantities of copper are refined by this process, a more detailed discussion of which will be found in Chapter 33 in connection with the production of this element. Aluminum, chromium, zinc, lead, gold, and silver are also refined electrolytically. The specialized Hoopes process used for the electrolysis of aluminum is discussed in section 4 of Chapter 15.

9. Alloys

One of the greatest contributions of the metallurgist has been the development and application of alloys. In section 8 of Chapter 13, alloys were discussed briefly and were defined in a more or less general way. Many of the metals and some of the elements which closely resemble the metals in their physical properties are capable of dissolving in each other when they are melted together. When the molten solution cools, an alloy is obtained. Examination of the crystals formed when the mixture cools shows that there are several general types of alloys. First, there are the *homogeneous alloys*. Notable among these are those which contain but one variety of crystal in which the component metals are present in the same proportion as in the molten solution. Some gold alloys belong to this class, whose members are also referred to as *solid solutions*. Certain other homogeneous alloys form no crystals and are therefore amorphous; they are regarded as *supercooled liquids*. Also homogeneous are the alloys in which the component metals appear to have reacted with each other in definite ratios (which are not necessarily the same as their proportions in the molten mixture) to form what are known as *intermetallic compounds*. The ordinary valences of the metals in such compounds do not seem to obtain, nevertheless strong evidence points to the existence of compounds.

Many alloys are *heterogeneous*. As the liquid mixture is cooled, the different elements present may form small pure crystals which interlock with those of the other elements. There are many such alloys, and they are of great practical importance. For example, many of the alloys used for bearings are of this type. Such products often appear to be homogeneous to the unaided eye, but closer examination reveals their true natures.

A given alloy often will belong to more than one of the physical classes mentioned above. Thanks to these differences in structure and to their widely varying properties, alloys serve a wide variety of purposes and fill many needs. Many alloys have been developed by the metallurgist to serve specific purposes, and, as a result of the knowledge already acquired and of that to be acquired from further research, still other alloys will be developed to meet requirements not yet satisfied. A number of specific alloys will be mentioned in succeeding chapters.

II. GERMANIUM, TIN, AND LEAD

10. *General Relationships*

Carbon, silicon, germanium, tin, and lead are the elements of the IV A family of the periodic classification of the elements. Together, they constitute a family which shows the same type of variations that are to be found in others of the regular families of the classification. Carbon and silicon are distinctly nonmetallic in their chemical behavior, though both occur in crystalline allotropes which possess certain characteristics in common with the metallic condition. Germanium, tin, and lead are definitely metallic in their appearance and other physical properties, but chemically they are all amphoteric. Carbon and silicon already have been discussed at some length, because of the great importance which attaches to their compounds; hence, in this chapter attention will be directed to the remaining elements of the family.

Germanium, tin, and lead all have four valence electrons and all can exist in the +4 oxidation state characteristic of the family, and in addition, because of the greater ease of removal of their two valence electrons of the number one sub-level, they also exist in the +2 oxidation state. This latter property they exhibit to a much more marked degree than do carbon and silicon. In fact, as atomic weights, atomic radii, and metallic properties increase, the +2 oxidation state (usually associated with metals) becomes increasingly stable, while the +4 state (usually associated with nonmetals) becomes decreasingly so. In the +2 state, all three elements form simple cations showing electrovalence, but their unions in the +4 state are principally covalent like those of the two lighter and nonmetallic members of the family. The tendency to covalency is well illustrated by the facts that the tetrachlorides are liquids and that all three elements have a pronounced tendency when in the $+4$ state to form organo-metallic compounds. All three of the elements are amphoteric in both states of oxidation.

11. General Physical Properties

A number of the physical and atomic properties of germanium, tin, and lead are listed in Table 32.

Table 32

PHYSICAL PROPERTIES OF THE METALLIC ELEMENTS OF THE IV A FAMILY

Property	Germanium (Ge)	Tin (Sn)	Lead (Pb)
Atomic weight.............	72.60	118.70	207.21
Isotopes..................	70, 72, 73, 74, 76	112,114,115,116,117,118, 119, 120, 122, 124	204, 206, 207, 208
Atomic number............	32	50	82
Electronic distribution.......	2, 8, 18, 4	2, 8, 18, 18, 4	2, 8, 18, 32, 18, 4
Ionization potential of gaseous atoms in volts			
1st valence electron........	8.09	7.30	7.38
2d valence electron........	15.86	14.5	14.96
3d valence electron........	34.07	30.5	31.9(?)
4th valence electron.......	45.5	39.4	42.11
Density, g./ml.............	5.36(20° C.)	7.31(20° C.)	11.34(16° C.)
Melting point, ° C..........	958.5	231.9	327.4
Boiling point, ° C..........	2700	2270	1613
Specific heat, cal./g........	0.074(0° to 100° C.)	0.0542(18° C.)	0.0306(20° C.)
Radius $+4$ ion in crystal, Å.U.....................	0.53	0.71	0.84

III. GERMANIUM

12. Occurrence

Germanium is never found free in nature. It is much less abundant than either tin or lead, and its compounds are so widely distributed that no marked concentrations of them have yet been found. It occurs usually as a component of the sulfide ores of some of the commoner metals such as silver, lead, tin, and zinc, and occasionally rare minerals of the element are found. Among these latter is *germanite*, deposits of which occur in South Africa.

The existence of germanium was predicted by Mendelejeff in 1871, and its discovery was achieved in 1886 by Winkler, who found it to be a component of the rare mineral *argyrodite*, whose formula is reported to be Ag_8GeS_6.

13. Preparation

Elementary germanium is a rather hard, silvery-white metal which shows little tendency to tarnish. It is quite brittle, and is a poor conductor of electricity. It is most readily prepared by reduction of its dioxide, GeO_2, which is readily obtained by the roasting of the sulfide ores. Among the various reducing agents which may be employed are carbon, aluminum, hydrogen, and potassium cyanide. Although germanium alloys readily with a number of other metals, few uses have been found for it.

14. Chemical Properties

The oxidation states in which germanium exists in its compounds are +2 and +4. It is amphoteric in both states so that, in addition to forming germanous and germanic compounds, it also forms germanites and germanates. The +4 oxidation state is more stable than the +2, which readily undergoes both oxidation and reduction.

Most familiar of the germanic compounds is the oxide GeO_2, which is readily formed by heating the metal above 600° C. or by roasting its simple and complex sulfides. It is soluble in neither sulfuric acid nor nitric acid, but does dissolve slowly in either hydrofluoric or hydrochloric acids to form the corresponding tetrahalides. The tetrachloride readily hydrolyzes to reform the acid and a hydrated variety of the dioxide, while the tetrafluoride forms some fluogermanic acid, H_2GeF_6, in addition to the analogous products. In alkalies, the dioxide dissolves to form germanates:

$$2NaOH + GeO_2 \rightarrow Na_2GeO_3 + H_2O$$

The metal also dissolves in molten alkalies, in molten alkali carbonates and nitrates, and in molten sodium peroxide to form germanates.

Germanium resembles silicon in that it forms several unstable hydrides, which may be prepared by reduction of germanium compounds with aluminum in alkaline solution. The compound GeH_4 is the principal product, but Ge_2H_6 and Ge_3H_8 are formed in traces.

Germanous acid, H_2GeO_2, is prepared by the hydrolysis of the compound $GeHCl_3$, which, in turn, is prepared by heating the metal in a stream of anhydrous hydrogen chloride. The acid dissolves in strong bases to form germanites, and upon heating yields germanous oxide, GeO, which dissolves in strong acids to form germanous salts.

Germanic sulfide, GeS_2, is precipitated by H_2S in massive form in strong sulfuric acid but in colloidal form in dilute acid. Upon careful heating, it yields germanous sulfide.

A wide variety of germano-organic compounds have been prepared, but few are of practical value.

IV. TIN

15. *Occurrence*

Tin is found in the elementary condition very rarely; principally, it is found in the combined condition. Most important of its ores is *cassiterite*, or *tinstone*, which contains the dioxide, SnO_2. The principal deposits of this mineral are in the Malay States, Bolivia, and the Dutch East Indies. Lesser deposits, which have been worked since as early as 1000 B.C., are located in Cornwall in England. Unfortunately, no noteworthy deposits of tin ore have been found in the United States. The Bolivian ores contain sulfides as well as the dioxide of tin.

16. *Preparation*

Tin dioxide is easily reduced, but the refining of its ores is complicated by the low percentage (1 to 5) of the dioxide and by the presence of a variety of other metals and nonmetals. The ore usually is concentrated by reverse flotation; it is then roasted to remove sulfur and arsenic as their volatile oxides; tungsten may be removed magnetically before the roasting or by fusion with sodium carbonate followed by leaching with water; the oxides of iron, zinc, copper, and other metals are next removed by treatment with sulfuric or hydrochloric acids; and lastly, the remaining dioxide of tin is reduced in a tin furnace with carbon. The product is still impure and is further refined by liquation (cf. section 8).

The ease with which tin ores are reduced no doubt accounts for the discovery of the element in prehistoric times. Bronze (an alloy of tin and copper) was prepared from it, and with the discovery of this alloy the transition from the Stone Age to those of metals was made possible. Tin is still in great demand, and for some uses is almost irreplaceable. During World War II, with the Japanese in control of the East Indian tin supplies, the United States obtained most of its supply of the metal from Bolivia. Prior to the war, Bolivian tin was refined almost entirely in England, but during the war a smelter was built at Texas City, Texas, to supply the needs of the United States.

The name *tin* is an Anglo-Saxon word; its symbol, *Sn*, is derived from *stannum*, the Latin name of the element.

17. Allotropes of Tin

Tin resembles carbon and silicon in that it exists in a variety of allotropic forms. These are three in number, and their names and transition temperatures are given in the accompanying diagram.

$$\text{Cubic tin} \underset{}{\overset{18°\,C.}{\rightleftarrows}} \text{Tetragonal tin} \underset{}{\overset{161°\,C.}{\rightleftarrows}} \text{Rhombic tin} \underset{}{\overset{231.9°\,C.}{\rightleftarrows}} \text{Liquid}$$

Cubic tin	Tetragonal tin	Rhombic tin	tin
(α-tin)	(β-tin or white tin)	(γ-tin)	
d = 5.75 g./ml.	d = 7.31 g./ml.	d = 7.31 g./ml.	

It is apparent from this diagram that tetragonal tin is the variety commonly encountered. It is silvery-white in color, with a high luster little affected by oxygen, moisture, or carbon dioxide. It is malleable and readily rolled into sheets of foil which find a wide use. Tetragonal tin is attacked only superficially by dilute acids, but strongly so by concentrated nitric acid and hot solutions of the alkalies. Rhombic tin forms above 161° C., and is so brittle that it cannot be rolled into foils. As the temperature is raised above the melting point, surface oxidation occurs, and, at white heat, the metal burns to form the dioxide.

The existence of allotropes of tin was first observed in very cold countries where tin organ pipes and other articles made of the metal were observed to crumble to a gray powder. At first, this was thought to be the work of an organism, and reference to a "tin pest" or "tin plague" became common. Later, the true nature of the change became apparent. At 18° C., the change from white tin to the powdery gray tin is very slow, but, at lower temperatures, the transformation is rather rapid and at −50° C. the change is said to become complete in a few days at most. Gray tin has a cubic lattice like that of diamond.

18. Uses of the Metal

Normally, about 50 per cent of the metallic tin imported into the United States is used in the preparation of *tin plate*, a majority of which is consumed in the manufacture of *tin cans*, most of which find ultimate use as food containers. For the preparation of tin plate, thin sheets of iron or steel are thoroughly cleaned by pickling in acid, and are then dipped in molten tin. After being dipped, they are rolled to remove excess tin and to insure uniformity of its thickness. Despite the fact that the tin so applied forms a layer whose average thickness is only 0.00009 in., a saving of some 60 per cent of this metal may be effected by substitution of an electroplating method for the dip-and-roll procedure.

The other half of domestic tin imports is used in the preparation of alloys; in the manufacture of collapsible tubes, pipes, and tubing; in the manufacture of foils; and in the manufacture of chemicals. Among the tin alloys which should be mentioned are solder (50-50 Sn and Pb), a variety of bronzes (alloys principally with copper), Babbitt metal (89 per cent Sn, 3.7 per cent Cu, 7.3 per cent Sb) and other bearing metals, and type metal (26 per cent Sn, 58 per cent Pb, 15 per cent Sb, 1 per cent Cu). The use of tanks lined with tin has already been mentioned (Chapter 23) as especially desirable for the storage of distilled water, and pipes of the metal are used for dispensing both distilled water and soda water. Extensive use of tin foil as a wrapper for many products is well known, and the use of the compounds of tin will be dealt with in succeeding sections.

19. *Chemical Properties*

Like germanium, tin forms compounds in which it exhibits oxidation numbers of $+2$ and $+4$. It is amphoteric in both states, although in the $+2$ condition it is more basic than acidic, while in the $+4$ state the reverse is true. Stannous compounds are readily oxidized to the stannic condition and hence make good reducing agents. Besides uniting directly with oxygen, tin will also combine directly with sulfur to form sulfides and with the halogens to form the tetrahalides. Although the element shows little tendency to displace hydrogen from dilute acids, it reacts with HCl to form the complex compound $HSnCl_3$, and it displaces hydrogen from solutions of the strongly basic hydroxides. Use is made of this latter behavior in one method of recovering tin from tin plate. The sodium salt formed is decomposed electrolytically to deposit the metal. Tin forms no complexes with ammonia and cyanides, but it does form complexes with OH^-, F^-, and Cl^- ions. The various ions of the element are colorless, but a number of its compounds are colored.

20. *Oxides and Hydroxides*

When strong basic hydroxides are added to solutions containing the stannous ion, Sn^{++}, a white precipitate of stannous hydroxide forms. Like other amphoteric hydroxides, this one is gelatinous and contains a varying quantity of water; it is, therefore, more properly referred to as a *hydrous oxide*, but, by custom, its formula is usually written $Sn(OH)_2$ rather than $SnO.xH_2O$. In an excess of strong base, the precipitate dissolves to form a stannite. Although there is some evidence to indicate that the formula of sodium stannite should be $Na_2[Sn(OH)_4]$, showing it to be a hydroxide complex, the formula is customarily represented as $NaHSnO_2$. In alkaline solution, the stannites are powerful reducing agents.

Careful dehydration of stannous hydroxide yields the corresponding oxide, SnO. This compound may also be prepared as a gray powder by heating the metal in a limited supply of air, or as a black powder by the pyrolytic decomposition of stannous oxalate in the absence of air.

Stannic oxide is obtained when tin is heated to white heat in an excess of air, or when stannous oxide is strongly heated in the open air. This oxide, being more acidic than basic, readily reacts with fused alkalies to form soluble stannates:

$$SnO_2 + 2NaOH \xrightarrow{\Delta} Na_2SnO_3 + H_2O$$

In accordance with the formula mentioned above for stannites, the formula for sodium stannate perhaps should be written more properly as $Na_2[Sn(OH)_6]$.

Stannic hydroxide of the formula $Sn(OH)_4$ is not known, but two forms of a hydrated stannic oxide are known. In its relation to water as demonstrated in these two compounds, stannic oxide shows its close kinship to the dioxide of silicon. When an acid is added to a solution of a stannate, a bulky, gelatinous precipitate of the hydrated oxide is formed. The precipitate will dissolve in either strong acids or strong bases when freshly prepared, but its solubility decreases with age. It is known as α-stannic acid. The insoluble form of the acid, known as β-stannic acid, may be prepared directly by the action of strong nitric acid upon the metal. The principal difference between the α and β forms seems to be physical rather than chemical, with the β form apparently having the larger particles. The behavior of nitric acid upon tin should be compared with that of the same acid upon antimony.

21. Chlorides

Both the dichloride and the tetrachloride of tin are of importance. Anhydrous stannous chloride is readily prepared by passing a stream of anhydrous hydrogen chloride over the heated metal. Hydrolysis occurs when the salt is added to water and the liquid is clouded by the formation of a basic chloride. Addition of an excess of hydrochloric acid to the solution reverses the equilibrium and restores the clarity of the fluid. The salt crystallizes from concentrated solutions as the dihydrate, $SnCl_2.2H_2O$. Acidified solutions of stannous chloride are powerful reducing agents—they reduce mercuric salts to the mercurous condition or to free mercury, ferric salts to ferrous, and a wide variety of salts of the heavier metals to lower valence states. Being so easily oxidized, solutions of the salt are attacked by the oxygen of the air. To prevent shelf solutions from being thus oxidized to the stannic condition, granular tin is usually added to them. This reduces any stannic ions formed back to the $+2$ state:

$$Sn + Sn^{+4} \rightarrow 2Sn^{+2}$$

Stannous chloride is known commercially as *tin salt*, and, in addition to being used as a reducing agent, is also used as a mordant in cotton printing and in the weighting of silk.

It is evident from the foregoing that stannic chloride may be prepared by the oxidation of the lower chloride. It is more readily prepared in the anhydrous condition, however, by the action of chlorine on the metal. Use is made of this reaction in the detinning of scrap tin plate, for, unless moisture is present, the chlorine has little action upon the iron. If both chlorides are formed they may be separated by fractional distillation, since anhydrous stannic chloride is a liquid which boils at 114.1° C., a figure considerably lower than the boiling point of ferric chloride. The liquid fumes in moist air, reacting with water to form hydrochloric acid and hydrous stannic oxide. It crystallizes from acidified aqueous solutions as the pentahydrate, known commercially as *butter of tin*, and in aqueous solutions strongly acidified with HCl it forms the complex chlorostannic acid, H_2SnCl_6:

$$2HCl + SnCl_4 \rightarrow H_2SnCl_6$$

Stannic chloride is used as a mordant and fire-proofing agent for cotton and as a weighting agent for silk. Ammonium chlorostannate, $(NH_4)_2SnCl_6$, is used in dyeing under the trade name of *pink salt*, despite the fact that it is colorless.

22. Sulfides

Stannous sulfide, SnS, may be formed as a gray mass by direct union of the elements under the influence of heat, or it may be precipitated from moderately acidic solutions of stannous ions as a brown solid by the action of hydrogen sulfide.

Stannic sulfide may also be prepared by direct union, but is more conveniently prepared by the action of hydrogen sulfide on weakly acidic solutions containing stannic compounds. Strong acids dissolve both sulfides, but the stannic compound is the less readily attacked of the two. The dry solid is used as a gilding pigment under the name of *mosaic gold*. The pigment is usually prepared by direct union in the presence of ammonium chloride and mercury, whose functions are not fully understood.

Stannic sulfide reacts with ammonium sulfide and the sulfides of the alkali metals to form the corresponding soluble complex thiostannate salts:

$$SnS_2 + Na_2S \rightarrow Na_2SnS_3$$

With the normal sulfides mentioned above, stannous sulfide forms no complexes, but it forms complex thiostannates with the polysulfides of ammonia and the alkali metals as a result of its oxidation to the stannic condition. The union of basic and acidic sulfides to form thiosalts is analogous to the union of basic and acidic oxides to form oxygen salts.

23. Analytical Tests

The sulfides of tin are precipitated along with the other metallic sulfides which form in weakly acidic solution. The mixed sulfide precipitate is then treated with a mixture of the normal sulfide and the polysulfide of ammonium which forms soluble thiosalts of tin, antimony, and arsenic. The sulfides are reprecipitated from the thiosalts by treatment with acid, and tin is separated from this mixture by treatment with moderately strong acid, its sulfides being more soluble than those of arsenic and antimony. The filtrate is treated with a more active metal to insure reduction to the stannous condition, and the presence of tin is confirmed by treatment with mercuric chloride. If tin is present, a white, black, or gray precipitate will form: white if mercurous chloride forms, black if free mercury forms, and gray if both form:

$$SnCl_2 + 2HgCl_2 \rightarrow SnCl_4 + \underline{Hg_2Cl_2}$$

and

$$SnCl_2 + HgCl_2 \rightarrow SnCl_4 + \underline{Hg}$$

V. LEAD

24. Physical Properties

Lead is a bright, silvery metal with a pronounced bluish cast. Because it tarnishes superficially in moist air to form a basic carbonate, it is usually observed to have a dull gray surface. Lead is one of our most dense metals, 1 ml. of it having a mass of 11.34 g. at 16° C. It is soft, malleable, ductile, and readily cut, but has little tensile strength. Pipes and wires are readily extruded under pressure through a die, especially when the metal has been heated to about 300° C. Octahedral and monoclinic modifications of the element are known.

25. *Occurrence*

Lead is occasionally found free in nature, but it occurs principally in combination. Its principal ore is *galena*, which contains the sulfide PbS. Galena is widely distributed in the United States and throughout the world. The United States, Mexico, Australia, and Canada are leading producers. The states of Missouri, Utah, and Idaho lead in domestic production. Less common than galena are *cerussite*, which contains $PbCO_3$, and *anglesite*, which contains $PbSO_4$. These ores are believed to have been formed by the weathering of galena, whose dark shiny cubes are easily recognized.

26. *Preparation*

Lead ores are so widely distributed and so easily reduced that the metal has been known since prehistoric times. The name *lead* is Anglo-Saxon, while the symbol Pb derives from the Latin name, *plumbum*.

Galena ores usually contain from 5 to 10 per cent of lead and an assortment of sulfides of other metals, notable among which are zinc and silver. Concentration is usually accomplished by flotation, a special modification of which permits some separation of the sulfides of lead and zinc. The concentrated ore is roasted for a time at temperatures between 450° to 750° C., with careful regulation of the air supply. During this treatment, much of the sulfur is eliminated as sulfur dioxide, while the lead is converted partly to the monoxide PbO, and partly to the sulfate $PbSO_4$:

$$4PbS + 7O_2 \rightarrow 2PbO + 2PbSO_4 + 2SO_2 \uparrow$$

Oxides of the other metals present are also formed.

The roasted ore is next mixed with raw ore, limestone, coke, and usually a little iron ore, Fe_2O_3, and placed in a furnace which in essence is a small blast furnace (cf. section 5, Chapter 33). The reactions which occur are not known with certainty, but the following are believed to be among those which take place:

$$PbO + C \rightarrow Pb + CO \uparrow$$
$$2PbO + C \rightarrow 2Pb + CO_2 \uparrow$$
$$PbO + CO \rightarrow Pb + CO_2 \uparrow$$
$$2PbO + PbS \rightarrow 3Pb + SO_2 \uparrow$$
$$PbSO_4 + PbS \rightarrow 2Pb + 2SO_2 \uparrow$$

and

$$PbS + Fe \rightarrow Pb + FeS$$

The limestone unites with any siliceous material present to form a fusible slag. As a result of the reactions which occur, three distinct layers collect in the base of the furnace for removal. These are (1) molten lead, which may contain copper, arsenic, antimony, bismuth, silver, and gold, (2) a *matte* which consists of the sulfides of iron, copper, and lead and may also contain gold and silver, and (3) the glassy slag. The matte may be treated further for the recovery of both copper and lead as well as the gold and silver, and the slag is discarded.

The lead bullion usually requires refining, though that obtained in Missouri and other Mississippi Valley states does not. The presence of the other metals, especially antimony, gives hardness to the lead but renders it unsuitable for the preparation of white lead pigment. To remove these metals, the bullion is melted and then stirred to permit the oxidation of antimony, arsenic, copper, and bismuth, which are more easily oxidized than lead. The oxides rise to the surface and may be skimmed off. Gold, silver, and some bismuth remain and are removed by use of either the Parkes or the Betts process.

In the Parkes process, zinc to the extent of about 2 per cent is added to the molten metal and the mixture is stirred. The impurities, being more soluble in zinc than in lead, are found principally in the zinc layer which rises to the top when the stirring ceases. This is a practical application of the partition principle. After several extractions, the zinc fractions are distilled to remove that metal. Gold and silver remain in the retort.

If the quantity of bismuth present in the crude bullion is relatively large, the Betts process may be used in preference to the Parkes. It is an electrolytic method of refinement in which plates of the bullion serve as anodes, thin sheets of pure lead serve as the cathodes, and lead fluosilicate, $PbSiF_6$, containing 8 to 12 per cent of fluosilicic acid and a little glue or gelatin is the electrolyte. When the current flows, lead leaves the anodes to deposit on the cathodes where the glue fosters a more coherent deposit. Bismuth, copper, arsenic, and gold form a slime or mud in the bottoms of the cells, while iron, cobalt, nickel, and zinc accumulate in the electrolyte and are subsequently recovered. This process is more expensive than the Parkes process and does not recover the valuable precious metals so well, but it does remove bismuth more completely, gives a purer product, and recovers more of the lead. Small quantities of contaminating metals may be removed by extraction with calcium. Last traces of this element and of bismuth may be removed by passing anhydrous chlorine through the molten metals.

27. *Uses*

Most of the uses of lead depend on its softness and low melting point or upon its relatively low chemical activity. The largest single use in times of peace is the manufacture of storage-battery plates for which an alloy containing about 6 per cent of antimony is used. Large quantities of the metal are also used in the manufacture of cable sheathing and of white lead pigment. Further, lead is the principal metal used in the manufacture of shot and bullets and is a component of many alloys, a number of which contain tin and were mentioned in section 18. Fuse metals and other low-melting alloys usually contain lead and bismuth as well as other metals, and terneplate used for roofing and for other jobs for which tin plate is too thin is a heavier sheet iron coated with a tin-lead alloy. Because of its low activity and its ability to form a closely adhering protective coating, sheet lead is used to line sinks, vats, tanks, and the lead chambers of sulfuric acid plants, and lead pipes are used for sewers and for the transfer of chemicals.

28. *Chemical Properties*

Lead, like germanium and tin, forms compounds in which it shows the oxidation numbers of $+2$ and $+4$, respectively. The lower valence state is essentially basic, though with the alkalies plumbous hydroxide, $Pb(OH)_2$, will form plumbites which are too unstable to be isolated. The higher valence state is essentially acidic, and is usually encountered in the plumbates, though it is sufficiently amphoteric for a few plumbic compounds to be formed. In the case of lead, the lower valence state is the more stable and the more important of the two.

Elementary lead oxidizes in moist air to form a closely adhering film of a basic carbonate. It forms the oxide Pb_3O_4 when heated above its melting point but below 545° C., while above 545° C. it yields lead monoxide, or plumbous oxide, PbO; contrast this behavior with that of germanium and tin. The metal combines directly with sulfur and with fluorine and chlorine to form plumbous compounds. Despite the fact that it is placed just above hydrogen in the activity series, this element displaces hydrogen very slowly from dilute acids, though it is rapidly oxidized by nitric acid. It displaces hydrogen from solutions of sodium hydroxide and other alkalies and is converted to a plumbite.

Soluble lead salts are poisonous, and the metal and its compounds are cumulative poisons; hence, all workers who come in contact with them should exercise great caution. Lead poisoning is commonly known as *painters' colic*, and vitamin C has been shown to be beneficial in its treatment. Water delivered through lead pipes is not suitable for human use, since soft water which contains dissolved air slowly reacts to form the hydroxide which is carried by the water. Hard waters containing sulfates, carbonates, or phosphates react with the pipes to form an adhering film which prevents further reaction.

29. Oxides and Hydroxides

Besides the regular oxides PbO and PbO_2, whose existence might be anticipated, lead forms three other oxides, Pb_2O, Pb_2O_3, and Pb_3O_4. The last two of these oxides are considered to be salts of the two regular oxides, and the existence of the suboxide, Pb_2O, is open to doubt, though large quantities of a substance held to be that compound are manufactured and sold.

Plumbous oxide, or lead monoxide, PbO, is commonly known as *litharge*, and is manufactured either by heating the metal above 545° C. in the open air or as a by-product in the manufacture of sodium nitrite from sodium nitrate:

$$Pb + NaNO_3 \xrightarrow{\Delta} PbO + NaNO_2$$

It is a yellowish or cream-colored powder. When treated with strong acids, it forms the corresponding plumbous salts which yield the Pb^{++} ion in solution; when treated with alkalies, it forms soluble plumbites. It is used in the manufacture of storage batteries and insecticides, as a glazing agent for pottery, and in the preparation of enamels, the manufacture of pigments, and the refining of oils. It makes a good cement for pipe fittings and for glass and crockery when mixed with glycerin or linseed oil.

The addition of an equivalent quantity of an alkali to a solution of a plumbous salt precipitates plumbous hydroxide, whose formula is usually written $Pb(OH)_2$ but which should be written $PbO.xH_2O$, since the precipitate is in reality a hydrous oxide. This compound reacts with acids to form plumbous salts and with alkalies to form soluble plumbites, and, upon being heated, loses water to yield PbO. The formula for sodium plumbite is usually written Na_2PbO_2, though, at least for the dissolved substance, it is more correctly written $Na_2[Pb(OH)_4]$.

Lead dioxide is a dark, reddish-brown powder which is usually manufactured by treating sodium plumbite with either chlorine or hypochlorites. The plumbite is prepared from sodium hydroxide and either plumbous oxide or a plumbous salt, and the oxidation in each case is that of a hypochlorite, since a base and chlorine react to form that compound:

$$Na_2PbO_2 + NaClO + H_2O \rightarrow \underline{PbO_2} + NaCl + 2NaOH$$

The dioxide is a strong oxidizing agent, especially in acid solution, and is so used in the laboratory. It will liberate chlorine from HCl and will oxidize the manganous ion Mn^{++} to the permanganate ion MnO_4^-. Its principal use is in the manufacture of anodes for lead storage batteries.

The dioxide is not very soluble in water, and it does not react with acids to give plumbic salts, but it does react with alkalies to yield soluble plumbates.

Lead sesquioxide, Pb_2O_3, is looked upon as being plumbous metaplumbate, $PbO + PbO_2 \rightarrow PbPbO_3$. It is precipitated as an orange-yellow powder when a plumbate is added to an aqueous solution of a plumbous salt. When the solid is treated with nitric acid, soluble plumbous nitrate is formed and lead dioxide remains:

$$PbPbO_3 + 2HNO_3 \rightarrow Pb(NO_3)_2 + PbO_2 + H_2O$$

Minium or red lead, Pb_3O_4, is held to be plumbous orthoplumbate, $2PbO + PbO_2 \rightarrow Pb_2PbO_4$. It is a bright orange-red powder which is prepared by heating lead in the open air to 450° to 500° C. Like the sesquioxide, when treated with nitric acid it yields plumbous nitrate and lead dioxide. Its principal uses are in the manufacture of storage batteries, as a pigment in paints applied to steel and iron to retard corrosion, and as an ingredient in the manufacture of flint glass, other glasses, and ceramic glazes.

The sub-oxide of lead, Pb_2O, is said to be the black powder obtained when plumbous oxalate is pyrolyzed:

$$2PbC_2O_4 \xrightarrow{\Delta} Pb_2O + 3CO_2 \uparrow + CO \uparrow$$

Whether this black substance is a true compound or not, it is prepared in large quantities for use in the manufacture of lead storage batteries. Upon being heated or treated with either acids or bases, the sub-oxide decomposes into lead and litharge.

30. *Plumbous Compounds*

One of the most soluble salts of lead, and therefore one of its most commonly used salts in the laboratory, is plumbous nitrate. It is manufactured by the action of nitric acid on either the metal or plumbous oxide. Its crystals are colorless and have the formula $Pb(NO_3)_2$; their pyrolytic decomposition was discussed in section 8 of Chapter 24. It is used as a mordant, as a component of certain explosives, and as a source of the Pb^{++} ion.

Plumbous acetate, $Pb(C_2H_3O_2)_2$, is another soluble salt of lead. It is usually prepared by the action of acetic acid on litharge, and, because of its sweetish taste (*Caution!*), it is known commonly as *sugar of lead*. It is used as a mordant, for the weighting of silk, in the preparation of hair dyes, and as a reagent.

The halides of lead are of low solubility and of little importance, though the chloride is precipitated in the analytical separation of the ion. The chloride is one of the three least soluble chlorides, but has a fair degree of solubility in hot water. It forms long white needles when crystallized slowly. The fluoride and bromide are also colorless solids of low solubility, while the iodide is a yellow solid of slight solubility.

Lead sulfide, PbS, has already been mentioned as occurring naturally in the mineral *galena*. It is readily precipitated as a black solid from solutions of lead salts by hydrogen sulfide, and the use of papers soaked with solutions of soluble lead salts for testing for the presence of hydrogen sulfide has been mentioned in section 12 of Chapter 21. It is insoluble in water, dilute acids, and alkali sulfides and polysulfides.

The addition of a solution containing sulfate ions to one containing plumbous ions results in the formation of a finely divided, crystalline precipitate of slightly soluble lead sulfate, $PbSO_4$. The formation of a protective coat of the sulfate on the walls of lead chambers, on the walls of sheet lead tanks and vats, and on lead pipes has been mentioned.

Lead arsenate, $Pb_3(AsO_4)_2$, is a colorless, insoluble salt used as a dusting insecticide for cotton and other farm crops. Its toxicity derives from both lead and arsenic.

31. *Plumbic Compounds*

Of the plumbic halides, only the chloride is known with certainty. It is a yellow fuming liquid which reacts with water to form HCl and PbO_2, and which decomposes at about $20°$ C. into chlorine and $PbCl_2$. It is made by treating with chlorine a suspension of $PbCl_2$ in concentrated HCl whose temperature is $10°$ to $15°$ C. The addition of ammonium chloride precipitates the product as ammonium hexachloroplumbate, $(NH_4)_2PbCl_6$, from which $PbCl_4$ is recovered by treatment with concentrated sulfuric acid.

Plumbic acetate, $Pb(C_2H_3O_2)_4$, is a colorless, crystalline solid which is a powerful oxidizing agent that finds some employment in organic chemistry. It is made by treating Pb_3O_4 with a mixture of glacial acetic acid and acetic anhydride at a temperature of about $70°$ C. It is readily hydrolyzed to plumbous acetate.

The preparation of tetraethyllead was discussed in section 13 of Chapter 26.

It is an important antiknock compound for addition to gasoline and is highly toxic.

32. Pigments

Because of their low solubility, good covering power, and variety of colors, a number of lead compounds are used as paint pigments. Most important of these is the basic carbonate known as *white lead*, which is one of the most widely used of all the white paints. Its formula is $Pb(OH)_2 \cdot 2PbCO_3$. This substance is precipitated when solutions of plumbous salts are treated with a solu-

LEAD BUCKLES AND THE POT FOR THEIR TREATMENT IN THE MANUFACTURE OF WHITE LEAD BY THE DUTCH PROCESS. (Courtesy, National Lead Co.)

tion of sodium carbonate, but on a commercial scale the preparation usually involves the action of acetic acid, air, and carbon dioxide on perforated lead plates or finely divided lead metal. There are a number of processes for preparing the pigment, and their products differ principally in physical characteristics. In the presence of acetic acid and air, the lead forms a basic acetate which is converted by the carbon dioxide to the basic carbonate. White lead is not suitable for use in chemical laboratories, since it is darkened by the hydrogen sulfide which is frequently present in their atmospheres.

The pigment known as *chrome yellow* is lead chromate, $PbCrO_4$, which is readily prepared by the addition of a soluble chromate to a solution of a plumbous salt. A very satisfactory green pigment is obtained by mixing chrome yellow with *prussian blue*, which is ferric berlinate, $Fe[Fe_2(CN)_6]_3$. A red pigment known as *chrome red* may be prepared by boiling chrome yellow with a dilute alkali. It is a basic lead chromate whose formula is Pb_2OCrO_4 or $PbCrO_4.PbO$.

The use of minium, Pb_3O_4, as a pigment for the painting of metal was mentioned in section 29.

33. *The Lead Storage Cell*

Many examples of electrolysis have been cited in preceding chapters. In these reactions, electrical energy is converted into chemical energy by the electrode reactions. Also cited in preceding chapters have been many oxidation-reduction reactions which occur spontaneously when the reagents are brought together in solution. When such reactions involve the use of ionic substances, a transfer of electrons occurs. If the substances of the reaction are arranged in a suitable cell so that the electrons cannot be transferred directly but must flow over an external metallic conductor, an electric current is developed and chemical energy has thus been converted into electrical energy. Such a reaction is then, in a sense, the reverse of electrolysis.

All batteries produce electric currents by reactions of the latter type. A storage battery is no exception to this general rule. The only difference between it and other batteries is that its interacting chemicals may be regenerated by passing a direct current of electricity through the cell in a direction opposite to that of current flow during discharge.

The most widely used of all the storage batteries is the lead cell, or *lead accumulator*, and the manufacture of such batteries constitutes the largest use for the metal. The cathodes of these cells are lead plates hardened by the presence of a few per cent of antimony, while, in essence, the anodes are plates of lead dioxide (lead plates with slots into which the dioxide has been stamped). The electrolyte is a solution of sulfuric acid whose density is about 1.28 g./ml. When the external circuit connecting the electrodes is closed so that electrons may flow, the following reactions occur: (a) at the cathode,

$$Pb + H_2SO_4 \rightarrow \underline{PbSO_4} + 2H^+ + 2\epsilon$$

and (b) at the anode,

$$PbO_2 + 2H^+ + H_2SO_4 + 2\epsilon \rightarrow \underline{PbSO_4} + 2H_2O$$

The two electrons liberated at the lead plates travel through the external circuit to reach the dioxide plates, where they and the hydrogen (hydronium) ions contained in the cell solution help in the reduction of the Pb^{+4} to Pb^{+2} and its subsequent conversion to lead sulfate. By adding the above two equations, the equation for the overall reaction is found to be:

$$Pb + PbO_2 + 4H^+ + 2SO_4^{--} \rightarrow \underline{2PbSO_4} + 2H_2O$$

Most of the lead sulfate formed adheres to the plates. It is apparent as the reaction progresses that both plates tend to attain the same composition, the density of the electrolyte decreases due to the removal of sulfuric acid, and the voltage of the cell decreases.

When the density of the acid has fallen to about 1.05 g./ml., the cell should be recharged, for, if used further, recharging becomes difficult or even

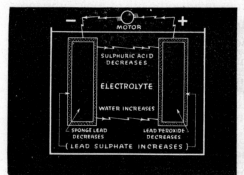 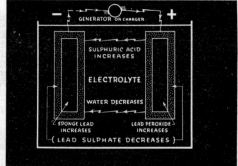

THE LEAD STORAGE CELL. (Courtesy, Willard Battery Co.)

impossible. Recharging consists of passing a direct current of electricity through the cell in a direction opposite to that of current flow during discharge. This reverses the chemical reactions and restores the electrodes to their original condition.

A fully charged lead accumulator cell has a voltage of about 2.2. By connecting the cells in series, their voltage becomes additive. The usual automobile battery has three cells and hence a maximum voltage of 3(2.2) or 6.6 v.

34. *Analytical Tests*

Lead chloride precipitates when a soluble chloride is added to moderately concentrated solutions of plumbous ion. This salt may be separated from precipitates containing silver and mercurous chlorides by dissolving it in hot water. The precipitation of lead sulfide has already been referred to in section 30. It is insoluble in ammonium polysulfide, but dissolves readily in dilute nitric acid. Plumbous sulfate is readily precipitated from solution by the addition of soluble sulfates and is dissolved by a hot solution of ammonium acetate. The plumbous ion is usually confirmed by the addition of a soluble chromate which causes the formation of a bright yellow precipitate of $PbCrO_4$.

(*See Appendix for Exercises*)

COLLATERAL READINGS

Anderson: White lead, *Ind. Eng. Chem.*, **26,** 1047 (1935).

Corse: *Bearing Metals*, Am. Chem. Soc. Monograph No. 53.

Creighton and Koehler: *Electrochemistry*, Vol. II, New York, John Wiley & Sons, Inc., 1944.

Furnas: *Roger's Industrial Chemistry*, Vol. II, New York, D. Van Nostrand Co., 1943.

Hoare and Hedges: *Tin Plate*, New York, Longmans, Green & Co., 1946.

Latimer and Hildebrand: *Reference Book of Inorganic Chemistry*, New York, The Macmillan Co., 1941.

Mantell: *Tin*, Am. Chem. Soc. Monograph No. 51.

Rohrman: Metals and alloys in chemical industry, *J. Chem. Education*, **13,** 53 (1936).

Tammann: *Textbook of Metallography*, Eng. translation by Dean & Swenson, New York, Chemical Catalog Co., 1925.

Vinal: *Storage Batteries*, New York, John Wiley & Sons, Inc., 1930.

Weeks: *Discovery of the Elements*, 5th ed., Mack Printing Co., 1945.

Metallurgy of lead, *Mineral Ind.*, **50,** 342 (1941).

Tin, *Fortune*, **5,** 74 (1932).

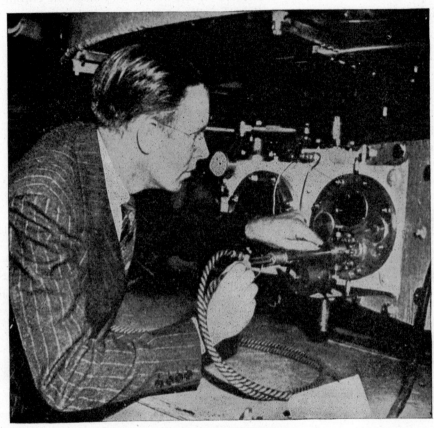

ERNEST ORLANDO LAWRENCE
(1901–   , American)

The most widely known achievement of Dr. Lawrence is his invention of the cyclotron, a huge "Rube Goldberg" device which has been used to accelerate positive particles for the bombardment of atomic nuclei. The use of the cyclotron in the laboratory of Professor Lawrence and in other laboratories where similar machines have been built has permitted the accomplishment of many elementary transmutations and the manufacture of many artificially radioactive substances. Still larger cyclotrons are planned for use in probing further the mysteries of the atom. Dr. Lawrence did his graduate work at Yale University, and, after receiving his degree, served on the faculty there until 1928 when he joined the faculty of the University of California, where he is now professor of physics and director of the Radiations Laboratory. For his invention of the cyclotron, he received the Nobel Prize in 1939. In addition, he has received many other medals, a number of honorary degrees, and other honors. (Courtesy World Wide Photos.)

32

The Transition Elements (Groups III B to VII B, Inclusive)

1. Introduction

In section 7 of Chapter 6, it was pointed out that the transition elements are those elements which contain valence electrons in two main energy levels. It was pointed out further that these elements occur in the long periods of the table, and that their possession of valence electrons in two main energy levels results from the filling up of partially filled underlying levels. The name *transition* is applied because the elements so designated form a series in which a change in the type of stability attained by the atoms as a result of reaction is occurring. Stability is attained in the elements which precede the transition series by the achievement of an inert gas configuration of eight electrons in the outermost level, while, as a result of the completion of underlying levels in the elements of the series, those which follow it achieve as the result of reaction a second type of stable configuration in which the outermost level contains 18 electrons. Transition elements occur first in the fourth period and are to be found in each of the succeeding periods, starting in every instance with the third element of the period. The fourth and fifth periods each contain 10 such elements, while in the sixth there are an additional 14 transition elements of a special type. These are known collectively as the *rare earth elements* and result from the filling up of a second, partially filled, underlying level. The seventh period comes to an end when only eight transition elements have appeared.

The last four of the elements of period seven are of synthetic preparation and their discovery was announced only in 1945. The discovery of elements 93 and 94 (neptunium and plutonium) was announced in August of that year and that of elements 95 and 96 (americium and curium) a few weeks later. Prior to the discovery of these elements, thorium, protoactinium, and uranium were classed as members of the regular transition families. Investigations of the properties of the four new radioactive elements have led to the promulgation by Seaborg and his co-workers of the hypothesis that elements 89 to 96, inclusive, are members of a series of special transition elements analogous to the rare earth elements of period six. It seems entirely likely that facts uncovered by future investigations will serve to establish this hypothesis. For the present, thorium, protoactinium, and uranium will be treated as members of the IV B, V B, and VI B families, respectively, but the student should realize that future discoveries may necessitate a revision of this classification.

Because of similarities of electronic structure, the transition elements form families just as do the regular elements, but because the outer-electronic configurations of adjacent elements in the same period are so similar (due to additions being made in an underlying level), often there is a greater similarity of behavior among these elements than among members of the same transition family. It is natural that these elements which differ principally in their underlying structures and which fit into the periodic classification of the elements between the second and third regular elements of a period should be very similar in behavior; for this reason it is convenient to consider them together. All are metals, and many are of importance in the manufacture of special steels.

A majority of the transition elements exhibit more than one oxidation number—this is especially true of those which appear in the B columns of higher numerical designation, though the elements which exhibit the greatest variety of oxidation states are to be found in the VII B family rather than in the VIII B. The $+2$ and $+3$ oxidation states represent true electrovalences in most instances, while those of higher value usually represent covalences of the type shown by the nonmetals in their higher states of oxidation. For a given element, the changes from low to high states of oxidation represent the same type of changes that one finds in the short periods as he progresses from left to right across the period. The intermediate states of oxidation are, therefore, characteristically amphoteric, while the higher ones are largely acidic and form compounds which enter into a variety of oxidation-reduction reactions. It should be pointed out in this connection that, while in such reactions the nonmetals usually undergo oxidation number changes of two or more units, under similar conditions the transition metals may change by one unit at a time. There is, in general, a smaller difference in properties between the compounds of the transition elements of the same period and like state of oxidation than between compounds of different oxidation number of the same element.

2. General Properties

The transition elements are all metals, and most of them show a variety of states of oxidation in their compounds. Save for copper which is reddish and for gold which is yellow, all of the metals are of some shade of gray. Chromium is possessed of an especially bright silvery-white luster. All are possessed of relatively high densities, which usually reach a maximum in each period toward the end of the series. The melting points vary in no regular manner through each period, but in every case the highest melting point for the entire period is that of the member of the VI B family. Electrical resistance also varies considerably, but is usually least with the elements of the I B family. In the fourth-period transition elements, it is least for copper and greatest for iron.

The compounds of these elements are characterized by the brilliant colors of many of their ions. This property should be contrasted with the general lack of color of the ions of the regular elements. It should be noted also that a given element exhibits a characteristic color for each of its states of oxidation. A second contrasting property is the tendency of many of the transition elements to form complex ions. The solubility of a majority of the compounds of these elements is good save for those of the amphoteric, intermediate states of oxidation.

A number of the transition metals are important both in their elementary states and in their compounds; others are important largely in their elementary conditions; and still others are of very slight importance. In this chapter, the space devoted to each element will be determined largely by its relative importance.

I. THE III B FAMILY AND THE RARE EARTH ELEMENTS

3. *General*

The elements of the III B family are scandium, yttrium, lanthanum, and actinium. Usually discussed in connection with lanthanum are the 14 rare earth metals whose outer electronic structures, as was pointed out in section 8 of Chapter 6 are identical with that of lanthanum. Actinium will be mentioned in Chapter 35 as a rare, radioactive element of slight practical importance. Scandium, yttrium, lanthanum, and the rare earth metals are also relatively scarce and of very slight importance, though lanthanum has been prepared in considerable quantities, and mixtures of the rare earth metals have uses as noted below. Properties of these several elements are given in Tables 33 and 34.

4. *Scandium*

Scandium was discovered by Nilson in 1879 and named by him in honor of Scandinavia. The pure metal has never been isolated, but a number of its

Table 33

PROPERTIES OF THE ELEMENTS OF THE III B FAMILY

Property	Scandium (Sc)	Yttrium (Y)	Lanthanum (La)	Actinium (Ac)
Atomic weight..................	45.10	88.92	138.92	227.05
Atomic number..................	21	39	57	89
Electronic distribution..............	2, 8, 9, 2	2, 8, 18, 9, 2	2, 8, 18, 18, 9, 2	2, 8, 18, 32, 18, 9, 2
Density, g./ml..................	3.02(?)	5.51	6.15	..
Melting point, °C..................	1200	1490	826	1800
Boiling point, °C..................	2400	2500	1800	1700
Color of salts..................	colorless	colorless	colorless	..

salts have been prepared from the oxide Sc_2O_3. The salts are colorless and of the
+3 valence state. The base of the element is weaker than the other bases of the
family, but is nevertheless strong enough to form a carbonate from solution.

5. Yttrium

This element was discovered by Gadolin in 1794. The free metal, which
is iron-gray in color, was prepared by Wöhler, who reduced YCl_3 with elementary potassium. It occurs naturally in *gadolinite, samarskite,* and other minerals
which contain the rare earths. Its base is intermediate in strength between that
of scandium and lanthanum. The free metal oxidizes readily upon exposure to
air and displaces hydrogen from hot water to form the hydroxide $Y(OH)_3$.

6. Lanthanum

Lanthanum was discovered by Mosander in 1839. It takes its name from
the Greek verb *to conceal* and is found in the minerals *cerite* and *monazite.* The
free metal may be prepared by displacement from its chloride by sodium or by
electrolysis of a molten mixture of the chloride, salt, and calcium fluoride.
The metal closely resembles iron in appearance and other physical properties.
The oxide La_2O_3 is formed when the metal burns in air. The hydroxide is a
base of moderate strength so that the lanthanum salts of strong acids are but
slightly hydrolyzed in solution. Uses of the metal and its salts are few.

7. The Rare Earth Metals

The rare earth elements are those which have atomic numbers from 57 to
71, inclusive; their names appear in Table 34. The first of these elements to be
discovered was cerium, which was identified in 1803 by Klaproth; illinium, the
last of the group to be identified, was discovered by Hopkins in 1926. Since
the structures of the atoms of these elements differ only in the electron content

of one of the internal energy levels, it follows that they will closely resemble each other in their chemical properties. This is indeed the case, but with increasing atomic number there is a slight decrease in atomic radius with its attendant slight decrease in the basic nature of the trivalent oxides and hydroxides. On the basis of this decreasing basicity, the group is divided into two sub-groups: the more basic elements from 57 to 62, inclusive, are known after cerium, the most plentiful member of the division, as the cerium sub-group, while the less basic ones from 63 to 71, inclusive, which more closely resemble in behavior the less basic yttrium, constitute the yttrium sub-group. Minerals which contain these rare elements are themselves rare. In general, these minerals are complex phosphates or silicates in which a number of the elements are represented. Prominent among these is *monazite*, which contains approximately 12 per cent of thorium phosphate and lesser quantities of the phosphates of various other ones of the rare earth elements, principally those of the cerium sub-group. Monazite sands are found in Brazil and India and in the states of Idaho and North Carolina. The mineral *xenotime* contains principally the phosphates of the yttrium sub-group. *Cerite* and *gadolinite* are silicate minerals which are sources of the metals of both sub-groups. *Thorianite* is also a source of the elements of the cerium sub-group.

A mixture of the rare earth metals is obtained by electrolysis of either their molten chlorides or their molten oxides to which a flux of the fluorides has been added; these processes follow, of course, a preliminary treatment of the ores to effect separation of the more abundant components. The alloy of the metals of the cerium sub-group obtained from *monazite* is known after the German designation as *mischmetall*, and, when alloyed with iron, forms a pyrophoric alloy which is used as the "flint" in gas and cigarette lighters and in the manufacture of tracer bullets. Mischmetall and other alloys of the rare earth metals are also used as a reducing agent for the liberation of strongly electropositive elements from their oxides (cf. the thermite process.)

Because of their pronounced similarity of properties, separation of the rare earth metals is difficult in the extreme. Mixtures of salts of the elements are gradually resolved by repeated fractional crystallization. This process takes advantage of the slight differences in solubility of various salts of the group. Fractional decomposition and fractional precipitation are also used in certain separations.

A number of the rare earth metals are reported to resemble iron in appearance. All combine directly with oxygen, hydrogen, and nitrogen to form the corresponding oxides, hydrides, and nitrides. In general, the oxides have a high heat of formation and are therefore stable. Cerium oxide is, in part, responsible for the brilliant white light provided by gas and gasoline lamps which use the common mantle. These mantles are cloth bags which have been soaked in solutions of thorium and cerium salts. When the mantle is burned, there remains a fragile ash which is largely a mixture of the oxides of cerium

and thorium in the ratio of 1:99. The characteristic valence of all the elements of the group is +3, but a few of the elements also show other valences. Thus cerium also exhibits a valence of +4 in the oxide CeO_2 and in the ceric salts, which are of an orange-red color as contrasted with the colorlessness of the cerous salts. The ceric salts are powerful oxidizing agents, and, as such, are finding an increasing use in volumetric analysis. Praseodymium, neodymium, and terbium all form dioxides, and the latter also forms the oxide Tb_2O_7; all of these are powerful oxidizing agents. Samarium, ytterbium, and europium are known to form compounds of the +2 valence state—these are, in general, powerful reducing agents. In the +3 state, the elements form isomorphous double sulfates, but these are not alums. Other information about the rare earth ele-

A WELSBACH GAS MANTLE AND ITS SUPPORT. (Courtesy, Welsbach Engineering and Management Corp.)

ments will be found in Table 34 on p. 661.

8. *Actinium*

Actinium is a radioactive element of great rarity. It was discovered in 1899 by DeBierne and has an atomic weight of approximately 227. Because of its rarity, little is known of it; however, it is the parent member of a series of radioactive disintegration products of which an isotope of lead is the final member (cf. section 7, Chapter 35).

II. THE IV B FAMILY

9. *General*

Members of the IV B family are titanium, zirconium, hafnium, and thorium; like all other transition elements, they are metals. All four are sufficiently electropositive never to be found free in nature, and all four are widely distributed in nature, the first two in relatively large quantities. Because all four rather closely resemble silicon in chemical properties, the presence of their

Table 34

INFORMATION CONCERNING THE RARE EARTH ELEMENTS

Element	Symbol	Origin of Name	Discoverer	Year of Discovery	At. No.	At. Wt.	Density	M.P.	B.P.	Solubility of Double Sulfates	Color of +3 Ions
Lanthanum	La	Greek, to conceal	Mosander	1839	57	138.92	6.15	826	1800	insoluble	colorless
Cerium	Ce	Planetoid, Ceres	Klaproth	1803	58	140.13	6.90	640	1400	insoluble	colorless
Praseodymium	Pr	Greek, green twin	von Welsbach	1885	59	140.92	6.5	940	..	insoluble	green
Neodymium	Nd	Greek, new twin	von Welsbach	1885	60	144.27	6.95	840	..	insoluble	pink
Illinium	Il	State of Illinois	Hopkins	1926	61	147	..	..	..	insoluble	..
Samarium	Sm	Samarski, a Russian	de Boisbaudran	1879	62	150.43	7.7-7.8	1300-1400	..	insoluble	yellow
Europium	Eu	Continent of Europe	Demarcay	1901	63	152.0	5.24	1100-1200	..	moderately soluble	rose
Gadolinium	Gd	Gadolin, Swedish chemist	Marignac	1880	64	156.9	7.95	..	..	moderately soluble	colorless
Terbium	Tb	Ytterby, a Swedish town	Mosander	1843	65	159.2	8.33	..	..	moderately soluble	colorless
Dysprosium	Dy	Greek, bard to speak with	de Boisbaudran	1886	66	162.46	8.56	..	..	very soluble	yellow
Holmium	Ho	Holmia, for Stockholm	Cleve	1879	67	164.94	..	..	..	very soluble	yellow
Erbium	Er	Ytterby, a Swedish town	Mosander	1843	68	167.2	4.77(?)	..	..	very soluble	red
Thulium	Tm	Thule, Northland	Cleve	1879	69	169.4	9.34	..	..	very soluble	green
Ytterbium	Yb	Ytterby, Swedish town	Marignac	1878	70	173.04	7.01	1800	..	very soluble	colorless
Lutecium	Lu	Lutece, old name of Paris	Urbain	1907	71	174.99	9.74	..	..	very soluble	colorless

compounds in silicate rocks often fails to be detected. Despite the availability of relatively large quantities of titanium minerals and of fair supplies of the minerals of the other three elements, the free metals in pure condition are seldom encountered because of the extreme difficulty of liberating and purifying them. Because of the marked chemical activity of the elements, they are difficult to set free from their compounds, and, once liberated, they have a strong tendency to unite with oxygen, nitrogen, carbon, and silicon to form binary compounds; they readily form alloys in the presence of other metals. The purest samples are obtained by the reduction of chlorides or complex fluorides with sodium metal, but the process is obviously expensive. More satisfactory methods of production would undoubtedly increase their use.

From the electronic distributions shown for the atoms of these elements in Table 35, it is obvious that the most stable compounds of these elements will be those in which their oxidation number is $+4$. Compounds in which the state of oxidation is either $+2$ or $+3$ are known, but, in general, these are unstable with respect to oxidation to the $+4$ state and are therefore good reducing agents. The $+2$ compounds of many of the transition elements are such strong reducing agents that they liberate hydrogen from their aqueous solutions.

A number of properties of the elements of the IV B family are presented in Table 35, from which it may be seen that all possess relatively high densities, melting points, and boiling points.

Table 35

PROPERTIES OF THE ELEMENTS OF THE IV B FAMILY

Property	*Titanium (Ti)*	*Zirconium (Zr)*	*Hafnium (Hf)*	*Thorium (Th)*
Atomic weight.....	47.90	91.22	178.6	232.12
Isotopes..........	46, 47, 48, 49, 50	90, 91, 92, 94, 96	176, 177, 178, 179, 180	232, (?)
Atomic number....	22	40	72	90
Electronic distribution...........	2, 8, 10, 2	2, 8, 18, 10, 2	2, 8, 18, 32, 10, 2	2, 8, 18, 32, 18, 10, 2
Density at 20°C. g./ml..........	4.5	6.4	13.3	11.3
Melting point, °C.	1800	1900	1700	1845
Boiling point, °C..	>3000	>2900	>3200	>3000
Color, $+2$ salts....	brown to black	black	..	..
Color, $+3$ salts....	violet	brown to black	..	..
Color, $+4$ salts.....	colorless to yellow	colorless	colorless	colorless

10. *Titanium*

Titanium is the ninth element in order of abundance in the earth's crust. It was discovered by Gregor in 1791 and takes its name from the Titans of Greek mythology. Its most common ores are: *ilmenite*, $FeTiO_3$, a ferrous titanate; *rutile*, TiO_2; and *arizonite*, $Fe_2O_3.3TiO_2$. Other ores containing titanates and titanosilicates are known, and there are two other minerals which contain the dioxide. Because of the intense whiteness of the purified dioxide and its resistance to tarnishing, it is used in large quantities as a pigment in paints, shoe polishes, and filler compounds. Its chief source is India, and it should be noted that the natural ores are not white. The dioxide is also used in the ceramic industries to produce a yellow glaze. The metal is seldom produced in the pure condition, but quantities of ferrotitanium are prepared for use in the manufacture of steel. Besides producing a very tough steel, it removes nitrogen which may be present in the molten metal. Titanium is reported to have a high electrical conductivity comparable to that of aluminum.

Titanium salts in which the element shows valences of $+2$, $+3$, and $+4$ are known, but the two lower states of oxidation are so easily oxidized that only compounds of the $+4$ condition are found in nature. Reduction of the dioxide with hydrogen at high temperatures yields the sesquioxide, while reduction with carbon also at high temperatures yields the monoxide:

$$2TiO_2 + H_2 \xrightarrow{\Delta} Ti_2O_3 + H_2O \uparrow$$

and

$$TiO_2 + C \xrightarrow{\Delta} TiO + CO \uparrow$$

The two lower oxides are both distinctly basic while the higher oxide, TiO_2, is amphoteric. It forms their corresponding titanic salts with acids, while, upon fusion with basic oxides or carbonates, it yields titanates of the type $CaTiO_3$ and K_2TiO_3. Addition of a base to a solution of a titanic salt precipitates the white gelatinous titanic hydroxide which resembles silicic acid in appearance and is usually represented by the formula $Ti(OH)_4$. This precipitate does not dissolve in an excess of the alkalies to form the titanates. Solutions of the soluble titanates are hydrolyzed to $Ti(OH)_4$ by boiling. The tetrachloride is a liquid which readily undergoes hydrolysis, and, as a consequence, is frequently used in smoke-screen formation. Reduction of this compound with hydrogen at high temperatures yields titanous chloride, $TiCl_3$. Titanous sulfate, $Ti_2(SO_4)_3$, may be prepared by the reduction of titanic sulfate, $Ti(SO_4)_2$, either with zinc or by electrolysis. Freshly prepared standard solutions of titanous salts or those stored carefully in inert atmospheres are used in volumetric analysis as reducing agents. Titanous hydroxide, $Ti(OH)_3$, is such a powerful reducing agent that it will absorb oxygen from the air, reduce nitrates to ammonia, and displace hydrogen from water. The use of titanic salts in the detection of hydrogen peroxide has been referred to in section 22 of Chapter 23; the reverse of this procedure may be used as a test for titanic salts.

11. Zirconium

This element was discovered by Klaproth in 1789 and was named from the Arabic word *zargun* meaning *of a gold color*. Its principal ores are *baddeleyite*, ZrO_2, and *zircon*, $ZrSiO_4$, and its principal production is in Brazil. The free metal is usually prepared by the thermite process, though an aluminum-zirconium alloy results. The two components of this alloy may be separated by distillation. Ferro-zirconium is used in the preparation of steels as a scavenger for oxygen and sulfur and as an agent of control of the size of the grain in the finished product.

Zirconium closely resembles titanium in its chemical properties, though the only oxide which is well known is the dioxide, ZrO_2. This oxide forms zirconic salts which yield the Zr^{+4} ion in solution, and upon fusion with alkaline oxides or carbonates it forms zirconates of the type Na_2ZrO_3. Freshly precipitated zirconium hydroxide, $Zr(OH)_4$, is of the hydrated oxide type, and the tetrachloride $ZrCl_4$ closely resembles $TiCl_4$ in behavior. Zirconyl chloride, $ZrOCl_2$, prepared by the partial hydrolysis of $ZrCl_4$, is used in tanning. The lower chlorides $ZrCl_2$ and $ZrCl_3$ can be prepared by reduction of $ZrCl_4$ with hydrogen, but they are too unstable to be used in aqueous solution. Naturally occurring zircon crystals are quite hard (7.5) and are valued as gem stones. Traces of other elements give them a variety of colors.

12. Hafnium

Although hafnium occurs to the extent of about 5 per cent of the zirconium content in most minerals of that element, it was not discovered until 1923 when Coster and Hevesy demonstrated its presence in a sample of Norwegian *zircon*. As might be expected from the foregoing statement, the chemical properties of these two elements are very similar, but because of its relative scarcity and difficulty of separation few of the compounds of hafnium have been prepared. Separation is reported to be best effected by careful fractional crystallization of the potassium hexafluorides of the two metals, K_2ZrF_6 and

K_2HfF_6. The dioxide and hydroxide of hafnium are apparently slightly more basic than are the corresponding compounds of zirconium. The name *hafnium* is derived from *Hafnia*, an old name of the city of Copenhagen.

13. Thorium

Thorium was discovered in 1828 by the great Berzelius, who named his find in honor of Thor, god of war in old Norse mythology. Although the element is not plentiful, it does occur in fair quantities in the minerals *thorite* and *orangite* which contain the silicate $ThSiO_4$, and in the mineral *thorianite* which contains the oxide ThO_2. In the United States, it is most readily obtained from *monazite*, in which its oxide may occur to the extent of 30 per cent. The free metal may be prepared by reducing with sodium the double chloride or fluoride which it forms with potassium. The metal burns in air to form the oxide ThO_2, but it is attacked by neither strong acids nor bases, though it does dissolve in *aqua regia*. The dioxide is exclusively basic, and is the only known oxide of the metal. Large quantities of the nitrate are used with cerium nitrate (*q.v.*) in the manufacture of Welsbach gas mantles, upon ignition of which are formed the oxides of thorium and cerium. In solution, thorium salts tend to hydrolyze to form thoryl compounds:

$$Th(SO_4)_2 + H_2O \rightarrow ThOSO_4 + 2H^+ + SO_4^{--}$$

The iodate $Th(IO_3)_4$ is one of the least soluble salts of the element. A coating of thorium upon the tungsten filament of incandescent electric bulbs improves their lighting qualities and reduces their tendency to disintegrate. The radioactivity of the element was not discovered until 1898 (cf. Chapter 35).

III. THE V B FAMILY

14. General

Vanadium, columbium, tantalum, and protoactinium are the members of the V B family. These elements are all of a silvery-gray color and are exceedingly hard, though they are malleable and ductile. In keeping with their transitional nature, they have high densities, high melting points, and high boiling points. In chemical nature, all of the elements of the family exhibit a reluctance to react which has caused them to be described as seminoble. Vanadium is attacked by nitric acid and other common strong oxidizing agents, but columbium and tantalum are attacked in the wet only by a mixture of nitric and hydrofluoric acids. All members of the family combine directly with oxygen, nitrogen, sulfur, and carbon upon heating, and their oxides are very difficult to reduce. Their characteristic and most stable state of oxidation is +5, but the lighter members of the family also exhibit electrovalences of +2, +3, and +4. With increasing atomic weight, the +5 state becomes more stable while the lower states become increasingly less stable. In the case of vanadium, the pentoxide is amphoteric, but as atomic weight increases the pentoxides become less susceptible to attack by either bases or acids. Only the pentavalent compounds of tantalum are stable in aqueous solutions. The free metals and their pentoxides are good catalysts for a variety of reactions. Some of the properties of the members of the family are set forth in Table 36.

Table 36

PROPERTIES OF THE ELEMENTS OF THE V B FAMILY

Property	Vanadium (V)	Columbium (Cb)(Nb)	Tantalum (Ta)	Protoactinium (Pa)
Atomic weight.............	50.95	92.91	180.88	231
Isotopes....................	51	93	181	231
Atomic number.............	23	41	73	91
Electronic distribution.........	2, 8, 11, 2	2, 8, 18, 12, 1	2, 8, 18, 32, 11, 2	2, 8, 18, 32, 18, 11, 2
Density at 20° C., g./ml.......	5.96(20° C.)	8.4	16.6	..
Melting point, ° C..........	1710	1950	2850	..
Boiling point, ° C...........	3000	3300 *ca.*	4100 *ca.*	6200
Color, +2 salts.............	green	..	..	..
Color, +3 salts.............	pink	blue	..	..
Color, +4 salts.............	red-brown	..	..	..
Color, +5 salts.............	yellow to red	colorless	colorless	..

15. Vanadium

This element, whose name is derived from that of *Vanadis*, the Icelandic counterpart of the Norse goddess Freya, was discovered by Sefström in 1830 but was not isolated until 1869. It is never found in the free condition, and usually is found as a vanadate of the heavier metals. One of its principal ores is *vanadinite*, which contains a lead chlorovanadate, but in the United States it is recovered principally from the *carnotite*, $2K(UO_2)VO_4.3H_2O$, ores of southwestern Colorado. Good supplies of vanadium ores have also been discovered in the states of Wyoming and Idaho, but Peru leads in the production of such ores. Vanadates are leached from their ores with acid, then precipitated as the ammonium salt when their solutions are treated with ammonium chloride. Roasting of the ammonium salt yields vanadium pentoxide:

$$2(NH_4)_3VO_4 \xrightarrow{\Delta} V_2O_5 + 3H_2O \uparrow + 6NH_3 \uparrow$$

Recovery of the pure metal from the pentoxide is very difficult, but reduction of a mixture of V_2O_5 and Fe_2O_3 with carbon yields ferrovanadium, used in great quantity for the manufacture of the vanadium steels, which are characterized by their fine grain and their high tensile strength. The pure metal, which is gray and highly infusible, may be prepared by reduction of the dichloride with hydrogen.

Vanadium forms compounds in which it exists in the $+2$, $+3$, $+4$, and $+5$ states of oxidation. The two lower states are exclusively basic, while the two higher states are amphoteric. Oxides corresponding to all four states are known, and the pentoxide is an important catalyst for a number of reactions including the manufacture of sulfuric acid, the oxidation of naphthalene to phthalic anhydride, and the oxidation of benzene to maleic anhydride. Compounds of the $+2$ and $+3$ states are easily oxidized, and thus make good reducing agents, while the $+5$ compounds act as weak oxidizing agents. The salts of the $+4$ and $+5$ states are easily hydrolyzed to form the blue vanadyl (VO^{++}) salts and the reddish pervanadyl (VO^{+++}) salts, respectively. The pentoxide is the anhydride of the ortho-, pyro-, meta-, and hexavanadic acids, salts of all of which are known. Vanadium compounds find use as pigments in the ceramic industry, in the dyeing industry, and in the manufacture of ink.

16. Columbium

Columbium was discovered in England in 1801 by Hatchett, and was so named because it was found in an ore sent from America by John Winthrop, first governor of Connecticut. The free metal was first prepared by Bloomstrand in 1864. The element is also known as *niobium*. It is rare, and is found principally in the mineral *columbite* as ferrous columbate, $FeCb_2O_6$. Columbium and tantalum usually occur together, and, after separation of their compounds, the former may be prepared by reduction of its complex alkali fluorides with sodium, reduction of its oxide with aluminum, or reduction of its chloride or oxide with hydrogen. The element is used principally as ferrocolumbium for the manufacture of rust-resistant steels. The ferrocolumbium is usually added to chrome-steels, which, in addition to becoming more resistant, become more ductile also. The free metal combines directly with oxygen, hydrogen, nitrogen, and carbon, respectively, when heated with them. The principal oxidation state of the element is $+5$, in which state its properties closely resemble those of pentavalent vanadium. Columbium compounds are rare, and of little practical value at present.

17. *Tantalum*

Tantalum was discovered in 1802 by Ekeberg, and was named for Tantalus, a character in Greek mythology. It is found principally in *tantalite* as ferrous tantalate, $FeTa_2O_6$, but is also found as the pentoxide in the complex oxide mixtures of other minerals. The free metal, which resembles platinum in appearance, may be prepared by methods entirely analogous to those mentioned above for columbium, and is highly resistant to the action of most chemicals. It is, however, attacked by fused alkalies. Because of its inertness, it is used for the manufacture of standard weights and measures; because of its high melting point and high electrical resistance, it was formerly used instead of tungsten in incandescent light bulbs. The hot metal absorbs gases readily, to become brittle; as a consequence of this property, it must be worked cold or *in vacuo*. Tantalum is hardened by alloying with various other metals. Such alloys are rust-proof, and sharp instruments made of them do not lose their edges when heated directly. Tantalum steels have properties closely resembling those of the columbium steels. Fine wires made of the metal are used for sewing severed nerves together, and plates of it are used to replace bone removed by surgery or by accident. Electrodes of tantalum allow an alternating current to pass in but one direction; hence, when used in conjunction with electrodes of another metal such as lead, they form a rectifier which delivers a pulsating direct current. An adhering layer of Ta_2O_5 is thought to explain this one-way action of the electrodes.

Tantalum unites directly with oxygen, nitrogen, and carbon to form the pentoxide, the nitride Ta_3N_5, and the carbide TaC, respectively. The carbide is a very hard substance, and is used in cutting tools and in devices which must withstand wear. Oxides of low stability may be prepared by reduction of Ta_2O_5. The compounds in which the metal exists in a state of oxidation lower than $+5$ are so easily oxidized that they displace hydrogen from water. The pentoxide is amphoteric. The pentahalides are readily hydrolyzed. A series of tantalates corresponding to the various tantalic acids of which Ta_2O_5 is the anhydride may be formed by fusion of the oxide with the oxides or carbonates of the alkali metals. In general, the compounds of tantalum, with the exception of the carbide and the pentoxide, are of little importance.

18. *Protoactinium*

This element is radioactive in nature and is extremely rare. It was discovered in 1917 by Hahn and Meitner and at almost the same time by Soddy and

Cranston. It is found in all uranium ores in slight traces and is isotopic with uranium X_2 (cf. Table 43 of Chapter 35). Its radioactive disintegration product is actinium, hence its name from the Greek word *protos*, meaning *first*. Proto-actinium is too rare to be of value, and little, if anything, is known of its chemical properties and compounds.

IV. THE VI B FAMILY

19. General

Chromium, molybdenum, tungsten, and uranium are the members of the VI B family of the periodic classification. None of these elements is ever found free in nature, but all are silvery metals of ultra-high melting and boiling points; their densities are also high, and all are unusually tough metals. Because of this toughness, and the toughness they impart to steels when alloyed with them, the first three members of the family are in great demand for the manufacture of special steels.

Like the other transition metals, these show a variety of positive states of oxidation, the highest of which corresponds to the column number. As a family, the VI B elements show the states $+2$, $+3$, $+4$, $+5$, and $+6$ in their compounds, though chromium, the lightest member of the family, shows only the $+2$, $+3$, and $+6$ states. In Table 37, which summarizes some of the properties of the individual elements, the important oxidation states of each

Table 37

PROPERTIES OF THE ELEMENTS OF THE VI B FAMILY

Property	Chromium (Cr)	Molybdenum (Mo)	Tungsten (W)	Uranium (U)
Atomic weight..........	52.01	95.95	183.92	238.07
Isotopes...............	50, 52, 53, 54	92, 94, 95, 96, 97, 98, 100	180, 182, 183, 184, 186	234, 235, 238
Atomic number.........	24	42	74	92
Electronic distribution....	2, 8, 13, 1	2, 8, 18, 13, 1	2, 8, 18, 32, 12, 2	2, 8, 18, 32, 18, 12, 2
Density at 20° C., g./ml.	7.1	10.2	19.3	18.68
Melting point, ° C......	1615	2620	3370	1850 *ca.*
Boiling point, ° C.......	2200	3700	5900	..
Color, +2 salts.........	blue	yellow	bluish	..
Color, +3 salts.........	green*	lime green*	..	red
Color, +4 salts.........	do not exist	brown	bluish	gray-green*
Color, +5 salts.........	do not exist	dark green*	black	gray-green
Color, +6 salts.........	yellow to orange*	colorless to yellow*	colorless*	yellow*

are marked with an asterisk. In their lower states of oxidation, these elements do not resemble each other so much as they do the corresponding states of the elements which precede and follow them in their respective periods. Family resemblance is much more marked in the +6 state, which in each case is exclusively acidic; in this state, all of the elements have properties which resemble the +6 state of the regular element sulfur. An important characteristic of the oxides of the +6 state is their pronounced tendency to form polyacids, a tendency which reaches its maximum with molybdenum. The +2 and +3 states, without exception, are exclusively basic, while the +4 and +5 states are amphoteric. Of the +4 state compounds, only the oxides are of any particular importance. Uranium, like the last member of the preceding families, is radioactive (cf. Chapter 35). Various properties of the elements are given in Table 37.

20. Occurrence, Preparation, and Uses of Chromium

Chromium, which takes its name from the Greek word for *color*, was discovered in 1797 by Vauquelin, who found it to be a constituent of the red mineral now known as *crocoite* which Lehmann had discovered in 1762. The free metal, albeit in an impure form, was also isolated by Vauquelin in the year following his discovery of the element. The principal ore of chromium is *chromite*, also known as *chrome iron ore*, which is a member of the group of minerals known as *spinels* and which contains the compound iron chromite, $Fe(CrO_2)_2$. This mineral is found chiefly in Turkey, the Philippines, and the Union of South Africa, though relatively small quantities of it are found in the states of Montana and California. Other chromium ores, such as *crocoite* which contains $PbCrO_4$, are found in various localities but constitute a less important source of the metal. The green color of many gem stones, such as jade and emerald, is caused by the presence of traces of trivalent chromium.

A major portion of the world's production of chromium is utilized in the manufacture of chrome steels, which are noted for their bright luster and their resistance to corrosion. For this purpose, ferrochrome is usually prepared by the reduction of chromite with carbon:

$$Fe(CrO_2)_2 + 4C \rightarrow Fe + 2Cr + 4CO \uparrow$$

The free metal may be prepared by the reduction of the oxide Cr_2O_3 with either aluminum or carbon. Soluble chromium compounds are usually prepared by heating the ground insoluble ore to a temperature of about 1200° C. with a mixture of lime and sodium carbonate. The purpose of the lime is to keep the mass porous and the reaction is

$$4Fe(CrO_2)_2 + 7O_2 + 8Na_2CO_3 \rightarrow 8Na_2CrO_4 + \underline{2Fe_2O_3} + 8CO_2 \uparrow$$

The soluble sodium chromate may be extracted by leaching the crushed fusion mass with water.

The metal is used chiefly in the preparation of steels and other alloys, though considerable quantities are used for the plating of iron, steel, copper, and other metals and alloys. Low chrome steels, which also contain small percentages of silicon and manganese, are very tough, while the high chrome steels (11 to 15 per cent Cr) possess great resistance to corrosion. An alloy of special importance is *nichrome*, which contains approximately 15 per cent Cr, 60 per cent Ni, and 25 per cent Fe. It has a high resistance to both corrosion and the passage of an electric current and is, therefore, suitable for use in various electrically heated devices. Other important alloys are *stellite* (Cr, Co, and either W or Mo) which is used for making high-speed cutting tools and *allegheny metal* (18 per cent Cr, 8 per cent Ni, 73 per cent Fe, and small percentages of Si, Mn, and C) which is even more resistant to corrosion than is stainless steel. Chrome plating will be discussed in a later section.

21. *Properties of Chromium*

In its silvery-white appearance and crystalline nature, chromium closely resembles iron, but it is much more resistant to chemical action and has a higher melting point. The metal produced by electrolysis is much more malleable than that produced by heat treatment in the presence of a reducing agent.

Chromium exists in both an active and a passive state. In either state, the metal will burn when heated to a sufficiently high temperature, but in the passive state it fails to dissolve in the dilute acids with which the active state reacts to evolve hydrogen and form solutions of chromous salts which are rapidly oxidized to the chromic state by the air. The passive state is believed to result from the formation of a very thin surface layer of a closely adhering coat of the oxide Cr_2O_3, and can be produced by dipping the metal in any one of a number of different oxidizing agents. The oxide which is formed when the metal burns in air is the green chromic oxide, Cr_2O_3. In general, the compounds produced by the direct union of chromium and another element are those of the chromic state. The various states of oxidation of the element and its compounds will be discussed in succeeding sections.

22. *Chromous Compounds*

Chromous oxide, CrO, is a black substance which is obtained by the atmospheric oxidation of chromium amalgam. It is exclusively basic in nature, reacts with acids to form chromous salts, is easily oxidized to chromic oxide by heating, and is pyrophoric. Chromous salts are all of a gray-blue color, and are so easily oxidized to the chromic condition that they are powerful reducing agents and cannot be kept in solution. They may be prepared by dissolving chromium in acids in the absence of oxygen or by reduction of acidified chromic and dichromate solutions with zinc or electrolytically, also in the absence of oxygen. The chloride $CrCl_2$ may be prepared by the action of anhydrous HCl gas on the metal. This salt and the sulfate are the most soluble salts of the series, and hence the most widely used. Chromous hydroxide forms as a yellowish precipitate when soluble bases are added to fresh solutions of chromous salts. It oxidizes rapidly in air, and, when heated in the absence of air, undergoes autooxidation-reduction, liberating hydrogen:

$$2Cr(OH)_2 \xrightarrow{\Delta} Cr_2O_3 + H_2O \uparrow + H_2 \uparrow$$

Chromous compounds are too readily oxidized to be easily used in volumetric quantitative analysis, but they are frequently used in gas analysis to absorb oxygen.

23. *Chromic Compounds*

Chromic compounds, in general, are green, though certain complexes containing trivalent chromium are of a lavender color. The most stable compound of the group is the oxide Cr_2O_3, which is formed as a green, very slightly soluble powder when the metal is burned in oxygen, when ammonium dichromate is pyrolyzed, and when dichromates of the alkali metals are heated with either sulfur or ammonium chloride:

$$(NH_4)_2Cr_2O_7 \xrightarrow{\Delta} Cr_2O_3 + 4H_2O \uparrow + N_2 \uparrow$$

and

$$K_2Cr_2O_7 + S \xrightarrow{\Delta} Cr_2O_3 + K_2SO_4$$

Under the name of *chrome green*, this compound is used as a pigment in paints and in ceramic glazes. It is but slightly soluble in acids, but upon fusion with the oxides of the alkali metals it forms chromates, the oxidation resulting from the action of atmospheric oxygen. Such fusions produce chromates in the absence of air.

Addition of a base to solutions of chromic salts results in the precipitation of a pale green gelatinous mass which is usually represented by the formula $Cr(OH)_3$, but which in reality is a hydrous chromic oxide which has much in common with hydrous aluminum oxide (q.v.), and should be represented by the formula $Cr_2O_3.xH_2O$. This compound dissolves in acids of moderate strength to form chromic salts, and in strong bases (in the absence of oxygen) to form a colloidal solution of the oxide and also chromites. Sodium peroxide converts the mass to sodium chromate. Because of its gelatinous nature, the hydrated oxide when precipitated in the fibers of cloth makes an excellent mordant.

Among the more important chromic salts are the chloride, the sulfate, the nitrate, and the somewhat less soluble acetate. The anhydrous chloride may be prepared by the direct union of chromium and chlorine, and also by passing chlorine over a hot mixture of chromic oxide and carbon:

$$Cr_2O_3 + 3C + 3Cl_2 \rightarrow 2CrCl_3 + 3CO \uparrow$$

When obtained by either of these methods, the product consists of violet plates which sublime at 1300° C. and are of slight solubility in water. Their solubility is increased by the presence of traces of reducing agents. The hydrated chloride, $CrCl_3.6H_2O$, appears to exist in three forms which are usually accounted for by the assumption that three different complex ions are formed. Accepted formulas of the three isomeric forms of the salt are $[Cr(H_2O)_6]Cl_3$, $[Cr(H_2O)_5Cl]Cl_2.H_2O$, and $[Cr(H_2O)_4Cl_2]Cl.2H_2O$. As might be expected, the first salt, which is violet in color, has all of its chlorine precipitated by silver nitrate, while the other two salts, both of which are green, have but two-thirds and one-third, respectively, of their chlorine precipitated when similarly treated. The chromic ion is, in fact, characterized by its ability to form a wide variety of complex salts—especially with water, ammonia, halides, cyanides, and thiocyanates. In each of these complexes, the coördination number (cf. section 8 of Chapter 5) of chromium is 6, and the union between the Cr^{+3} ion and its six coördinated groups is very stable.

Chromic sulfate is usually prepared by the action of sulfuric acid on the metal and is precipitated by the addition of alcohol. In the hydrated form, as usually prepared, this salt is lavender, and has the formula $Cr_2(SO_4)_3.18H_2O$. Like the chloride, it also forms several complexes, notable among which is the green one formed by heating the hydrated salt mentioned above. Only one-third of the available sulfate radicals of this latter form are ionic, and it is not precipitated by alcohol. A violet-colored chrome alum of the formula $KCr(SO_4)_2.12H_2O$ is readily prepared by the reduction of an acidified solution of potassium dichromate, $K_2Cr_2O_7$, with sulfur dioxide, though it is usually obtained as a by-product in the manufacture of certain dyes. This salt is used industrially in considerable quantities. Its aqueous solutions turn green upon being heated. The nitrate is known in both green and violet forms and finds some use as a laboratory reagent.

24. The Compounds of Hexavalent Chromium

Most important of the salts of chromium are those in which the metal has an oxidation number of $+6$. Despite the fact that it is most readily prepared from them, chromium trioxide, CrO_3, may be thought of as the parent compound of these salts. It exists in the form of brilliant red needles and is a powerful oxidizing agent. As such, it finds a wide use in organic chemistry. Ordinarily, it is prepared by the addition of concentrated sulfuric acid to a concentrated solution of an alkali dichromate:

$$K_2Cr_2O_7 + H_2SO_4 \rightarrow K_2SO_4 + H_2O + \underline{2CrO_3}$$

The resulting mixture is commonly employed in the laboratory as *cleaning solution*. The red crystals of the trioxide melt at 196° C., decompose into CrO_2 at 250° C., and upon further heating yield Cr_2O_3. This oxide finds application in many industries as an oxidizing agent.

Chromium trioxide, also known as chromic anhydride and "chromic acid," dissolves readily in water with which it reacts to form chromic acid, H_2CrO_4, and a series of polychromic acids in which two, three, and even more molecules of the anhydride have united with one molecule of water. None of these acids is of practical importance because of their instability, but the salts of chromic and dichromic acids are of great importance as oxidizing agents.

The preparation of sodium chromate from chromite ores has already been described in section 20. Potassium chromate may be prepared by an entirely analogous method, and both salts are so prepared industrially. At about 20° C., the potassium salt crystallizes from solution in the anhydrous condition while the sodium salt forms the decahydrate. Each of these salts is isomorphous with its corresponding sulfate, and both are of a brilliant yellow color, as are the majority of chromates. Slightly soluble silver chromate is noteworthy in that it has a brick-red color. Soluble chromates are poisonous; nevertheless, they are widely used both industrially and in the laboratory as oxidizing agents. The use of chromates of low solubility as pigments has already been referred to (cf. section 32, Chapter 31). Zinc chromate is widely used as a nontarnishing yellow pigment. Acid chromates are not known despite the fact that chromic acid, H_2CrO_4, is apparently dibasic.

When acid is added to a solution of a soluble chromate, the corresponding dichromate is formed and the color of the solution changes from yellow to orange. Addition of a base reverses this change. Just as the chromates are analogous to sulfates, the dichromates are analogous to pyrosulfates, but, unlike the latter, they are quite stable in solution. The dichromates are also stable to heat, though in general they are less so than are the corresponding chromates. The notable exception to this statement is ammonium dichromate, whose thermal decomposition was referred to in section 23 above. Most important of the dichromates are those of potassium, sodium, and ammonium. In acid solution these salts are powerful oxidizing agents, and it is in this capacity that they find their principal use both industrially and in the laboratory. The chrome plating of other metals is carried out in a dichromate bath of carefully regulated pH. Industries which use these salts are plating, tanning, dyeing, waterproofing of fabrics, and photography.

In section 22 of Chapter 23, reference was made to a perchromic acid produced by treatment of a dichromate with hydrogen peroxide. The compound is very unstable and is of little importance save in the analytical procedures cited.

Hexavalent chromium forms no binary halides, but chromyl fluorides and chlorides are known. These compounds may be prepared by heating a mixture of a dichromate, sulfuric acid, and a salt of the proper halide:

$$Na_2Cr_2O_7 + 4NaCl + 3H_2SO_4 \rightarrow 2CrO_2Cl_2 + 3Na_2SO_4 + 3H_2O$$

Chromyl chloride, CrO_2Cl_2, is a dark red liquid which is readily distilled from the reaction mixture. It boils at $117°$ C. and is readily hydrolyzed (cf. the oxyhalides of sulfur):

$$CrO_2Cl_2 + 2H_2O \rightarrow H_2CrO_4 + 2HCl \uparrow$$

25. *Analytical Tests for Chromium*

Chromium is most easily identified by the color changes accompanying the oxidation of its compounds, by the precipitation of the highly colored, insoluble chromates of lead, silver, and barium, and by the perchromic acid test described in section 22 of Chapter 23 (*q.v.*).

26. *Molybdenum*

Molybdenum, which takes its name from the Greek word for *lead*, was first recognized as an element by Scheele in 1778 but was not isolated until 1782. Credit for its isolation goes to Hjelm. The principal ores of the element are *molybdenite* (MoS_2) and *wulfenite*, ($PbMoO_4$). The sulfide ore is refined by

THE MOLYBDENUM MINE AT CLIMAX, COLORADO. (Courtesy, Climax Molybdenum Co.)

being roasted to the oxide which is subsequently reduced with carbon or hydrogen. In the United States, the metal is mined principally at Climax, Colorado, where the supply is adequate to meet the present domestic demand.

Molybdenum is a silvery-white metal of high density, high ductility, and great toughness which finds its principal use in the production of alloy steels and other ferrous and nonferrous alloys. The free metal also finds many uses. The toughness of steel is greatly increased by the addition of the metal, and its use in conjunction with other steel-forming metals greatly reduces the normal requirement for them. A cobalt-molybdenum alloy has the valuable property of having the same coefficient of expansion as glass. The free metal is used in the manufacture of electrical contact points, supports for filaments in radio tubes and light bulbs, and parts for various electrical circuit-breaking devices.

In its compounds, molybdenum shows oxidation numbers from $+2$ to $+6$, inclusive. Of these, those of the highest valence state are of the greatest importance. The oxide MoO_3, which may be made by the roasting of MoS_2, is a valuable catalyst, especially for hydrogenation processes. Despite the fact that it is but slightly soluble in water, this oxide is the anhydride of molybdic acid, H_2MoO_4, and a series of complex polymolybdic acids. Normal molybdates of the type K_2MoO_4 are most readily formed by the fusion of MoO_3 with the proper basic oxides or carbonates. In solution, both molybdic acid and the soluble normal molybdates tend to form polymolybdates whose complexity increases as the pH of the solution is decreased. The action of mild reducing agents upon MoO_3 produces the well-known *molybdenum blue*, which appears to be a molybdenyl molybdate.

The most important of the molybdenum compounds in the laboratory is ammonium molybdate, whose formula is usually represented as $(NH_4)_6\cdot Mo_7O_{24}\cdot 4H_2O$. When a solution of this reagent is added to a solution of an orthophosphate acidified with nitric acid, there forms a brilliant yellow precipitate of ammonium phosphomolybdate whose formula is usually represented as $(NH_4)_3PO_4\cdot 12MoO_3$, although the quantity of MoO_3 present varies somewhat with the experimental conditions. This precipitate is soluble in ammonia, alkalies, and phosphoric acid, but insoluble in other acids. Arsenic forms a similar ammonium arsenomolybdate under analogous conditions. Other phosphomolybdate complexes are known.

Lead molybdate precipitated simultaneously with the chromate and sulfate of lead forms the pigment *molybdenum red*.

Hydrogen peroxide reacts with normal molybdates to form the unstable, red permolybdic acid, H_2MoO_8. Similar treatment of the polymolybdic acids yields the perpolymolybdic acids.

27. *Tungsten*

Tungsten was discovered in 1783 by the d'Elhujar brothers and takes its name from the Swedish words meaning *heavy stone*. Its symbol *W* is derived from the German *wolfram*. Most important of its ores are *wolframite* (Fe, $MnWO_4$) and *scheelite* ($CaWO_4$). China is a leading producer of these ores, but small quantities of them are found in Idaho, Nevada, Colorado, and other of the western states. The ores are usually refined by fusion with sodium carbonate to yield the soluble sodium tungstate, Na_2WO_4, which, upon treatment with acid, yields tungstic acid, H_2WO_4, as a precipitate. Upon dehydration, this yields the oxide WO_3, which may then be reduced with carbon, aluminum, or hydrogen. Relatively pure ferrous tungstate may be reduced directly to ferrotungsten for use in the preparation of steel.

Metallic tungsten is of greater importance than are its compounds. It is a gray-black metal of great hardness and tensile strength, of high density, and of very high melting point. Since the temperature of the reduction process by which it is produced is far below its melting point, it is obtained as a dark powder which is sintered into rods by passage of an electric current. After having been worked to break up their crystalline structures, these rods may be drawn into wires which are used principally as the filaments of incandescent electric bulbs. The metal is also used for making contact points for various electrical devices, cathodes and targets for x-ray tubes, and the facing of valves for internal combustion engines. The major use of the metal is still the production of alloy steels of great hardness, toughness, tensile strength, and elasticity. Tungsten steels are especially useful in the manufacture of high-speed cutting tools which do not lose their cutting edge when heated to redness by the friction of the process. Such steels often contain 10 to 25 per cent of the metal. A number of nonferrous tungsten alloys are also of importance; notable among these are the *stellites*, which contain varying percentages of tungsten, cobalt, chromium, and other metals. They are hard, resistant to corrosion, and retain a cutting edge well. The free metal may be deposited electrolytically, but coats of a tungsten-nickel alloy are more frequently employed. These have a high resistance to corrosion.

Among the numerous compounds of the metal, only those in which it exhibits an oxidation number of +6 are important as a family. The preparation of the yellow trioxide, WO_3, from naturally occurring ores has been described above. In analogy to the corresponding oxide of molybdenum, tungsten trioxide is of low solubility but is, nevertheless, the anhydride of tungstic acid, H_2WO_4, and a host of polytungstic acids. The simple tungstates are best prepared by fusion of WO_3 and the proper metallic oxide or carbonate. Of the many simple and complex tungstates, only those of the alkali metals are readily soluble. Normal sodium tungstate, $Na_2WO_4.2H_2O$, is easily prepared, but the commercial salt used as a mordant in dyeing is usually the paratungstate, $Na_{10}W_{12}O_{41}.28H_2O$. Again in analogy to molybdenum, tungsten forms a phosphotungstic acid, $H_3PO_4.12WO_3$, and its simple and polytungstates when treated with hydrogen peroxide yield *per-* acids. Tungstyl halides may also be prepared.

Tungsten carbide, WC, is of note because of its hardness and its ability to retain this hardness at high temperatures. These properties make it valuable for use in the form of high-speed cutting tools.

28. *Uranium*

Uranium, the naturally occurring element of highest atomic weight and highest atomic number, is radioactive and is the only one of the naturally occurring, heavy, radioactive elements which is found in appreciable quantities. It derives its name from the planet uranus, which, in turn, derives its name from a deity of Greek mythology. Its principal ores are *pitchblende* or *uraninite* which contains the oxide U_3O_8 along with other metallic oxides, *carnotite* which contains the potassium uranyl vanadate $2K(UO_2)VO_4.3H_2O$, and *autunite* which contains the calcium uranyl phosphate $Ca(UO_2)_2(PO_4)_2.8H_2O$. Although the element was discovered by Klaproth in 1789, it was not prepared in the free state until 1842, when Peligot reduced its chloride with potassium. At the present time, the first step in the refining of the oxide ores is usually fusion with sodium carbonate, followed by leaching with sulfuric acid. The extracted soluble, UO_2SO_4, is usually converted either to the oxide which is reduced by carbon in an electric furnace or to potassium uranium fluoride which is electrolyzed after fusion.

The metal is silvery-white, and has the high density of 18.7 g./ml. Its melting point is 1850° C. Metallic uranium has few uses, though it is a constituent of several alloys. Alloys which contain more than 20 per cent of the metal are pyrophoric. Ferrouranium is used in the preparation of a few special alloy steels. The use of the isotope of weight 235 is discussed in Chapter 35.

Uranium regularly shows a maximum oxidation number of $+6$ and for this reason has long been classed as a member of the VI B family, but, like chromium and the other members of the family, it also shows a number of intermediate oxidation numbers in its various compounds. Its most important oxidation states are $+4$ and $+6$. The oxide UO_2 is exclusively basic in its behavior, while the oxide UO_3 is amphoteric and capable of forming uranates of the type K_2UO_4 and uranyl salts of the type UO_2SO_4 and $(UO_2)_3(AsO_4)_2$. The uranyl acetate, nitrate, sulfate, and halides are soluble, and the uranyl salts in general are highly fluorescent. Among the common uranium salts are the diuranates of the type $Na_2U_2O_7$, which are insoluble in water but soluble in acids. The sodium diuranate is known as *uranium yellow*, and is used in the manufacture of fluorescent uranium glass and colored ceramic glazes. Ammonium diuranate is similarly used. Uranium salts are also used as mordants for silk and wool; the oxide UO_2 is used in the manufacture of certain types of electric lamp bulbs; and the carbide is used industrially as a catalyst. Large quantities of uranium compounds are available since carnotite is mined in large quantities for the recovery of vanadium. The element is radioactive, but in this respect it is weak as compared with radium, and little if any practical use is made of the activity of the naturally occurring isotopic mixture save in the production of the artificial transuranic elements. Its radioactive nature was discovered by Becquerel in 1896, and radium is one of its disintegration products. Further discussion of the radioactive nature of the element will be found in Chapter 35.

V. THE VII B FAMILY

29. General

Manganese, masurium, and rhenium are the members of the VII B family. Of these elements, only manganese was known prior to 1925. Masurium and rhenium were discovered in that year by the Germans Noddack and Tacke, who named them for those German territories parts of which were forfeited under the terms of the Versailles Treaty. Little is known of masurium, but research has established much of the chemistry of rhenium, and at the beginning of World War II Germany was producing some 400 lb. of the metal annually.

Like the transition elements of the preceding families, in their compounds manganese and rhenium show a variety of states of oxidation with the highest of these corresponding to the column number. Their compounds of the +7 state somewhat resemble the halogen compounds of the +7 state, and the permanganates and perrhenates have somewhat similar properties, though the former are much more potent oxidizing agents than are the latter. In their lower states of oxidation, the VII B elements more closely resemble the preceding and succeeding elements of their respective periods than they do each other.

Since manganese is of importance both industrially and in the laboratory, it will be discussed in some detail. Rhenium will be discussed briefly and the other member of the family not at all.

30. Occurrence and Preparation of Manganese

The discovery of manganese, (which, incidentally, takes its name from *magnes*, the Latin word for *magnet*) took place in 1774 and is usually credited to Gahn, who isolated the metal, despite the fact that earlier in the same year Scheele had distinguished between iron and manganese ores, which had long been confused. This element, which ranks ninth among the metals in order of their abundance, is never found free in nature. Its principal ores are *pyrolusite*, which contains the dioxide, MnO_2, and *psilomelane*, which contains an impure manganese dioxide. Less common ores include *braunite*, Mn_2O_3, *manganite*, $Mn_2O_3.H_2O$, and *hausmannite*, Mn_3O_4. Russia, India, and Brazil are among the principal producers of manganese. In the United States, only a small portion of the demand for this important substance is supplied by domestic production. States in which ores of the metal are mined are Montana, Arkansas, Minnesota, and Virginia.

Metallic manganese is usually prepared by reduction of the dioxide with either carbon or aluminum, though an electrolytic process is also frequently used. The use of aluminum yields a more nearly pure product, since carbon tends to unite with the liberated metal to form the carbide Mn_3C. Because the major portion of all manganese produced is consumed in the manufacture of steel, an iron-manganese alloy is more frequently the product of reduction than is the free metal. Ferromanganese containing from 70 to 80 per cent of manganese is generally prepared by reduction of the mixed ores in a blast furnace (cf. section 5, Chapter 33). Another common alloy of the two metals is *spiegeleisen* (mirror iron), a brilliantly lustrous metal which contains from 5 to 15 per cent of manganese.

31. Properties and Uses of Manganese

Manganese is a silvery-gray metal with a reddish cast. It closely resembles iron in appearance, though when pure it is softer than that well-known metal. The presence of small quantities of carbon renders it both hard and brittle. The atomic number of the element is 25, its atomic weight 54.93, its melting point 1260° C., its boiling point 1900° C., and its density 7.2 g./ml. at 20° C. It tarnishes readily in moist air, displaces hydrogen slowly from cold water but rapidly from acids, burns when heated in air to form the oxide Mn_3O_4, is readily attacked by a wide variety of oxidizing agents, and combines directly with a majority of the nonmetals to form binary compounds.

The principal use of the element is in the manufacture of steels, in which connection its functions are several: it deoxidizes and desulfurizes the iron employed; it improves the rolling and forging qualities of the product; and it yields a steel which is very hard, tough, and resistant to wear. A manganese bronze containing about 30 per cent of the element is especially resistant to corrosion by sea water, and the alloy *manganin* which contains 12 per cent manganese, 84 per cent copper, and 4 per cent nickel and which has an unusually low temperature coefficient of resistance is used in the manufacture of many electrical devices. Many other alloys containing the metal are in common use.

32. The Oxidation States and Oxides of Manganese

The states of oxidation exhibited by manganese in its compounds are $+2$, $+3$, $+4$, $+6$, and $+7$. Of these the $+2$ and $+3$ are exclusively basic; the $+4$ is amphoteric; and the two higher states are exclusively acidic. The $+3$ and $+6$ states are so unstable that their compounds are of but slight importance. Of the $+4$ state compounds only the dioxide is of pronounced importance.

The oxides MnO, Mn_2O_3, MnO_2, MnO_3, and Mn_2O_7, corresponding to the valence states listed above, are known. In addition, the oxide Mn_3O_4, which appears to have the composition $MnO.Mn_2O_3$, is also known. It occurs naturally in the ore hausmannite and is obtained when the metal is burned in air, when the dioxide is heated in air, and when the monoxide is heated in air. The dioxide is the most important of these compounds.

33. Manganous Compounds

Manganese compounds in which the metal has an oxidation number of $+2$ are known as manganous, and, in general, are of a pale pink color, although crystalline varieties of the oxide and sulfide are green. Most important of these compounds are the chloride, sulfate, and nitrate, which are usually prepared by reduction of the dioxide:

$$MnO_2 + 4HCl \rightarrow MnCl_2 + 2H_2O + Cl_2 \uparrow$$

and

$$MnO_2 + 2NaCl + 2H_2SO_4 \rightarrow MnSO_4 + Na_2SO_4 + 2H_2O + Cl_2 \uparrow$$

In their solubility relationships, these salts resemble those of magnesium and iron. Addition of alkali or ammonium hydroxides to solutions containing manganous ions precipitates the pink hydroxide, which rapidly turns dark due to atmospheric oxidation; addition of alkali or ammonium carbonates precipitates the pink carbonate. The hydroxide and carbonate are both soluble in an excess of ammonium salts (cf. the corresponding magnesium salts). A pinkish variety of the sulfide MnS is precipitated when hydrogen sulfide is passed into neutral or basic solutions of the ion. The sulfide is soluble in even dilute acids. Other slightly soluble manganous salts are the ammonium phosphate $MnNH_4PO_4$, the oxalate $MnC_2O_4.2H_2O$, and the ferrocyanide $Mn_2Fe(CN)_6$, all of which are important in analytical work.

Solutions of the manganous salts of strong acids do not undergo air oxidation as do the corresponding chromous and ferrous salts, but the salts of weak acids are slowly oxidized.

Careful dehydration of manganous hydroxide in the absence of air yields MnO, as does the reduction of MnO_2 by hydrogen.

34. Manganic Compounds

Manganic compounds are those in which the metal has an oxidation number of $+3$. The majority of such compounds are violet in color, and are so unstable in solution with respect to spontaneous autooxidation-reduction as to be of little value. The oxide Mn_2O_3 occurs naturally in the form of black octahedral crystals, and the compounds $Mn(OH)_3$ and $MnO(OH)$ are among the products formed by the air oxidation of manganous hydroxide. The only manganic compounds which may be prepared in aqueous solution are those of low solubility. Manganic fluoride is prepared by direct union of the elements, while the chloride is prepared by the decomposition of $MnCl_4$. Complex halides of the type K_2MnCl_5 are also known, and an unstable sulfate and unstable manganic alums have been prepared. In aqueous solution, the manganic salts undergo the following reaction:

$$2Mn^{+3} + 2H_2O \rightarrow Mn^{+2} + \underline{MnO_2} + 4H^+$$

35. Manganese Dioxide and the Manganites

Manganese dioxide is the only important compound of the $+4$ oxidation state of manganese. It occurs in nature as a black powder, and may be precipitated in a hydrous form which is brown. Although it is amphoteric in nature, it is insoluble in and unattacked by solutions of most acids and bases. It reacts with cold hydrochloric acid to form a greenish solution of the unstable tetra-chloride. A sulfate is also known, but it too is very unstable. The complex fluoride K_2MnF_6 is of fair stability:

$$MnO_2 + 2KHF_2 + 2HF \rightarrow K_2MnF_6 + 2H_2O$$

When fused with basic oxides, manganese dioxide reacts to form rather complex manganites of doubtful purity. Calcium manganite of the formula $CaMn_2O_5$ may be prepared by oxidizing manganous oxide with bleaching powder, while a potassium manganite of the formula $K_2Mn_5O_{11}$ results when carbon dioxide is passed into a solution of potassium manganate.

The use of the dioxide in the manufacture of chlorine in the laboratory, in the neutralization of the green color of ferrous salts in glass, and in the common dry cell as a depolarizer has been mentioned in previous chapters.

This compound is also used as a catalyst in the preparation of quick drying oils for paints and varnishes and as a component of a number of specialized catalysts. Its use in the laboratory to catalyze the evolution of oxygen from potassium chlorate is well known. In the presence of strong acid it is a powerful oxidizing agent capable even of liberating oxygen from water. Stains of the dioxide are best removed by reduction to the manganous condition with either sulfurous acid or sodium bisulfite.

36. Manganates

Salts containing manganese in the $+6$ oxidation state are known as manganates and yield solutions which are green in color. These salts are most easily prepared by fusing manganese dioxide with an alkali hydroxide or carbonate in the presence of a strong oxidizing agent such as an alkali chlorate or nitrate:

$$2MnO_2 + 4KOH + O_2 \rightarrow 2K_2MnO_4 + 2H_2O$$

The most important of the manganates are those of potassium and sodium (K_2MnO_4 and $Na_2MnO_4.10H_2O$). In the crystalline form, these salts are isomorphic with the corresponding sulfates of their parent metals.

Manganic acid is very unstable, rapidly undergoing autooxidation-reduction:

$$3H_2MnO_4 \rightarrow MnO_2 + 2HMnO_4 + 2H_2O$$

For the foregoing reason, manganates in solution are stable only in the presence of bases. The acidified solutions are powerful oxidizing agents.

Manganese trioxide, MnO_3, the anhydride of manganic acid, is also extremely unstable, but it may be prepared according to the following equation:

$$2(MnO_3)_2SO_4 + 2Na_2CO_3 \rightarrow 4MnO_3 + 2Na_2SO_4 + 2CO_2 \uparrow + O_2 \uparrow$$

It is described as a reddish, deliquescent substance.

37. Permanganates

Manganese exhibits its maximum state of oxidation in the permanganates, whose solutions are easily identified by their brilliant reddish-purple color. The formation of permanganates by the autooxidation-reduction of manganates was cited in the preceding section, but, on the commercial scale, they are usually prepared by the chlorine oxidation of solutions of manganates which, in turn, have been prepared from the dioxide. Permanganates may also be prepared by anodic oxidation, and, in the laboratory, they are prepared by the oxidation of acidic solutions of manganous salts with either lead dioxide or sodium bismuthate (*q.v.*).

Most important of these salts is potassium permanganate, which is second in importance only to the dioxide among the compounds of manganese. Like most of the other permanganates, it is highly soluble, but is less so than the sodium salt and is, therefore, more easily recovered and purified. In the solid state, it forms dark crystals of a purplish cast and a semimetallic glint. It is widely used both industrially and in the laboratory as an oxidizing agent, and is capable of serving in this capacity in acidic, basic, and neutral solutions. From previous discussions (cf. section 16, Chapter 8), it should be recalled that in acidic solutions the manganese is always reduced to the manganous condition, while in neutral and basic solutions the reduction product is always the dioxide:

$$KMnO_4 + 5FeCl_2 + 8HCl \rightarrow MnCl_2 + KCl + 5FeCl_3 + 4H_2O$$

and

$$2KMnO_4 + 3MnSO_4 + 2H_2O \rightarrow \underline{5MnO_2} + K_2SO_4 + 2H_2SO_4$$

Acidified solutions of the permanganates are the more frequently employed. Since even neutral solutions of the permanganates are so easily reduced by light, dust particles, etc., standard solutions must be rechecked frequently; this is done by titrating them against pure oxalic acid or pure sodium oxalate:

$$5H_2C_2O_4 + 2KMnO_4 + 3H_2SO_4 \rightarrow 2MnSO_4 + K_2SO_4 + 10CO_2 \uparrow + 8H_2O$$

In addition to the above-mentioned uses of potassium permanganate, it finds use as an antiseptic (Condy's fluid) and in the treatment of poison-ivy infection and snake bite.

Permanganic acid may be prepared by treating barium permanganate with a stoichiometric amount of sulfuric acid. The acid is also purple in color and is unstable to light, heat, and reducing agents. Careful treatment of either the acid or its salts with concentrated sulfuric acid produces the green salt $(MnO_3)_2\text{-}SO_4$, which, upon addition of water, is decomposed into manganese heptoxide, Mn_2O_7, a violently explosive, dark reddish-brown oil. It is the anhydride of permanganic acid, which is not a true *per-* acid in the sense that persulfuric and perphosphoric acids are; rather it is of the type of perchloric acid.

38. Analytical Tests for Manganese

Qualitatively, manganese is precipitated from alkaline solutions containing the manganous ion as the pinkish sulfide MnS, and after separation of the other members of the group it is identified by the purple color produced when it is oxidized to the heptavalent condition.

Quantitatively, it may be precipitated as NH_4MnPO_4 and ignited to the pyrophosphate $Mn_2P_2O_7$ for weighing.

39. Rhenium

Rhenium is a very rare element which is obtained principally from the copper-bearing slates of Germany. In the United States, it has been found in small quantities in Wisconsin *molybdenite*. The metal is obtained by the electrolysis of potassium perrhenate, $KReO_4$, and is soft, ductile, and quite active. Upon direct oxidation, it forms the oxide Re_2O_7. It also combines directly with other nonmetals to form binary compounds, in which it exhibits a variety of valences ranging from $+3$ to $+7$, inclusive. Most important of the rhenium compounds are the perrhenates. They are the salts of perrhenic acid, $HReO_4$, which is formed when its anhydride, the colorless oxide Re_2O_7, is dissolved in water. It is a strong acid, and has but weak oxidizing powers. The potassium and silver perrhenates are of low solubility. Treatment of the parent acid with an excess of base forms the so-called mesoperrhenates of the type $Ba_3(ReO_5)_2$. Because of the scarcity of the metal and its high cost, few uses have been found for it and its compounds.

(See Appendix for Exercises)

COLLATERAL READINGS

Ephraim: *Inorganic Chemistry*, 3d Eng. ed., London, Gurney and Jackson, 1939.

Hopkins: *Chapters in the Chemistry of the Less Familiar Elements*, Champaign, Ill., Stipes Publishing Co., 1939.

Killefer: Chromium plating, *Ind. Eng. Chem.*, **19**, 773 (1927).

Latimer and Hildebrand: *Reference Book of Inorganic Chemistry*, New York, The Macmillan Co., 1941.

Levy: *The Rare Earths*, New York, Longmans, Green & Co., 1924.

Phalen: Uses of manganese dioxide ores, *Chem. & Met. Eng.*, **21**, 196 (1922).

Priestley: Chromium and its alloys, *Ind. Eng. Chem.*, **28**, 1381 (1936).

Roscoe and Schorlemmer: *A Treatise on Chemistry*, New York, The Macmillan Co., 1923.

Sykes: Metallurgy of tungsten and molybdenum, *J. Chem. Education*, **17**, 190 (1940).

Thornton: *Titanium*, Am. Chem. Soc. Monograph, Chemical Catalog Co., 1927.

Venable: *Zirconium and Its Compounds*, New York, Chemical Catalog Co., 1922.

Weeks: *Discovery of the Elements*, 5th ed., Mack Printing Co., 1945.

Discovery and properties of hafnium, *Chem. Rev.*, **2**, 1 (1925).

Element number forty two, Fortune, **14**, 105 (1936).

Manganese, *Ind. Eng. Chem.*, **32**, 1168 (1940).

Spices for wartime steel, *Fortune*, **28**, No. 5, 90 (1943).

33

The Transition Elements—Continued
(Groups VIII B and I B)

1. Introduction

With manganese and the related elements of the VII B family, the transition elements reach their maximum states of oxidation in their oxygen salts. In the remaining elements of each of the transition series, there occurs a general decrease in valence, which indicates that the underlying level is approaching its goal of 18 electrons and which brings the valence back into the proper magnitude for continuance of the period with the third regular element. There remain four elements in each of the complete transition series. Three of these, which differ only in the number of electrons in the level underlying the outermost, possess a number of common properties and are incorporated into the periodic chart in the space usually occupied by a single element. The three triads of the fourth, fifth, and sixth periods constitute the VIII B family. The remaining elements in each of these three periods (namely, copper, silver, and gold) constitute the I B family, which ends the transition series.

2. Complex Compounds

Occasional reference to *complex compounds* has been made in the preceding chapters of this textbook. A general discussion of such compounds has been postponed to the present juncture because the last four elements of each of the transition series show such a marked tendency to form them and, therefore, furnish many examples of the type.

Complex compounds are those which, in solution, give rise to complex ions. These latter result from the union of two or more simple ions or from the union of simple ions and molecules. It is readily seen from this statement that the majority of simple ions when put in solution become complex as the result of their becoming hydrated. As has been seen from previous discussions of hydration (cf. section 10, Chapter 14) and from the formulas given for various complex compounds, the unions which occur in the formation of such compounds are not in accord with the oxidation numbers of the substances involved, although they are influenced by both the oxidation numbers of the ions present and their ionic radii—in other words, by their ionic potentials. In general, elements of high ionic potential (i.e., of high oxidation number and small ionic radius) tend to form complexes; however, there are other factors which also exert a marked influence. Since the transition elements show a far greater tendency to form such compounds than do the regular elements, and since this tendency is often far more marked than would be indicated by the ionic potential alone, it is assumed that a level containing more than eight electrons immediately underlying the outermost valence level exerts a powerful influence in this direction.

It is now believed that complex ions result from the sharing of electron pairs by the simple ion and the ions or molecules which become attached to it. Both electrons of the shared pair are furnished by the same atom or ion, and the union is, therefore, essentially of the coördinate covalent type discussed at some length in connection with ammonia and ammonium compounds (cf. section 23, Chapter 24). The simple ions or molecules which add to the central coördinating ion to form complex ions must, therefore, contain atoms which have an unshared pair of electrons in their outermost energy level. As is the case with other types of chemical reactions, those which result in complex formation occur as the result of the universal tendency toward greater stability; in the case of transition elements, their goal appears to be the acquisition of an interest in sufficient electrons to establish a stable outer electronic configuration. These electrons may enter an incomplete level or may build a new outer level.

The first investigator to evolve a general theory of the chemistry of the complex compounds was the Swiss chemist, Alfred Werner. The concept of the coördination number (cf. section 8, Chapter 5) was proposed by him, as was the name *coordination compounds* and the general system of nomenclature for such compounds commonly in use now. Since Werner enunciated his theory in 1893, a number of other workers have proposed additions and modifications; notable among these investigators are Sidgwick and Pauling. Investigation has shown that the coördination number of the central ion or atom in a complex ion is always even, and may vary from 2 to 12, though for a given ion or atom it is usually invariable. The coördination numbers most commonly shown are 4 and 6. The entities which enter into the formation of complexes usually lose most of their individual identities and, as a consequence, no longer undergo their characteristic reactions.

A number of the metallic cations of the transition series form complex cations by union with neutral molecules such as ammonia and water, and complex anions by union with simple negative ions such as halides, cyanides, carbonates, thiocyanates, and nitrites. Examples of such compounds are $[Co(NH_3)_6]Cl_3$, $[Co(NH_3)_5Cl]Cl_2$, $K_3[Co(NO_2)_6]$, and $K_2[Co(CN)_6]$. In writing the formulas of these substances, it is customary to enclose the formula of the complex ion in brackets, and it must be remembered that the portion of the formula so enclosed acts as a single homogeneous unit. In writing the formulas of these compounds and in naming them, as in other compounds the cation takes precedence. In naming the complex ions, groups are named as follows and take precedence as indicated:

(a) acid radicals: Cl^- *chloro*, CO_3^{--} *carbonato*, CN^- *cyano*, SCN^- *thio-cyanato*, NO_2^- *nitro*, $C_2O_4^{--}$ *oxalato*;

(b) water or oxygen groups: H_2O *aquo*, O^{--} *oxo*, and OH^- *hydroxo*;

(c) ammonia: NH_3 *ammino*;

(d) name of positive element.

If the complex ion is positive, the name of the positive element is given characteristic endings to designate its valence: $+1$, *a*; $+2$, *o*; $+3$, *i*; $+4$, *e*. If the complex ion is negative, the endings *-ite* or *-ate* are used.

Examples of the use of the above system of nomenclature are:

$[Cu(NH_3)_4]SO_4$—tetrammino cuprosulfate;

$[Co(NH_3)_5H_2O]Cl_3$—aquopentammine cobaltichloride;

$K_3[Co(NH_3)_3(NO_2)_3]$—potassium trinitrotriamminocobaltiate.

Complex compounds are to be found in nature as well as in the laboratory, and many of both categories are useful. Many of the compounds used in electroplating and in the recovery of the noble metals are complex; many dyes belong to this class; and the hematin of the blood and the chlorophyll of green plants are naturally occurring members of the family. Specific examples will be encountered throughout the remainder of this chapter.

I. IRON, COBALT, AND NICKEL

3. General

Iron, cobalt, and nickel are the three elements of the fourth period which occupy the VIII B column of the periodic chart. They show a marked resemblance in appearance and other physical properties. They also show considerable similarity chemically, although the tendency to exist in the $+3$ state of oxidation diminishes from iron to nickel. All three metals form salts in which their state of oxidation is $+2$. Under the influence of very powerful oxidizing agents, iron will form salts in which it exhibits a maximum oxidation number of $+6$, while cobalt and nickel when similarly treated reach their maximum with the $+4$ state. These salts of the higher valence states are unstable and of little importance.

Because of the close resemblance of iron, cobalt, and nickel, and because of their slight resemblance as a group to the other two triads which occupy column VIII B, these three elements are discussed together rather than in connection with the other two triads whose members do resemble each other more closely.

A number of the physical and atomic properties of iron, cobalt, and nickel are listed in Table 38.

Table 38

PROPERTIES OF IRON, COBALT, AND NICKEL

Property	Iron (Fe)	Cobalt (Co)	Nickel (Ni)
Atomic weight	55.85	58.94	58.69
Mass of isotopes	54, 56, 57, 58	57, 59	58, 60, 61, 62, 64
Atomic number	26	27	28
Distribution of planetary electrons	2, 8, 14, 2	2, 8, 15, 2	2, 8, 16, 2
Melting point, ° C	1535	1480	1455
Boiling point, ° C	3000	3000	2900
Density, g./ml. at 20° C	7.86	8.9	8.9
Ionizing potential, volts			
1st electron	7.83	7.81	7.61
2nd electron	16.16	17.3	18.2
Electrode potential of $+2$ ions	0.441	0.278	0.231
Ionic radius of $+2$ ions, Ångström units	0.75	0.72	0.70
Specific heat, cal./g. at 20° C	0.107	0.100	0.105

4. Occurrence of Iron

Iron is a silvery-white metal which is malleable, ductile, and highly paramagnetic. It is sufficiently active never to be found free, save in specimens of meteoric origin, and its discovery is lost in antiquity. The name *iron* is of Anglo-Saxon origin, while the symbol *Fe* is derived from the Latin name *ferrum*.

In order of its abundance in the earth's crust, iron ranks fourth among the elements and second among the metals. The central core of the earth, whose radius is believed to be about 2200 miles, is held to consist principally of iron containing some nickel. In addition to being plentiful, iron is widely distributed throughout the earth's crust, but its concentration in most soils and rocks is too low to warrant their use as ores. It is also an important constituent of the hemoglobin of the blood. The principal ores of the metal are *hematite*, Fe_2O_3;

magnetite, Fe_3O_4; *martite*, a ferric oxide ore having the crystalline structure of magnetite; *limonite*, $2Fe_2O_3.3H_2O$; and *siderite*, $FeCO_3$.

For many years, the United States has been the chief iron-producing country of the world. The principal iron-producing region of the country is the Lake Superior district, which contains the famous *hematite* deposits of the Mesabi Range of northern Minnesota. Other less important ore sources are the deposits

ORE TRAINS IN A HUGE OPEN-PIT IRON MINE. (Courtesy, U.S. Steel Corp.)

of the Birmingham district of Alabama and those of eastern Wyoming. In France and Germany, *limonite* is the principal iron ore, while Great Britain produces chiefly *siderite*, and the Scandinavian peninsula chiefly *magnetite*. *Pyrite*, FeS_2, which occurs in great quantities in many localities, has thus far not been used as a source of iron.

5. *The Production of Pig Iron*

In essence, iron is obtained by reduction of its ores with hot carbon monoxide. The reduction is a stepwise process whose various individual reactions are reversible, and whose points of equilibrium are dependent upon the relative pressures of CO and CO_2 in the reaction chamber. The modern method of reduction involves the use of the blast furnace, in which the successive steps proceed continuously, with molten iron being drawn off at the base of the tower.

The blast furnace is essentially a circular steel tower lined with highly refractory fire bricks. Its diameter usually measures 20 to 25 ft. and its height 90 to 100 ft. It is provided at the top with a double bell arrangement to permit the entry of the charging material without the loss of the hot gases from within and with a vent pipe for the removal of excess gas. Near the bottom, there are tapholes for the removal of slag and molten iron, and above these are the tuyères

A BLAST FURNACE AND ITS STOVES. Note that the hot gases escaping from the furnace are used to heat the incoming air. (Courtesy, U.S. Steel Corp.)

through which air preheated to about 500° to 700° C. is forced under a pressure of about 15 lb. per sq. in. (see accompanying illustration).

To place the blast furnace in operation, a charge of coke is introduced, ignited, and burned in the presence of the hot air forced through the tuyères. When the furnace has thus been preheated, alternate layers of ore, limestone, and coke are introduced at such intervals as to keep the tower filled. The carbon monoxide produced by the burning coke is the active reducing agent (any carbon dioxide produced by the burning of the lower layers of coke or by the decomposition of the limestone is reduced as it rises through successive layers of hot coke). In the upper reaches of the furnace, where the temperature is 400° to 600° C., *hematite* is reduced to the magnetic oxide, Fe_3O_4. As the material moves downward through the furnace to hotter regions, the successive stages of reduction take place, limestone is converted to lime, and the latter reacts with the siliceous earthy material of the ore to form a fluid calcium silicate slag. By the time the material of a single charge of ore has reached the bottom of the furnace, it has been completely converted to molten iron and its siliceous material to slag. The molten metal collects in the bottom of the furnace with the slag floating upon it. Both are drawn off from time to time.

The essential reactions of the blast furnace and the temperatures at which they occur principally are:

$$3Fe_2O_3 + CO \rightarrow 2Fe_3O_4 + CO_2 \uparrow, 500° \text{ C. } ca.$$
$$Fe_3O_4 + CO \rightarrow 3FeO + CO_2 \uparrow, 850° \text{ C. } ca.$$
$$FeO + CO \rightarrow Fe + CO_2 \uparrow, 1000° \text{ C. } ca.$$
$$CaCO_3 \rightarrow CaO + CO_2 \uparrow, 800° \text{ to } 1000° \text{ C.}$$

and

$$CaO + SiO_2 \rightarrow CaSiO_3 \quad \text{and} \quad CaO + Al_2O_3 \rightarrow Ca(AlO_2)_2$$

The hot gases drawn from the top of the furnace are passed through a dust-removing device and are then used to heat the stoves in which air for the furnace is preheated. Unreacted carbon monoxide in the mixture is the fuel. The slag produced is usually a waste product, though some of it is used for the production of spun slag insulating and packing material. The molten iron drawn from the furnace usually contains small percentages of carbon, silicon, sulfur, phosphorus, and manganese, and is thus far from pure (92 to 94 per cent). When drawn off, it may be carried directly to the furnaces while still in the molten state, where it will be converted into steel, or it may be cast into molds. The blast-furnace product is commonly called *pig iron* because the old method of casting it involved the use of depressions in a bed of sand which were said to resemble a pig's bed or wallow.

Blast furnaces operate continuously until they have to be shut down for repairs. In a 24-hour period, a modern furnace will produce about 1000 tons of pig iron, 500 tons of slag, and 150,000,000 cu. ft. of fuel gas. These products result from 2000 tons of ore, 400 tons of limestone, 900 tons of coke, and 3000 tons of air.

6. Cast Iron

Because of the impurities which it contains, pig iron melts in the 1150° to 1250° C. range, while pure iron melts at 1535° C. If pig iron is cooled rapidly, the iron carbide Fe_3C, known as *cementite*, formed during the heat treatment is held in solid solution and gives the cast a bright silvery-white appearance. When cast in this fashion, the product is known as *white cast iron*. If the cast is

A TYPICAL BLAST FURNACE INSTALLATION. (Courtesy, U.S. Steel Corp.)

cooled slowly, the *cementite* decomposes into graphite and the product is of a dull appearance and is known as *gray cast iron*. Both varieties of cast iron crack easily when subjected to great strain or sudden shock, but of the two the gray variety is the stronger. A variety of objects which will be subjected to very little strain or shock are made of cast iron; among these are stoves, radiators, pipes, etc.

7. Wrought Iron

The need for a product stronger than cast iron found its first solution in wrought iron. This material is iron of 99.8 to 99.9 per cent purity prepared from pig iron by heating it with a basic flux in a reverberatory furnace. Flames from the furnace are directed upon the material contained on the hearth by the low, curved roof. Carbon is removed largely as its gaseous oxides, while the other impurities form a slag which contains ferric phosphates and silicates, ferrous sulfide, and silicates of manganese. The reacting mass is stirred, and, as the impurities are removed, its melting point rises until its consistency is that of a stiff paste. Balls of the pasty mass (blooms) weighing about 100 lb. are removed on the puddling rods. Rolling of the blooms removes most of the adhering slag and leaves a tough fibrous product of great tensile strength which is both malleable and ductile.

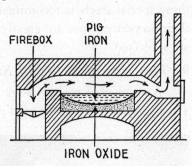

DIAGRAM OF A REVERBERATORY FURNACE.

It was formerly used to make chain, wire, horseshoes, etc., but today its former place of industrial importance has been taken largely by mild steel.

8. Steel

Steel is the name applied to iron which contains from 0.05 to 2.0 per cent of carbon and is capable of being hardened by quenching in oil or water. *Mild steels* contain up to about 0.25 per cent of carbon and are soft enough to be quite ductile. *Medium steels* contain up to about 0.7 per cent of carbon and are much harder and more elastic; the *high carbon steels* are very hard, but are also inclined to be brittle.

The properties of a given sample of steel depend not only upon its carbon content but upon its heat treatment, or tempering. If the sample be reheated and allowed to cool slowly, it is said to be *annealed*, and is much less hard and brittle than if cooled rapidly by quenching.

Steels which must be tough and elastic and at the same time withstand wear on their outer surfaces are usually subjected either to *casehardening* or *nitriding*. The former process consists of packing the given object in either carbon or sodium cyanide and heating it until a layer of high carbon steel of the desired thickness is formed. By heating the object in an atmosphere of ammonia, a hard coating of nitrides is formed. This last process is especially suitable for many of the alloy steels containing the steel-forming metals discussed in the preceding chapter.

Knowledge of the ferrous alloys has been greatly expanded by investigations conducted during the present century. The special alloy steels, whose properties have been suggested in the discussions of the various elements used in their preparation, are of great importance in the modern world, and, in many instances, have displaced simple steels. A review of the sections dealing with these special steels is recommended, and attention is directed to the fact that their properties, too, are greatly affected by the heat treatments to which they are subjected.

9. The Manufacture of Steel

A number of processes are used for the conversion of pig iron into steel. The two most commonly used processes are the Bessemer and the open-hearth

A BESSEMER CONVERTER IN ACTION. (Courtesy, Bethlehem Steel Co.)

(Siemens-Martin). Of these, the former is the older but the latter is the more widely used, accounting for more than 90 per cent of the total output of steel in the United States.

A. THE BESSEMER PROCESS. This process consists of blowing air through molten pig iron to burn out the impurities, followed by the addition of the requisite quantity of carbon. The operation is carried out in a special pear-shaped furnace known as a *Bessemer converter*. This furnace has tuyères in its bottom, is mounted on trunnions so that it may be tilted for charging and discharging, and is capable of containing about 10 tons of iron. In the United States, only iron low in phosphorus and sulfur is treated by the Bessemer process, hence the furnace is lined with bricks of an acidic nature to serve as slagging agents for the basic impurities to be removed. Thomas and Gilchrist introduced the idea of using a lining of basic bricks so that acidic impurities may be removed by the process. During the air blast, which lasts about 15 to 20 min., manganese and silicon are burned to their oxides, and then the carbon is partially burned away. The heat of the process keeps the metal molten. At the end of the air blast, the carbon in the form of a high-carbon steel is added, and just before the batch is discharged a scavanging agent is introduced.

The Bessemer process is quick and relatively inexpensive, but it does not remove acidic impurities and therefore produces a steel which rusts easily and cannot withstand too much shock or sudden strain. The process is too rapid to permit of any analytical control of the composition of the product.

B. THE OPEN-HEARTH PROCESS. In this process, pig iron, scrap steel, and some unrefined *hematite* are melted together on the hearth of a specially designed reverberatory furnace (see the accompanying illustration). The shallow saucer-shaped hearth may be lined with either acidic or basic bricks, as the nature of

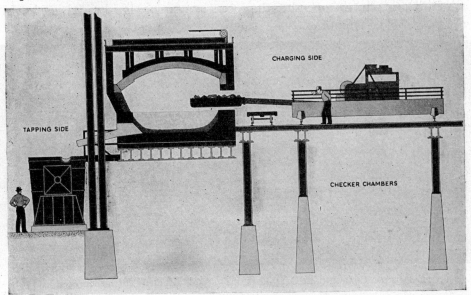

THE OPEN-HEARTH FURNACE. The diagram shows a typical open-hearth installation. The checker chambers for heating the incoming gases are not shown though their position is indicated. (Courtesy, Bethlehem Steel Co.)

the impurities to be removed demands. The high temperature required for the process is obtained by preheating the air and gaseous fuel by passing them over a hot checkerwork of brick or tile. The exhaust gases heat a like checkerwork on the opposite side of the furnace, and the direction of flow is frequently reversed so that the incoming gases may always be very hot. The furnace may hold 50 to 100 tons of iron at a time.

In the open-hearth process, a charge of 50 tons usually requires 8 to 10 hr. for conversion to steel. Being much slower than the Bessemer process, it permits of the analysis of samples and, therefore, of a much more careful control of the quality of the product. The use of a basic lining of the furnace also permits of the removal of sulfur and phosphorus, and, therefore, the production of a purer and stronger product. The process also permits of a better and more complete removal of the slag formed. After the removal of impurities, there are added the requisite quantities of carbon, manganese, and other alloying agents, along with scavangers which remove air bubbles which, if left, would cause weaknesses in the casts to be made.

c. THE DUPLEX PROCESS. When special purification of iron to be made into steel is required, it may be treated first by the Bessemer process to remove basic impurities, then by the open-hearth process in a furnace lined with basic bricks to remove acidic impurities.

APPARATUS FOR CHARGING AN OPEN-HEARTH FURNACE. (Courtesy, Bethlehem Steel Co.)

d. CRUCIBLE STEEL. Relatively small quantities of very tough steel capable of taking and retaining a good cutting edge are prepared by heating small batches of wrought iron or open-hearth iron with carbon in refractory crucibles. The steels so produced usually contain 0.75 to 1.5 per cent of carbon.

e. ELECTRIC-FURNACE STEEL. The electric furnace is used principally for the manufacture of special alloy steels. It consists of a steel box lined with basic refractory material into which molten steel from either the Bessemer or open-hearth furnace may be charged, usually in quantities of from 10 to 15 tons. Arcs are formed between the molten metal and carbon electrodes which are lowered into position above its surface. Again, the composition of the product may be carefully controlled by analysis. Steels so produced are very low in sulfur and phosphorus content, and are very dense.

10. Properties of Iron

Pure iron is seldom encountered, but can be prepared by reduction of the oxides in an atmosphere of hydrogen. A number of its physical and atomic properties were listed in Table 38. The metal is tetramorphous. At ordinary temperatures, it forms cubic crystals of the body-centered type, in which form it is designated as α-iron or *ferrite*. At 766° C., α-iron changes into β-iron. Here the change seems to be electronic and involves no change in structure. At 895° C., γ-iron is formed; its structure is cubic but of the face-centered type. Above 1400° C., δ-iron, of which little is known, is formed. Alpha-iron is easily magnetized, but does not retain its magnetic properties so well as steel. The other varieties are but slightly paramagnetic.

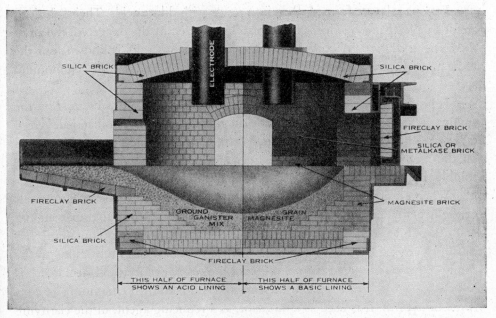

DIAGRAM OF AN ELECTRIC FURNACE USED IN THE PREPARATION OF ALLOY STEELS. (Courtesy, U.S. Steel Corp.)

Pure iron reacts readily with dilute acids to liberate hydrogen, but is rendered passive by various strong oxidizing acids. It does not liberate hydrogen from cold water, but does react slowly with steam. The metal is converted to the magnetic oxide Fe_3O_4, as it is when burned in air or oxygen. At very high temperatures, the product of direct combustion is Fe_2O_3.

From the practical standpoint, the most undesirable property of iron is its tendency to *rust*. The formation of the well-known reddish-brown scales or powder is to be noted wherever unprotected iron or steel surfaces are exposed. The *rust* is a hydrated variety of ferric oxide, and presumably is formed by the galvanic action of the iron and small particles of other metals contained in it in contact with the acidic solutions formed by the dissolution of carbon dioxide in rain water and dew. By the galvanic action, there are formed solutions of ferrous salts which are rapidly oxidized by the air to the ferric condition. Hydrolysis and drying of the solution complete the formation of hydrated ferric oxide.

Iron forms two regular series of salts—*ferrous*, in which its oxidation number is +2, and *ferric*, in which its oxidation number is +3.

11. Ferrous Compounds

Ferrous salts are formed when iron reacts with dilute acids. Their solutions are of a delicate green color, and are readily oxidized by the oxygen of the air to the ferric condition. A complete series of the ferrous salts is known, but the more important members are the chloride, sulfate, and ferrous ammonium sulfate.

Ferrous chloride may be prepared as anhydrous colorless crystals by the action of gaseous hydrogen chloride on the metal. The familiar pale green crystals of the tetrahydrate are obtained by the action of dilute hydrochloric acid on the metal. The other ferrous halides are like the chloride in being quite soluble, but they are much less frequently used.

When crystallized from solution, ferrous sulfate forms pale green crystals of the heptahydrate $FeSO_4.7H_2O$. These crystals effloresce in the open air and gradually undergo oxidation to the ferric condition. Solutions containing ferrous ions are oxidized more rapidly by the air if a base has been added to the solution. Ferrous sulfate is a by-product of the *pickling* of iron and steel which is to be coated with zinc, tin, or other metals, and is known commonly as *green vitriol* or *copperas*. It is used as a mordant, as a reducing agent, in the clarifying of water, and in the manufacture of inks and pigments.

More resistant to oxidation than the simple sulfate is the double salt, ferrous ammonium sulfate, $FeSO_4.(NH_4)_2SO_4.6H_2O$. This compound, known as Mohr's salt, is often used as a substitute for the simple sulfate.

Ferrous hydroxide, $Fe(OH)_2$, is formed as a colorless, flocculent precipitate when basic solutions are added to a solution of a ferrous salt. In the presence of air or oxygen it is rapidly oxidized, turning first green, then almost black, and finally the rusty brown characteristic of ferric oxide. The oxide, FeO, has never been prepared in a high state of purity, but is best obtained by the pyrolytic decomposition of ferrous oxalate, FeC_2O_4, at relatively low temperatures. The black powder so produced is pyrophoric.

Ferrous sulfide, FeS, which is so widely used for the preparation of hydrogen sulfide, is usually prepared by the direct union of the constituent elements, a reaction which is exothermal when once initiated. The same compound is precipitated from solutions of ferrous salts by the addition of alkaline sulfides. When heated with an excess of sulfur, ferrous sulfide forms iron pyrites, FeS_2, whose natural occurrence and wide distribution have been noted already.

While there are many varieties of inks, one of the most common types of black and blue-black inks contains ferrous sulfate and an extract of nutgalls, one component of which is tannic acid. A colorless ferrous tannate is formed which, when spread on paper and thus exposed to the air, is oxidized to black ferric tannate. Such inks usually contain a dye so that the writing may be visible before the oxidation has taken place. Solutions of oxalic acid and of ammonium oxalate are used to remove the stains of such inks from cloth.

12. Ferric Compounds

Reference has already been made to the natural occurrence of both anhydrous and hydrated varieties of ferric oxide, Fe_2O_3. This compound reacts with solutions of acids to form ferric salts, but it does not react with solutions of bases; however, when fused with basic oxides it reacts to form ferrites of the type $NaFeO_2$. Magnetic oxide of iron, Fe_3O_4, is such a compound, being ferrous ferrite, $Fe(FeO_2)_2$. When bases are added to solutions of ferric salts, there is formed a brown, gelatinous precipitate which is commonly known as ferric hydroxide but which actually consists of the hydrated oxide. Four forms of the precipitated hydrous oxide are known. The color of ferric oxide varies from reddish-brown to red, and depends somewhat upon the heat treatment to which it has been subjected. Under the name of *Venetian red*, it is used as a pigment, and more highly purified forms known as *rouge* are used as cosmetics and for the polishing of lenses and other articles requiring a high polish.

Because of the extreme weakness of ferric oxide as a base, solutions of ferric salts, whether prepared by direct dissolution or by oxidation of ferrous salts in solution, are highly hydrolyzed and in consequence contain colloidally dispersed particles of the hydrated oxide. The addition of negative ions fosters coagulation and the addition of acid tends to reverse the hydrolysis, causing the solutions to clear somewhat.

Anhydrous ferric chloride is prepared by passing chlorine over heated iron. When so prepared, it has the form of plates or scales which are green by reflected light and red by transmitted light. The fluoride and bromide may be prepared in similar fashion, but the iodide may not be so prepared because of the oxidation-reduction reaction which occurs. The anhydrous chloride has the formula Fe_2Cl_6 and is apparently covalent, since it is soluble in organic solvents. The crystals obtained from solution when ferric oxide is treated with hydrochloric acid or when ferrous chloride is oxidized are of a bright yellow color and have the formula $FeCl_3.6H_2O$.

Anhydrous ferric sulfate is nearly colorless, but the hydrated variety, $Fe_2(SO_4)_3.9H_2O$, is yellow. It is used in the preparation of ferric ammonium alum, $FeNH_4(SO_4)_2.12H_2O$, which is usually of a pale violet color.

When a solution of a ferric salt is added to a solution containing the thiocyanate ion, a deep blood-red color is developed. This colored substance is usually referred to as ferric thiocyanate and represented by the formula $Fe(SCN)_3$, but there is still some question as to its exact nature.

Solutions of ferric ions are moderately strong oxidizing agents. They are reduced by iodide ion, stannous chloride, etc. For analytical purposes, they are usually reduced by passage over amalgamated zinc.

13. The Complex Cyanides of Iron

When potassium cyanide is added in excess to solutions of either ferrous or ferric ions, there are formed complex cyanides of great stability:

$$Fe^{++} + 2KCN \rightarrow Fe(CN)_2 + 2K^+$$

and

$$Fe(CN)_2 + 4KCN \rightarrow K_4[Fe(CN)_6]$$

Most widely used of the complex cyanides of iron are those containing potassium as a cation.

Potassium ferrocyanide, which is also known as *yellow prussiate of potash*, is obtained commercially as a by-product in the distillation of coal. Hydrogen cyanide liberated by the distillation is removed by being passed through hydrated ferric oxide, which it converts to a cyanide of iron. Upon treatment with lime, this latter substance is converted to calcium ferrocyanide, $Ca_2[Fe(CN)_6]$, which may then be converted to the potassium salt, $K_4[Fe(CN)_6]$. The old method of making this latter compound consisted of treating scraps of hoofs, hides, hair, dried blood, and other nitrogenous animal matter with iron filings and potassium carbonate. Potassium ferrocyanide may be recovered from solution in the form of large, yellow, monoclinic crystals of the trihydrate $K_4[Fe(CN)_6].3H_2O$.

Potassium ferricyanide, *red prussiate of potash*, is usually prepared by oxidizing aqueous solutions of the ferrocyanide with chlorine:

$$2K_4[Fe(CN)_6] + Cl_2 \rightarrow 2K_3[Fe(CN)_6] + 2KCl$$

The ferricyanides are mild oxidizing agents and in aqueous solutions exposed to light they are gradually reduced to ferrocyanides. Both complexes are sufficiently stable to show none of the characteristic behaviors of iron or cyanide ions.

In preceding sections, reference has been made to the precipitation of a number of ferrocyanides. At this juncture, the reaction of soluble ferro- and ferricyanides with both ferrous and ferric ions should be mentioned, since they are often used in qualitative tests for these ions. An intense blue color develops when ferric ions are added to an excess of ferrocyanide ions. The compound formed has the formula $K[Fe_2(CN)_6]$ and is known as *soluble Prussian blue* or potassium berlinate. The addition of an excess of ferric ions results in the formation of a precipitate of *Prussian blue*, $Fe[Fe_2(CN)_6]_3.10H_2O$, ferric berlinate. Ferric ions added to a solution of a ferricyanide produce no precipitate but yield a brown solution. When added to a solution of a ferricyanide, ferrous ions bring about an oxidation-reduction reaction which produces ferric and ferrocyanide ions and the final product is again the *soluble Prussian blue*, $K[Fe_2(CN)_6]$. The further addition of an excess of ferrous ions produces $Fe[Fe_2(CN)_6]_2$, ferrous berlinate, an insoluble blue precipitate known commonly as *Turnbull's blue*. As ordinarily prepared, however, this latter precipitate is of variable composition. Ferrous ions, upon addition to a solution of potassium ferrocyanide, cause the precipitation of a white (more often very pale blue) precipitate of potassium ferrous ferrocyanide, $K_2Fe[Fe(CN)_6]$.

The reaction of ferrous ions and ferricyanide ions is made use of in the production of blue print paper. The paper is treated in the dark with ferric ammonium citrate and potassium ferricyanide. When this paper is covered with the tracing cloth bearing the inked drawing and exposed to sunlight, the ferric ions of the citrate are partially reduced by the light to the ferrous condition, save where they are protected by the inked areas of the cloth. When covered with water, the exposed portions of the paper become coated with *Turnbull's blue*, while the chemicals of the shaded areas are washed away to leave the traced pattern in white.

Turnbull's blue and Prussian blue are used as pigments and for the bluing of clothes that have been laundered.

In addition to forming cyanide complexes, iron also forms a host of other complex ions of less importance than those discussed above.

14. Iron Carbonyls

When finely divided iron is heated with carbon monoxide, a number of different carbonyls may be formed. Most important of these is the pentacarbonyl $Fe(CO)_5$, which is a viscous yellow liquid which freezes at $-21°$ C. and boils at $102.8°$ C. under a pressure of 749 mm. A very pure variety of iron is obtained by its thermal decomposition.

15. Analytical Tests for Iron

Because the ferrous ion is so easily oxidized, the ferric ion is usually the one tested for. Qualitatively, it is precipitated with its group as a sulfide in basic solution and is confirmed by the blood-red color which it produces with thiocyanates or by the blue precipitate which it yields with ferrocyanides. Quantitatively, iron is precipitated as hydrous ferric oxide and ignited to constant weight or reduced to the ferrous condition and titrated with a standard oxidizing agent which brings it back to the ferric condition. Because of the color of the solutions, titration procedures usually require the use of an external indicator or of an electrical method of determining the end-point.

16. Occurrence of Cobalt and Nickel

Early confusion of the ores of iron and cobalt and of those of copper and nickel was attributed to the presence of evil spirits; hence, when cobalt was finally discovered in 1735 by Brandt and nickel in 1751 by Cronstedt, the former was named from the German word *Kobald* meaning *goblin* and the latter for the *Old Nick*. Ores of the two metals nearly always occur together, and are usually associated with iron, arsenic, and sulfur. Many copper ores also contain some nickel. The principal source of the two metals in North America is the rich silver-nickel-cobalt ores of the province of Ontario, Canada. The principal ores of cobalt are *smaltite*, $CoAs_2$; *cobaltite*, $CoAsS$; *erythrite*, $Co_3(AsO_4)_2.8H_2O$; and *linnaeite*, Co_3S_4. Other cobalt-producing countries are the Belgian Congo, Chile, Burma, Finland, Morocco, the Union of South Africa, and Italy. The principal ores of nickel are *pentlandite*, $NiS.2FeS$, and *garnierite*, $[Ni, Mg]SiO_3.nH_2O$. The latter ore and other silicate ores of the metal are mined chiefly on the island of New Caledonia, which is second only to Canada in nickel production.

17. The Refining of Cobalt and Nickel Ores

The refining of cobalt and nickel ores is made difficult by the presence of a wide variety of other elements and by the similarity of the properties of the two metals. Smelting of the Canadian ore in a small blast furnace usually yields free silver and a mixture of the arsenides of the remaining metals (*speiss*). Iron and arsenic are next removed by a series of roastings with a variety of fluxes. Cobalt, nickel, copper, and any remaining silver are then converted to their chlorides by roasting with salt. Extraction with water removes the chlorides of the first three of the foregoing metals, and copper is separated by reduction and filtration. The nickel and cobalt are then precipitated as their hydroxides which are roasted to the corresponding oxides, and then reduced to the free metals.

There are several other processes for refining nickel and cobalt ores. In general, these depend largely upon the composition of the ores.

The final step in a majority of these processes is the separation of cobalt and nickel, which is usually accomplished by use of the Mond process. By this method, the mixture of finely divided reduced metals is heated to 50° to 100° C. in a stream of carbon monoxide. Under these conditions, nickel forms a volatile carbonyl, $Ni(CO)_4$, whose boiling point is 43° C. The cobalt is left behind, and the distilled nickel carbonyl is pyrolytically decomposed to free nickel and carbon monoxide. Cobalt forms carbonyls only under very high pressures of carbon monoxide.

Nickel is purified electrolytically in a bath of nickel sulfate. The oxides of both metals may be reduced to the free metal by heating with either carbon or aluminum.

18. Properties and Uses of Cobalt and Nickel

A number of the properties of both metals are listed in Table 38. Cobalt is a silvery metal with a faint tinge of pink, and is hard, brittle, and strongly paramagnetic. Nickel is also silvery, but with a faint tinge of yellow; it is also hard and paramagnetic, but it is also malleable, ductile, and in addition takes an unusually high polish. Both metals exist at low temperatures in the form of face-centered cubes, and both become nonmagnetic at definite transition temperatures: 1150° C. for cobalt and 360° C. for nickel. Cobalt displaces hydrogen from dilute acids less readily than does iron, and nickel is still less active. Nitric acid renders cobalt passive, but reacts readily with nickel. The latter metal, when exposed to the open air, shows little tendency to oxidize and is also very resistant to the action of even hot alkalies.

Cobalt is used principally in the preparation of special steels and other alloys. Its alloys are especially resistant to oxidation, take a high polish, and retain their hardness and temper well even at rather high operating temperatures. *Stellite* alloys containing cobalt have been referred to in previous chapters. When used with thorium, the metal serves as a catalyst in a number of processes, notable among which is the Fischer-Tropsch process for making hydrocarbons from water gas.

The uses of nickel closely parallel those of cobalt. A large portion of the metal is used in the production of special steels of great hardness and low susceptibility to oxidation. In addition, it forms a wider variety of other alloys than does cobalt. Notable among these latter are *nichrome* (cf. section 20, Chapter 32), *permalloy*, containing 78 per cent Ni and 21 per cent Fe, which is highly permeable by a magnetic field, and German silver, containing 25 per cent Ni, 25 per cent Zn, and 50 per cent Cu, which is a white metal used for the manufacture of many articles. Much nickel is used in plating other metals, either for their protection or in order to increase their beauty. Chromium plating is now more common, but the article to be so plated is usually given a primary plating of nickel to increase the life of the subsequent plate of chromium. For nickel plating, the electrolyte is usually nickel ammonium sulfate.

Finely divided nickel is a good catalyst, especially for reactions in which hydrogen is one of the reactants. The hydrogenation of unsaturated vegetable oils for the production of cooking fats is conducted in the presence of such a catalyst (cf. section 8, Chapter 23).

19. Cobalt and Nickel Compounds of the +2 Valence State

Cobaltous salts may be prepared by the action of acids on the metal, cobaltous oxide, or cobaltous hydroxide. The chloride crystallizes from solution as the hexahydrate, $CoCl_2.6H_2O$, which is of a brilliant cherry-red color. Upon dehydration, the crystals crumble to a blue powder. As a result of this behavior of the salt, its dilute solutions are sometimes used as a "sympathetic ink." Marks made with the solution become visible when the paper is warmed and fade as the salt again absorbs moisture from the air. Cobaltous sulfate and nitrate are also common laboratory reagents. In the crystalline state, the former is of a bright red color, has the formula $CoSO_4.7H_2O$, is isomorphous with ferrous sulfate heptahydrate, and is capable of forming with ammonium sulfate a double salt of the type of Mohr's salt. The nitrate crystals have the formula $Co(NO_3)_2.6H_2O$, are of the monoclinic system, and are of a somewhat yellowish-red color.

A blue precipitate of the hydroxide is obtained when alkalies are added to solutions of cobaltous ion. The color of this precipitate gradually becomes lavender, and finally pink as hydration progresses. The precipitate dissolves in ammonium hydroxide, forming a brownish-red solution of the complex compound $[Co(NH_3)_6](OH)_2$, which is rapidly oxidized by the air to $[Co(NH_3)_6](OH)_3$. Dehydration of the blue hydroxide yields cobaltous oxide, CoO, which may be obtained also by heating the oxalate CoC_2O_4 in an atmosphere of hydrogen. This oxide is a greenish powder which is used in the preparation of cobaltous salts and in the preparation of blue glasses and ceramic glazes.

Nickel has few compounds in which it shows a valence other than $+2$. The hydrated nickelous ion is green, and a majority of its salts are readily soluble. Most important of the nickel salts are the sulfate, nitrate, and chloride whose hydrated crystals have the formulas $NiSO_4.7H_2O$ (the hexahydrate is also formed), $Ni(NO_3)_2.6H_2O$, and $NiCl_2.6H_2O$, respectively. Nickel ammonium sulfate, $NiSO_4.(NH_4)_2SO_4.6H_2O$, is also widely used, especially as the electrolyte in plating cells. Addition of an alkali to a solution of nickelous ion results in the precipitation of the hydroxide as pale green flocs. Dehydration of this precipitate produces the oxide NiO, which is usually black, though as it occurs naturally in the ore *bunsenite* it is green. It may also be obtained by pyrolytic decomposition of the nitrate or the carbonate. Both the hydroxide and the oxide dissolve in an excess of ammonium hydroxide to form a pale blue solution of $[Ni(NH_3)_6](OH)_2$.

The sulfides of cobalt and nickel are precipitated by hydrogen sulfide only from basic solutions, but the precipitates so formed, both of which are black, are but slowly soluble in dilute acids. Three varieties of the nickelous sulfide of varying degrees of solubility are reported to exist.

20. Compounds of the +3 Valence State

Cobalt forms a few simple cobaltic salts of the $+3$ valence, but, in general these are unstable. Cobaltic oxide, Co_2O_3, is obtained as a dark powder when cobaltous nitrate is pyrolyzed at moderately high temperatures. The solutions formed by dissolving the powder in acids maintained at relatively low temperatures are believed to contain the cobaltic ion, which is reduced to the cobaltous condition when the solutions are warmed. Cobaltic hydroxide is formed as a black precipitate when an alkali hypochlorite is added to solutions containing cobaltous ions. It is perhaps the most stable of the cobaltic compounds and upon being heated yields the corresponding oxide. A hydrated cobaltic sulfate having the formula $Co_2(SO_4)_3.18H_2O$ is obtained by the electrolysis of a saturated solution of cobaltous sulfate in dilute sulfuric acid. Like the other cobaltic salts, it is unstable, especially in solution, but it is capable of forming deep blue cobaltic alums of the type $NH_4Co(SO_4)_2.12H_2O$. Cobaltic fluoride has also been prepared and described.

In the trivalent condition, nickel is even less stable than is cobalt. An oxide said to be Ni_2O_3 is obtained as a black powder by the careful pyrolysis of nickelous nitrate. The existence of nickelic hydroxide as a simple compound is even more doubtful, though its preparation has been reported.

21. Other Oxides of Nickel and Cobalt

In addition to the two oxides of cobalt already mentioned, the metal forms two other oxides. Upon being heated to temperatures which lie between 373° C. and 700° C., cobaltic oxide is converted to a black powder of the formula Co_3O_4. This oxide is analogous to Fe_3O_4. Upon being heated above 905° C., it decomposes into CoO. Cobalt dioxide, CoO_2, is obtained as a black precipitate by the strong oxidation of solutions of cobaltous salts with either alkali hypochlorites or hypoiodites.

It is reported that when either nickelous or nickelic oxide is heated in oxygen, the oxide Ni_3O_4 is obtained as a gray-black powder. There is some doubt, however, as to the exact composition of this product. Nickel dioxide is obtained from solutions of nickelous salts as a black precipitate in a manner entirely analogous to that used for the production of cobalt dioxide. When freshly precipitated, this oxide is hydrous and is used to form the anode of the Edison storage cell. The cathode of this cell is iron; its electrolyte is sodium hydroxide; and its electromotive force is 1.35 v. The equation for the reaction which occurs during its discharge is:

$$NiO_2 + Fe + 2H_2O \rightleftarrows Ni(OH)_2 + Fe(OH)_2$$

22. Complex Compounds of Cobalt and Nickel

Both cobalt and nickel exhibit a marked tendency to form complex compounds, but they differ in that the former exhibits oxidation numbers of both +2 and +3 in its complexes with a marked preference for the higher state, while the latter metal shows only the lower state of oxidation in its complexes. Attempts to oxidize nickelous complexes usually result in their decomposition and the formation of a precipitate of the hydrous dioxide. A wide variety of complex compounds of each of the metals is known, among the commonest of which are $[Co(NH_3)_6](OH)_2$ and $[Ni(NH_3)_6](OH)_2$. Equally well known is the yellow precipitate of potassium hexanitrocobaltiate (commonly called potassium cobaltinitrite), $2K_3[Co(NO_2)_6].3H_2O$, which is formed when an excess of potassium nitrite is added to a solution of a cobaltous salt acidified with acetic acid. The formation of this substance is commonly used as a test for both potassium and cobalt. Ammonium ions interfere, but the ions of nickel and of the other common heavy metals do not. Under the name of *cobalt yellow*, the substance is sometimes used as a pigment.

23. Analytical Tests for Cobalt and Nickel

Both metals are precipitated as sulfides in an alkaline solution. Their separation from the other sulfides is based first upon their failure to form soluble salts when treated with strong bases and secondly upon the insolubility of these sulfides in dilute acids. Separation of the metallic ions from ferric ions depends upon their ability to form soluble complexes with ammonium hydroxide while iron is precipitated as ferric hydroxide. Usually, no attempt is made to separate the two metals from each other. After the removal of iron, one portion of the solution is tested for cobalt, the other for nickel. The former metal may be tested for by the method mentioned in the preceding section, or the test solution may be acidified with hydrochloric acid and then treated with ammonium thio-cyanate solution and a few milliliters of an ether-amyl alcohol mixture. If cobaltous ions are present, a blue to green color will develop in the ether-alcohol layer.

The addition of a solution of dimethylglyoxime, $(CH_3)_2C_2(NOH)_2$, to a slightly ammoniacal solution containing nickelous ions results in the formation of a brilliant strawberry-red precipitate. Nickel may be determined quantitatively by the collection, drying, and weighing of this precipitate. Under the conditions described, cobalt does not form a precipitate.

II. THE PLATINUM METALS

24. General

Ruthenium, rhodium, and palladium are the VIII B metals of the fifth period, while osmium, iridium, and platinum are the VIII B metals of the sixth period. All six of these elements resemble each other closely and are known collectively after the commonest member of the group as the *platinum metals*. Although these elements have some properties in common with iron, cobalt, and nickel, they are much less susceptible to oxidation and are in general inert to all save the most drastic treatment. Further general information is presented in Table 39.

25. Properties

The general atomic and physical properties of the platinum metals, along with a few chemical properties, are also listed in Table 39. All of the metals are dense; all have high melting points; and all possess a silvery luster.

None of these metals is oxidized at ordinary temperatures, and only osmium and ruthenium burn when finely divided and heated in oxygen. Only palladium is converted to the nitrate by treatment with nitric acid, but by similar treatment very finely divided osmium is converted to the oxide OsO_4, a pale yellow, volatile solid (m.p. 40° C.). All of the metals are attacked by *aqua regia*, though iridium and rhodium are but slightly so, and the state of oxidation effected varies considerably with the metal. A variety of states of oxidation is shown by each metal, but only ruthenium and osmium are capable of reaching the +8 state. Each of the metals resembles members of the iron family in its ability to form complex compounds. Most important of these latter are the complex halides and cyanides. In the +4 state of oxidation, each of the metals forms complexes of the type K_2MX_6, where M stands for the metal and X for the halogen involved. These salts all crystallize in the cubic system, are isomorphous, and are of low solubility even when the positive ion is an alkali metal or ammonium. Solutions of salts of the platinum metals are easily reduced.

Table 39

PROPERTIES OF THE PLATINUM METALS AND OTHER DATA CONCERNING THEM

Property	Ruthenium (Ru)	Rhodium (Rh)	Palladium (Pd)	Osmium (Os)	Iridium (Ir)	Platinum (Pt)
Atomic weight.........	101.7	102.91	106.7	190.2	193.1	195.23
Mass of isotopes.......	96, 98, 99, 100, 101, 102, 104	101, 103	102, 104, 105, 106, 108, 110	186, 187, 188, 189, 190, 192	191, 193	192, 194, 195, 196, 198
Atomic number........	44	45	46	76	77	78
Distribution of planetary electrons........	2, 8, 18, 15, 1	2, 8, 18, 16, 1	2, 8, 18, 18	2, 8, 18, 32, 14, 2	2, 8, 18, 32, 15, 2	2, 8, 18, 32, 16, 2
Melting point, °C.....	2450	1985	1553	2700	2350	1773.5
Boiling point, °C......	> 2700	> 2500	2200	> 5300	> 4800	4300
Density, g./ml. at 20°C.	12.2	12.5	12.16	22.48	22.42 (17° C.)	21.37
States of oxidation (positive)	3, 4, 6, 8	3	2, 4	2, 3, 4, 8	3, 4	2, 4
Discoverer............	Klaus	Wollaston	Wollaston	Tennant	Tennant	Ulloa
Date of discovery......	1844	1803	1803	1803	1803	1735
Derivation of name.....	*Ruthenia*, (Russia)	*rose*, Greek	*Pallas*, a planetoid	*odor*, Greek	*rainbow*, Latin	*little silver*, Spanish
Color of the metal	silvery-gray	brilliant silvery-white	silvery with bluish cast	silvery-gray	silvery-white	silvery with bluish cast
Color of salts..........	brown, red	yellow, red	yellow, red	red, brown, green	green, red, violet	yellow, brown, green

Nickel, palladium, and platinum, corresponding members of the three VIII B triads, are noted for their ability to adsorb hydrogen, especially when they are in a high state of subdivision. Palladium possesses this property in the highest degree, but all three metals are excellent hydrogenation catalysts. Platinum used catalytically on an industrial scale represents a large investment and is easily "poisoned" (cf. section 7, Chapter 16) by a number of substances, the most notable of which is arsenic. Nickel, because of its relative cheapness, is widely used as a catalyst for hydrogenation and for a number of other reactions.

26. Occurrence

The platinum metals are always found free in nature, usually as small grains or nuggets in placer deposits. The largest of these are found in Russia, Alaska,

Colombia, and the Union of South Africa. Canada and the United States have lesser deposits. Crude platinum usually contains small quantities of the other metals of the family, as well as gold and some iron and copper. Also occurring naturally is *osmiridium*, which is, essentially, an alloy of osmium and iridium containing small percentages of the other elements of the family. All of the metals save osmium are obtained, also, from the residues of the nickel-cobalt ores of Ontario. All members of the family are relatively scarce.

27. Uses

Platinum is the most plentiful member of the family and is also the most widely used. Its general inertness, high melting point, and good malleability render it especially useful for the manufacture of various pieces of scientific equipment. Platinum crucibles, evaporating dishes, and electrodes are widely used in laboratories. Vessels made of a platinum-rhodium alloy are even less susceptible to loss of weight on heating than are those made of platinum alone. Platinum-iridium alloys possess great hardness and a low coefficient of expansion. They are used for making penpoints, electrical contacts, and standard weights and measures. Platinum is used in the manufacture of jewelry, in dentistry, and as a catalyst. In Russia, a few coins have been made of it. Platinum leaf finds some use in decoration and in the preparation of signs. The most important platinum compound is chloroplatinic acid, H_2PtCl_6, which is prepared by the action of *aqua regia* on the metal and is decomposed by heat to form the catalytically active platinum-black. Potassium chloroplatinate finds some use in photography.

In point of quantity used, palladium ranks second. It closely resembles platinum in both appearance and properties but is softer and has the lowest melting point of the family. It is also more reactive and a more effective hydrogenation catalyst. It, too, finds use in the jewelry, electrical, and dental goods industries, and its leaf is also used for decoration. It combines directly with chlorine and a number of other nonmetals when heated with them. Some of its salts find a slight use in photography. When carbon monoxide comes in contact with a solution of palladous chloride, $PdCl_2$, finely divided palladium-black is formed by reduction. This test is so sensitive that as little as one part of the monoxide in 10,000 parts of air will affect a solution containing the chloride in a dilution of 1:10,000.

Iridium ranks third in use. It is very hard and more brittle than is platinum. Its chief use is for alloying with the latter metal to give it greater hardness and more resistance to wear. The platinum-iridium tips of gold fountain-pen points are highly resistant to the constant wear to which they are subjected. The finely divided metal is possessed of good catalytic activity, and some of its compounds find use in photography. When the finely divided metal is heated in the air to a temperature of 1100° C., the dioxide, IrO_2, is formed. It finds some use as a pigment in porcelain glazes.

Rhodium is used principally for alloying with platinum and for plating jewelry and other decorative metal objects. It has a brilliant silvery-white luster, and is so inactive in the massive form as to be almost tarnish-proof. The massive metal is very resistant even to the action of *aqua regia*. Because of their very high melting point, rhodium-platinum alloys are used to make wires for thermo-couples and electric furnaces and special pieces of heat-resistant laboratory ware. Many of the spinnerets used in the manufacture of rayon threads are also made of this alloy. Rhodium is rather susceptible to attack by free chlorine.

Ruthenium and osmium also find their chief use as hardeners in the preparation of alloys of the platinum metals. Alloys of the latter element are sometimes used instead of jewels as bearings in precision instruments. Both metals form their tetroxides when treated with *aqua regia*, and osmium also forms its tetroxide by direct combination. Ruthenium tetroxide is a yellow solid which melts at 25.5° C. and boils with decomposition at 100° C. Osmium tetroxide resembles it in appearance, but melts at about 40° C. and boils at 130° C. Both oxides are volatile with steam; both are powerful oxidizing agents; and the osmium compound is poisonous. Osmium tetroxide is soluble in water, alcohol, and a variety of other solvents. Its aqueous solutions are used for hardening and staining tissues to be used in microscopical work. It also finds some use in fingerprint work. Osmium is the most dense of all the metals.

Many compounds of the platinum metals are known, since all are characterized by the ability to exist in several states of oxidation and by a marked tendency to form double salts and complex compounds. These compounds, in general, are expensive, and, save in the instances noted and from a theoretical standpoint, are of little importance.

28. Care of Platinum Laboratory Ware

Although platinum and alloys of the platinum metals are highly resistant to many types of chemical action, there are, nevertheless, a number of precautions which should be observed in the use of laboratory ware made of them. Certain metals should never be heated in platinum since they alloy readily with it; notable among these are mercury, tin, lead, and bismuth. If heated with carbon, silicon, phosphorus, or sulfur, the metal becomes brittle, and it is also attacked by free fluorine and free chlorine. One should also avoid heating the alkali hydroxides in platinum and its alloys. The action of these strong bases is especially pronounced when oxidizing agents are present. Ferric chloride also attacks these metals. Often nickel crucibles and dishes may be used for the conducting of fusions for which neither platinum nor porcelain vessels are suitable.

III. COPPER, SILVER, AND GOLD

29. General

Copper, silver, and gold are the members of the I B family. Because all three metals occur in the free state, they have been known for thousands of years, and because all three are used in coinage, they are known collectively as the *currency metals*. Like the metals of the I A family, each of the I B metals has but a single electron in its outermost energy level, but the next lower level contains 18 electrons rather than eight, as in the case of the alkali metals. Since one or two of the 18 electrons may also be lost, these currency metals may show valences in excess of the characteristic +1; indeed, the +2 copper ion and the +3 gold ion are more stable to reduction than are the +1 ions of the respective metals. The I B and I A metals differ also in the slight activity of the former, the lower solubility of their hydroxides, oxides, sulfides, and monohalides, and their marked tendency to form complex ions. A further difference to be noted is that whereas the I A metals increase in activity as the weights of their atoms increase, the I B metals decrease in activity with increasing weight. The low activities,

Table 40

PROPERTIES OF COPPER, SILVER, AND GOLD

Property	Copper (Cu)	Silver (Ag)	Gold (Au)
Atomic weight..........................	63.57	107.880	197.2
Mass of isotopes.........................	63, 65	107, 109	197
Atomic number..........................	29	47	79
Distribution of planetary electrons............	2, 8, 18, 1	2, 8, 18, 18, 1	2, 8, 18, 32, 18, 1
Melting point, ° C........................	1083	960.5	1063
Boiling point, ° C........................	2300	1950	2600
Density, g./ml. at 20° C..................	8.94	10.50	19.32 (17.5° C.)
Ionizing potential, volts			
1st electron.............................	7.68	7.54	9.18
2nd electron............................	20.34	21.4	19.95
Electrode potential +1 ions, volts............	−0.470	−0.798	−1.50
Ionic radius of +1 ions, Ångström units......	0.96	1.26	1.37
Specific heat, cal./g.......................	0.0921 (20° C.)	0.0558 (20° C.)	0.0312 (18° C.)

high boiling points, and relatively high ionizing potentials of the I B metals indicate that the separation of their atoms is accomplished only with difficulty. The family is unusual in that it is the only one whose members regularly exhibit states of oxidation in excess of the family number, and also in that copper and gold are the only metals whose colors are not some shade of gray. Metals of the I A and I B families resemble each other in the property of low electrical resistance, but chemically the I B elements more closely resemble the platinum metals than they do the elements of any other family. A number of important properties of the members of the currency family are given in Table 40.

30. Occurrence of Copper

The name *copper* and the symbol *Cu* are derived from the Latin *cuprum*, which in turn is derived from *Cyprus*, a Mediterranean island from which the

AN ARIZONA OPEN-PIT COPPER MINE. (Courtesy, Phelps Dodge Corp.)

Romans obtained the metal. Although the metal occurs in the free state, especially in the Lake Superior region, its chief sources are the ores in which it occurs in combination with nonmetals. Over 70 per cent of the annual copper production in the United States is derived from sulfide ores, notable among which are *chalcocite*, Cu_2S; *chalcopyrite*, $CuFeS_2$; *bornite*, Cu_3FeS_3; and *covellite*, CuS. Certain oxygen-containing ores are also of importance; notable among these are *cuprite*, Cu_2O; *tenorite*, CuO; *malachite*, $Cu_2(OH)_2CO_3$; *azurite*, $Cu_3(OH)_2(CO_3)_2$; and *chrysocolla*, $CuSiO_3.2H_2O$. The most important copper-producing states in the order of production are Arizona, Utah, Montana, Nevada, Michigan, and New Mexico. Japan, Mexico, Chile, Alaska, Siberia, the Belgian Congo, and the Union of South Africa are also copper-producers.

31. *Refining of Copper*

The methods used in the recovery of copper from its ores vary considerably with the nature of the ore. Native copper is usually recovered by purely mechani-

A MASS OF COPPER SULFATE CRYSTALS PRODUCED BY AN ELECTROLYTIC METHOD. (Photograph from Canadian Chemistry and Process Industries—courtesy, Canadian Copper Refiners, Ltd.)

cal processes, and the oxygen-containing ores are usually smelted with coke and a suitable flux. The treatment of sulfide ores is rendered much more complex by the presence of both sulfur and iron. The treatment of such ores usually involves five steps: (a) concentration by the froth-flotation process (especially for low-grade ores); (b) roasting to remove the volatile oxides of arsenic and antimony, to convert a part of the copper to the oxide, and to remove a portion of the sulfur as gaseous SO_2; (c) smelting with sand or calcium carbonate to remove some of the iron as a slag and more of the sulfur as SO_2, and to leave a *copper matte* consisting mostly of cuprous and ferrous sulfides; (d) reduction of the *matte* to *blister copper* by subjecting it to an air blast in a converter, closely

DISCHARGE OF MOLTEN METAL FROM A MODERN COPPER CONVERTER. (Courtesy, Anaconda Copper Mining Co.)

resembling the Bessemer converter, where the iron oxide formed is removed as slag and the cuprous sulfide reduced to the free metal; and (e) electrolysis of the *blister copper* in a bath of cupric sulfate. Gold and silver recovered from the anode mud of the electrolytic process are often of sufficient value to pay for the current used.

32. *Uses of Copper*

Copper is widely used and is, therefore, a highly important metal. As a conductor of electricity, it rates next to silver, and finds wide use in the manufacture of wire for electrical circuits and in the construction of various electrical devices. Because of its great heat-conducting ability, it finds common use in the manufacture of cooking kettles, pots, and pans. The sheet metal is used for the covering of roofs and ships' bottoms, and for the manufacture of gutters, drain pipes, etc. The ability of the molten metal to dissolve gases which are given up to form blisters when cooling takes place renders it unsuitable for the making of castings. Copper plating is a common procedure, and its use in the production of electrotype plates from which books and magazines are printed should be noted. The metal also finds wide use in the production of alloys. Reference to a number of these alloys has been made in preceding chapters, and special attention is directed to the beryllium alloys (cf. section 5, Chapter 30). Listed below are several important copper alloys.

Table 41

ALLOYS OF COPPER

Aluminum bronze............	Cu 90–98%, Al 2–10%
Aluminum silicon bronze.......	Cu 91%, Al 7%, Si 2%
Bell metal...................	Cu 78%, Sn 22%
Brass.......................	Cu 60–82%, Zn 18–40%
Bronze.....................	Cu 70–95%, Zn 1–25%, Sn 1–18%
Constantan.................	Cu 60%, Ni 40%
German silver..............	Cu 55–60%, Zn 20%, Ni 20–25%
Gun metal.................	Cu 90%, Sn 10%
Nickel coin.................	Cu 75%, Ni 25%
Silver coin.................	Cu 10%, Ag 90%
Sterling....................	Cu 7.5%, Ag 92.5%

33. *Chemical Properties of Copper*

Like the other members of its periodic family, copper is below hydrogen in the activity series, hence it liberates hydrogen from neither water nor dilute acids. It does react, however, with oxidizing acids, and with nonoxidizing acids in the presence of air or oxygen. In moist air, the metal is even attacked by the very dilute carbonic acid solutions formed by the dissolution of atmospheric carbon dioxide in water. As a result of the action of this substance there is formed the well-known green deposit which appears on copper exposed to the weather. The formula of the deposit is $Cu_2(OH)_2CO_3$. The metal is not attacked by fused alkalies, but is dissolved slowly by ammonium hydroxide in the presence of air. It will combine directly with oxygen or sulfur when heated, and it is attacked by the halogens. Two common series of copper salts are known, and compounds of the +3 oxidation state have been prepared but are very unstable. All soluble salts of the metal are highly toxic.

34. *Cuprous Compounds*

Most cuprous salts are prepared from the corresponding cupric salts by reduction. Cuprous salts of the oxygen acids, in general, are both soluble and so unstable that they are seldom encountered. Those most frequently found in the laboratory are either binary compounds which are insoluble or which form stable complex compounds. In solution, most cuprous salts tend to undergo oxidation to the cupric condition. The cuprous ion and most of its complexes are colorless, or nearly so, though the oxide and sulfide are colored. Most important of the salts of the $+1$ state of oxidation are the oxide, sulfide, halides, cyanide, and thiocyanate.

As precipitated from solution, cuprous oxide, Cu_2O, is a yellow powdery substance which turns red upon being heated. It may be prepared by treating an alkaline solution of cupric sulfate and sodium potassium tartrate (known as Fehling's solution) with dextrose or other reducing sugars, or other mild reducing agents. Other methods of preparation are the heating of sodium carbonate with cuprous chloride and the maintenance of cupric oxide, CuO, at temperatures in excess of red heat. It is used in making some types of ruby glass, red porcelain glazes, and some types of photoelectric cells.

Cuprous hydroxide, $CuOH$, may be precipitated by the addition of an alkali hydroxide to a solution of cuprous chloride in hydrochloric acid, which solution presumably contains the complex acid $HCuCl_2$.

The sulfide, Cu_2S, is a black, insoluble substance obtained by heating cupric sulfide either alone in the absence of air or in a current of hydrogen, or by heating the free metal with an excess of sulfur.

Cuprous chloride is a colorless solid whose solubility in water is very slight. It may be prepared by reduction of solutions of the corresponding cupric salt with either copper or sulfur dioxide. It dissolves readily in either ammonium hydroxide or hydrochloric acid as the result of the formation of soluble complexes, which are colorless but which undergo oxidation upon standing. Reference has already been made to the use of these solutions for the absorption of carbon monoxide (cf. section 11, Chapter 27). The preparation of the bromide is analogous to that of the chloride, but the iodide is prepared simply by adding solutions containing iodide ions to solutions of the cupric ion:

$$2Cu^{++} + 4I^- \rightarrow \underline{2CuI} + I_2$$

The preparation of the cyanide is analogous to that of the iodide.

Cuprous thiocyanate, $CuSCN$, is prepared by reduction of the cupric salt with sulfur dioxide.

35. Cupric Compounds

In general, the cupric salts of the oxygen acids are more important than the binary salts. Most widely used of these salts is the sulfate. The hydrated cupric ion is of a bright blue color.

Cupric oxide is a hard, dark substance which is prepared by heating the metal to red heat in the air, or by the pyrolysis of the hydroxide, the carbonate, or the nitrate. At red heat it is a good oxidizing agent for a number of substances including a wide variety of organic compounds. It is used industrially to desulfurize petroleum oils and as a coloring agent in ceramic glazes.

Cupric hydroxide, $Cu(OH)_2$, is formed as a pale blue, gelatinous precipitate when an alkali hydroxide is added to solutions which contain the cupric ion. It is easily converted to the oxide and may be so converted simply by boiling the solution from which it is formed. It is essentially weakly basic, but is amphoteric enough to be dissolved slightly by concentrated solutions of strong bases. It dissolves readily in ammonium hydroxide, forming the deep blue complex $[Cu(NH_3)_4](OH)_2$, whose solution is capable of dissolving cellulose and is so used in one method of manufacturing rayon; treatment of this latter solution with an acid causes the cellulose to be reprecipitated.

Cupric sulfate, $CuSO_4$, known also as *bluestone* or *blue vitriol*, is obtained by treating copper or its ores with dilute sulfuric acid. Beautiful blue, triclinic crystals of the pentahydrate are obtained from solution. Water is driven off when these crystals are heated, leaving behind the anhydrous salt in the form of a white powder. Like most of the other cupric salts of strong acids, it forms solutions which, due to hydrolysis, are acidic. The salt is both a germicide and fungicide, and, as such, is added to water in reservoirs and swimming pools and is used as a component of Bordeaux mixture for spraying plants and trees. It also finds use in electroplating, the solutions of certain types of batteries, the preparation of pigments, the preparation of other copper salts, and calico-printing. The anhydrous salt is used as a drying agent.

The sulfide, CuS, may be formed by direct union of the elements when they are heated together, or by the action of hydrogen sulfide on acidic solutions of cupric ions. It is soluble in both strong nitric acid and *aqua regia*.

Cupric nitrate, $Cu(NO_3)_2.6H_2O$, cupric chloride, $CuCl_2.2H_2O$, and cupric acetate, $Cu(C_2H_3O_2)_2.H_2O$, are all common laboratory reagents. The basic carbonate, $Cu_2(OH)_2CO_3$, is precipitated by the action of sodium carbonate on a warm cupric solution and is a common compound. Cupric arsenite, $CuHAsO_3$ and cupric acetoarsenite (*Paris green*), $Cu(C_2H_3O_2)_2.Cu_3(AsO_3)_2$, are commonly used as dusting insecticides, and the former is used as a pigment under the name of *Scheele's green*.

Both the cuprous and the cupric ion form a wide variety of complexes, most important of which are the ammino cations and the halo and cyano anions. Best known of the complex ions is the deep blue tetramminocupro ion $[Cu(NH_3)_4]^{++}$.

36. *Analytical Tests for Copper*

Since the cuprous ion is so easily oxidized, the qualitative tests for copper are essentially those of the cupric ion. Cupric sulfide is precipitated as described above and dissolved in nitric acid. Confirmation is obtained either by the formation of the deep blue tetrammino complex or by the formation of a dull red precipitate of cupric ferrocyanide whose formula is usually represented as $Cu_2[Fe(CN)_6]$, though more correctly as $Cu[Cu_3[Fe(CN)_6]_2]$. The latter test is the more delicate.

Quantitatively, copper may be precipitated electrolytically on a weighed cathode, or it may be determined volumetrically by any one of several reactions. One method involves the titration with standard thiosulfate of the free iodine liberated by the action of cupric ions on iodide ions (cf. section 34).

37. *Occurrence of Silver*

The discovery of silver is lost in antiquity, but its name is derived from the Anglo-Saxon word *seolfor* and its symbol, *Ag*, is derived from the Latin *argentum*, meaning *white*. In nature, the metal occurs both free and in the combined state. When free, it is often alloyed with varying quantities of the other noble metals, copper, and mercury, and its compounds frequently occur in ores which contain compounds of other metals. Most important of the naturally occurring silver compounds is the sulfide, AgS, which is sometimes found alone as the mineral *argentite* or *silver glance*, but is more frequently found associated with the sulfides of lead, copper, nickel, antimony, and arsenic. Silver chloride also occurs naturally as the mineral *cerargyrite* or *horn silver* and is an important ore, samples of which sometimes contain the bromide and iodide also. Selenides, tellurides, and sulfates of silver have also been discovered. The western hemisphere leads in the production of the metal, with Mexico, the United States, and Canada, in the order given, being the principal countries of production.

38. *The Refining of Silver*

The recovery of silver which occurs with copper has been dealt with above in section 31, and its separation from lead has been treated in section 26 of Chapter 31 (*q.v.*). The metal is recovered from relatively pure silver ores either by amalgamation or by the cyanide process, or by some combination of the two. In the amalgamation process, the crushed ore is passed over plates on which mercury has been spread. Ultimately, the amalgam is scraped off and the mercury distilled from the silver for reuse. In the cyanide process, the crushed ore is extracted with a solution of sodium cyanide. Silver is removed as the soluble complex compound $Na[Ag(CN)_2]$, from which it is recovered by displacement with zinc. The latter process does not work well on sulfide ores or on large particles of native silver, hence its use is frequently preceded by amalgamation or by roasting the ore with sodium chloride so that the readily attacked silver chloride will be formed. Molten silver dissolves large quantities of oxygen, which escape with a spitting sound as the mass cools.

39. *Uses of Silver*

Silver is used principally for the manufacture of coins, jewelry, tableware, and ornamental goods, though some laboratory ware is made of it. It also finds use in dental alloys, and its salts are used in the production of photo-

SILVER INGOTS STORED FOR LATER CONVERSION TO SILVER HALIDES TO BE USED IN THE PREPARATION OF PHOTOGRAPHIC FILMS, PLATES, AND PAPERS.

graphic films, plates, and papers and in the silvering of mirrors. Large quantities of the metal are used in the plating of objects made of a variety of the baser metals. The metal is very malleable and ductile, a good conductor of heat and electricity, and a good reflector of light. It takes a high polish, and tarnishes but slightly save in the presence of hydrogen sulfide. Since it is a very soft metal, it is common practice to increase its hardness and wearing qualities by alloying it with copper. Coin and sterling alloys are listed in Table 41. Plating is usually carried on in a bath of potassium argenticyanide, $K[Ag(CN)_2]$, with the object to be plated serving as the cathode. The plate thus obtained is of a much finer grain and takes a much higher polish than that obtained when silver nitrate serves as the electrolyte. Mirrors are prepared by pouring on a cleaned glass plate a mixture of an ammoniacal solution of silver nitrate and a mild reducing agent such as formaldehyde or dextrose. The deposited film of the metal is washed, dried, and then shellacked or varnished.

40. Chemical Properties of Silver

Since it is below hydrogen in the activity series, silver does not displace hydrogen from acids, but it is attacked by nitric acid and hot sulfuric acid, which reagents convert it to its nitrate and sulfate, respectively. It is not attacked by strong bases. It is not attacked by oxygen under ordinary conditions, although it is oxidized by ozone to the peroxide, Ag_2O_2. Hydrogen sulfide tarnishes silver by forming a thin surface film of the sulfide. Eggs and other substances which contain sulfur also cause tarnishing (cf. section 5, Chapter 30). Silver forms but a single series of stable, simple salts. In these its oxidation number is $+1$, as is also its electrovalence; in addition, however, it also forms a variety of both simple and complex compounds in which its state of oxidation is $+2$ and $+3$. The monovalent ion has a strong tendency to form salts of the oxygen acids and but a slight tendency toward hydration. A peculiarity of the monovalent ion is that although it is itself colorless, it frequently unites with colorless anions to form colored compounds; on combination with colored anions it usually intensifies their color.

41. Compounds of Silver

Silver hydroxide, AgOH, is exclusively basic in its behavior, but it is so unstable that when it is precipitated by the addition of a base to solutions of silver nitrate, it immediately decomposes into a brown, amorphous form of the oxide Ag_2O. This latter compound may also be prepared by heating the finely divided metal to 300° C. in an atmosphere of oxygen maintained under a pressure of 15 atm. Under ordinary pressures, it decomposes into its elements at 250° C. It dissolves in strong ammonium hydroxide to form the complex diamminoargentahydroxide, $[Ag(NH_3)_2]OH$, which is a moderately strong base.

Because of its ease of preparation and its solubility in water, the nitrate is one of the most generally useful of the silver salts. It is prepared by dissolving the metal in nitric acid and is readily crystallized from the concentrated solution in the form of colorless rhombic prisms of the formula $AgNO_3$. The salt melts at 212° C. and is frequently melted and cast into sticks for medicinal use. In this form it is sometimes known as *lunar caustic* and is used to cauterize wounds and to remove warts. Solutions of the salt are readily reduced by organic matter in the presence of light. This property accounts for the black stains which appear around bottle necks and on skin with which solutions of the salt come in contact. Most other silver salts are prepared from the nitrate.

Silver fluoride, AgF, is a colorless salt of high solubility which is prepared by dissolving silver oxide in hydrofluoric acid. The other halides are of a low solubility which decreases with the increasing weight of the combined halogen. They are usually prepared by addition of solutions of the proper anion to solutions of silver nitrate. The chloride is colorless, the bromide cream-colored, and the iodide a bright yellow. The chloride is much more soluble in ammonium hydroxide than are the bromide and iodide. All three are reduced to their constituent elements upon exposure to light, a property which makes them highly useful in photography.

The acetate, sulfate, carbonate, nitrite, and cyanide are frequently used as laboratory reagents, and the thiocyanate, AgSCN, and the chromate, Ag_2CrO_4, are frequently precipitated in laboratory work. The sulfide, Ag_2S, is readily precipitated as a black solid when hydrogen sulfide is passed into even strongly acidic solutions of argentous ions. Although most argentous salts are of low solubility in water, any compound in the following list may be formed at the expense of any which precedes it: Ag_2SO_4, $AgC_2H_3O_2$, $AgNO_2$, Ag_2CO_3, $Ag_2C_2O_4$, Ag_2CrO_4, AgCl, AgSCN, AgBr, AgCN, AgI, and Ag_2S.

Argentous ion, like the ions of copper, forms a wide variety of complex ions, the most notable of which are diamminoargenta ion, $[Ag(NH_3)_2]^+$, and the dicyanoargentate ion, $[Ag(CN)_2]^-$. The use of the latter in the recovery of the metal and in silver plating has already been mentioned.

While compounds containing di- and trivalent silver are less common and less important than those of the monovalent ion, many of them exist, and the student should be aware of the fact. The sesquioxide, Ag_2O_3, is prepared by the action of potassium perdisulfate upon $AgNO_3$, but decomposes readily into Ag_2O and oxygen. It is believed that certain of the catalytic actions of silver are due to the presence of the Ag^{+3} ion. When $AgNO_3$ is treated with both sodium carbonate and potassium perdisulfate, the oxide AgO is formed. It dissolves in sulfuric, perchloric, and nitric acids to give solutions which have great oxidizing power and which are believed to contain the corresponding unstable argentic salts. Argentic fluoride, AgF_2, has been prepared and described, and argentic nitrate, $Ag(NO_3)_2$ is said to be formed when argentous nitrate dissolved in nitric acid is treated with lead dioxide. A number of crystalline complex compounds which contain divalent silver are known.

42. *Photochemistry and Photography*

There have been a number of previous references to reactions which bear a definite relationship to their condition of exposure to light. The study of such relationships is known as *photochemistry*. Many substances have the ability to absorb light energy in varying degrees, but their behavior as the result of the absorption is far from uniform. The fate of the energy absorbed and the study of any reactions which may result from the absorption are the concern of the photochemist. Many substances as a result of light-energy absorption simply attain a higher temperature, i.e., greater molecular motion, while the molecules of other substances become excited and thus exist for a time in an unstable state. The excited molecules may regain stability by emission of energy, in which case the phenomenon of *fluorescence* is observed. On the other hand, the excess energy may be passed on to other particles by collision or it may result in the dissociation of the molecule into its constituent atoms. These two possibilities are both potentially capable of starting chemical reactions. If the reaction so initiated is endothermal, it will continue only so long as light energy continues to be supplied, but in many instances, such as the explosion of irradiated mixtures of hydrogen and chlorine, the reaction once initiated will evolve energy and thus go to completion. There are many photochemical reactions, some of which, like *photosynthesis*, are of great importance. The field is far too broad and involved to be discussed here in anything but the most cursory manner. It may also be said that photochemistry offers a fertile field for further scientific investigation.

Photography is based upon the fact that the halides of argentous silver undergo a not-very-well-understood photochemical change of some sort when they are exposed to light. Photographic films, plates, and papers are coated with an emulsion of finely divided particles of silver bromide suspended in gelatin, which serves both as an adhesive and as a protective colloid. The chloride and iodide are frequently used in conjunction with the bromide, and silver sulfide is employed in small quantities to increase the sensitivity of the halides. When light reflected by some object, or series of objects, is admitted to the sensitized plate or film through a system of focusing lenses, the halides undergo no visible change, but are nevertheless rendered more susceptible to reduction by the mild reducing agents of the developer. The speed of reduction is proportional to the intensity of the admitted light. The visible image formed is called a negative, because the light-colored, highly reflecting portions of the original scene appear as dark areas of finely divided silver on the plate or film. The unreduced halides are removed by treatment with the fixing agent, usually sodium thiosulfate (cf. section 29, Chapter 21). Positive prints are obtained by projecting light through the negative onto sensitized paper. Again the shading of the areas is reversed and a positive whose highlights and shadows correspond to those of the original is produced. Prints must be developed, fixed, and washed just as films and plates are. In essence, this is the photographic process, though there are many different films, plates, papers, developers, and specialized processes from which to choose.

43. Analytical Tests for Silver

Silver ions are usually precipitated along with those of lead and mercurous mercury as the chloride. The lead chloride is removed by dissolution in hot water, and the silver chloride is then dissolved in strong ammonium hydroxide, with which the mercurous chloride reacts to give a black or gray precipitate. From the ammoniacal solution the silver chloride may be reprecipitated by the addition of nitric acid. Upon exposure to sunlight, or ultraviolet light, the white solid turns first lavender then black. Silver sulfide is black, the chromate brick-red, the phosphate yellow, and the arsenate chocolate-brown. All are of slight solubility.

44. The Occurrence of Gold

Gold is believed by many to be the first metal to be used by man. The name *gold* is of Anglo-Saxon origin, and the symbol *Au* is derived from the Latin name *aurum*, whose meaning is given as *shining dawn*. The metal is usually found in the free condition distributed through a hard quartz matrix. The weathering of such deposits accounts for the finding of placer gold. Ores of copper, lead, silver, and nickel usually contain small quantities of the metal. Its only naturally occurring compounds are the tellurides such as *calaverite*, $AuTe_2$, *petzite*, $(Au, Ag)_2Te$, and *sylvanite* $(Au, Ag)Te_2$, which are found principally in Colorado and in the Hungarian province of Transylvania. Leading gold producers are the Union of South Africa, Russia, Canada, and the United States. States which lead in production of the yellow metal are California, South Dakota, Utah, Colorado, Arizona, and Nevada.

45. *Recovery of Gold*

All the earlier methods of recovering gold from alluvial deposits involved the use of water to wash away the lighter sandy and earthy material. All of these methods—from the "panning" of the lone worker to the complicated sluiceways and powerful streams of water of more involved placer methods—were far from efficient in the recovery of the metal. The modern method usually combines amalgamation and cyanide extraction, as described for silver recovery. In the cyanide extraction process, the soluble compound usually formed is

MANUAL PLACER MINING OF GOLD. (Courtesy, The Denver *Post.*)

$Na[Au(CN)_2]$, from which the precious metal is displaced by zinc. This procedure, which was introduced in 1889, is especially valuable for the treatment of low-grade ores. A third process occasionally used is chlorination, by which method the ore is treated with free chlorine; the soluble auric chloride, $AuCl_3$, formed is extracted with water and then treated with hydrogen sulfide; and the metal is recovered from the precipitated sulfide by ignition.

Gold obtained by any of the above methods is usually alloyed with silver, copper, and other base metals, hence refining, or *parting*, is necessary. Usually, parting is accomplished by treating the alloy with sulfuric acid, which reacts with silver and other metals to leave the gold unaffected. Nitric acid is more expensive, but is sometimes used. Neither acid works well unless the mixture

J. Robert Oppenheimer
(1904–   , American)

Best known as the top scientific director of the atomic bomb project, Dr. Oppenheimer is a physicist of distinction, an expert mathematician, an outstanding teacher, and an administrator of rare ability, whom Secretary of War Stimson cited for "genius and leadership." His physical contributions in the realm of the sub-atomic have been fundamental and outstanding. He is a graduate of Harvard University, received the Ph.D. degree at Göttingen, and has studied at a number of other American and foreign universities. He has held professorships at the California Institute of Technology and at the University of California, and is the recipient of many honors in the scientific world.

Enrico Fermi
(1901–   , Italian [by birth])

Fermi is an Italian-born scientist of great skill and ability. He was trained in the universities of Italy, Germany, and Holland, and, after teaching at the University of Florence, he became professor of theoretical physics at the University of Rome in 1926. From 1934 to 1938 he worked on the production of radioactive isotopes of nonradioactive elements by the bombardment of stable atoms with neutrons. In an effort to create atoms heavier than those of uranium, he bombarded that element with neutrons. Repetition of this experiment by Hahn and his co-workers and its interpretation by Meitner led directly to the atomic bomb project. Because of his antifascist ideals, Fermi came to the United States in the late 1930's to join the faculty of Columbia University. During World War II, he was an active member of the group of scientists who were engaged in the atomic bomb project. He is now a professor at the Institute of Nuclear Studies of the University of Chicago. Fermi has received many decorations, degrees, and honors, included among which are the Nobel Prize in physics (1938) and the Hughes Medal (1943).

contains at least 70 per cent of silver. Electrolytic refining is also used. If the alloy is rich in gold, auric chloride in 10 per cent hydrochloric acid is usually used as the electrolyte, and the metal is deposited on a pure gold cathode. For less pure alloys special modifications of the method are used.

46. Uses of Gold

Gold has long been used for the manufacture of coins, pieces of jewelry, and art objects. The metal is so soft that it does not wear well, and for that reason it is frequently alloyed with silver, copper, or nickel. The quantity of gold in such alloys is usually expressed either in terms of degrees of fineness or in terms of carats. The pure metal is 1000 degrees or 24 carats fine. Because of its low activity, the metal is used extensively in dental work and for plating objects made of less valuable metals. It is the most malleable and ductile of all metals, and can be rolled into sheets whose thickness is as small as 0.00001 mm. Thin sheets of the foil, known as *gold leaf*, are used in preparing signs, in book-binding, and for architectural decorations.

47. Properties of Gold

Gold is the only pure metal which is yellow by reflected light. By trans-mitted light, it is green. Although it can be drawn into very fine wires, it has only about 70 per cent of the efficiency of copper in conducting the electric current. Chemically it is among the least active of the metals. It is not attacked by air, water, oxygen, or sulfur, or by any single acid save selenic. Even fused alkalies attack it but slowly. It is attacked by free halogens, *aqua regia*, selenic acid, and solutions of the alkali cyanides. Compounds of the aurous ($+1$) and auric ($+3$) series are known, but the simple compounds are in general unstable. A few very unstable compounds of the $+2$ oxidation state are known.

48. The Compounds of Gold

In the aurous condition, gold is distinctly basic and readily forms complex ions; in the auric condition, it is somewhat amphoteric and has an even more pronounced tendency to form complexes. All compounds of the metal are unstable to heat and reducing agents.

The oxides of gold cannot be prepared directly, but both Au_2O and Au_2O_3 are known. They are of little importance.

Chloroauric acid, $HAuCl_4$, is formed when the metal is treated with *aqua regia*. By evaporation of the solution, one may obtain yellow, deliques-cent crystals of the formula $HAuCl_4.4H_2O$, which, upon being heated to $120°$ C., yield hydrogen chloride and auric chloride. At $175°$ C., the latter compound decomposes into aurous chloride and chlorine, and at still higher temperatures gold and chlorine are the decomposition products. Aurous chloride is not soluble in water, but when treated with hot water it undergoes autooxidation-reduction:

$$3AuCl \rightarrow AuCl_3 + 2Au$$

Evaporation of chloroauric acid solutions to which sodium chloride has been added yields yellow crystals of sodium chloroaurate dihydrate, $NaAuCl_4.2H_2O$, which is used in photography as a toning agent.

The addition of a strong base to solutions of chloroauric acid precipitates orange-colored auric hydroxide, $Au(OH)_3$, which dissolves in an excess of the base to form aurates of the type $KAuO_2$, and which may be dehydrated to give the brown auric oxide, Au_2O_3. Reduction of this oxide with hydriodic acid yields aurous iodide:

$$Au_2O_3 + 6HI \rightarrow 2AuI + 2I_2 + 3H_2O$$

From a practical standpoint, the most important compounds of gold are the auro- and auricyanides of the alkali metals. These salts are of the type $Na[Au(CN)_2]$ and $Na[Au(CN)_4]$. They are prepared by the action of solutions of the alkali cyanides on aurous and auric salts, respectively, and are used as electrolytes in gold-plating.

49. Analytical Tests for Gold

Gold is most easily tested for by treating its solution in *aqua regia* with stannous chloride solution. As a result of the reduction, free gold is liberated in colloidal form and absorbed on a hydrosol of stannic acid. The sol so formed is of a brilliant purple color, and is commonly known as *purple of Cassius*. The test is a very delicate one, since the color develops when the concentration of gold in the original solution is as little as one part in one hundred million. The color of gold sols varies considerably with the size of the dispersed particles. With decreasing particle size, the color shifts from blue through purple to red and finally to orange. The beautiful red of antique stained glass is due to colloidally dispersed gold.

(See Appendix for Exercises)

COLLATERAL READINGS

Addicks: *Silver in Industry*, New York, Reinhold Publishing Corp., 1940.
Backert: *The A, B, C, of Iron and Steel*, 4th ed., Cleveland, Penton Publishing Co., 1921.

Bailar: The oxidation states of silver, *J. Chem. Education*, **21**, 523 (1944).

Baldwin: The story of nickel, *J. Chem. Education*, **8**, 1749, 1954, 2325 (1931).

Burchard: Sources of our iron ores, *J. Chem. Education*, **10**, 195, 288 (1933).

Carter: Precious metals as materials of construction, *Ind. Eng. Chem.*, **27**, 751 (1935).

Creighton and Koehler: *Electrochemistry*, Vol. II, 4th ed., New York, John Wiley & Sons, Inc., 1943.

Crook: Alloy steels and their uses, *J. Chem. Education*, **4**, 583 (1927).

Davis: *The Story of Copper*, New York, Century Co., 1924.

Emeleus and Anderson: *Modern Aspects of Inorganic Chemistry*, London, George Routledge & Sons, Ltd., 1938.

Fraser: Nickel as a catalyst, *Trans. Electrochemical Soc.*, **71**, 1 (1937).

Gilchrist: The platinum metals, *Chem. Rev.*, **32**, 277 (1943).

Johnstone: Some aspects of steel chemistry, *Ind. Eng. Chem.*, **28**, 1417 (1936).

Keller: The coordination theory and coordination compounds of the platinum group metals, *J. Chem. Education*, **18**, 134 (1941).

Latimer and Hildebrand: *Reference Book of Inorganic Chemistry*, New York, The Macmillan Co., 1941.

Lee: Silver, gold, tantalum, and the platinum metals, *Ind. Eng. Chem.*, **28**, 1412 (1936).

Mathews: The steel age, 1876–1926, *Ind. Eng. Chem.*, **18**, 913 (1926).

Morgan and Burstall: *Inorganic Chemistry*, Cambridge, W. Heffer & Sons, Ltd., 1938.

Nelson: Red hot speed, *Nature*, **36**, 181 (1943).

Sheppard: Fifty years of photography, *J. Chem. Education*, **4**, 298, 465, 749 (1927).

Silliman: Beryllium-copper alloys, *Ind. Eng. Chem.*, **28**, 1424 (1936).

Vines: *The Platinum Metals and Their Alloys*, New York, International Nickel Co., 1941.

Walker: The story of steel, *Sci. American*, **130**, 5, 28, 108, 162, 234, 310, 396 (1924); **131**, 98, 174 (1924).

Weeks: *Discovery of the Elements*, 5th ed., Mack Printing Co., 1945.

Spices for wartime steel, *Fortune*, **28**, No. 5, 90 (1943).

Steel, *Fortune*, **3**, No. 5, 84 (1931); **4**, No. 2, 41 (1931); **5**, No. 6, 30 (1932); **20**, No. 5, 75 (1939).

34

Zinc, Cadmium, Mercury, and Their Compounds

1. Introduction

Group II B of the periodic classification of the elements contains the metals zinc, cadmium, and mercury. These elements are not transition elements according to the usual definition of the term, but they do serve to complete the series of variations of properties which begin with and extend through the transition elements. With them the characteristic valence is brought to $+2$, and after them come the regular elements of the III A family. In view of the fact that the members of the II B family are neither regular nor transition elements, it is not strange that they differ in a number of respects from the elements which precede and follow them immediately in their respective periods. Their melting and boiling points are lower in general than are those of the metals of the I B family, and their activity is much greater, as is shown by their higher electrode potentials. The family is also peculiar in that chemical activity within the family (and the electrode potential) does not increase with increasing atomic number as is the case in the regular A families; rather the exact opposite is true, as was the case also in the I B family.

The three members of the II B family each have two valence electrons and hence characteristically show an electrovalence of $+2$ in a majority of their compounds, but they differ from the members of the II A family in that their valence electrons are immediately underlaid by a level of 18 electrons, while those of the latter family are underlaid by a level of eight electrons. There is, therefore, considerable difference of chemical properties between the members of the II A and II B families, though less than between the members of the I A and I B families. Ions of the II B family are smaller than the comparable ions of the II A family, and hence the hydroxides of the former group are less soluble and less active as bases than are those of the latter.

Zinc and cadmium resemble each other more closely than either resembles mercury (whose behavior, incidentally, approaches that of the noble metals in a number of respects). For example, the oxides and hydroxides of mercury are much less stable than are those of zinc and cadmium. Zinc shows only a valence of $+2$ in its compounds, while cadmium also exhibits a valence of $+1$ in one or two unusual and unstable compounds, and mercury is unusual in that it forms a well-defined series of mercurous compounds in which it exhibits a valence of $+1$. Mercury also shows the regular family valence in a series of mercuric compounds. Zinc is the only markedly amphoteric member of the family, all of whose members have a strong tendency to form complexes, a property which increases in strength from zinc to mercury. A further unusual property of the family is the low degree of ionization of its chlorides, bromides, and iodides.

2. General Physical Properties

The three members of the II B family are all silvery in color, and all have a high luster when fresh surfaces are exposed. All are fair conductors of electricity. Mercury is noteworthy as being a liquid at about 20° C. Many of its uses are dependent upon this property.

A number of general physical and atomic properties of zinc, cadmium, and mercury are summarized in Table 42.

Table 42

PHYSICAL PROPERTIES OF THE ELEMENTS OF THE II B FAMILY

Property	Zinc (Zn)	Cadmium (Cd)	Mercury (Hg)
Atomic weight	65.38	112.41	200.61
Mass of isotopes	64, 66, 67, 68, 70	106, 108, 110, 111, 112, 113, 114, 116	196, 197, 198, 199, 200, 201, 202, 204
Atomic number	30	48	80
Distribution of planetary electrons	2, 8, 18, 2	2, 8, 18, 18, 2	2, 8, 18, 32, 18, 2
Melting point, ° C	419.5	320.9	−38.87
Boiling point, ° C	907	767	356.9
Density, g./ml. at 20° C	7.14	8.65	13.546
Ionizing potential, volts			
1st electron	9.36	8.96	10.39
2nd electron	17.89	16.84	18.65
Electrode potential, volts	+0.76	+0.40	−0.85
Ionic radius, of +2 ions, Ångström units	0.74	0.97	1.10
Specific heat, cal./g	0.0925 (20° C.)	0.0552 (27.9° C.)	0.03325 (20° C.)

I. ZINC

3. Physical Properties

Zinc is a silvery metal with a slightly bluish cast. It is highly crystalline and possessed of moderate hardness and a distinct brittleness at ordinary temperatures. At temperatures between 100° and 150° C., its malleability and ductility have increased sufficiently for it to be rolled into thin sheets or pulled into wires. Foils and wires so produced do not become brittle on cooling. The metal becomes so brittle when its temperature is raised to 200° to 300° C. that it may be pulverized easily. The melting point and the density of zinc both vary some-what according to the physical treatment which the sample has previously received. The metal is a good conductor of both heat and electricity, and, since it expands upon cooling, it gives sharp castings.

4. Occurrence

Thanks to its activity, zinc is found naturally only in combination. Its principal ore is *sphalerite* or *zinc blende*, which contains the sulfide and is found associated with galena in the states of Missouri, Kansas, and Oklahoma in the vicinity of Joplin. The sulfide ore is also found in large quantities in the states of Montana, Idaho, and Colorado. *Smithsonite* is a carbonate ore which is mined in the states of Colorado and Arkansas and in various foreign countries. The zinc ores of New Jersey are *franklinite* (an oxide ore of zinc, iron, and manganese), *zincite* (ZnO), and *willemite* (Zn_2SiO_4). Also worthy of note is *calamine*, a hydrated silicate ($Zn_2SiO_4.H_2O$), which is of some importance in certain foreign countries. In the production of zinc, the United States stands first. Belgium, Canada, and Germany also are important producers.

The earliest use of zinc ores in the preparation of brass is lost in antiquity. It appears entirely likely that the free metal was isolated by various ones of the earlier workers who smelted zinc ores; at present, however, isolation of the metal commonly is attributed to Marggraf, who in 1746 reduced *calamine* in a closed vessel with charcoal.

5. Preparation

The methods used for the recovery of zinc from its ores depend to a large extent upon the specific nature of the ore in question and the percentage of other metals which it contains.

Sulfide ores of the Joplin district are concentrated by the froth-flotation method and then roasted to the oxide. Care must be taken to prevent the temperature from rising to a point sufficiently high to volatilize the oxide formed. The by-product, sulfur dioxide, may be made into sulfuric acid:

$$2ZnS + 3O_2 \rightarrow 2ZnO + 2SO_2 \uparrow$$

The oxide is mixed with coal and charged into fire-clay retorts to which are sealed clay condensers in which the zinc vapors are liquefied. Casts made of this metal (which contains small quantities of lead, cadmium, iron, and arsenic) are known as *spelter*, and may be used without further refinement for the coating of iron, for which purpose the lead impurity is an asset.

Lower-grade sulfide ores and those which contain considerable quantities

MOLTEN ZINC WHICH HAS BEEN REFINED BY REDUCTION OF THE OXIDE AND SUBSEQUENT DISTILLATION. (Courtesy, New Jersey Zinc Co.)

of metallic impurities are refined by an electrolytic process. After concentration, the ore is roasted to a mixture of sulfates and oxides which is then extracted with a solution of sulfuric acid whose concentration is in the neighborhood of 10 per cent. The sulfates of lead and silver are of low solubility, and may be removed by filtration. Other impurities are removed largely by treating the solution with lime, zinc, and a blast of air followed by filtration. The purified solution is then electrolyzed with aluminum sheets serving as cathodes. Zinc produced by this method is about 99.95 per cent pure and is especially useful in the preparation of brass. As the electrolysis progresses, the acidity of the solution is restored so that it may be used again.

The New Jersey oxide ores are refined by reduction with coal. Zinc, being more volatile than the other metals liberated, readily distils from the mixture and may be collected, though air under pressure is usually admitted to the hot vapors. Zinc oxide is formed as a very fine powder which is collected in canvas

THE CASTING OF ZINC PLATES TO BE REFINED ELECTROLYTICALLY. (Courtesy, N. J. Zinc Co.)

dust bags. It is used as a pigment, as a filler for rubber, and in the preparation of other zinc compounds.

6. Uses

The largest single use of zinc is as a coating for other metals, chief among which is iron. Primary protection is offered because of the tendency of zinc to become coated with a closely adhering coat of its basic carbonate, and zinc-coated iron is further protected since zinc, being the more active of the two metals, is oxidized first, maintaining the iron in a reduced condition. *Galvanized* iron is prepared by both a *hot* and a *cold* process. In the former, after being cleaned by pickling in an acid bath or by blasting with sand, iron is dipped in molten zinc and rolled; in the latter, zinc is deposited electrolytically from a solution of its salts. *Sherardized* iron is prepared by baking objects made of the metal at a temperature of about 800° C. in a closed and rotating drum which contains zinc dust. A durable zinc-iron alloy is formed on the surface of all objects treated by this process. Coatings of zinc may also be applied by spraying the molten metal.

Zinc is also used in the preparation of a number of important alloys, notable among which is brass (Zn, 10 to 40 per cent; Cu, 60 to 90 per cent). Admiralty metal and manganese bronze are used in the manufacture of a variety of marine fittings. German silver and Babbitt metal also are widely used alloys of zinc.

Rolled zinc finds considerable use, though galvanized iron often serves as a substitute for it. The metal finds use as an electrode in many primary electric cells; this is the case with the well-known dry cell whose zinc container serves as one electrode. Silver and gold are displaced from their complex cyanide solutions by zinc, and the metal is used to make zinc oxide, whose uses are numerous. Many lesser uses might be listed if space permitted.

7. *Chemical Properties*

In the presence of a trace of moisture, zinc is sufficiently active to combine with oxygen at about 20° C. Since carbon dioxide is usually a constituent of the atmosphere, fresh surfaces of the metal upon exposure to the air soon become coated with a closely adhering film of a basic carbonate, $Zn(OH)_2.ZnCO_3$, which prevents further reaction. The massive metal ignites only when heated above 500° C., but the dust will ignite spontaneously in moist air. The flame of burning zinc is of a bluish-white color, and the product is the oxide. Zinc will dissolve in both acids and the very strong bases to liberate hydrogen, but in dilute acids it is almost insoluble because of the high overvoltage (cf. section 6, Chapter 23) of hydrogen. Copper, platinum, or another metal of low overvoltage, when placed in contact with the zinc, remedies this situation. The presence of such metals in commercial zinc accounts for its ready reaction with dilute acids as compared with the slow action of the pure metal. In the form of the dust, the metal will liberate hydrogen from hot water. Zinc reacts with acids to form the corresponding zinc salts containing the Zn^{++} ion, but with the alkali hydroxides it reacts to form zincates of the alkali metals which contain the zincate ion whose formula is usually represented as ZnO_2^{--}. The products of the reaction with nitric acid are usually zinc nitrate, ammonium nitrate, and oxides of nitrogen. A strong tendency to form complex ions is another noteworthy property of the metal.

8. *Oxide and Hydroxide*

Zinc oxide is found in nature as the mineral *zincite*, but since known deposits of this mineral are not large, the oxide is usually prepared by burning the metal in the form of its dust or by roasting other ores of the metal with carbon in an air blast so that the metallic vapors burn as they distil from the mixture. The product is yellow when hot, but when cool it is intensely white. It is used in large quantities as a white pigment and as such is frequently mixed with white lead (*q.v.*). It is also used as a filler for white rubber goods, plastics, oilcloth, linoleum, etc. It is well known in zinc oxide ointment and is a component of many other ointments; the adhesive material on *adhesive tape* also contains zinc oxide.

Zinc oxide does not dissolve in water to form the hydroxide, but it does dissolve in acids to form solutions of their zinc salts. Addition of alkalies to these solutions in stoichiometric quantities precipitates the hydroxide as a flocculent white substance which, despite being somewhat hydrated, is usually represented by the formula $Zn(OH)_2$. It is distinctly amphoteric in its behavior, since it dissolves in acids to form their zinc salts and in the strong bases to form zincates of their cations:

$$Zn(OH)_2 + 2HCl \rightarrow ZnCl_2 + 2H_2O$$

and

$$Zn(OH)_2 + 2NaOH \rightarrow Na_2ZnO_2 + 2H_2O$$

Zinc hydroxide also dissolves in an excess of ammonium hydroxide, but in this instance dissolution is due to the formation of the soluble tetrammino complex:

$$Zn(OH)_2 + 4NH_4OH \rightarrow [Zn(NH_3)_4](OH)_2 + 4H_2O$$

Other zinc salts characteristically form this complex in the presence of an excess of ammonium hydroxide.

9. *Compounds*

One of the most important zinc salts is the chloride, which may be prepared by the action of hydrochloric acid on the oxide, the carbonate, or the metal itself, or by the direct union of the elements. Being a salt of an amphoteric base and a strong acid, zinc chloride is extensively hydrolyzed in solution, yet very little hydrogen chloride is evolved upon evaporation of its solutions. The anhydrous salt melts at 365° C. and while molten is cast into sticks which are both deliquescent and soluble. It is used as a drying agent and as a catalyst. Because of the acid reaction of the moist salt, it is used to clean metal to be soldered or welded. Since solutions of the salt convert cellulose to a gelatinous mass, they are used in parchmentizing paper and in the preservation of wood, in which latter use the toxicity of zinc ion is also of value. Solutions of the salt are also used in the preparation of embalming fluid and other such fluids for the preservation of animal specimens. White of eggs is used as an antidote for zinc chloride poisoning and for zinc ion poisoning in general.

Also of importance is zinc sulfate, which is prepared both by the careful roasting of sulfide ores and by the action of sulfuric acid on either the metal or its oxide. It crystallizes from solution in large rhombic prisms of the formula $ZnSO_4.7H_2O$. The crystals effloresce readily. Solutions of this salt are less toxic than are those of the chloride, and find some use medicinally as astringents and antiseptics. The sulfate also finds use as a mordant and in the preserving of hides, but its principal use is in the manufacture of lithopone (cf. section 29. Chapter 30).

The acetate of zinc may be prepared readily by the action of acetic acid on the oxide or carbonate of the metal. From solution it forms monoclinic crystals of the dihydrate, and it finds use as a laboratory reagent and as a mordant.

Zinc sulfide is used as a white pigment alone or in lithopone. After exposure to sunlight, the naturally occurring sulfide phosphoresces, as it also does when exposed to x-rays. This latter property makes it useful for the manufacture of the screens so frequently used in x-ray examinations. Synthetic zinc sulfide may be rendered capable of phosphorescing by a heat treatment. The sulfide is precipitated readily only from slightly basic solutions of zinc ion, hence ammonium sulfide is an excellent precipitating agent while, because of the ready hydrolysis of zinc salts, hydrogen sulfide works well only if ammonia has been added.

Zinc nitrate, $Zn(NO_3)_2$, is a common and useful salt of zinc. The carbonate, $ZnCO_3$, finds some use in medicine, as do the borate, ZnB_4O_7, and the stearate, $Zn(C_{18}H_{35}O_2)_2$. The bromide, $ZnBr_2$, and the iodide, ZnI_2, are of good solubility, but the fluoride, ZnF_2, is but slightly soluble, and the cyanide, $Zn(CN)_2$, and the ferrocyanide, $Zn_2[Fe(CN)_6]$ or $Zn[Zn_3[Fe(CN)_6]_2]$, are of very slight solubility.

10. Analytical Tests

Along with the ions of iron, cobalt, nickel, and manganese, those of zinc are precipitated as the sulfide from a slightly basic solution. The ready solubility of zinc sulfide in dilute acid and the amphoteric nature of the element are utilized in separating the ion from the others of the general group. The confirmatory test usually consists of reprecipitating the ion, after its separation, as the white sulfide. In this test, finely divided free sulfur is often formed and is confusing.

Upon treatment with a solution of ammonium thiocyanate, a neutral solution of zinc ion to which a drop or two of pyridine (C_5H_5N) has been added will yield a heavy white precipitate whose formula is reported to be $Zn(C_5H_5N)_2(SCN)_2$.

Upon evaporation to dryness, treatment with a few drops of a solution of cobaltous nitrate, and ignition to dryness on charcoal, zinc ion solutions yield a green substance known as Rinmann's green, which is generally considered to be a zinc cobaltiate, $ZnCo_2O_4$.

II. CADMIUM

11. Occurrence

Like zinc, cadmium is not found free in nature. It is much less common than zinc, and although it is occasionally found as the rare mineral *greenockite*, whose color is orange or yellow and which contains the sulfide CdS, it is usually obtained from zinc ores, in which it is usually present to the extent of about 1 per cent. *Calamine* and the other silicate ores of zinc customarily contain about 3 per cent of cadmium.

12. Preparation

Because of its occurrence with zinc, cadmium was not discovered until 1817, when it was isolated by Stromeyer. Zinc ores from the Black Sea region were at that time known as *cadmia*, so, having found his new element in the residues of the cadmia furnaces, Stromeyer named it *cadmia fornacum*. In time, this name evolved into *cadmium*.

Being less active than zinc, cadmium is reduced along with it during the smelting of its ores. The boiling points of the two metals are sufficiently far apart to permit their separation by fractional distillation. They may also be separated by chemically dissolving the two metals in sulfuric acid and precipitating the cadmium as its sulfide by treatment of the diluted solution with hydrogen sulfide. A third method of separation involves electrolysis of the acid solution; cadmium, being less active than zinc, is deposited at a lower voltage.

13. Uses

It is only within relatively recent years that cadmium has been in great demand. The metal is used in the preparation of alloys, in the coating of iron, and in the preparation of its compounds. Among its important alloys are many of low melting point and a number which are in demand as bearing metals. Wood's metal, one of the commonest of the low-melting alloys, contains 12.5 per cent of cadmium and melts at 65.5° C. Cadmium-coated iron is more resistant to weathering than is galvanized iron. The coating is usually deposited electrolytically, after which the coated article is heated so that a cadmium-iron alloy may form on its surface. When alloyed with copper, 1 per cent of cadmium greatly increases its tensile strength without appreciably decreasing its conductivity.

14. Chemical Properties

Cadmium is a silvery metal with a bluish cast. It is of lower activity than zinc, and, therefore, does not tarnish so readily. It is harder than either tin or zinc, and at ordinary temperatures is more malleable and ductile than the latter. It, too, becomes more brittle at higher temperatures. It is less amphoteric than zinc, and readily displaces hydrogen from acid solutions. Otherwise, its general chemical behavior closely parallels that of zinc. It forms complexes readily and its salts are toxic, a property which accounts for their occasional use in insecticides or as insecticides.

15. Oxide and Hydroxide

Cadmium oxide, CdO, is a brown solid which may be prepared by methods analogous to those given for the preparation of zinc oxide. It reacts with acids to form cadmium salts whose solutions contain the Cd^{++} ion. Its uses are at present few.

The hydroxide, $Cd(OH)_2$, is produced as a white precipitate when solutions of strong bases are added to solutions containing the cadmium ion. It is more soluble than zinc hydroxide, and considerably more basic. It reacts readily with acids to form cadmium salts, but does not dissolve in strong bases to form cadmates. It is reported, however, that cadmates are formed when CdO is fused with potassium hydroxide and other strongly basic substances. The hydroxide dissolves in an excess of ammonium hydroxide to form cadmium-tetrammino hydroxide, $[Cd(NH_3)_4](OH)_2$.

16. Compounds

Among the important compounds of cadmium are the nitrate, the acetate, the sulfate, and the halides. The nitrate, $Cd(NO_3)_2.4H_2O$, and the acetate, $Cd(C_2H_3O_2)_2.3H_2O$, are common laboratory reagents which are readily soluble. The sulfate, $3CdSO_4.8H_2O$, is also used in the laboratory.

The halides and cyanide of cadmium are unusual in that in solutions of moderate or strong concentration they are but weakly ionized. This low degree of ionization is associated with the strong tendency of cadmium to form complex ions. In these cases, it is believed that there are formed homoatomic complexes of the type $Cd[Cd(CN)_4]$ and $Cd[CdX_4]$, where X represents any one of the common halogens.

Insoluble cadmium sulfide, CdS, is of a bright yellow color and finds use as a pigment under the name *cadmium yellow*. It is readily soluble in dilute acid. The selenide, CdSe, is also used as a pigment.

17. Cadmous Compounds

Although cadmium regularly exhibits a valence of $+2$, a few compounds in which it apparently shows a valence of $+1$ have been reported. Cadmous chloride, Cd_2Cl_2, is said to be formed by heating a mixture of $CdCl_2$ and Cd at a temperature of 800° C. Addition of a base to solutions of this salt is said to precipitate cadmous hydroxide, $Cd_2(OH)_2$. This substance is a powerful reducing agent and upon being heated loses water to form cadmous oxide, Cd_2O.

18. Analytical Tests

Along with the ions of copper, bismuth, lead, mercuric mercury, arsenic, antimony, and tin, cadmium ions are precipitated from a weakly acidic solution as sulfides. The acidity of the solution must be carefully controlled, since cadmium sulfide will fail to precipitate in the presence of too great a concentration of H^+ ions. Separation of cadmium from the other elements of the mixed sulfide precipitate is based upon the insolubility of CdS in either $(NH_4)_2S$ or $(NH_4)_2S_x$ and upon its solubility in very dilute acid. After separation, the ion is usually confirmed by reprecipitation as the bright yellow sulfide.

III. MERCURY

19. Physical Properties

Mercury is unusual in that it is the only metal which is stable in the liquid state at about 20° C. It has a bright silvery luster, shows little tendency to tarnish at ordinary temperatures, and is a good conductor of both heat and electricity. Because of its uniform expansion over a wide range of temperature, it is well adapted to use in thermometers, and because of its high density, low coefficient of expansion, and slight vapor pressure at ordinary temperatures, it is well suited for use in the ordinary liquid-type barometer. Despite its high boiling point, mercury does show a small vapor pressure even at ordinary temperatures; at

20° C. this pressure is 0.0013 mm. Mercury is a cumulative poison, hence those who work with it should beware of regularly breathing even minute quantities of the vapor. When raised to a temperature considerably above its boiling point, mercury vapor readily conducts electricity, at the same time emitting a ghostly, lavenderish radiation which is rich in ultraviolet rays. Most other metals dissolve in mercury to form alloys known as *amalgams*. A number of amalgams are used in dentistry for the filling of teeth. Iron and platinum are not wet by mercury, and hence do not form amalgams. If the liquid metal is rubbed in a mortar with a fat or oil, it becomes divided into many extremely small droplets; such finely divided mercury is used in a number of mercurial ointments which find use in medicine.

20. Occurrence

Since mercury approaches the noble metals in chemical behavior, it is not strange that droplets of it are frequently found distributed in rocky matrices. Small quantities of amalgams of gold and silver also are found occasionally. The usual source of the metal, however, is the mineral *cinnabar*, whose principal

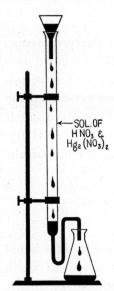

component is red mercuric sulfide, HgS. In the United States, California, Texas, and Arkansas are the principal producers of cinnabar. Other countries in which large deposits of the ore are found are Spain, China, and Mexico. The metal has been known since at least the fourth century B.C. and was of great interest to the ancients and to the alchemists, who called it *liquid silver* or *quicksilver*. The symbol *Hg* is derived from the Latin name *hydrargyrum*, said to have been given the metal by Pliny. The English name *mercury* is derived from that of the planet, which, in turn, was named for the messenger of the gods in Roman mythology.

SOL. OF
H NO₃ &
Hg₂ (NO₃)₂

DEVICE FOR THE LAB-
ORATORY PURIFICATION
OF MERCURY.

21. Preparation

Cinnabar ores are usually concentrated by the froth-flotation process. The concentrates are then distilled in the presence of air:

$$HgS + O_2 \rightarrow Hg + SO_2 \uparrow$$

The sulfur dioxide formed is usually wasted, but is occasionally collected and used. The mercury vapors are condensed, and the liquid so formed may be further purified by filtration through chamois skin and by washing with dilute nitric acid. If necessary, it may be redistilled. The metal is sold in iron flasks whose capacity is 76 lb.

22. Uses

The use of mercury in thermometers and barometers was referred to above. It also finds use in many other scientific instruments. Its use in the recovery of gold and silver has been mentioned. Amalgamation also figures in some of the electrolytic processes for the preparation of hydroxides of the alkali metals. Amalgams of tin and some of the noble metals are used in dentistry, sodium amalgam is a frequently used reducing agent, and other amalgams are variously employed. Mercury vapor lamps are used in indoor photography, in silk mills, for sterilizing water, and for a number of other purposes. Mercury also finds use in some of the so-called "neon" signs—notably the blue and green ones. A number of turbines which use mercury vapor instead of steam have been built and are in operation; because of the high boiling point of the metal these machines are more efficient than are their steam counterparts. Large quantities of the metal are used in the preparation of its compounds, many of which are used in medicine. There are a host of these latter compounds, among which are calomel, bichloride of mercury, merthiolate, and mercressin. Other mercury compounds manufactured in large quantities are the pigment *vermilion* (HgS) and the detonating agent mercury fulminate ($Hg(ONC)_2$). Other compounds used as laboratory reagents are also manufactured from the metal.

23. Chemical Properties

At ordinary temperatures, mercury is attacked neither by oxygen nor by very many other gases. Among those gases with which it does react is hydrogen sulfide. At temperatures in the neighborhood of 350° C., the metal unites with oxygen to form mercuric oxide, HgO, but at more advanced temperatures the compound is decomposed into the elements. Mercury and sulfur combine when rubbed together in a mortar, and the metal will also combine directly with the halogens.

Mercury forms two rather complete series of salts in which it shows the valences $+1$ and $+2$, respectively. Being lower than hydrogen in the activity series, it does not displace hydrogen from solutions of the acids, but it does react with the oxidizing acids to form their respective salts. With an excess of such acids, mercuric salts are formed; while with an excess of the metal, mercurous salts are the products. In their insolubility and instability with respect to light, the mercurous halides resemble those of silver. Mercury also resembles silver in the instability of its hydroxides with respect to their conversion to the oxides. The salts of the element are unusual in that they are but slightly ionized in solution. This is believed to be due to their strong tendency to form auto-complexes—a tendency which is more pronounced with mercury than with cadmium.

The oxides of mercury are both exclusively, though weakly, basic in their behavior; because of this weakness, the mercury salts are easily hydrolyzed, and as a result a number of oxy salts are formed. Mercury also forms a variety of salts with ammonia. All soluble mercury salts are poisonous, though some of them are used medicinally in small quantities. Antidotes commonly used for poisoning by mercury salts are emetics, milk, white of egg, and finely divided iron.

24. Mercurous Compounds

It may be seen from Table 42 that the mercury atom contains two valence electrons underlaid by 18 electrons in the next lower energy level. When one of the valence electrons is lost, there is formed an "odd" ion which overcomes its "oddness" by associating itself with another such ion to form the complex ion $(Hg:Hg)^{++}$. This ion exists not only in solution but also in the solid compounds and in their vapors, and is not easily oxidized to the mercuric condition. It is formed by the action of oxidizing acids upon an excess of mercury and by the mild reduction of mercuric salts. Only a limited number of mercurous salts will be discussed in detail.

The oxide Hg_2O is formed by the action of alkalies upon solutions of mercurous salts. Any of the hydroxide originally formed rapidly loses water to form the oxide, which in turn is decomposed by both heat and light into mercury and mercuric oxide, HgO. It is of little importance. Mercurous sulfide is also unstable, even at about $20°$ C., and decomposes in an analogous manner into mercury and mercuric sulfide.

One of the most important of the mercurous compounds is the chloride, Hg_2Cl_2, which is a white, insoluble substance frequently used in medicine as a purgative under the name of *calomel* (Greek: *beautiful black*). The name derives from the fact that, when treated with ammonia, the salt is partially converted to a black, finely divided precipitate of free mercury:

$$Hg_2Cl_2 + 2NH_3 \rightarrow NH_4Cl + \underline{HgNH_2Cl} + \underline{Hg}$$

The mercuric amidochloride formed simultaneously is a white precipitate, so that often the combined precipitate is gray rather than black. The amidochloride is also known as *ammoniated mercury,* and is used in the preparation of ointments.

Calomel is usually prepared commercially by heating either a mixture of mercury and mercuric chloride or a mixture of mercury, mercuric sulfate, and salt. It may be prepared in the laboratory by adding solutions of chloride ions to solutions of mercurous ions or by the careful reduction of mercuric chloride with stannous chloride; too much of the latter reagent will cause complete reduction to mercury (cf. section 23, Chapter 31). Calomel is easily oxidized to the highly toxic mercuric chloride by the action of light. Its uses also include the decorating of china and the preparation of pyrotechnics. When calomel is used internally, care must be exercised to prevent its oxidation to toxic mercuric salts which produce the condition known as *salivation*.

Mercurous bromide and iodide also find some use in medicine.

The mercurous salt most widely used in the laboratory is the nitrate, $Hg_2(NO_3)_2.2H_2O$, which is the most soluble compound of the family. It is prepared by the action of cold, dilute nitric acid on mercury, and in solution is easily oxidized by the oxygen of the air to mercuric nitrate; to prevent this action a little free mercury is usually added to the solution. Very dilute solutions of the salt usually become clouded by the formation of the basic salt, $Hg_2(OH)NO_3$. The addition of nitric acid will clear the solution by reversing the equilibrium:

$$Hg_2(NO_3)_2 + HOH \rightleftharpoons Hg_2(OH)NO_3 + H^+ + NO_3^-$$

25. *Mercuric Compounds*

Mercuric oxide is obtained as a bright, orange-red, finely crystalline substance either by heating mercury in air as mentioned above, or by the pyrolysis of mercuric nitrate. It is also obtained as a yellow precipitate when soluble, basic hydroxides are added to solutions of mercuric nitrate; the hydroxide which at first forms undergoes spontaneous decomposition. The yellow oxide seems to differ from the red only in that its particles are of smaller size. It is used medicinally in ointments. Upon being heated it changes into the red modification.

The other mercuric salts are usually prepared by treating either the oxide or free mercury with the appropriate acid. In general, they are more soluble than the corresponding mercurous salts. Among the most important of the mercuric salts is the chloride, $HgCl_2$, which is commonly known both as *bichloride of mercury* and as *corrosive sublimate*. It is usually prepared by heating a mixture of mercuric sulfate and salt, from which it sublimes, although it may also be prepared by the action of chlorine on mercury. The salt is moderately soluble in water, in which it is but slightly ionized, and it is also soluble to some extent

ALFRED WERNER

(1866–1919, French-Swiss)

Werner was a prolific and indefatigable worker who published nearly 170 scientific papers. At the present time, he is most generally remembered for his work on complex compounds and for the coördination theory which he evolved. For this work, he was awarded the Nobel Prize in chemistry in 1913. His other contributions include work on the Walden inversion and other organic problems, the hydration of metals, and the spatial relationships of the atoms in the molecules of certain nitrogenous compounds. He was graduated from the University of Zurich in 1890, and in 1892 he returned there to spend the remainder of his life as a member of the faculty. He is reported to have been a capable and inspiring teacher who attracted many students.

in both alcohol and ether. It is a violent poison, but in dilution it is used as a sterilizing agent and for dressing wounds. It hydrolyzes, in dilute solutions, forming basic salts, and its tendency to form autocomplexes and other complexes is pronounced. Its reduction by stannous chloride has already been discussed.

Mercuric sulfide, HgS, is also of importance as the pigment *vermilion*, which is used in paints, printer's inks, rubber, paper, etc. As precipitated from slightly acid solutions of mercuric salts, it is first white, then yellow and brown, and finally black, though only the black precipitate appears to have the simple

THE VOLUMINOUS ASH PRODUCED BY THE COMBUSTION OF A PHARAOH'S SERPENT EGG. At the right on the black paper is an *egg* of the same size as that whose combustion produced the ash pictured.

formula HgS. Upon being heated, the black substance changes to the brilliant red *vermilion*. It is not attacked by dilute acids, but is slowly attacked by hot concentrated hydrochloric or nitric acid, and rapidly by *aqua regia*. It is also soluble in the alkali sulfides as a result of the formation of the complex ion $[HgS_2]^{--}$.

Mercuric nitrate is an important laboratory reagent. It is prepared by the action of hot concentrated nitric acid on mercury and crystallizes from solution as the octahydrate, $Hg(NO_3)_2.8H_2O$.

Mercuric iodide, HgI_2, is of interest because it exists in two colored modifications. It is yellow when precipitated from solution, but upon standing it rapidly changes to scarlet. The scarlet variety is stable at about 20° C., but changes to the yellow modification at temperatures in excess of 126.5° C. It is insoluble in water, but dissolves readily in a solution of potassium iodide to form the complex salt $K_2[HgI_4]$. This complex, added to an excess of potassium hydroxide, is known as Nessler's reagent, which is used in water analysis for the detection and estimation of nitrogen compounds. Both the iodide and the complex find some use in medicine. The iodide is moderately soluble in both alcohol and ether.

Mercuric sulfate, $HgSO_4$, is prepared by the action of sulfuric acid on mercury and is a common reagent. The cyanide $Hg(CN)_2$ is a colorless, water-soluble salt which forms the complex ion $[Hg(CN)_4]^{--}$ and is easily pyrolyzed into cyanogen gas:

$$Hg(CN)_2 \xrightarrow{\Delta} Hg + (CN)_2 \uparrow$$

The thiocyanate $Hg(SCN)_2$ is prepared by the action of potassium thiocyanate upon mercuric chloride. When mixed with gummy materials and pressed into pellets, it is known as *Pharaoh's serpent eggs* because of the voluminous snake-like ash produced when it burns. Mercuric fulminate, $Hg(ONC)_2$, is a widely used detonating agent which is prepared by the action of nitric acid on mercury in the presence of alcohol.

26. Ammonia Derivatives

From the interaction of mercuric salts and ammonia, there results a variety of compounds which Latimer and Hildebrand divide into four groups: (1) Soluble complexes which contain the $Hg(NH_3)_4^{++}$ ion (tetrammino mercuric ion); (2) salts of the type $HgCl_2.2NH_3$ (known as *fusible white precipitate* because heat drives off the ammonia and melts the remaining salt); (3) salts such as $HgNH_2Cl$, mentioned in section 24, which are formed by the negative ions derived from ammonia by a process of ammonolysis similar to hydrolysis; and (4) salts of the type HO-Hg-NH-Hg-OH which are formed as a result of both ammonolysis and hydrolysis having occurred. Salts of the second and third classes are the most important. Those of the first class are stable only in the presence of a large excess of ammonia. The salt given as an example of the fourth class of derivatives is known as Millon's base, and is prepared as a yellow powder by warming HgO with ammonium hydroxide.

27. Analytical Tests

Both mercurous and mercuric ions are colorless. Mercurous ions are usually precipitated as the colorless chloride which, after removal of lead and silver chlorides, gives a black precipitate when concentrated ammonium hydroxide is added.

Mercuric ion is usually precipitated as a sulfide from a slightly acid solution along with cadmium and the other ions listed in section 18. The black mercuric sulfide is not soluble in ammonium sulfide and polysulfide as are arsenic, antimony, and tin, and it is more resistant to the action of 3 N nitric acid than are the other undissolved sulfides of its analytical sub-group. After dissolution of the other sulfides of the sub-group in the nitric acid, the mercuric sulfide precipitate is dissolved in *aqua regia* and the solution treated with a limited quantity of stannous chloride solution whose action on mercuric chloride was discussed in section 23 of Chapter 31.

(*See Appendix for Exercises*)

COLLATERAL READINGS

Burns and Schuh: *Protective Coatings for Metals,* New York, Reinhold Publishing Corp., 1939.

Creighton and Koehler: *Electrochemistry,* Vol. II, 4th ed., New York, John Wiley & Sons, Inc., 1943.

Ephraim: *Inorganic Chemistry,* 3d Eng. ed., London, Gurney and Jackson, 1939.

Hanley: The story of zinc, *J. Chem. Education,* **10,** 600, 682 (1933); **11,** 33, 111 (1934).

Jordan and Barrows: Mercury poisoning, *Ind. Eng. Chem.,* **16,** 898 (1924).

Latimer and Hildebrand: *Reference Book of Inorganic Chemistry,* New York, The Macmillan Co., 1941.

Weeks: *Discovery of the Elements,* 5th ed., Mack Printing Co., 1945.

Cadmium platings, *Metals & Alloys,* **12,** 339 (1940); **13,** 358 (1941).

New supplies of quicksilver, *Chem. & Met. Eng.,* **47,** 644 (1940).

MARIA SKLODOWSKA CURIE
(1867–1934, Polish [by birth])

Madame Curie is known throughout the world as the discoverer of radium. She also discovered the element polonium and throughout her adult life made numerous contributions to the knowledge of radioactive substances and radioactivity. In 1903 she, her husband, Prof. Pierre Curie, and Henri Becquerel jointly received the Nobel Prize; in 1920 she received the prize alone for her further contributions. After the accidental death of Pierre Curie in 1906, Mme. Curie succeeded him as professor of physics at the Sorbonne. In 1921 President Harding presented her with a gram of pure radium salts purchased by her admirers in the United States, and again in 1929 a fund of $50,000 raised by American friends was presented to her by President Hoover.

35

Radioactivity and the Radioactive Elements

1. The Discovery of Radioactivity—Polonium and Radium

Uranium, the naturally occurring element of highest atomic weight and of atomic number 92, was discovered in 1789, but that the element, its salts and its ores emit rays which are capable of penetrating black paper to reduce the silver salts of photographic plates wrapped in it was not discovered until 1896. The discovery was made by the French physicist Henri Becquerel while he was engaged in the study of the fluorescence (*q.v.*) of certain minerals, among which was *carnotite*, an ore of uranium. This ability of uranium and certain other elements spontaneously to emit rays of the type mentioned above has become known as *radioactivity*. Its discovery intrigued Becquerel, and, upon his suggestion, further investigation of uranium and its ores was undertaken by Monsieur and Madame Curie, Parisian scientists of his acquaintance. During their study, they obtained evidence which suggested the presence in the ores of some substance which was much more radioactive than uranium itself. Excited by this discovery, the Curies undertook further work upon the residues of Austrian uranium ores from the St. Joachimsthal in Bohemia, and on July 18, 1898, they were able to announce to the French Academy of Sciences the discovery of a new element which was strongly radioactive. This element they named *polonium* in honor of Poland, the native country of Mme. Curie, who was born Maria Sklodowska. On December 26 of the same year, these same investigators were able to announce the discovery of a second element which, because of its even more marked radioactivity, they named *radium*. This latter element had chemical properties very similar to those of barium, while those of polonium related it to bismuth. For their important discoveries the Curies and Becquerel jointly were awarded the Nobel Prize.

2. The Preparation and Properties of Radium

Because radium is not a plentiful element, and because it is rather widely distributed in nature, it is seldom found in anything but minute concentrations.

Since it is one of the radioactive disintegration products of uranium, it is always found in ores of that element, and commercially it is recovered from such ores. The process of extraction is expensive, for, because of the decomposition equilibria (to be discussed in a later section), the ratio of radium to uranium in an old uranium ore can never exceed 1 to 3,000,000. This means that radium is present in high-grade uranium ores to the extent of about 0.2 g. per ton, and that its recovery is always expensive, especially when one considers that most uranium ores are not rich in that element. The exact method used in extracting radium depends upon the nature of the ore and upon its quality. Limited space does not permit the discussion of the many steps involved; that they consume much time and effort and large quantities of chemicals goes without saying.

Until 1913, European ores from Austria and Portugal were the chief source of radium. From 1913 to 1925, the carnotite ores (containing a potassium uranyl vanadate) of southwestern Colorado were the principal source. During the latter year, production shifted to the Belgian Congo, where ores richer in radium had been discovered a few years previously. The discovery in Canada in 1931 of pitchblende ores (containing the oxide U_3O_8) which are still richer in radium has shifted preëminence in production to that country. The ore deposits are located near Great Bear Lake not far from the Arctic Circle, and air, rail, and water transportation are used in moving the ore. Since the time that commercial production of radium was begun in 1910, the price of the metal has dropped from about $100,000 per gram to about $20,000.

Radium is a brilliant, silvery-white metal of high chemical activity which in both physical and chemical properties closely resembles barium, its nearest relative of the II A family. It melts at 960° C., boils at 1140° C., and is reported to have a density of about 5 g./ml. The metal is so active that it must be protected from both oxygen and moisture. It shows the characteristic family valence of +2 in all of its compounds. The hydroxide $Ra(OH)_2$ is more soluble than the corresponding barium compound, and is a stronger base. The sulfate $RaSO_4$ is even less soluble than the very slightly soluble sulfate of barium. Also in keeping with the general family solubility trends are the decreased solubilities of the radium halides as compared with those of barium. Radium is unusual only in its radioactivity, in which property it exceeds all other known substances. Its radiations are so intense that in the dark its salts glow with a bluish light, and as a result of the action of the radiations the salts undergo partial decomposition. The rate of radiation is unaffected by changes in external conditions of any kind.

3. The Other Radioactive Elements

Of the pronouncedly radioactive elements, only uranium and thorium were known at the time of Becquerel's important discovery. The subsequent discovery of two new radioactive elements by the Curies stimulated other investigators to seek to discover still other elements of that type; success attended many of these efforts. In 1899 actinium (Ac) was discovered by Debierne; in 1900 radon (Rn) was discovered by Dorn; in 1901 a radioactive isotope of lead was discovered by Hofmann and Strauss; in 1907 mesothorium (MsTh) was discovered by Hahn; in 1917 protoactinium (Pa) was discovered by Hahn and Meitner; and many radioactive isotopes of these and others of the radioactive elements have been discovered. In 1945 discovery of elements number 93, 94, 95, and 96 was announced, although the first two of these were discovered in 1940. Names assigned to these elements are *neptunium, plutonium, americium,* and *curium,* respectively. Neptunium was discovered by McMillan and Abelson of the University of California while the other three of these transuranic elements were discovered by Glenn T. Seaborg and his associates. Most of these radioactive elements exist in such small quantities as to be of little value save for scientific purposes, although plutonium was produced for use in the atomic bombs. Actinium is of a high degree of activity, but, so far as is known, exists only in the most minute of concentrations.

It will be noted that these elements are all of high atomic weight. Investigation has shown that, of the lighter naturally occurring elements, potassium and rubidium possess a slight radioactivity, as do the three rare earth elements neodymium, samarium, and lutecium. In each case, this activity is attributed to a single isotope of less than normal stability.

4. The Nature of Radioactive Emanations

From Becquerel's discovery, as described in section 1, it is apparent that radioactive elements are characterized by the ability to emit spontaneously certain radiations which early investigations showed to be of a complex nature. Credit for the identification of the various components of the radiations goes largely to Sir Ernest Rutherford and his co-workers. Their brilliant work demonstrated that the rays were of three distinct types. One of the simplest experiments by which the existence of the three varieties of emanations may be demonstrated consists of allowing a narrow beam of rays from radium or other radioactive materials to pass through the electric field between two highly charged metallic plates. The paths taken by the rays in the field may be followed by allowing them to fall on a photographic plate or film or on a fluorescent screen. In the field, the original beam is split into three smaller beams, as indicated by the accompanying diagram. The alpha ray is deflected slightly toward the negatively charged plate and the beta ray sharply toward the positively charged plate, while the gamma ray is undeflected.

PHOTOGRAPHIC PLATE

$-$ α γ β $+$

LEAD CUP

RESOLUTION OF BECQUEREL RAYS IN AN ELECTRICAL FIELD.

Further study of these rays, as was stated in section 13 of Chapter 4, has shown the alpha rays to consist of a stream of alpha particles, the beta rays to consist of a stream of electrons, and the gamma rays to be ultrashort electromagnetic waves. Alpha particles are expelled from the atoms of radioactive elements with tremendous force, in some instances attaining speeds as great as one-fifteenth that of light. They will penetrate from 2.6 to 8.6 cm. of air at ordinary pressure, knocking off electrons from oxygen and nitrogen molecules as they go. When the alpha particle with its double positive charge acquires two extra electrons, it becomes an ordinary helium atom. The electrons of the beta ray are expelled with even greater force than are the heavier alpha particles, and attain speeds approaching that of light. They, too, ionize the gases through which they pass by knocking electrons out of the gaseous atoms. Because of their lightness, they are more sharply deflected in an electric field than are the alpha particles. Since the gamma rays are electromagnetic in nature, they travel with the speed of light and are not deflected in an electric field. Their wave-

ALPHA RAY TRACKS IN NITROGEN. (Courtesy, Prof. W. D. Harkins, Chicago University.)

length is even shorter than that of ordinary x-rays, hence they have great energy and great penetrating power. They are able to penetrate considerable thicknesses of lead and to cause the ionization of gases, and they are largely responsible for the effect of Becquerel rays on wrapped photographic plates and films.

5. *The Origin of Radioactive Emanations*

The nucleus of the atom was discussed at some length in section 6 of Chapter 4. A review of this section reveals that all atomic nuclei are believed to contain protons and a lesser number of electrons (save in the case of ordinary hydrogen) which pair off with the protons to form neutrons. Furthermore, in atoms in which such behavior is possible, pairs of neutrons and pairs of protons are believed to form the larger units known as alpha particles (helium nuclei). Since the atomic nuclei of radioactive elements differ from those of nonradioactive elements only in the numbers of protons and electrons which they contain, it is believed that radioactivity results from an inherent instability of certain atomic nuclei. The theory that radioactive emanations result from the disintegration of atomic nuclei was first proposed by Rutherford and Soddy in 1902, and has since been well established. When particles are expelled from an atomic nucleus, the matter which remains naturally forms the nucleus of a different atom. This new atom may be stable, or it may in turn decompose spontaneously, as did its parent. Disintegration will continue through a series of expulsions and their resulting atoms until a stable nucleus ultimately results.

6. *Radioactive Transformations*

The instability of certain atoms seems to be directly related to the ratio of neutrons to protons in their nuclei. For every atom there appears to be a range of stable ratios which if exceeded in either direction produces instability. This range is greater for atoms of even atomic number than for those of odd number, and accounts for the former having generally greater numbers of isotopes than do the latter.

If the number of neutrons in a given nucleus is greater than the range of stability permits, β-ray emission (electron emission) usually results. The emitted electron is obtained by the disruption of a neutron, so that as a result of its omission the number of neutrons present in the nucleus is decreased by one while the number of protons present is increased by one. In certain other cases, notably in the case of artificially radioactive substances, the number of excess neutrons present may be reduced by neutron expulsion.

If the number of protons in a given nucleus is in excess of that which gives a stable ratio, the atom then has a positive charge which is too large in relation to its mass. At present there appear to be four ways in which this situation may be rectified: (1) An alpha particle (whose mass is 4 and whose charge is $+2$) may be expelled, as is commonly the case with naturally occurring radioactive elements; (2) a proton (whose mass is 1 and whose charge is $+1$) may be expelled, as is the case with some of the lighter, artificial, radioactive elements; (3) a planetary electron of the atom may be captured by one of the nucleic protons to form a neutron, a change which is accompanied by the emission of x-rays; and (4) a positron (whose mass is the same as that of the electron and whose charge is $+1$) may be expelled. Thus far, positron emission has been noted only in the case of artificial radioactive elements. The positron is not a particle which has an existence in the nucleus. So far as is known, it is produced by the energetic changes taking place within the nucleus at the time of its expulsion. After expulsion, its life is very short because of the mutual attraction which exists between it and free electrons. The union of the two particles destroys both of them and produces gamma rays.

The emission of gamma rays by radioactive elements may accompany the emission of either alpha or beta particles. As has been stated, they are of very short wavelength, and therefore large quantities of energy must have been consumed in their formation. This energy is released at the time of the expulsion of the particles and is associated with the violent changes taking place within the nucleus.

From the foregoing discussion it should be apparent that a given atom undergoes only one variety of change. When either an alpha particle or an electron (the particles commonly expelled by naturally occurring radioactive elements) has been expelled, the original element, or its atom, no longer exists; further changes, if any, are then those of a new element. The fact that radium evolves both alpha and beta rays shows that not only is radium decomposing, but also its decomposition products are undergoing spontaneous disintegration.

Alteration of physical conditions has no effect upon the rate at which radioactive changes take place, nor does the state of chemical combination.

7. The Displacement Law

Since the naturally occurring radioactive atoms always expel either an alpha particle or an electron when they disintegrate, and since each variety of atom always undergoes a specific type of change, it follows tnat there is a definite relationship between the parent atom, the offspring, and the type of particle expelled. When an alpha particle of mass 4 and charge of $+2$ is expelled from a nucleus, there remains behind the nucleus of a new atom whose mass is four units less and whose positive charge is two units less—i.e., whose atomic number is two units less. In consequence of this change, the new atom will have the same atomic number as the element in the second column of the periodic table to the left of the parent element, and will be either identical with that element or an isotope of it. When an electron of -1 charge is expelled from a nucleus whose net charge was already positive, the effect is to increase that net positive charge by one unit. The new element will have, therefore, the same atomic number as the element in the first column of the periodic table to the right of the parent element, but, since the mass of the electron is negligible, the new atom will have virtually the same mass as its parent and is said to be an *isobar* of the parent. It will be an isotope of the naturally occurring element of the space in the table to the right of the parent. Concisely, the displacement law states that *an alpha-ray change produces an element which falls two places to the left in the periodic table, while a beta-ray change produces one which falls one place to the right.*

8. Transformation Series

The foregoing sections suggest that an atom whose neutron-proton ratio greatly exceeds the limits of stability will have to undergo a whole series of changes before stability is finally attained. Such is indeed the case, and each change of such a series produces a new element. Three such series are so well known that they are often discussed in textbooks; they are the uranium, thorium, and actinium series. Because of space limitations, we shall consider only the uranium series. In the accompanying illustration, the successive disintegration products of uranium and their periodic relationships are shown in diagrammatic form. The figures above the symbols are the atomic numbers; those below are the atomic weights. Further data on this series is given in Table 43.

It will be noted that the end-product of the uranium series is a stable isotope of lead. The same is true of the thorium and actinium series. Since actinium is always present in small quantities in uranium ores, the actinium series is believed to be but a branch of the uranium series, probably deriving from the uranium isotope of mass 235. Since the alpha particles emitted during these changes become helium atoms, it may be said that the final products of the disintegration of the markedly radioactive, naturally occurring elements are the simpler elements lead and helium.

9. The Rate of Radioactive Disintegration—Radioactive Equilibrium

While all of the atoms of a given radioactive substance are inherently unstable, only a certain definite fraction of them will attain in a given period of time a condition which permits their disintegration. From this it follows that

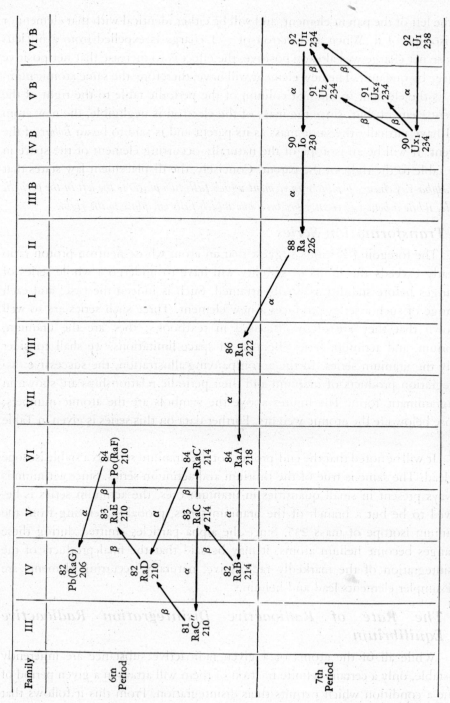

THE PERIODIC RELATIONSHIPS OF THE RADIOACTIVE DISINTEGRATION PRODUCTS OF THE URANIUM SERIES.

the rate of decay of any such substance is proportional to the quantity present. By measurement of the rate at which decomposition proceeds, one may calculate the time required for the disintegration of half of the sample. This time is known both as the *half-life* and also as the *period* of the substance in question. At the end of two such periods, one-fourth of an original sample would remain; at the end of three periods one-eighth would remain. Thus, theoretically, a given sample would never entirely vanish, though practically, in time it would approach the vanishing point. The half-life is brief for highly unstable substances, while for more stable ones it may be long; for example, the half-life of thorium C is less than one-millionth of a second, while that of uranium I is 4,500,000,000 years. Again, it must be emphasized that the rate of decay, being an atomic property, is wholly independent of both chemical and physical conditions. Table 43 gives the half-life of the members of the uranium series, together with other pertinent data.

Table 43

THE URANIUM SERIES

Element	Atomic Wt.	Atomic No.	Element of Which an Isotope	Half-life Period	Particle Expelled
Uranium I.................	238	92	Uranium	4.67×10^9 yrs.	Alpha
Uranium X$_1$...............	234	90	Thorium	24.6 days	Beta
Uranium X$_2$...............	234	91	Protoactinium	1.15 min.	Beta
Uranium Z.................	234	91	Protoactinium	6.7 hrs.	Beta
Uranium II................	234	92	Uranium	2×10^6 yrs.	Alpha
Ionium....................	230	90	Thorium	6.9×10^4 yrs.	Alpha
Radium...................	226	88	Radium	1690 yrs.	Alpha
Radon....................	222	86	Radon	3.85 days	Alpha
Radium A.................	218	84	Polonium	3.0 min.	Alpha
Radium B.................	214	82	Lead	26.8 min.	Beta
Radium C.................	214	83	Bismuth	19.5 min.	Beta
Radium C'.................	214	84	Polonium	10^{-6} sec.	Alpha
Radium C".................	210	81	Thallium	1.4 min.	Beta
Radium D.................	210	82	Lead	16.5 yrs.	Beta
Radium E.................	210	83	Bismuth	5.0 days	Beta
Polonium (Radium F)............	210	84	Polonium	136 days	Alpha
Lead (Radium G)................	206	82	Lead	stable	None

When the first member of a radioactive series begins to decompose into the second, the second will decompose into the third at a very slow rate because little of it is present. As number 1 continues to decompose, however, the quantity of number 2 increases, as does also its rate of decomposition. Ultimately, as more of number 2 is formed and its rate of disintegration increases, a time will be reached when the quantity of number 2 being formed in a given period of time is just equal to the quantity of it which is disintegrating. A condition of equilibrium then obtains. As time goes on, similar equilibria will be established for the other intermediate members of the series. The last member of the series, being stable, does not disintegrate, and once its formation is begun it continues at a constant rate. Since lead is the end-product of the uranium

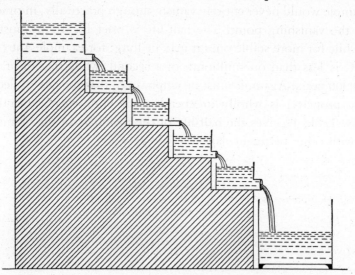

DIAGRAM OF THE WATER ANALOGY OF RADIOACTIVE EQUILIBRIA. Holes of various sizes in the different containers are analogous to the various half life periods. Ultimately all of the water will collect in the lowest container just as ultimately all of a given radioactive substance will ultimately be converted to a nonradioactive substance.

series, it is always present in the natural uranium ores. By assuming that this lead derives entirely from uranium and by measuring the relative quantities of the two metals in the sample, it has been possible to calculate the age of the sample, and, hence, presumably, the age of the earth. The method was first suggested by Boltwood in 1905, and application of it has confirmed the contention of the geologists that the earth is of great age. The maximum thus obtained is 1,852,000,000 years, a figure reported by Kovarik and based upon the study of ores from southern Russia.

10. Uses of Radium and Radon

Radon is the radioactive inert gas which is produced by the disintegration of radium. Its atomic weight is about 222 and its melting and boiling points are $-110°$ C. and $-61.8°$ C., respectively. The uses of both radium and radon depend almost entirely upon their ability spontaneously to emit radiations of high energy content. The quantity of energy liberated by even small samples of these elements is enormous. Thus the energy liberated by the complete disintegration of 1 g. of radium into lead is equivalent to that obtained by the combustion of more than half a ton of coal of good quality. The source of this energy was for a long time a mystery, but it is now believed to result from the conversion of small quantities of matter in accordance with Einstein's equation (cf. section 6 of Chapter 4).

Aside from its uses in research laboratories, radium is used chiefly in the treatment of cancers and tumors and in the preparation of luminous paints. Either the metal or its salts may be used for these purposes, and radon pumped from the containers of the element and its salts is sealed into small glass capsules and used also for the treatment of cancerous growths. The theory of the therapeutic use of radioactive substances is that the diseased tissues are more quickly affected by the emanations than are healthy cells. Inexpert or overlong applications may stimulate the growth of healthy cells to the point of developing cancer or may cause severe burns which result in loss of hair, in destruction of nerve endings, oil glands, and sweat glands, and in sterility. Luminous paint whose luminosity is not dependent upon previous exposure to light

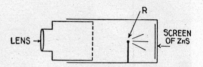

THE SPINTHARISCOPE. This is a simple device for magnifying the flashes produced by the collision of alpha particles from the radioactive material at R with a zinc sulfide screen.

is prepared by mixing one part of radium with several thousand parts of the impure zinc sulfide whose preparation is referred to in section 9 of Chapter 34. The zinc sulfide glows under the continuous bombardment of alpha particles from the radium.

The chemical effects of radium emanations upon both living and inanimate matter are both interesting and striking; they are, however, too numerous to be considered here.

11. Transmutation

Since the days of the alchemists, the possibility of changing one element into another (preferably cheap ones into valuable ones) has tantalized even the least self-seeking of laboratory workers. It became apparent with the discovery of radioactivity that elements were not immutable, but, even so, control of such changes remained beyond the grasp of man because of the tremendous energies involved. In time, as the nature of the atom and its nucleus and the nature of radioactivity became better understood, it became apparent that transmutation could be effected only by subjecting the nucleus to sufficiently energetic attack to cause its alteration—that is, to change the atomic number of the nucleus. Since the nucleus of any atom is extremely small and surrounded by a field of potential energy, bombardment with a "shotgun charge" of particles of small size and of extremely large energy content and penetrating power seemed the logical attack. Only particles of sub-atomic size would be small enough to fulfill the requirements, and at the time the above conclusion was reached the only known sub-atomic particle of sufficient energy was the alpha particle expelled from naturally occurring radioactive substances. By use of these particles, Rutherford was able to announce in 1919 the accomplishment of the first artificial transmutation; by bombarding nitrogen he was able to produce oxygen and hydrogen. Since a given alpha particle cannot be aimed at a given nucleus, it follows that the process, employing as it does a "shotgun charge," is highly inefficient. In the Rutherford

THE GIANT SPHERES OF A VAN DER GRAAFF ELECTROSTATIC GENERATOR. (Courtesy, Massachusetts Institute of Technology.)

experiment, it is estimated that about 1 out of every 50,000 atoms bombarded underwent transmutation.

During the years which have elapsed since Rutherford's initial experiment, many transmutations have been effected, but the process is still inefficient and of little value save in the production of artificially radioactive elements whose use, except in the case of plutonium, is limited largely to the laboratory. It was realized early that the alpha particle with its double positive charge was not well suited for atomic bombardment because of its repulsion by the positively charged nuclei. The singly charged proton and the neutral neutron and later the deuteron (the nucleus of heavy hydrogen) were recognized as better projectiles for the purpose, but since none of these particles was expelled from naturally radioactive substances, their use had to be postponed until such time as means could be found to give them a velocity of sufficient magnitude to permit them to strike with enough force to have the desired effect. The proton and deuteron are the nuclei of ordinary and heavy hydrogen atoms, respectively, and as such are rather easily produced. Two means of accelerating these positively charged particles have been found. Both are electrical and both involve the acceleration of the particle through a potential difference of several millions of volts. One method requires the use of specially designed electrostatic generators which are capable of developing potentials as high as 5,000,000 volts. The other employs a machine invented by Lawrence of the University of California which he named the "cyclotron." In this machine the particles are whirled

A CYCLOTRON. (Courtesy, University of California.)

in a strong magnetic field between electrodes on which the charge alternates at intervals equal to the time of half revolution of the particle. The cyclotron produces greater accelerations than do the various types of static machines, and the new one at the University of California will operate at a potential difference of 1,000,000 volts and will be capable of accelerating protons to a kinetic energy of 100,000,000 electron-volts.

In the early 1930's, it was discovered that the neutron can be produced as a disintegration product by the bombardment of beryllium and other light elements with alpha particles. Because it is not electrically charged, the neutron cannot be accelerated by use of electrical machines, but, fortunately, slow-moving ones appear to be more effective than are those of greater speed.

A new device for smashing the atom makes use of none of the sub-atomic particles but rather shoots pure energy in the form of x-rays into atomic nuclei. Known as the *betatron*, this device is, in essence, an x-ray tube of super power, and was developed in the laboratories of the General Electric Company. The first of the betatrons was tested early in 1946, and is reported to have developed x-rays at a potential of 100,000,000 volts. Early reports indicate that its powerful energy beam is capable of shattering not only atomic nuclei but also the protons and neutrons of which the nuclei are composed.

A still later device now under construction at the University of California and known as the *synchrotron* is expected to be ready for use early in 1947. It will combine the principles of the cyclotron and the betatron with a new principle

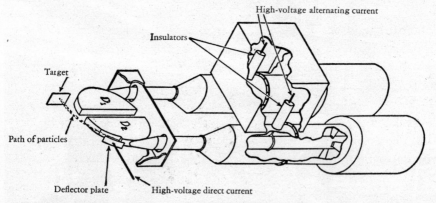

DIAGRAM OF THE CYCLOTRON. (Courtesy, White, Harvey E.: "Classical Modern Physics," D. Van Nostrand Co., Inc.)

developed independently by the American physicist Edwin M. McMillan and the Russian scientist V. Veksler. The University of California synchrotron is designed to accelerate electrons to a kinetic energy of 300,000,000 electron-volts and will make possible a wide range of sub-nuclear investigations which should increase greatly man's knowledge of the ultimate nature of his physical world. It is predicted that synchrotrons capable of accelerating electrons to a kinetic energy of 1,000,000,000 electron-volts eventually will be designed and constructed.

12. Transmutation Equations

A system whereby transmutations may be represented by equations has been evolved. In this system, as commonly employed, the atom is as usual represented by its symbol. The atomic number is written as a subscript preceding the symbol while the atomic mass to the nearest whole number is written as a superscript following the symbol. By this notation, hydrogen and deuterium are $_1H^1$ and $_1D^2$, respectively, and the chlorine isotopes are $_{17}Cl^{35}$ and $_{17}Cl^{37}$, respectively, while the original Rutherford transformation becomes

$$_2He^4 + {_7}N^{14} \rightarrow {_8}O^{17} + {_1}H^1$$

It will be noted that the oxygen formed is an isotope of the common oxygen ($_8O^{16}$).

In equations of this type, the atomic numbers must balance among themselves, and the atomic mass numbers must do likewise.

13. Artificially Radioactive Elements

In 1934, while studying the effects of bombarding the lighter elements with alpha particles, Irène Curie Joliot (elder daughter of Mme. Curie of radium fame) and her husband Frédéric Joliot discovered that in certain instances there were formed transmutation products which were radioactive. These products were the first artificially radioactive substances to be produced, and they were also the first known radioactive isotopes of the light elements of low atomic number. Following the announcement of this discovery, many investigators undertook to prepare by similar methods radioactive isotopes of other elements which are not naturally radioactive. As a result of this work, many artificially radioactive elements have been prepared and a host of such isotopes are known. Equations representing the formation of radioactive isotopes of some of the lighter elements are:

$$_4Be^9 + {_2}He^4 \rightarrow {_6}C^{12} + {_0}n^1$$
$$_5B^{10} + {_2}He^4 \rightarrow {_7}N^{13} + {_0}n^1$$

and

$$_{13}Al^{27} + {_2}He^4 \rightarrow {_{15}}P^{30} + {_0}n^1$$

Artificial radioactive elements, like natural ones, are characterized by rates of disintegration which are proportional to the numbers of their atoms present in a given sample and to the degree of instability of the particular variety of atoms in question; hence each variety of these atoms is also characterized by a definite half-life. The half-life is relatively short for most of the artificially radioactive substances. Of the elements whose preparation was described in the foregoing equations, the radioactive nitrogen decomposes thus, expelling a positron and forming an isotope of carbon:

$$_7N^{13} \rightarrow {_6}C^{13} + {_1}\epsilon^0$$

The equation for the decomposition of the radioactive phosphorus is:

$$_{15}P^{30} \rightarrow {}_{14}Si^{30} + {}_{1}\epsilon^0$$

The half-life of the nitrogen isotope is 11 min. while that of the phosphorus isotope is 2.5 min. The periods of other radioactive isotopes of some of the light elements are given in Table 44.

A 7,000,000 ELECTRON-VOLT BEAM OF PROTONS FROM A CYCLOTRON.
(Photograph by Paul H. Donaldson, Cruft Laboratory, Harvard University.)

As indicated in section 12, investigation has also revealed that the proton, the deuteron, and the neutron may also be used to produce transmutations. Of these particles, the neutral and relatively slow-moving neutron has been found to be especially effective. When it strikes an atomic nucleus, one of the

Table 44

PROPERTIES OF SOME ARTIFICIAL RADIOACTIVE ELEMENTS

Symbol	Method of Production	Half-life	Particle Ejected	Product of Decomposition
$_1H^3$	$_1H^2 + {}_1D^2 \rightarrow {}_1H^3 + {}_1H^1$	30 yrs.	Electron	$_2He^3$
$_6C^{11}$	$_5B^{10} + {}_1D^2 \rightarrow {}_6C^{11} + {}_0n^1$ or $_5B^{11} + {}_1H^1 \rightarrow {}_6C^{11} + {}_0n^1$	20.5 min.	Positron	$_5B^{11}$
$_8O^{15}$	$_7N^{14} + {}_1D^2 \rightarrow {}_8O^{15} + {}_0n^1$ or $_8O^{16} + {}_0n^1 \rightarrow {}_8O^{15} + 2_0n^1$	126 sec.	Positron	$_7N^{15}$
$_{12}Mg^{27}$	$_{12}Mg^{26} + {}_1D^2 \rightarrow {}_{12}Mg^{27} + {}_1H^1$ or $_{13}Al^{27} + {}_0n^1 \rightarrow {}_{12}Mg^{27} + {}_1H^1$	10.2 min.	Electron	$_{13}Al^{27}$
$_{16}S^{35}$	$_{17}Cl^{35} + {}_0n^1 \rightarrow {}_{16}S^{35} + {}_1H^1$	80 days	Electron	$_{17}Cl^{35}$
$_{19}K^{42}$	$_{20}Ca^{42} + {}_0n^1 \rightarrow {}_{19}K^{42} + {}_1H^1$ or $_{21}Sc^{45} + {}_0n^1 \rightarrow {}_{19}K^{42} + {}_2He^4$	12.2 hr.	Electron	$_{20}Ca^{42}$
$_{53}I^{128}$	$_{53}I^{127} + {}_0n^1 \rightarrow {}_{53}I^{128}$ or $_{52}Te^{128} + {}_1H^1 \rightarrow {}_{53}I^{128} + {}_0n^1$	25 min.	Electron	$_{54}Xe^{128}$

following changes may occur: (a) An alpha particle may be expelled; (b) a proton may be expelled; (c) the neutron may be captured, with the energy of the reaction being radiated as gamma rays; or (d) sufficient energy to cause the expulsion of a neutron may be captured from especially energetic bombarding neutrons. Since transmutations may be produced by different types of projectiles and by different types of nuclear reactions as a result of collision with a given type of projectile, it follows that a given artificially radioactive isotope may be produced by several different reactions. For example, the active sodium isotope, $_{11}Na^{24}$, is produced by the following reactions:

$$_{11}Na^{23} + {}_1D^2 \rightarrow {}_{11}Na^{24} + {}_1H^1$$
$$_{12}Mg^{24} + {}_0n^1 \rightarrow {}_{11}Na^{24} + {}_1H^1$$
$$_{13}Al^{27} + {}_0n^1 \rightarrow {}_{11}Na^{24} + {}_2He^4$$
$$_{11}Na^{23} + {}_0n^1 \rightarrow {}_{11}Na^{24} + \gamma\text{-rays}$$

and

$$_{12}Mg^{24} + {}_1D^2 \rightarrow {}_{11}Na^{24} + 2{}_1H^1$$

However prepared, a given radioactive element always decomposes spontaneously in the same manner. In the case of the above-mentioned isotope of sodium, decomposition is always into magnesium as the result of electron expulsion:

$$_{11}Na^{24} \rightarrow {}_{12}Mg^{24} + {}_{-1}\epsilon^0$$

At the present time, radioactive isotopes of every known element have been prepared, and in addition there have also been prepared radioactive isotopes of several elements whose existence in nature has never been established with certainty. Among these latter elements are masurium (at. no. 43), illinium (at. no. 61), alabamine (at. no. 85), and virginium (at. no. 87). Masurium has been prepared by proton or deuteron bombardment of molybdenum; illinium is reported to have been prepared by deuteron bombardment of neodymium; alabamine was prepared by alpha-particle bombardment of bismuth; and virginium is reported to be a member of the actinium series. The artificial preparation of neptunium (at. no. 93) and plutonium (at. no. 94) was referred to in section 3. They are products of the radioactive disintegration of $_{92}U^{239}$ which is obtained by bombarding $_{92}U^{238}$ with neutrons. The preparation of elements 95 (americium) and 96 (curium) has also been reported. That elements 85, 87, 93, 94, 95, and 96 should be radioactive is predictable from their position in the periodic system and from their large masses.

14. *Use of the Products of Transmutation*

In their chemical properties, artificially produced radioactive isotopes differ in no wise from the naturally occurring element. If such an isotope is mixed uniformly with a sample of the natural, nonradioactive element, then the presence of even minute samples of the mixture may be detected by the effects produced by the emanations of the radioactive atoms. Various devices are available for detecting and rather closely measuring the quantities of these emanations. Because the radioactive isotopes when mixed as mentioned above permit the location of even small quantities of a given element, they have become known as *tracer elements*. The use of the various radioactive isotopes is largely conditioned by the length of their half-lives. If the period is either too short or too long, then the use of the element as a tracer is not satisfactory. Fortunately, the half-life of many of the active isotopes of the common, light elements is of a magnitude to permit their use in the manner described.

The tracer elements have found their chief application thus far in the study of the various organic functions of humans, domestic animals, and plants. For example, the fate of foods in the body may be studied by the use of specially prepared fats, proteins, and carbohydrates which contain tracer elements, and photosynthesis may be investigated more thoroughly than formerly by the use of "tagged" molecules of carbon dioxide and water. Application of such elements to inanimate systems also has been made both in the laboratory and in industry.

Artificially produced plutonium has thus far found use only in the atomic bomb, though in time it may serve as a source of energy for industrial use.

15. *Nuclear Fission*

As a result of attempts to prepare isotopes of elements of atomic number greater than 92, a new type of transmutation, commonly called *nuclear fission*, was discovered. In ordinary cases of transmutation discussed in the preceding sections of this chapter, it will be noted that unstable nuclei ordinarily disintegrate into particles of disparate mass and charge. In these cases, the larger particle is usually an atom whose mass differs not at all, or by only a few units, from that of the parent atom. When, in the attempt to prepare atoms of an atomic number higher than that of uranium, that element was bombarded with slow-moving neutrons, it was found that some of its atoms were split into two particles whose mass and charge while not equal were nearly so. Disintegration of this type was named *nuclear fission*, and was found to be accompanied by the evolution of tremendous quantities of energy. Other naturally occurring atoms which have been observed to undergo this type of transmutation are those of thorium and protoactinium. Rapidly moving neutrons seem to move too quickly to be captured by the uranium nucleus whose instability is greatly increased by such a capture. The speed of neutrons may be decreased by their passage through layers of water, oils, carbon, metals, etc.

Apparently the capture of a neutron by the atoms of uranium, thorium, and protoactinium results in the formation of heavier isotopes whose instability is so great that they undergo the unusually violent decompositions of the type under discussion. As a result of these disintegrations, pairs of elements whose atomic numbers are of approximately median value are formed. The heavier fragment may range in identity from $_{52}$Te to $_{57}$La, while the lighter fragment will be a member of the group $_{34}$Se to $_{42}$Mo; both fragments resulting from a given disintegration contain a relatively large number of neutrons in excess of the permissible neutron-proton ratio, and are therefore themselves radioactive and isotopes of the natural elements of the same atomic numbers. In some instances, several different radioactive isotopes of a given element may be formed by fission.

In the radioactive isotopes formed, the ratio of neutrons to protons is considerably in excess of the limit of stability, hence their formation is followed by a series of radioactive changes which ultimately result in the formation of stable atoms. Stability may be attained either by the emission of the excess neutrons which causes a decrease in mass but no decrease in charge (atomic number), or by the emission of electrons which causes an increase in charge but no appreciable change of mass. As a result of changes of both types, a series of radioactive intermediate products is formed.

Fission is caused by the capture of a neutron, yet, as was shown in the preceding paragraph, as a result of the fission of a single uranium atom many neutrons are set free along with large quantities of energy. It seemed logical to suppose that these liberated neutrons would be captured by surrounding atoms of uranium which in turn would decompose to liberate still more neutrons and still more energy, thus establishing a chain of reactions of ever-increasing violence. Observation showed that no such chain of increasingly violent disintegrations develops. Reasons for this failure may be several. In the first place, the ejected neutrons may be expelled too violently and may travel too rapidly to be captured; in the second place, samples of uranium are usually far from pure and the ejected neutrons may be captured by atoms which do not become unstable as a result of their capture; and in the third place, it is $_{92}U^{235}$, one of the less plentiful isotopes of uranium, rather than the more plentiful isotope $_{92}U^{238}$ which undergoes fission. In the light of these considerations, it seemed likely that the concentration of neutrons produced by fission was not sufficiently large to undergo the losses mentioned above and still set up in the relatively scarce $_{92}U^{235}$ atoms a self-perpetuating chain of disintegrations.

At the time of the precipitation of the United States into World War II late in 1941, the foregoing facts were common knowledge among the scientists of the world, and the conclusion derived from them was that if the uranium isotope of mass 235 could be separated from the other isotopes of the metal, it might undergo a self-perpetuating series of disintegrations which would liberate tremendous quantities of energy. It was conceivable that the quantities of energy liberated by such a disintegration would be sufficiently large to cause the disintegration of the more stable atoms of surrounding material, thus touching off a series of changes which would result in the complete disordering, on this planet at least, of the organized energy which we know as matter. It also seemed entirely possible, however, that means of controlling such evolutions of sub-atomic energy could be found. There matters rested at that time.

16. The Atomic Bomb

On Monday, August 6, 1945, the best-kept secret of World War II was revealed when the President of the United States released the following statement: "Sixteen hours ago an American airplane dropped one bomb on Hiroshima . . . That bomb had more power than 20,000 tons of T.N.T. It is an atomic bomb . . . a harnessing of the basic power of the universe." This announcement made plain that in the race to accomplish the liberation of sub-atomic energy, scientists of the United Nations were the victors. The story of the establishment of a research center in the mountains of north-central New Mexico; of the gathering there of leading scientists from the United States, Great Britain, Canada, and a number of other countries; of the erection of plants for processing uranium concentrates in the states of Washington and Tennessee; of the expenditure of $2,000,000,000 on the overall project; of the test of the first atomic bomb in the wastelands of southern New Mexico; and of the dropping of two atomic bombs, one on Hiroshima, the other on Nagasaki, is to be read in the publications of the day. At the present writing, much secrecy still surrounds the discoveries which preceded the fabrication of the bombs and the details of their manufacture. From material which has been made public, however, it appears that, despite the like chemical behavior of the isotopes of uranium and the very slight difference in their masses, means of concentrating the 235 isotope were found; that the processes hit upon involved the use of tremendous quantities of electrical energy; that means of initiating the reaction at the desired time were found; that the evolution of energy from a limited quantity of material undergoing nuclear fission does not serve to initiate the destruction of the earth; that the explosion of such bombs above the surface of the ground does not leave dangerous radioactive substances in the earth; and that hopes for the future use and control of subatomic energy are good. The discovery of neptunium and plutonium has been mentioned, and it is stated that the latter element also undergoes nuclear fission and was used in conjunction with uranium 235 in the bombs.

Uranium as concentrated from naturally occurring ores contains 99.3 per cent of $_{92}U^{238}$, 0.7 per cent of $_{92}U^{235}$, and a negligible percentage of $_{92}U^{234}$. Since separation of these isotopes by chemical means is impossible, physical means taking advantage of the slight differences in atomic mass had to be employed. Four such methods, all of which involve prior vaporization of the metal, and all of which have been tried, are: (a) gaseous diffusion through a porous barrier; (b) centrifugation;

COLUMN OF SMOKE ARISING FROM THE EXPLOSION OF AN ATOMIC BOMB. (Official Photo, U.S.A.A.F.)

(c) thermal diffusion; and (d) selective deflection of the gaseous particles in a strong magnetic field. Each of these methods is both tedious and expensive.

Plutonium for use in the bomb was prepared from the naturally occurring uranium. By action of the neutrons emitted by $_{92}U^{235}$ on $_{92}U^{238}$, there was

AERIAL VIEW OF THE PLANT ERECTED AT HANFORD, WASH., FOR THE PREPARATION OF PLUTO-
NIUM. (Courtesy, War Department, U.S. Engineer Office.)

formed an artificial radioactive isotope $_{92}U^{239}$ which upon spontaneous disintegration yielded $_{93}Np^{239}$, whose half-life is of the order of a few days, and which
in turn disintegrated, yielding the more stable $_{94}Pu^{239}$:

$$_{92}U^{238} + _{0}n^{1} \rightarrow _{92}U^{239}$$
$$_{92}U^{239} \rightarrow _{93}Np^{239} + _{-1}\epsilon^{0}$$

and

$$_{93}Np^{239} \rightarrow _{94}Pu^{239} + _{-1}\epsilon^{0}$$

Preparation of this latter substance was carried on in a plant at Hanford, Washington, where the production units were several huge "piles." These were large
blocks of graphite into which had been bored holes to contain cylinders of
uranium sealed in aluminum cans for protection from the cooling water circu-
lated through the pile. The encasing carbon served to slow the flight of emitted
neutrons and the size, design, and control of each pile was such that the chain
reaction once begun would continue at a steady rate. The plutonium formed
was separated from the excess of uranium by chemical means. The evolution
of heat by the processes taking place within the piles suggests a possible means
of utilizing sub-atomic energy industrially.

For the successful use of sub-atomic energy as an agent of destruction, it
is requisite that its evolution be instantaneous; that is, the chain reaction must
proceed very rapidly. Such considerations imply the use of a mass of the explo-

sive material of sufficient size to prevent the fruitless escape of a majority of the evolved neutrons; in other words, for an instantaneous explosion to occur, there must be present for a given shape of the charge a certain mass of it. From this it is apparent that within the bomb there must have been a suitable mechanism for bringing together at the proper moment several small masses of radioactive material whose total mass exceeded the critical value.

Reports issued to the press state that the bomb dropped on Hiroshima utilized only about one-tenth of 1 per cent of the total energy which could be obtained under optimum conditions from the fission of the uranium atom. This would indicate that perhaps concentration of the 235 isotope and of plutonium was carried only to a certain point so that these substances remained mixed with some inert material. At the present time, the methods employed for this degree of concentration are far too costly to make atomic energy a competitor of electricity, coal, oil, and other common sources of energy. The problems connected with the harnessing and directing of this energy must also be solved. That cheaper and more efficient means of obtaining the materials which release sub-atomic energy will be found seems likely, as does the discovery of means of controlling this unleashed genie for the accomplishment of the useful work of the world, but how long the solution of these problems will take is a matter of conjecture. It seems likely, however, that within the next decade limited utilization of atomic energy for a few specialized commercial processes which warrant the use of a premium fuel may be expected, if government regulations permit. At the moment, it further appears that in the hands of the unscrupulous, the inept, or the incautious, sub-atomic power will remain a threat to the very existence of our civilization, if not to the earth itself. It is apparent, therefore, that the problems connected with this chapter of scientific development are moral, ethical, social, and economic as well as scientific. Success in the solution of all of these problems may well achieve the inauguration of a new era in the history of man; failure may accomplish his utter destruction. Here conjecture must cease.

(See *Appendix for Exercises*)

COLLATERAL READINGS

Coryell: The scientific importance of the nuclear power projects, *J. Chem. Education*, **23,** 395 (1946).

Curie: *Madame Curie*, New York, Doubleday, Doran & Co., Inc., 1937.

Daniels: Peacetime use of atomic power, *Chem. & Eng. News*, **24**, 1514 (1946).

DeMent and Dake: *Uranium and Atomic Power*, New York, Chemical Publishing Co., 1945.

Eidinoff: Uranium fission, *J. Chem. Education*, **23**, 60 (1946).

Evans: Applied nuclear physics, *J. Applied Phys.*, **12**, 260 (1941).

Hevesy and Paneth: *A Manual of Radioactivity*, New York, Oxford University Press, 1941.

Kovarik: The age of the earth: radioactive methods of its determination, *Sci. Monthly*, **32**, 309 (1931).

Latimer and Hildebrand: *Reference Book of Inorganic Chemistry*, New York, The Macmillan Co., 1941.

Pollard and Davidson: *Applied Nuclear Physics*, New York, John Wiley & Sons, Inc., 1942.

Ridenour and Yost: Artificial radioactivity, *Chem. Rev.*, **18**, 457 (1936).

Robertson: *Atomic Artillery*, New York, D. Van Nostrand Co., 1945.

Rosenblum: Isotopes as indicators, *J. Chem. Education*, **17**, 567 (1940).

Rutherford: *The Newer Alchemy*, New York, The Macmillan Co., 1937.

——, Chadwick, and Ellis: *Radiations from Radioactive Substances*, London, Cambridge University Press, 1930.

Seaborg: The impact of nuclear chemistry, *Chem. & Eng. News*, **24**, 1192 (1946).

Sheppard: Atom smashing: two methods, *Sci. American*, **164**, 282 (1941).

Solomon: The physics of the bomb, *Fortune*, **33**, No. 5, 115 (1946).

Timm: Putting tagged atoms to work, *J. Chem. Education*, **20**, 54 (1943).

Urey: The separation and use of stable isotopes, *J. Applied Phys.*, **12**, 270 (1941).

Weeks: *Discovery of the Elements*, 5th ed., Mack Printing Co., 1945.

Williams: Nuclear reactions, *J. Chem. Education*, **23**, 423 (1946).

Plutonium laboratory, *Life*, p. 69, July 8, 1946.

The atomic bomb, *Life*, 87B, Aug. 20, 1945.

The cyclotron, *Life*, p. 42, Feb. 5, 1940.

The great radium mystery, *Fortune*, **9**, 70 (1934).

The Inert Gases

1. Introduction

Helium, neon, argon, krypton, xenon, and radon are the inert gases which make up the VIII A family of the periodic system. Discussion of these elements has been relegated to the end of this textbook because they form no stable compounds, but this in no wise reflects upon the importance of their discovery and its subsequent influence upon the theories of the structure of the atom and the nature of chemical change. Until the discovery of argon in 1894, the existence of a group of elements of no chemical activity had scarcely been suspected, but so firm was the establishment of the periodic classification by that time that no sooner was the first of this new type of element discovered than there

Table 45

PHYSICAL PROPERTIES OF THE ELEMENTS OF THE VIII A FAMILY

Property	Helium (He)	Neon (Ne)	Argon (A)	Krypton (Kr)	Xenon (Xe)	Radon (Rn)
Atomic weight.........	4.003	20.183	39.944	83.7	131.3	222
Mass of isotopes.......	4	20, 21, 22	36, 38, 40	78, 80, 82, 83, 84, 86	124, 126, 128, 129, 130, 131, 132, 134, 136	222
Atomic number........	2	10	18	36	54	86
Distribution of planetary electons........	2	2, 8	2, 8, 8	2, 8, 18, 8	2, 8, 18, 18, 8	2, 8, 18, 32, 18, 8
Melting point, ° C......	below −272.2 (26 atm.)	−248.67	−189.2	−157	−112	−110
Boiling point, ° C	−268.9	−245.9	−185.7	−152.9	−107.1	−61.8
Critical temperature, ° C.	−267.9	−228.7	−122.4	−63	16.6	104
Density, g./l...........	0.177	0.8990	1.7839	3.708	5.85	9.73
Ionizing potential, volts						
1st electron..........	24.46	21.47	15.68	13.93	12.08	10.7
2nd electron.........	54.14	40.9	27.76	26.4	21.1(?)	(?)
Heat of vaporization, cal./g...............	25	405	1600	2240	3100	3600
Occurrence in atmosphere (by volume)....	1 part: 200,000 parts	1 part: 65,000 parts	1 part: 106 + parts	1 part: 1,000,000 parts	1 part: 11,000,000 parts	zero

was begun work which resulted in the discovery of most of the other members of the family.

With the exception of helium, whose atom contains only the two electrons of the first energy level, the inert gases possess atoms which contain eight electrons in their outermost energy levels. This configuration apparently confers great stability upon the atoms, making them resistant to both chemical and physical attacks. A very few compounds of the inert gases have been reported, but these are of such extreme instability that for all practical purposes these elements may be thought of as forming no compounds. Knowledge of the inertness and of the atomic structure of these elements has been of prime theoretical importance.

2. Physical Properties

At about 20° C., the members of the VIII A family are all colorless gases of very low boiling and freezing points. The numerical values of these transition temperatures and the numerical values of other physical properties of the various members of the family are given in Table 45.

The great stability and low affinity of these gases is shown by their existence in the monoatomic condition, their very low boiling and freezing points, and their low heats of solidification. The stability of the atoms may also be inferred from their relatively high ionizing potentials. The gases are all slightly soluble in water, and become increasingly soluble as the atomic mass increases.

Helium, the lightest of the gases, has properties which are of especial interest. Like hydrogen, it is slightly more than a perfect gas, as is shown by its warming slightly when it expands at about 20° C. When cooled to temperatures below $-262°$ C. (11° A.), it will, however, cool on expansion, and when the liquid is evaporated *in vacuo*, temperatures only 0.7° above the absolute zero have been reached. When cooled to a temperature of 2.2° A., the liquid undergoes a strange change. Its thermal conductivity increases, its viscosity decreases, and in general it seems to have attained a new state in which it behaves as if it were a solid with the general properties of a gas. Substances in such a state are referred to as *degenerate gases*.

3. Discovery of the Inert Gases

Argon was almost discovered by Cavendish in 1785 when he showed that, after the removal of oxygen and nitrogen from a sample of air, there still remained a relatively tiny volume of gas which further treatment did not diminish. By concluding that experimental error accounted for the observation, he missed making an important discovery which was not made until more than 100 years later. While engaged in the determination of the densities and molecular weights of a number of gases, in 1894 J. W. Strutt, who later became Lord Rayleigh, observed that the density of the nitrogen obtained by the decomposition of pure ammonium nitrate was always slightly less than that obtained by the removal of oxygen and other known components from samples of air. Reference to the memoirs of Cavendish convinced Strutt that the deviation in the density of his samples of nitrogen was caused by the presence in the air of small quantities of some unknown and inert gas. The isolation of the suspected substance was undertaken by Sir William Ramsay, professor of chemistry in the University College of London. So successful was his work that later in the same year he and Strutt were able to announce the discovery of a new element which was characterized by extreme inertness and by a brilliant line in the red end of the spectrum. This element they named argon (Greek, *inert* or *lazy*).

Helium, the lightest of the inert gases, was discovered by Sir William Ramsay in 1895, but the story of the discovery has its beginning in 1868, in which year the French astronomer, Janssen, discovered in the solar spectrum a brilliant yellow line which was unknown in the spectra of any of the terrestial elements. This discovery was also made in the same year by Lockyer and Frankland. The conclusion was, naturally enough, that there existed in the sun an element not known on the earth. Lockyer gave to this new solar element the name *helium*, derived from the Greek word for *sun*. After his discovery of argon, Ramsay was naturally interested in the possible existence of other inert elements, hence it is not strange that his attention was attracted by a report of the American chemist, Hillebrand. In 1889, while studying various uranium ores, Hillebrand discovered that upon treatment with acid some of these evolved small volumes of an inert gas which he supposed to be nitrogen and which he investigated no further. Upon repeating these experiments in 1895, by treatment of a sample of Norwegian *cleveite* Ramsay obtained a gas whose spectrum proved to be identical with that of the solar helium. Later, Kayser showed that helium is also present in the air, though in very minute concentrations. With the discovery of radioactivity, it was found that helium is usually present in the minerals of radioactive elements. This is accounted for by the capture of two electrons by the alpha particles (helium nuclei) which are emitted during the course of many radioactive disintegrations.

From his knowledge of the periodic classification of the elements, Ramsay concluded that there should be other inert elements besides helium and argon, and that one of these unknowns should have a weight intermediate between the weights of the two already discovered gases. He chose air as a likely source of this intermediate substance and by the use of processes of fractional distillation and fractional absorption he and his co-worker, Travers, were able to isolate not one, but three, new members of the family of inert elements. All three of these were gases at about 20° C., all were colorless, and each was best characterized by its spectrum. The lightest of these was named *neon* (Greek, *new*), the one of atomic weight 83.7 *krypton* (Greek, *hidden*), and the one of atomic weight 131.3 *xenon* (Greek, *stranger*). As shown in Table 45, all three of these gases are present in the air in very small quantities.

Radon, the heaviest of the inert gases, was discovered in 1900 by Dorn. As was shown in Chapter 35, this element is the disintegration product of radium and is radioactive itself; nevertheless, it was soon recognized that its chemical properties showed it to be a member of the family of inert elements. The element was isolated in 1908 by Ramsay and Gray, who named it *niton* from the Latin word *nitens* which means *shining*. It was renamed *radon* in 1923 to show its relationship to radium.

4. Helium

From the standpoint of the variety of its uses, helium is the most important of the inert gases. Despite the facts that its discovery was long delayed and that it was once believed to be very rare, in reality this gas is rather plentiful though very widely distributed. It is present to the extent of 0.0004 per cent by volume in the air and is also found in various naturally occurring minerals and gases. At the present time, the United States is the only large-scale producer of the gas, and the source is certain natural gases of Texas, Kansas, Oklahoma, and New Mexico, which contain about 2 per cent of helium, save in the case of the gas from the Rattlesnake Field in New Mexico, which contains 7 to 8 per cent. Production is entirely in the hands of the Bureau of Mines of the Federal Government. An extraction plant has been maintained at Amarillo, Texas, since 1929, and during World War II four new plants were established by the Government—one at Shiprock, New Mexico, one in Texas, and two in Kansas. The price of the gas has been in the neighborhood of $10.00 per thousand cubic feet. Liquid helium has been of great importance in scientific investigations conducted at low temperatures. It is the most difficult gas to liquefy—its liquefaction was not accomplished until 1908. The largest use of the gas is in the filling of the bags of lighter-than-air craft. Its lifting power as compared with that of hydrogen is only 92.6 per cent, but whereas hydrogen is highly inflammable, helium is perfectly safe under all operating conditions, including those of battle. The burning of the German dirigible *von Hindenburg*, a hydro-

A Tank Car Used for the Transportation of Helium Gas under High Pressure. (Courtesy, U.S. Department of the Interior, Bureau of Mines.)

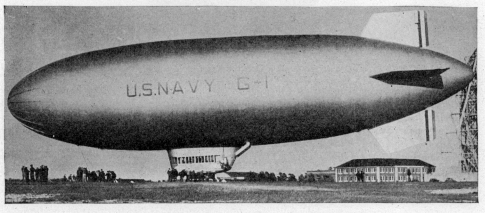

A Helium-filled Balloon. (Courtesy, U.S. Navy.)

gen-filled balloon, at Lakehurst, New Jersey, furnishes an outstanding example of the fate which may overtake hydrogen-filled balloons.

Another important use of helium is in a mixture with oxygen for use as a synthetic atmosphere by divers and others who work under high pressures.

SIR WILLIAM RAMSAY
(1852–1916, Scottish)

William Ramsay was educated at the University of Glasgow and in Germany. During his lifetime he held professorships at a number of Scottish and English universities. He was a remarkably skillful experimentalist who made many original contributions to chemical knowledge. His most important achievements were the discovery of the inert gases and his studies on radioactivity. After his discovery of argon, as suggested by the work of Lord Rayleigh on the density of atmospheric nitrogen, he discovered helium, and later, with the aid of Travers, neon, krypton, and xenon. For his work on the noble gases, he received the Nobel Prize in chemistry in 1904, and in 1902 he was knighted by the British Crown. In every sense of the word, Ramsay was a scholar; he spoke several languages fluently and was proficient in a number of other fields. In addition he was a sportsman, a traveler, and a raconteur and wit.

Nitrogen dissolves in the blood of those who work at high pressures in an ordinary atmosphere. As the pressure is reduced on these individuals, the dissolved gas is liberated and tends to form bubbles which collect in the blood vessels—especially those of the joints. These bubbles cause the painful condition known both as "the bends" and as "caisson disease." Fatalities from the condition have been known to occur. To prevent the development of "the bends" in workers who have spent some time under pressure, they are required to spend a considerable period in a chamber where the pressure is reduced slowly enough for the nitrogen to be removed by the lungs as it is released. Helium is much less soluble in blood than is nitrogen, hence workers who have breathed the artificial atmosphere in which helium has replaced nitrogen may be depressurized much more quickly and are much less susceptible to "the bends" than are those who have worked in an atmosphere of air. Similar artificial atmospheres have been used in the treatment of respiratory diseases and for administration during anesthesia.

Helium has been used in certain instances to cool electrical generators and other electrical equipment. A wider use of the gas may be anticipated for the future.

5. Neon

Neon is obtained as a by-product of the liquid-air industry. It is a component of the "crude" argon obtained from the atmosphere and is separated from the other members of the mixture by both fractional distillation and fractional liquefaction. Between 40 and 50 tons of air must be processed to yield 1 lb. of neon. The principal use of the gas is in the manufacture of "neon" signs and lights. These are simply Crookes tubes of various designs in which the gas is used at very low pressures. Neon alone in a clear glass tube gives a bright red light of an orange cast. When mixed with other gases or when used in tubes of colored glass, it yields other colors. It is also used in the Pintsch neon-glow lamps. Many so-called "neon" signs are made of tubes which contain gases and vapors of substances other than neon.

6. Argon

Argon is the most plentiful of the inert gases of the atmosphere and as such is obtained in considerable quantities as a by-product of the air liquefaction industry. Its principal uses are the filling of ordinary tungsten-filament light bulbs to slow the rate of evaporation of the hot filament when the bulb is in use and the filling of the tubes used in fluorescent lighting. When tubes of the latter type are operating, the effective gas is a mixture of mercury vapor and argon. Argon is also used in "neon" type signs and in clear glass tubes gives a characteristic red glow. Occasionally the gas is used for other purposes that require an inert atmosphere.

7. Krypton and Xenon

. These two gases, as shown in Table 45, are present in the atmosphere in extremely small proportions. Of such small magnitudes are these proportions that when liquid air is fractionated usually no attempt is made to separate the two. Discharge tubes containing a mixture of these gases under reduced pressure are used in photography and in other scientific work where very brilliant illuminations of ultrashort durations are required. The price of xenon was quoted in 1939 as $600.00 per liter.

8. Radon

Radon, as has been pointed out, is the direct disintegration product of radium, and, as such, is always found to a greater or lesser extent in radioactive ores which contain radium. Samples of radium salts always contain some radon, the last vestiges of which they release only upon being heated to about 800° C. The gas is always carefully collected from samples of radium and its salts and is sealed in small glass capsules which are used in the treatment of cancers and tumors. By use of these capsules a small sample of radium can be made to serve for the treatment of a number of patients at once; also by their use the danger of loss or theft of valuable radium samples is considerably decreased. Scientific students often are able to make a portion of their expenses by pumping radon from radium samples and preparing the capsules. Continued exposure to the emanations of the two elements must be avoided, however. Radon is also a good source of alpha particles for use in scientific investigations.

9. Conclusion

This textbook reaches its conclusion with the consideration of the inert gases. It is the hope of the author that the students who have used it will have come to a greater appreciation of the extreme orderliness of nature as manifested in matter, its composition and properties, and the changes which the various types of matter undergo. It is hoped further that the student will have been impressed most forcibly not with the individual facts set forth, but rather with the overall relationship of these facts and with the achievements of those who by application of the scientific method have given to the world a knowledge of the tiny particles and the great forces of the atomic and sub-atomic worlds.

Lastly, it is the earnest hope of the author that some of the students who have attended classes in which this book has been used as a text will be inspired to build a career in chemical science upon the foundation thus acquired, and that all who have studied its pages will find their lives richer for the knowledge gained and for the habits of mind acquired. The frontiers of science are wide, offering great opportunities to the qualified explorer, and demands for individuals who have the habits of close observation and correct interpretation coupled with the traits of thoroughness and dependability are numerous in all fields.

(See Appendix for Exercises)

COLLATERAL READINGS

Ackerman: Balloon juice, *Popular Sci.*, **143**, 89 (1943).

Bartlett: Some uses of atmospheric gases, *J. Chem. Education*, **5**, 1327 (1928).

Harrow: *Eminent Chemists of Our Time*, 2d. ed., New York, D. Van Nostrand Co., 1927.

Hopkins: *Chemistry of the Rarer Elements*, Boston, D. C. Heath & Co., 1923.

Keesom: *Helium*, New York, Elsevier Publishing Co., 1946.

Latimer and Hildebrand: *Reference Book of Inorganic Chemistry*, New York, The Macmillan Co., 1941.

Metzger: Traces from tons, *Ind. Eng. Chem.*, **27**, 112 (1935).

Ramsay: *Gases of the Atmosphere*, New York, The Macmillan Co., 1915.

Siebel: The production of helium at Amarillo, *Ind. Eng. Chem.*, **30**, 848 (1938).

Snyder and Bottoms: Properties and uses of helium, *Ind. Eng. Chem.*, **22**, 1189 (1930).

Weeks: *Discovery of the Elements*, 5th ed., Mack Printing Co., 1945.

Mightiest nothing, *Sci. American*, **173**, 364 (1945).

Appendix

A. VAPOR PRESSURE OF WATER

Temperature, °C.	Pressure, mm. of Hg	Temperature, °C.	Pressure, mm. of Hg	Temperature, °C.	Pressure, mm. of Hg
0	4.57	24	22.15	50	91.98
5	6.51	25	23.52	60	148.88
8	7.99	26	24.96	70	233.31
10	9.14	27	26.47	80	354.87
15	12.67	28	28.07	90	525.47
16	13.51	29	29.74	100	760.00
17	14.40	30	31.51		
18	15.33	31	33.37		
19	16.32	32	35.32		
20	17.36	33	37.37		
21	18.47	34	39.52		
22	19.63	35	41.78		
23	20.85	40	54.87		

B. SOLUBILITY PRODUCT CONSTANTS

Substance	$K_{s.p.}$	Substance	$K_{s.p.}$	Substance	$K_{s.p.}$
$Al(OH)_3$	1.9×10^{-33}	CuS	4×10^{-38}	HgS	1×10^{-53}
$BaCrO_4$	2×10^{-10}	$Fe(OH)_3$	1×10^{-38}	NiS	1.4×10^{-24}
$BaSO_4$	4×10^{-10}	FeS	1×10^{-19}	AgCl	1×10^{-10}
CdS	1.4×10^{-28}	$PbCl_2$	1.8×10^{-4}	Ag_2CrO_4	1.1×10^{-12}
$CaCO_3$	9×10^{-10}	$PbCrO_4$	2×10^{-14}	AgI	1.7×10^{-16}
CaC_2O_4	4×10^{-10}	PbS	1×10^{-29}	$SrCO_3$	4.6×10^{-9}
$CaSO_4$	3.5×10^{-6}	$Mg(OH)_2$	5×10^{-12}	$SrCrO_4$	5×10^{-5}
CoS	1×10^{-26}	MnS	1.6×10^{-16}	$Zn(OH)_2$	4×10^{-17}
				ZnS	4.5×10^{-24}

C. LOGARITHMS OF NUMBERS

Natural Numbers	0	1	2	3	4	5	6	7	8	9	Proportional Parts								
											1	2	3	4	5	6	7	8	9
10	0000	0043	0086	0128	0170	0212	0253	0294	0334	0374	4	8	12	17	21	25	29	33	37
11	0414	0453	0492	0531	0569	0607	0645	0682	0719	0755	4	8	11	15	19	23	26	30	34
12	0792	0828	0864	0899	0934	0969	1004	1038	1072	1106	3	7	10	14	17	21	24	28	31
13	1139	1173	1206	1239	1271	1303	1335	1367	1399	1430	3	6	10	13	16	19	23	26	29
14	1461	1492	1523	1553	1584	1614	1644	1673	1703	1732	3	6	9	12	15	18	21	24	27
15	1761	1790	1818	1847	1875	1903	1931	1959	1987	2014	3	6	8	11	14	17	20	22	25
16	2041	2068	2095	2122	2148	2175	2201	2227	2253	2279	3	5	8	11	13	16	18	21	24
17	2304	2330	2355	2380	2405	2430	2455	2480	2504	2529	2	5	7	10	12	15	17	20	22
18	2553	2577	2601	2625	2648	2672	2695	2718	2742	2765	2	5	7	9	12	14	16	19	21
19	2788	2810	2833	2856	2878	2900	2923	2945	2967	2989	2	4	7	9	11	13	16	18	20
20	3010	3032	3054	3075	3096	3118	3139	3160	3181	3201	2	4	6	8	11	13	15	17	19
21	3222	3243	3263	3284	3304	3324	3345	3365	3385	3404	2	4	6	8	10	12	14	16	18
22	3424	3444	3464	3483	3502	3522	3541	3560	3579	3598	2	4	6	8	10	12	14	15	17
23	3617	3636	3655	3674	3692	3711	3729	3747	3766	3784	2	4	6	7	9	11	13	15	17
24	3802	3820	3838	3856	3874	3892	3909	3927	3945	3962	2	4	5	7	9	11	12	14	16
25	3979	3997	4014	4031	4048	4065	4082	4099	4116	4133	2	3	5	7	9	10	12	14	15
26	4150	4166	4183	4200	4216	4232	4249	4265	4281	4298	2	3	5	7	8	10	11	13	15
27	4314	4330	4346	4362	4378	4393	4409	4425	4440	4456	2	3	5	6	8	9	11	13	14
28	4472	4487	4502	4518	4533	4548	4564	4579	4594	4609	2	3	5	6	8	9	11	12	14
29	4624	4639	4654	4669	4683	4698	4713	4728	4742	4757	1	3	4	6	7	9	10	12	13
30	4771	4786	4800	4814	4829	4843	4857	4871	4886	4900	1	3	4	6	7	9	10	11	13
31	4914	4928	4942	4955	4969	4983	4997	5011	5024	5038	1	3	4	6	7	8	10	11	12
32	5051	5065	5079	5092	5105	5119	5132	5145	5159	5172	1	3	4	5	7	8	9	11	12
33	5185	5198	5211	5224	5237	5250	5263	5276	5289	5302	1	3	4	5	6	8	9	10	12
34	5315	5328	5340	5353	5366	5378	5391	5403	5416	5428	1	3	4	5	6	8	9	10	11
35	5441	5453	5465	5478	5490	5502	5514	5527	5539	5551	1	2	4	5	6	7	9	10	11
36	5563	5575	5587	5599	5611	5623	5635	5647	5658	5670	1	2	4	5	6	7	8	10	11
37	5682	5694	5705	5717	5729	5740	5752	5763	5775	5786	1	2	3	5	6	7	8	9	10
38	5798	5809	5821	5832	5843	5855	5866	5877	5888	5899	1	2	3	5	6	7	8	9	10
39	5911	5922	5933	5944	5955	5966	5977	5988	5999	6010	1	2	3	4	5	7	8	9	10
40	6021	6031	6042	6053	6064	6075	6085	6096	6107	6117	1	2	3	4	5	6	8	9	10
41	6128	6138	6149	6160	6170	6180	6191	6201	6212	6222	1	2	3	4	5	6	7	8	9
42	6232	6243	6253	6263	6274	6284	6294	6304	6314	6325	1	2	3	4	5	6	7	8	9
43	6335	6345	6355	6365	6375	6385	6395	6405	6415	6425	1	2	3	4	5	6	7	8	9
44	6435	6444	6454	6464	6474	6484	6493	6503	6513	6522	1	2	3	4	5	6	7	8	9
45	6532	6542	6551	6561	6571	6580	6590	6599	6609	6618	1	2	3	4	5	6	7	8	9
46	6628	6637	6646	6656	6665	6675	6684	6693	6702	6712	1	2	3	4	5	6	7	7	8
47	6721	6730	6739	6749	6758	6767	6776	6785	6794	6803	1	2	3	4	5	5	6	7	8
48	6812	6821	6830	6839	6848	6857	6866	6875	6884	6893	1	2	3	4	4	5	6	7	8
49	6902	6911	6920	6928	6937	6946	6955	6964	6972	6981	1	2	3	4	4	5	6	7	8
50	6990	6998	7007	7016	7024	7033	7042	7050	7059	7067	1	2	3	3	4	5	6	7	8
51	7076	7084	7093	7101	7110	7118	7126	7135	7143	7152	1	2	3	3	4	5	6	7	8
52	7160	7168	7177	7185	7193	7202	7210	7218	7226	7235	1	2	2	3	4	5	6	7	7
53	7243	7251	7259	7267	7275	7284	7292	7300	7308	7316	1	2	2	3	4	5	6	6	7
54	7324	7332	7340	7348	7356	7364	7372	7380	7388	7396	1	2	2	3	4	5	6	6	7

C. LOGARITHMS OF NUMBERS (*Continued*)

Natural Numbers	0	1	2	3	4	5	6	7	8	9	Proportional Parts								
											1	2	3	4	5	6	7	8	9
55	7404	7412	7419	7427	7435	7443	7451	7459	7466	7474	1	2	2	3	4	5	5	6	7
56	7482	7490	7497	7505	7513	7520	7528	7536	7543	7551	1	2	2	3	4	5	5	6	7
57	7559	7566	7574	7582	7589	7597	7604	7612	7619	7627	1	2	2	3	4	5	5	6	7
58	7634	7642	7649	7657	7664	7672	7679	7686	7694	7701	1	1	2	3	4	4	5	6	7
59	7709	7716	7723	7731	7738	7745	7752	7760	7767	7774	1	1	2	3	4	4	5	6	7
60	7782	7789	7796	7803	7810	7818	7825	7832	7839	7846	1	1	2	3	4	4	5	6	6
61	7853	7860	7868	7875	7882	7889	7896	7903	7910	7917	1	1	2	3	4	4	5	6	6
62	7924	7931	7938	7945	7952	7959	7966	7973	7980	7987	1	1	2	3	3	4	5	6	6
63	7993	8000	8007	8014	8021	8028	8035	8041	8048	8055	1	1	2	3	3	4	5	5	6
64	8062	8069	8075	8082	8089	8096	8102	8109	8116	8122	1	1	2	3	3	4	5	5	6
65	8129	8136	8142	8149	8156	8162	8169	8176	8182	8189	1	1	2	3	3	4	5	5	6
66	8195	8202	8209	8215	8222	8228	8235	8241	8248	8254	1	1	2	3	3	4	5	5	6
67	8261	8267	8274	8280	8287	8293	8299	8306	8312	8319	1	1	2	3	3	4	5	5	6
68	8325	8331	8338	8344	8351	8357	8363	8370	8376	8382	1	1	2	3	3	4	4	5	6
69	8388	8395	8401	8407	8414	8420	8426	8432	8439	8445	1	1	2	2	3	4	4	5	6
70	8451	8457	8463	8470	8476	8482	8488	8494	8500	8506	1	1	2	2	3	4	4	5	6
71	8513	8519	8525	8531	8537	8543	8549	8555	8561	8567	1	1	2	2	3	4	4	5	5
72	8573	8579	8585	8591	8597	8603	8609	8615	8621	8627	1	1	2	2	3	4	4	5	5
73	8633	8639	8645	8651	8657	8663	8669	8675	8681	8686	1	1	2	2	3	4	4	5	5
74	8692	8698	8704	8710	8716	8722	8727	8733	8739	8745	1	1	2	2	3	4	4	5	5
75	8751	8756	8762	8768	8774	8779	8785	8791	8797	8802	1	1	2	2	3	3	4	5	5
76	8808	8814	8820	8825	8831	8837	8842	8848	8854	8859	1	1	2	2	3	3	4	5	5
77	8865	8871	8876	8882	8887	8893	8899	8904	8910	8915	1	1	2	2	3	3	4	4	5
78	8921	8927	8932	8938	8943	8949	8954	8960	8965	8971	1	1	2	2	3	3	4	4	5
79	8976	8982	8987	8993	8998	9004	9009	9015	9020	9025	1	1	2	2	3	3	4	4	5
80	9031	9036	9042	9047	9053	9058	9063	9069	9074	9079	1	1	2	2	3	3	4	4	5
81	9085	9090	9096	9101	9106	9112	9117	9122	9128	9133	1	1	2	2	3	3	4	4	5
82	9138	9143	9149	9154	9159	9165	9170	9175	9180	9186	1	1	2	2	3	3	4	4	5
83	9191	9196	9201	9206	9212	9217	9222	9227	9232	9238	1	1	2	2	3	3	4	4	5
84	9243	9248	9253	9258	9263	9269	9274	9279	9284	9289	1	1	2	2	3	3	4	4	5
85	9294	9299	9304	9309	9315	9320	9325	9330	9335	9340	1	1	2	2	3	3	4	4	5
86	9345	9350	9355	9360	9365	9370	9375	9380	9385	9390	1	1	2	2	3	3	4	4	5
87	9395	9400	9405	9410	9415	9420	9425	9430	9435	9440	0	1	1	2	2	3	3	4	4
88	9445	9450	9455	9460	9465	9469	9474	9479	9484	9489	0	1	1	2	2	3	3	4	4
89	9494	9499	9504	9509	9513	9518	9523	9528	9533	9538	0	1	1	2	2	3	3	4	4
90	9542	9547	9552	9557	9562	9566	9571	9576	9581	9586	0	1	1	2	2	3	3	4	4
91	9590	9595	9600	9605	9609	9614	9619	9624	9628	9633	0	1	1	2	2	3	3	4	4
92	9638	9643	9647	9652	9657	9661	9666	9671	9675	9680	0	1	1	2	2	3	3	4	4
93	9685	9689	9694	9699	9703	9708	9713	9717	9722	9727	0	1	1	2	2	3	3	4	4
94	9731	9736	9741	9745	9750	9754	9759	9763	9768	9773	0	1	1	2	2	3	3	4	4
95	9777	9782	9786	9791	9795	9800	9805	9809	9814	9818	0	1	1	2	2	3	3	4	4
96	9823	9827	9832	9836	9841	9845	9850	9854	9859	9863	0	1	1	2	2	3	3	4	4
97	9868	9872	9877	9881	9886	9890	9894	9899	9903	9908	0	1	1	2	2	3	3	4	4
98	9912	9917	9921	9926	9930	9934	9939	9943	9948	9952	0	1	1	2	2	3	3	4	4
99	9956	9961	9965	9969	9974	9978	9983	9987	9991	9996	0	1	1	2	2	3	3	3	4

Index

A

Abelson, discovery of neptunium, 753
Absolute zero, 136
Acetic acid, 560
  ionic equilibrium of, 297
  ionization constant of, 298
  preparation of from wood, 542
Acetone, 542
Acheson, E. G., 320
  biographical sketch and portrait of, 582
  manufacture of graphite by, 542
Acid(s), acetic, 560
  cyanic, 561
  definition of, 161, 236
  degree of ionization of, 161
  fatty, 560
  fluosilicic, 329
  formic, 560
  fulminic, 561
  hydrocyanic, 561
  hypothetical, definition of, 328
  isocyanic, 561
  isothiocyanic, 562
  malonic, 561
  meta, 265
  molecular, 236
  muriatic, 161
  ortho, 265
  oxalic, 560
  silicic, 327
    table of, 328
  strength of, 161
  thiocyanic, 562
Acidimetry, 307
Actinium, discovery of, 753
  discussion of, 660
  physical properties, table of, 658
Activity, of electrolytic solutions, 242
Activity coefficient. (*See* Coefficient, activity)
Activity series, table of, 101
Addition reactions, of hydrocarbons, 524
Adhesive tape, 737
Adsorption, definition of, 278

Aerosols, agglomerating, 346
  precipitation of, 351–352
  preparation of, 351
Agent, oxidizing, 64
  reducing, 64
Air, 498
  liquid, 465
Alabaster, 614
  oriental, 616
Alchemy, 4
Alclad, 269
Alclor process, 265
Alkali, definition of, 105
Alkali metals, general, 587
  physical properties, table of, 588
Alkalimetry, 307
Alkaline earth metals, general, 605
  physical properties, table of, 606
Allegheny metal, 671
Allison, 19, 515
Allotropy, definition of, 190
  and polymorphism, 190
Alloys, 230
  heterogeneous, 635
  homogeneous, 634
  of aluminum, 269
  pyrophoric, 659
  solid solutions, 634
  supercooled liquids, 634
Alpha particle, definition of, 46
Alpha rays, nature of, 754
Aluminic acid, *meta,* 265
  ortho, 265
Aluminon, 271
Aluminothermy, definition of, 259
  use of, 259
Aluminum, 251*ff.*
  alloys, 269
  analytical tests for, 270
  bronze, 270
  chemical properties of, 257
  combination reactions of, 257
  displacement reactions of, 258
  electrode potential of, 252

G

Gadolin, discovery of yttrium, 658

Gadolinite, 658, 659

Gahn, isolation of manganese, 680

Galena, 386, 644

Gallium, 581

Gamma rays, nature of, 754

Gangue, 630

Garden, chemical flower-, 213

Garnierite, 704

Gas, degenerate, 776

  laws, 134

    deviation from, 140

    general, 137

    perfect, 134

Gases, critical pressure of, 147

  critical temperature of, 147

  density of, 146–147

  energy relationships of, 178–179

  glowing of in electrical discharge tube, 47–48

  in refrigeration, 181

  Joule-Thompson effect of, 179

  liquefaction of, 178

    machine for, 179–180

  rate of diffusion of, 149

  solubility of, 148

  volcanic, 387

Gay-Lussac, J. L., 570

    gas law of, 137

    law of combining volumes of, 143–144

    names iodine, 527

Geber, 487, 598

Gelatin, 349

General gas law. (*See* Gas, laws, general)

Generator, gas, Kipp, 391

    Starkey, 392

German silver, 706

Germanite, 636

Germanium, 635*ff.*

  acids of, 637

  chemical properties of, 637

  general, 635

  occurrence of, 636

  oxides, 637

  physical properties, table of, 636

  preparation of, 637

  sulfides, 637

Gibbsite, 253

Glass, 330*ff.*

  Bohemian, 330

Glass—(*Continued*)

  borosilicate, 331

  colored, 332

  cut, 331

  etching of, 330

  flint, 331

  manufacture of, 330

  phosphorus, 331

  potash-lead, 331

  Pyrex, 331

  soda-lime, 330

Glucinium, 607

Goiter, simple, 532

    map of incidence of, 532

Gold, analytical tests for, 729

  chlorides, 728

  compounds, 728

    complex, 729

  general, 713

  leaf, 728

  mosaic, 642

  occurrence of, 725

  oxides, 728

  physical properties, table of, 713

  properties of, 728

  recovery of, 726

  uses of, 728

Goldschmidt process, 259

Goldstein, 41

Graham, Thomas, 337

Graham's law, 148

  and hydrogen diffusion, 440

Gram, definition of, 30

Gram-atomic weight, definition of, 115

Gram-ion, definition of, 236

Gram-molecular volume, definition of, 141

  value of, 141

Gram-molecular weight, definition of, 118

Gram-molecule, definition of, 118

Graphite, occurrence of, 541

  physical properties of, 539

  preparation of, 542

  structure of, 539

Gravitational attraction, definition of, 131

  law of, 131

  vs. escaping tendency, 131–132

Greenockite, 739

Gregor, discovery of titanium, 663

Guldberg and Waage, law of, 280

Gunpowder, black, 598

Gypsum, 366, 386, 610, 614

Problems and Questions

Exercises for Chapter 1

1. What are the two great fields of knowledge?
2. How does a physical science differ from a biological science?
3. Which of the following sciences are: (a) biological; (b) physical?

astronomy	hygiene	chemistry	medicine
entomology	geology	botany	surgery
physiology	meteorology	parasitology	physics

4. What are the principal concerns of chemistry?
5. What change always accompanies a change in the nature of matter, and what use is made of a knowledge of this other change?
6. What is: (a) a law; (b) a hypothesis; (c) a theory?
7. From the list of sciences given in problem 3, select those which you think are exact sciences, and be prepared to give reasons for your answers.
8. What type of scientist would be able to furnish the best information concerning:

> (a) the magnetic behavior of a metal;
> (b) the production of alcohol from corn;
> (c) the identification of a flower;
> (d) the production of heat from a piece of coal;
> (e) the identification of a rock;
> (f) the identification of the materials composing the rock.

Exercises for Chapter 2

1. What are some of the outstanding properties of: water, iron, salt, alcohol, lead, copper, granite, sulfur?
2. Given a block of iron, which is silvery-gray, weighs 500 g., has a density of 7.86 g. per cc., is in the shape of a cylinder 2 cm. thick, dissolves in hydrochloric acid, has a temperature of 25° C., and has a melting point of 1535° C.: which of these attributes of the iron are conditions and which are properties?
3. Which of the properties identified in problem 2 are physical and which are chemical?
4. Which of the following varieties of matter are materials and which are substances?

rock salt (natural)	wood	candy
granite	bluestone	sugar (table)
iron	tin	flour
copper	cornstalks	pepper

5. How do ordinary mixtures and solutions differ?

6. How could a mixture of salt and sawdust be separated so that the salt could be used on the table?

7. Of the materials listed in problem 4, which are: (a) elements; (b) compounds; (c) mixtures?

8. Which of the following are chemical changes and which are physical?

> (a) the changing of cider into vinegar;
> (b) the burning of gasoline;
> (c) the melting of paraffin;
> (d) the stretching of rubber;
> (e) the souring of milk;
> (f) the grinding of corn.

9. Why is it that, although aluminum is more abundant in the earth's crust than is iron, the latter was used for hundreds of years before the former came into general use?

10. Define: (a) atom; (b) molecule; (c) ion.

Exercises for Chapter 3

1. What are the usual steps involved in accurately measuring a given quantity?

2. Name and describe some of the measuring devices used in the chemical laboratory.

3. What instrument would one use if he wished to measure very carefully 8.6 ml. of a liquid into a flask?

4. Name the factors which influence the sensitivity of a balance.

5. Why should a student know the load limits of all balances provided in his laboratory?

6. How many cubic centimeters are there in: (a) a cubic inch; (b) a cubic foot?

7. The speed of light is 186,000 mi. per sec. Express this quantity as centimeters per second, employing powers of 10.

8. Prove the given relationship for the kilometer and the mile.

9. How many liters of water could be stored in a tank which is 1 yd. long by 2 ft. wide by 8 in. deep?

10. Would it be cheaper to buy potatoes at $.10 per lb. or at $.24 per kg.?

11. In Mexico, gasoline formerly sold for about $.05 per l. At this rate, how much did it cost per gal.?

12. The normal temperature of the body is 98.6° F. What is its normal temperature on the Centigrade scale?

13. At sea level, the boiling point of ethyl alcohol is 78.5° C. What is its boiling point on the Fahrenheit scale?

14. In a certain calorimeter, 2.2 g. of an unknown substance was burned. The calorimeter contained 300 g. of water which increased in temperature from 21.5° to 36.8° C. Neglecting the heat absorbed by the calorimeter, calculate the number of calories furnished by the combustion of each gram of the sample.

15. In an aluminum calorimeter which weighed 1000 g. was burned 2 g. of coal. The mass of the water in the calorimeter was 2000 g., and its initial temperature was 20° C. The final temperature of the water was 25° C. What was the heat of combustion in calories per gram of the coal? (Specific heat of aluminum = 0.214 cal. per g.)

16. The barometer in a certain classroom records a pressure of 585 mm. of mercury. What is the pressure there in kilograms per square centimeter? (The density of mercury is 13.6 g. per cc.)

17. How should the sum of 3.678, 4.531, 0.368, and 30.5 be expressed?

18. If the last figure in each of the quantities 46.083 and 5.068 is doubtful, how should their product be expressed?

19. What is the density of a substance, 650 ml. of which has a mass of 1018.5 g.?

20. What is meant by a derived unit?

Exercises for Chapter 4

1. What is the atomic number of an atom? What two bits of information about an atom does it yield?

2. If all atoms are made of protons and electrons, how do you account for the fact that there are many different kinds of atoms?

3. What are isotopes? Why do the isotopes of a given element behave alike chemically?

4. In view of the existence of isotopic atoms, how would you define an element in terms of its atomic constitution?

5. Name and characterize the four small particles associated with the structure of the atom.

6. Why do the protons and electrons within the atomic nucleus assume special groupings?

7. What is a quantum?

8. State the formulas used for calculating the maximum number of electrons which may occupy: (a) a given main quantum level; (b) a sub-quantum level.

9. Why are the atomic weights of many elements fractions?

10. Complete the following table according to the example given:

Atom	Symbol	At. Wt.	At. No.	Structure in Terms of p's and e's	Complete Structure
Lithium.....................	Li	6.94	3	$(7p, 4\epsilon)3\epsilon$	$(1\alpha, 2n, 1p)2\epsilon, 1\epsilon$
Carbon					
Oxygen....................					
Fluorine...................					
Aluminum.................					
Phosphorus................					
Sulfur.....................					

Exercises for Chapter 5

1. Read the history of the discovery of the inert gases and make an outline of the important steps involved.

2. Explain why most elements undergo chemical reactions.

3. What are the means employed by atoms to bring about chemical changes?

4. What is valence?

5. What types of valence result from the various types of electronic changes that an atom may undergo?

6. Using the Lewis system of notation, represent the changes which might be expected when: (a) lithium reacts with bromine; (b) carbon reacts with hydrogen; (c) phosphorus reacts with oxygen.

7. Name the compounds prepared in problem 6.

8. Define oxidation and reduction in terms of: (a) electrons; (b) valence.

9. How does the oxidation number of an element which develops electrovalences differ from that of an element which develops covalences?

10. Why may some elements have several different oxidation numbers while others have only one, or even none?

11. Make a list of the oxidation numbers of each element in the following compounds: Na_2SO_4, K_3PO_4, $KClO_4$, $HClO_3$, K_2CrO_4, and HNO_3.

12. Distinguish between (a) polar and nonpolar compounds, and (b) ionic and covalent compounds.

13. What is the coördination number of an element?

14. What are the types of chemical reactions?

15. Into how many types of reactions may elements enter?

16. What information concerning a chemical reaction may a chemist want to know? Why?

17. How much of this information does a simple chemical equation supply, and how may more of this information be written into an equation?

18. Write simple chemical equations for the action of: (a) sodium and oxygen; (b) aluminum and chlorine; (c) hydrogen and chlorine; (d) magnesium and oxygen.

Exercises for Chapter 6

1. By consulting Table 3, select the elements which should have chemical properties similar to those of: (a) nitrogen; (b) zinc.

2. What would you expect the electronic structures of the following real or imaginary ions to be: Ca^{+2}, Cr^{+3}, Cr^{+6}, Cl^{+7}, Cl^{-1}, V^{+5}?

3. Write the formulas for the oxides of the following elements in their highest valences: Cl, Cr, S, P, C.

4. Write the formulas for the chlorides of the following elements in their highest valence: Mg, As, Ti, Sn, Al.

5. State the periodic law, and explain just what it means.

6. What are the transition elements, and what accounts for their existence?

7. How many electrons could the fifth main energy level contain as a maximum, and what is the maximum number of electrons which the 5_4 sub-level might contain?

8. How many electrons might the sixth main level contain as a maximum, and how would these be distributed among the sub-levels?

9. What are the uses of the periodic chart?

10. Discuss the weaknesses of the periodic classifications of the elements.

11. Assuming that the ions exist in their maximum valence state, how do the radii of the ions of a given period vary as one passes from left to right across a given period of the table?

12. How do the radii of the ions of a given column vary as one passes down the column?
13. Name the types of elements found in the periodic chart, and tell where each type is located in the chart.
14. What is meant by the "ionic potential"? How does this differ from the "ionizing potential"?

Exercises for Chapter 7

1. What are the principal physical properties of sodium?
2. Which contains a greater percentage of sodium and by how much: sodium chloride or sodium hydroxide?
3. If a fused mixture of sodium chloride and zinc chloride were electrolyzed, which element would be liberated first at the cathode? Why?
4. What reason could you advance for cesium having a higher electrode potential than sodium?
5. What explanation might be offered for the fact that metallic sodium cannot be obtained successfully by the reduction of the oxide with carbon?
6. What explanation might be offered for the fact that elementary sodium was not discovered until after the discovery of electricity?
7. How is sodium used in sodium vapor lights, and why are these lights preferred to others for highway lighting?
8. How many grams of sodium are theoretically obtainable from 10 kg. of salt?
9. Write equations for the combination reactions of sodium with: (a) bromine; (b) sulfur; (c) fluorine; (d) phosphorus; (e) selenium. Name the compounds formed.
10. What is: (a) an anhydride; (b) a basic anhydride?
11. Assuming that in each case an insoluble hydroxide is formed, write metathetical equations for the reaction of a solution of sodium hydroxide with solutions of each of the following: (a) magnesium chloride; (b) aluminum chloride; (c) stannous chloride ($SnCl_2$); (d) zinc sulfate ($ZnSO_4$); (e) silver nitrate ($AgNO_3$).
12. Calculate the weight of sodium which could be obtained theoretically from 10 g. of $Na[Sb(OH)_6]$ and from 10 g. of $NaAl(SiO_3)_2$.
13. Write equations for the following metatheses: (a) sodium carbonate and calcium chloride ($CaCl_2$); (b) sodium carbonate and magnesium sulfate ($MgSO_4$); (c) sodium carbonate and cupric nitrate ($Cu(NO_3)_2$); (d) sodium chloride and silver nitrate ($AgNO_3$); (e) sodium chloride and lead nitrate ($Pb(NO_3)_2$); (f) sodium phosphate and calcium nitrate ($Ca(NO_3)_2$); (g) sodium hydroxide and hydrochloric acid (HCl); (h) sodium hydroxide and sulfuric acid (H_2SO_4).

Exercises for Chapter 8

1. Define: (a) stoichiometry; (b) gram-atomic weight; (c) mole; (d) gram-equivalent weight.
2. State: (a) the law of the conservation of mass; (b) the law of the conservation of energy. What justification is there for integrating these two laws into a single law?
3. Why are relative atomic weights more commonly used than absolute atomic weights? What is the standard of comparison for relative atomic weights?

4. State: (a) the law of definite proportions; (b) the law of multiple proportions. What is the basis for the truth of these laws?

5. Analysis reveals that a certain compound contains 92.24 per cent carbon with the remainder of the compound being made up of hydrogen. If the molecular weight of this compound is found to be 78.05, what is its formula?

6. A 1-g. sample of an oxide of copper, when heated in a stream of hydrogen, is found to yield 0.2262 g. of water. If the molecular weight of the oxide is 79.57, what is the formula of the compound?

7. What weight of sodium would be required to prepare 12 g. of sodium chloride by reaction with chlorine?

8. What weight of hydrogen could be prepared by electrolysis in aqueous solution of the sodium chloride prepared in problem 7?

9. What weight of iron could be displaced from a solution of iron chloride ($FeCl_2$) by 3 g. of finely divided zinc?

10. By the factor method calculate the quantity of sodium phosphate (Na_3PO_4) which can be made from 15 g. of salt if all of the sodium is converted to the new compound.

11. How much pure silver could be obtained theoretically from 20 g. of silver chloride?

12. Upon analysis, an oxide of sulfur reveals that it contains 50 per cent S and 50 per cent O. What is the equivalent weight of the sulfur in this compound?

13. Phosphorus forms two common oxides, one of which contains 56.35 per cent phosphorus, the other of which contains 43.68 per cent phosphorus. What is the equivalent weight of phosphorus in each compound? What is the ratio of these equivalent weights, and what law is illustrated?

14. Calculate the simplest formula for each of the oxides mentioned in problem 13.

15. Calculate the mass in grams of one atom of: (a) nitrogen; (b) chromium; (c) iodine.

16. A certain metal has a specific heat of 0.224 cal./g. One gram of the metal will combine with 0.888 g. of oxygen. What is the valence of this element in this compound, and what is its atomic weight?

17. A current of 5 amp. acting for 8 min. 25 sec. will deposit 3.04 g. of a certain metal from a solution of one of its compounds. If the valence of this metal is 2, what is its atomic weight?

18. One equivalent weight of Na_2S will react by metathesis with how many gram-molecular weights of each of the following compounds: (a) $AgNO_3$; (b) $CuCl_2$; (c) $Bi(NO_3)_3$; (d) $ZnSO_4$; (e) $SbCl_3$?

19. Calculate the equivalent weight as an oxidizing agent of the first compound in each of the following equations:

$$\text{(a) } K_2CrO_4 + 3FeCl_2 + 8HCl \rightarrow 2KCl + CrCl_3 + 3FeCl_3 + 4H_2O$$
$$\text{(b) } K_2Cr_2O_7 + 6FeCl_2 + 14HCl \rightarrow 2KCl + 2CrCl_3 + 6FeCl_3 + 7H_2O$$

20. How many milliequivalents of sodium chloride are contained in 5.85 g. of the substance? How many milliequivalents of sodium hydroxide may be produced from this quantity of salt? What will be the weight of the lye produced?

21. Complete and balance the following metathetical equations:

(a) $Na_2S + CuCl_2 \rightarrow$

(b) $H_2S + Bi(NO_3)_3 \rightarrow$

(c) $Ca(OH)_2 + Na_2CO_3 \rightarrow$

(d) $Ca(OH)_2 + HNO_3 \rightarrow$

(e) $ZnS + H_2SO_4 \rightarrow$

(f) $NaOH + H_2SO_4 \rightarrow$

(g) $K_2CO_3 + CaCl_2 \rightarrow$

(h) $CaCO_3 + HCl \rightarrow$

(i) $KOH + H_3PO_4 \rightarrow$

(j) $FeS + HCl \rightarrow$

(k) $NH_4NO_3 + NaOH \rightarrow$

(l) $NaCl + H_2SO_4 \rightarrow$

Exercises for Chapter 9

1. Name the forces at work among the molecules of a gas, give evidence in support of the existence of each, and show how they oppose each other.
2. State the principal assumptions of the kinetic molecular theory, and give evidence in support of each.
3. What is meant by the term "perfect gas"?
4. What would be the volume at standard conditions of the volumes of gas mentioned below if measured under the conditions stated?

(a)	30 ml.	0° C.	780 mm.
(b)	380 ml.	25° C.	580 mm.
(c)	550 ml.	20° C.	585 mm.
(d)	66 ml.	15° C.	720 mm.

5. What would be the volume at 740 mm. and 24° C. of the volumes of gas mentioned below if measured under the conditions stated?

(a)	400 ml.	28° C.	770 mm.
(b)	350 ml.	20° C.	730 mm.
(c)	210 ml.	26° C.	720 mm.
(d)	560 ml.	20° C.	760 mm.

6. Fifty ml. of hydrogen gas is collected over water at 24° C. in a laboratory where the barometric pressure is 585 mm. What weight of sodium would be required to produce this gas by action on water?
7. What would be the volume of hydrogen produced by the action of 10 g. of zinc on a solution of hydrogen chloride in a laboratory where the temperature is 20° C. and the pressure is 700 mm.?
8. What volume of nitrogen gas at 755 mm. and 30° C. would be required to prepare 1 kg. of ammonia by the following reaction, assuming 100 per cent conversion: $N_2 + 3H_2 \rightarrow 2NH_3$.
9. What weight of water could be prepared from 400 l. of hydrogen at a pressure of two atmospheres and a temperature of 227° C.?
10. A sample of a certain substance weighing 0.132 g. when volatilized displaces from a Victor Meyer apparatus 40.3 ml. of air at a temperature of 25° C. The gas is caught over water and the barometric reading is 746.5 mm. What is the approximate molecular weight of the substance?

11. A certain glass bulb has a volume of 568 ml. and when empty weighs 250.363 g. When filled with a certain substance in the gaseous form at room conditions, it weighs 250.489 g. The temperature of the room is 20° C. and the barometric pressure is 710 mm. What is the approximate molecular weight of the substance?

12. What relative volumes of gases are involved in each of the following reactions? Are these relationships correct to the third or fourth decimal place? Give reasons for your answers.

$$C_{(s)} + H_2O_{(g)} \rightarrow CO_{(g)} + H_{2(g)}$$
$$N_2 + O_2 \rightarrow 2NO_{(g)}$$
$$Cl_2 + CO_{(g)} \rightarrow COCl_{2(g)}$$
$$CO + 2H_2 \overset{\Delta}{\rightarrow} CH_3OH_{(g)}$$

13. What volume of chlorine gas at 25° C. and 765 mm. will be required to react with 8.5 l. of hydrogen gas under the same conditions?

14. What volume of sulfur dioxide gas at 40° C. and 760 mm. can be prepared by direct union of the elements from 3.35 l. of oxygen at the same conditions?

15. Which of the following gases are heavier than air and which lighter: C_3H_8, C_2H_2, CO, PH_3, Cl_2, NO, N_2, CH_4, O_3, CO_2?

16. What volume will 3 g. of oxygen occupy at S.T.P.?

17. From the solubility of oxygen stated in section 21, calculate the weight of oxygen dissolved in an aquarium full of water if the aquarium is 1 m. long, 40 cm. deep, and 30 cm. wide. The temperature of the water is 20° C. and the pressure of the oxygen gas above the water is 190 mm.

18. Ammonia gas (NH_3) and hydrogen chloride gas are released at the same time at opposite ends of an evacuated glass tube 2 m. long. A white band will form on the inside of the tube at the point where the two gases meet. From purely theoretical considerations, how far should this band be from the end of the tube at which the hydrogen chloride was released?

19. Explain why it is that gases, though they vary widely in mass and chemical properties, behave so similarly physically.

Exercises for Chapter 10

1. Calculate the true value of the G.M.V. of chlorine and the percentage of deviation of this value from the theoretical value.

2. Explain why gases deviate from Avogadro's law.

3. If one should assume that chlorine does not react with water, what would be the molar concentration of chlorine in 1 l. of chlorine water at 0° C.?

4. What volume would 5 g. of chlorine at S.T.P. occupy?

5. Given 100 g. of pure hydrogen chloride, by which of the two laboratory methods for the production of chlorine could you obtain the most chlorine? What weight of chlorine would be obtained by this method?

6. Write equations for the union of chlorine with: (a) potassium; (b) aluminum; (c) iron; (d) silicon; (e) strontium.

7. What quantity of heat should be liberated by the union of 1 kg. of chlorine with hydrogen? How much water would this amount of heat raise from the freezing point to the boiling point?

8. How many moles of hydrogen chloride are contained in 1 l. of the constant boiling mixture at a pressure of 760 mm.?

9. What weight of hydrogen chloride could be prepared from 50 g. of chlorine? What volume of water at $0°$ C. would be required to dissolve this weight of hydrogen chloride at S.T.P.?

10. A certain solution of hydrogen chloride has a density of 1.11 g./ml. and contains 22.09 per cent of the reagent. What weight of the reagent is contained in 5 l. of the solution, and how many moles of the reagent are there per liter of solution?

11. Write equations for the reaction of hydrochloric acid with:

(a) Na_2CO_3	(f) CaO	(k) $Ga(OH)_3$	(p) Na
(b) $MgCO_3$	(g) Al_2O_3	(l) KOH	(q) Mg
(c) $KHCO_3$	(h) SnO	(m) $Mg(OH)_2$	(r) Cu
(d) $BaCO_3$	(i) Na_2O	(n) $AgOH$	(s) Cd
(e) $ZnCO_3$	(j) SnO_2	(o) $Ba(OH)_2$	(t) Fe

12. Write equations for the reaction of sulfuric acid (H_2SO_4) with each of the reagents of problem 11.

13. Balance the following equations by employing the change-of-oxidation-number method.

(a) $K_2CrO_4 + FeSO_4 + H_2SO_4 \rightarrow K_2SO_4 + Cr_2(SO_4)_3 + Fe_2(SO_4)_3 + H_2O$

(b) $KMnO_4 + FeCl_2 + HCl \rightarrow KCl + MnCl_2 + FeCl_3 + H_2O$

(c) $K_2Cr_2O_7 + TiSO_4 + H_2SO_4 \rightarrow K_2SO_4 + Cr_2(SO_4)_3 + Ti(SO_4)_2 + H_2O$

(d) $KMnO_4 + H_2C_2O_4 + H_2SO_4 \rightarrow K_2SO_4 + MnSO_4 + CO_2 + H_2O$

(e) $HNO_3 + Cu \rightarrow Cu(NO_3)_2 + NO + H_2O$

(f) $HNO_3 + C \rightarrow CO_2 + NO_2 + H_2O$

(g) $HNO_3 + H_3PO_3 \rightarrow H_3PO_4 + NO_2 + H_2O$

(h) $HNO_3 + H_2S \rightarrow \underline{S} + NO + H_2O$

(i) $K_2CrO_4 + H_2S + HCl \rightarrow \underline{S} + KCl + CrCl_3 + H_2O$

(j) $FeCl_3 + SnCl_2 \rightarrow FeCl_2 + SnCl_4$

Exercises for Chapter 11

1. Define: (a) viscosity; (b) fluidity; (c) surface tension; (d) refractive index.

2. What are the characteristics of a state of equilibrium? Give examples of systems in equilibrium.

3. Water is often cooled in desert regions by keeping it in tightly woven canvas bags. Explain how water so kept is cooled.

4. Define: (a) vapor pressure; (b) boiling point.

5. Explain why one must apply Dalton's law to obtain the pressure of a gas collected over water.

6. Offer an explanation of the heat of vaporization of water being so much higher than its heat of fusion.
7. How much water at 100° C. could be converted into steam at the same temperature by the quantity of heat required to raise the temperature of 500 g. of water from 20° C. to 100° C.?
8. How much steam at 100° C. would have to be mixed with 100 g. of ice at 0° C. to convert the mixture to water at 25° C.?
9. What is an associated liquid, and why is it associated?
10. Define: (a) critical temperature; (b) critical pressure.
11. What factors must be taken into consideration when it is desired to liquefy a gas?
12. Why are gases of low molecular weight usually difficult to liquefy?
13. What is the Joule-Thompson effect, and how is it explained?
14. What characteristics must a gas have to make it a satisfactory refrigerant?
15. Explain how an absorbing agent may take the place of a compressor in a refrigerating system.
16. List the characteristic properties of the states of matter and state how the existing differences are accounted for by the kinetic-molecular theory.
17. Define: (a) space lattice; (b) unit cell; (c) melting point; (d) heat of fusion.
18. How do true solids and amorphous substances differ, and why may true solids be made to exist for a time in an amorphous condition?
19. How does the cubic system of crystals differ from: (a) the rhombic system; (b) the triclinic system?
20. What are the units of which crystals may be built?
21. Calculate the total number of ions contained in a cube of salt 1 cm. on an edge, assuming that there is only one whole ion to a unit cell (this is true because the ions at the corners of a unit cell are shared with other unit cells).
22. Define the terms: (a) metastable; (b) polymorphic; (c) isomorphic; (d) allotropic; (e) enantiotropic.
23. Wet clothing hung out to dry may freeze immediately, nevertheless it will dry without first thawing. Explain.
24. How may it be shown that isomorphic substances which form a mixed crystal have not reacted to form a new substance which is responsible for the homogeneous crystals?

Exercises for Chapter 12

1. What is a solution, and why is a knowledge of the properties of solutions essential to the chemist?
2. What is the characteristic which distinguishes solutions from other mixtures?
3. Define: (a) unsaturated; (b) saturated; (c) supersaturated solutions.
4. How might one easily determine whether a given solution of sodium sulfate was saturated, unsaturated, or supersaturated?
5. List the factors which have an effect upon solubility, and explain why they have the effect they do.

6. State Henry's law, and explain its operation.
7. How are the solubilities of solids, liquids, and gases usually expressed?
8. What is a *standard* solution?
9. What are the types of standard solutions which the chemist most commonly employs?
10. What is a normal solution, and what is the advantage of employing solutions whose concentrations are so expressed?
11. The density of a 12 per cent aqueous solution of silver nitrate ($AgNO_3$) at 20° C. is 1.108 g./ml. What weight of the salt should be required to prepare 3 l. of such a solution?
12. What is the percentage strength of a solution of sodium chloride which is prepared by mixing 17.5 g. of salt with 232.5 g. of water?
13. What is the percentage strength of a lithium bromide (LiBr) solution which contains 112.5 g. of the solute in 512.5 g. of water? If the solution so prepared occupies a volume of 546.7 ml., what is its density?
14. What weight of zinc bromide ($ZnBr_2$) should be required to make 800 g. of a 4 per cent solution of that salt?
15. Calculate the number of grams of solute required to make each of the following standard solutions:

(a) 200 ml. of 3 N Na_2SO_4
(b) 1.8 l. of 2 N $MgCl_2.6H_2O$
(c) 1500 ml. of 1.2 N $Al_2(SO_4)_3.18H_2O$
(d) 750 ml. of 0.5 N NaBr

(e) 2.5 l. of 6 N NaOH
(f) 3 l. of 16 N H_2SO_4
(g) 1000 ml. of 0.1 N Na_3PO_4
(h) 4 l. of $N/2$ $MgSO_4.7H_2O$

16. Calculate the molarity of each of the solutions mentioned in the preceding problem.
17. What volume of 3 N solution could be prepared from each of the following quantities of solute:

(a) 117 g. of NaCl
(b) 1333.2 g. of $Al_2(SO_4)_3.18H_2O$

(c) 1320 g. of KI
(d) 50 g. of $Zn(C_2H_3O_2)_2.2H_2O$

18. Given a solution of hydrogen chloride whose density at 20° C. is 1.1345 g./ml., and which contains 26.56 per cent of the solute, what volume of this solution should be required to prepare 1 l. of 2 N hydrochloric acid? What will be the molarity of the prepared solution?
19. What is the molarity of a solution of hydrogen sulfate whose density is 1.46 g./ml. at 20° C. and which contains 56 per cent of the solute?
20. What weight of solute is contained in each of the following:

(a) 3 l. of 5 M $C_{12}H_{22}O_{11}$
(b) 50 ml. of 6 M HNO_3
(c) 400 ml. of 0.2 M $Na_2S_2O_3$

(d) 10 l. of 0.5 M KOH
(e) 5 ml. of 3 M Na_2CO_3
(f) 7 l. of 1.75 M KNO_3

21. A certain solution is prepared by dissolving 215 g. of $Fe(NO_3)_3$ in 285 g. of water. The volume of the solution so prepared is 354.6 ml. What is: (a) the percentage strength of this solution; (b) its normality; (c) its molarity?

22. What is the mole per cent standard of a solution prepared by dissolving 100 g. of NaCl in 918 ml. of water?

23. A given solute is five times more soluble in ether than in water. A solution of 10 g. of the solute in 100 ml. of water is shaken with 3 ml. of ether. What weight of solute is left in the water?

24. A solution of 12 g. of a given solute in 200 ml. of water is shaken with two separate 20-ml. portions of a solvent in which the solute is four times as soluble. What weight of solute is removed from the original solution by the two extractions?

25. Define: (a) deliquescence; (b) drying agent; (c) dehydrating agent; (d) azeotropic mixture.

26. What effect does the addition of a solute have upon the escaping tendency of a solvent? Why?

27. How does fractional distillation differ from ordinary distillation?

28. In what instances does fractional distillation fail in its purpose?

29. Explain the operation of a fractionating tower or column.

30. State Raoult's law.

31. What is the relationship between vapor pressure depression and boiling point elevation?

32. Define: (a) semipermeable membrane; (b) osmosis; (c) osmotic pressure.

33. What is the molal freezing point constant of a liquid?

34. Explain how osmotic pressure determinations might be employed to determine the molecular weight of a water-soluble solid.

35. Twelve grams of a certain solid when dissolved in 1200 g. of water yields a solution whose freezing point is $-0.2°$ C. What is the molecular weight of this solid?

36. Ten grams of alcohol (C_2H_5OH) is dissolved in 130 g. of water. At what temperature should the solution freeze?

37. When dissolved in 80 g. of acetic acid, 5 g. of an organic substance raises the boiling point of the latter $0.97°$ C. What is the molecular weight of the organic substance?

Exercises for Chapter 13

1. What are the physical properties of magnesium?

2. Where and how does magnesium occur, and how is it refined?

3. Prepare a diagram illustrating the assumed constitution of the magnesium nucleus and the number and distribution of its extranuclear electrons. From this diagram, would you expect magnesium to be active or inactive chemically, and to what degree? Would you expect it to be easily prepared in the free state?

4. Would you expect soapstone to be a good source of magnesium metal? Give reasons for your answer.

5. What quantity of magnesium could be prepared theoretically from 10 kg. of dolomite which is 95 per cent pure?

6. Ten grams of magnesium is burned in a calorimeter surrounded by 800 g. of water. The water is at a temperature of $21°$ C. before the combustion starts. If one neglects the heat capacity of the material of which the calorimeter is made, what should be the temperature of the water after the combustion is complete?

7. What volume of dry ammonia gas at 21° C. and 585 mm. of mercury should be produced by the hydrolysis of the magnesium nitride which could be prepared from 5 g. of magnesium?

8. What weight of hydrated magnesium nitrate could be prepared from 200 g. of magnesite which is 80 per cent pure?

9. What volume of 6 N hydrochloric acid is required in theory to dissolve 2 g. of magnesium? What volume of hydrogen at S.T.P. would be produced?

10. What weight of zinc could be displaced from a solution of one of its salts by the action of 1 g. of magnesium?

11. Given a solution containing both sodium and magnesium ions, how might you separate them? Be explicit.

12. Select five examples of oxidation and reduction mentioned in this chapter, and indicate the oxidizing agent, the reducing agent, and the changes of oxidation number involved in each case.

13. How might one prepare magnesium oxalate?

14. Name three important compounds of magnesium, and list several uses for each.

15. Discuss the present uses of magnesium alloys and suggest possible future uses for them. What general industrial field in particular profits by their use?

16. Give two analytical tests for the magnesium ion.

17. What is: (a) an alloy; (b) a lake?

18. A certain sample of a magnesium ore weighs 0.7660 g. The sample is dissolved in acid and the magnesium which it contains is precipitated as $MgNH_4PO_4.6H_2O$, which is then heated to yield magnesium pyrophosphate. The mass of this latter substance is found to be 0.9732 g. What percentage of magnesium does the ore contain?

19. Write equations for the reaction of each of the following magnesium compounds with each of the following acids: (a) magnesium hydroxide, (b) magnesium oxide, (c) magnesium carbonate; and (1) HCl, (2) HNO_3, (3) H_3PO_4, (4) H_2SO_4, (5) $HC_2H_3O_2$, (6) HBr, (7) $HClO_4$.

20. Complete and balance the following metathetical equations:

   (a) $MgSO_4 + NaOH \rightarrow$
   (b) $MgCl_2 + NaOH \rightarrow$
   (c) $Mg_3(PO_4)_2 + KOH \rightarrow$
   (d) $Mg(C_2H_3O_2)_2 + HCl \rightarrow$
   (e) $MgC_2O_4 + H_2SO_4 \rightarrow$
   (f) $MgCl_2 + H_2SO_4 \rightarrow$
   (g) $Mg(NO_3)_2 + H_3PO_4 \rightarrow$
   (h) $Mg(C_2H_3O_2)_2 + H_2SO_4 \rightarrow$

Exercises for Chapter 14

1. What are electrolytes?

2. What are the main classes of electrolytes?

3. What pieces of evidence showed that electrolytes must differ markedly from other solutes?

4. Who was the man first to arrive at a plausible explanation of the peculiar behavior of electrolytes?

5. How may one account for the presence of ions in a solution of sodium bromide?

6. How may one account for the presence of ions in a solution of hydrogen bromide?

7. What is the source of the charge on ions?

8. What is the hydronium ion, and how is it formed?

9. The vapor pressure of a solution of sodium bromide should be how many times lower than that of a glycerol solution of the same molal strength? Why is the actual lowering in solutions of moderate concentration not in entire agreement with the prediction?

10. What explanation can you offer to account for the fact that the solutions of many acids do not appear to be completely ionized?

11. What is the interionic attraction theory?

12. State Coulomb's law, and point its relation to the interionic attraction theory.

13. What is meant by: (a) a weak electrolyte; (b) a strong electrolyte? How may one account for this difference in strength?

14. What is meant by the term: (a) heat of hydration; (b) heat of solution?

15. Why is a solution best prepared in a beaker or other flask, before being transferred to a volumetric flask for exact dilution?

16. What is meant by the activity of an electrolytic solution?

17. What factors influence the activity of an electrolytic solution?

18. How is the activity of an electrolytic solution usually expressed?

19. In chemical work, what is a radical?

20. What is meant by electrolysis?

21. What occurs during electrolysis?

22. Why do ions migrate?

23. What would be produced at each electrode by the electrolysis of each of the following aqueous solutions: (a) nickelous chloride; (b) lithium hydroxide; (c) silver nitrate; (d) potassium bromide? Represent each electrode reaction by an ion-electron equation.

24. Suppose a given cell contained a mixed solution of sodium chloride and zinc chloride. What would you expect to happen if the lowest voltage at which the cell seemed to work well were employed?

25. How do the primary products of electrolysis differ from secondary products?

26. How is the equivalent weight defined in terms of electricity?

27. What apparently is proved by the fact that solutions of electrolytes are electrically neutral?

28. A current of 2 amp. acts for 45 min. 40 sec. on a solution of cadmium sulfate. What is produced at each electrode, and what is the mass of each product?

29. How long should a 5-amp. current have to act to liberate from a solution of an acid 5 l. of hydrogen gas measured at 700 mm. and 21° C.?

30. What is the apparent degree of ionization of a solution of sodium chloride containing 11.70 g. of solute per 500 g. of water if the freezing point of the solution is − 1.09° C.?

Exercises for Chapter 15

1. What reasons may be offered to explain why aluminum has less tendency than sodium to form ionic compounds?

2. What is meant by the term heat of hydration, and how is this quantity related to the square root of the ionic potential?

3. What are the physical properties of aluminum?

4. Where and how does aluminum occur?

5. Why are clays not more generally used as an industrial source of aluminum?

6. How is aluminum: (a) refined; (b) purified?

7. What quantity of aluminum should be obtainable from 1 kg. of gibbsite which is 96.5 per cent pure?

8. If the gibbsite of problem 7 were purified by the Serpek process, what weight of anhydrous ammonia should be obtained as a by-product? What volume would this ammonia occupy as a gas at S.T.P.?

9. Why has the cost of aluminum progressively dropped since the introduction of the Hall process?

10. What quantity of aluminum sulfate octadecahydrate could be prepared from 200 g. of pure kaolin?

11. What volume of methane at 20° C. and a pressure of 740 mm. of mercury should be theoretically obtainable from the aluminum carbide prepared from 100 g. of pure aluminum oxide?

12. Given a solution of the chlorides of sodium, magnesium, and aluminum in water, how could you separate the cations by the use of chemical processes?

13. How much electricity would be required in theory to prepare 1 lb. of aluminum by the Hall process? If the electricity is delivered at the rate of 10 amp., how long would be required for the task?

14. What volume of 6 N nitric acid would be required to react with 10 g. of aluminum "hydroxide"?

15. Discuss the factors which influence the manner in which a hydroxide may ionize.

16. What is alundum?

17. What is an ampholyte?

18. What is the distinction between *ortho* and *meta* acids in inorganic chemistry?

19. Name three important compounds of aluminum, and list several uses for each.

20. What is an alum?

21. What explanation may be offered for the fact that aluminum rusts very little in air?

22. Why is aluminum "hydroxide" more properly referred to as hydrous aluminum oxide? In general, what are the characteristics of hydrous oxides which distinguish them from true hydroxides?

23. What is ultramarine, and for what is it used?

24. What is a mordant?

25. List some of the alloys of aluminum and their uses.

26. How may one test analytically for the presence of aluminum ions?

27. Complete and balance the following equations:

(1) $Al_2O_3 + C \rightarrow$

(2) $Al_2O_3 + KOH \rightarrow$

(3) $Al_2O_3 + HCl \rightarrow$

(4) $Al(OH)_3 + H_2SO_4 \rightarrow$

(5) $Al(OH)_3 + HNO_3 \rightarrow$

(6) $Al(OH)_3 + NaOH + H_2O \rightarrow$

(7) $Al + O_2 \rightarrow$

(8) $Al + S \rightarrow$

(9) $Al + C \rightarrow$

(10) $Al + N_2 \rightarrow$

(11) $Al + Cl_2 \rightarrow$

(12) $NaAlCl_4 + Na \rightarrow$

(13) $Al + SiO_2 \rightarrow$

(14) $Al + Cr_2O_3 \rightarrow$

(15) $Al + Fe_2O_3 \rightarrow$

(16) $H_4Al_2Si_2O_9 + H_2SO_4 \rightarrow H_2SiO_3 +$

(17) $Al + CO \rightarrow Al_4C_3 +$

(18) $Al + HC_2H_3O_2 \rightarrow$

(19) $Al + HCl \rightarrow$

(20) $AlCl_3 + NaOH \rightarrow$

(21) $Al(NO_3)_3 + Ca(OH)_2 \rightarrow$

(22) $AlCl_3 + H_2SO_4 \rightarrow$

(23) $NaAl(SO_4)_2.12H_2O + NaOH \rightarrow$

(24) $Al(C_2H_3O_2)_3 + NaOH \rightarrow$

(25) $AlCl_3 + AgNO_3 \rightarrow$

Exercises for Chapter 16

1. What is a reversible reaction?
2. What is meant by chemical equilibrium?
3. What is meant by the "point of equilibrium," and how is it described?
4. In what terms might the point of equilibrium for the following processes be described:

$$(a)\ \ 2(CaSO_4.2H_2O)_{(s)} \overset{\Delta}{\rightleftarrows} 2CaSO_4.H_2O_{(s)} + 3H_2O_{(g)}$$

$$(b)\ \ 2H_2O_{(g)} \overset{\Delta}{\leftrightarrows} 2H_2 + O_2$$

(c) $HCN \rightleftarrows H^+ + CN^-_{(all\ in\ solution)}$

(d) $CaF_{2(s)} \rightleftarrows Ca^{++} + 2F^-_{(in\ solution)}$

5. What practical advantage arises from a knowledge of chemical equilibrium?
6. What is the velocity of a reaction, and how is it described?
7. What factors influence the velocity of a reaction?
8. What is a catalyst? What are the various sub-classes of catalysts?
9. How does a homogeneous catalyst differ in behavior from a heterogeneous one?

10. What is the relationship between velocity constants and the equilibrium constant?
11. What may one determine from the numerical value of the equilibrium constant?
12. For each of the equilibria represented by the following equations, formulate the equilibrium expression:

$$\text{(a)} \quad N_2 + 3H_2 \rightleftarrows 2NH_3$$
$$\text{(b)} \quad 2KCl + Mg(NO_3)_2 \rightleftarrows MgCl_2 + 2KNO_{3\text{(all in solution)}}$$
$$\text{(c)} \quad PCl_{5(s)} \overset{\Delta}{\rightleftarrows} PCl_{3(g)} + Cl_2$$
$$\text{(d)} \quad H_2C_2O_4 + 2C_2H_5OH \rightleftarrows 2H_2O + (C_2H_5)_2C_2O_{4\text{(all in solution)}}$$

13. State the principle of Le Chatelier, and give two examples to illustrate its operation.
14. Which occupies the larger volume: 1 g. of liquid water or 1 g. of ice? What would be the effect of exerting pressure upon ice?
15. In the following reactions, predict in which direction equilibrium would be shifted by an increase in temperature:

$$\text{(a)} \quad CO_2 + H_2 \rightleftarrows CO + H_2O - 10,600 \text{ cal.}$$
$$\text{(b)} \quad 2H_2 + O_2 \rightleftarrows 2H_2O + 113,120 \text{ cal.}$$
$$\text{(c)} \quad N_2 + O_2 \rightleftarrows 2NO - 43,200 \text{ cal.}$$
$$\text{(d)} \quad 4HCl + O_2 \rightleftarrows 2H_2O + 2Cl_2 + 28,000 \text{ cal.}$$

16. In the following reactions, predict in which direction equilibrium would be shifted by an increase of pressure:

$$\text{(a)} \quad 3O_2 \rightleftarrows 2O_3$$
$$\text{(b)} \quad 2NO + O_2 \rightleftarrows 2NO_2$$
$$\text{(c)} \quad H_2 + Cl_2 \rightleftarrows 2HCl$$
$$\text{(d)} \quad N_2O_4 \rightleftarrows 2NO_2$$

17. What effect does a catalyst have upon the point of equilibrium?
18. What factors affect the value of the equilibrium constant? Give the reasons involved in your answer.
19. Under what circumstances can the law of chemical equilibrium be applied to heterogeneous systems?
20. In what sense is the decomposition of a hydrate a physical process, and in what sense is it a chemical process?
21. Why should the hydrate formed by a salt used as a drying agent have a small vapor pressure at about 20° C.?
22. How many times faster should a given reaction go at 90° C. than it does at 30° C.?
23. What effect upon the point of equilibrium should be noted when more Cl_2 is added to the following equilibrium mixture:

$$4HCl + O_2 \rightleftarrows 2H_2O + 2Cl_2$$

24. The equilibrium constant for the following hypothetical reaction is $0.36 : 2C + D \rightleftarrows E + F$. At equilibrium, which of the several substances will be present in the greater quantities?

Exercises for Chapter 17

1. Why is it that many metathetical reactions do not go to completion?
2. What are the circumstances under which metathetical reactions will go to completion?
3. Submit equations to represent five metathetical reactions which go to completion.
4. What is a complex ion?
5. What is the solubility product of a substance, and for what kind of substances are solubility products of sufficient accuracy to be valuable?
6. Is the solubility product of a given substance variable, and if so what will cause variation to occur?
7. Using $K_{s.p.}$ to represent the solubility product constant, formulate its value for each of the following substances: $BaSO_4$, $Cr(OH)_3$, PbI_2, and CaC_2O_4.
8. Calculate the numerical value of the solubility product constant for: (a) calcium carbonate if its solubility is 0.0014 g. per 100 ml. of water at 25° C.; (b) silver phosphate, Ag_3PO_4, if its solubility is 0.00065 g. per 100 ml. of water at 19.5° C.
9. The solubility product constant for magnesium carbonate is 3×10^{-5} at 20° C. Calculate the solubility of this substance in grams per 100 ml. of water at that temperature.
10. The solubility product constant for silver sulfate is 6.5×10^{-5} at 20° C. Calculate the solubility of this substance in grams per 100 ml. of water at that temperature.
11. What is the "common-ion effect," and of what practical value is it?
12. Using the principles of chemical equilibrium, explain why it is that a precipitate of magnesium hydroxide will dissolve when it is shaken with a moderately concentrated solution of ammonium chloride.
13. When aqueous solutions of ferric chloride are first prepared they are homogeneous, but, upon standing, they gradually become opaque due to the formation of a precipitate of ferric hydroxide: $Fe^{+3} + 3Cl^- + 3HOH \rightleftarrows \underline{Fe(OH)_3} + 3Cl^- + 3H^+$

    (a) How might the formation of this substance be prevented?
    (b) How might the complete conversion of the ferric salt to the hydroxide be fostered?

14. Giving reasons for each answer, to what extent would you expect the following reactions to proceed:

    (a) Sodium acetate + sulfuric acid
    (b) Calcium carbonate + nitric acid
    (c) Silver sulfate + nitric acid

15. Of what significance are the ionization constants of electrolytes?
16. Calculate the ionization constant for hydrocyanic acid, HCN, in a 0.1 M solution in which the acid is ionized to the extent of 0.0145 per cent.
17. Calculate the ionization constant for nitrous acid, HNO_2, in a 0.1 M solution in which the acid is ionized to the extent of 6.3 per cent.
18. What is a buffer solution, and what is the practical value of such solutions?
19. Why are the successive stages of ionization of a polybasic acid or a polyacid base progressively weaker?

20. By use of the principles dealt with in this chapter, explain why it is that phosphoric acid will form a tertiary orthophosphate only with strong bases.
21. What is a neutral aqueous solution? What is the pH of such a solution?
22. What is the hydrogen-ion concentration of a 0.015 M solution of sodium hydroxide?
23. What are: (a) acid salts; (b) normal salts; (c) mixed salts?
24. What is the pH of a solution? What are the advantages in using it rather than conventional concentration units?
25. Calculate the pH of a solution in which the hydrogen-ion concentration is 4.2×10^{-4} gram-ions (moles) per liter.
26. What is the pH of a solution in which the hydroxyl-ion concentration is 8.6×10^{-10} gram-ions (moles) per liter?
27. Find the hydrogen-ion concentration of a solution whose pH is: (a) 3.8; (b) 12.4.
28. In its essence, what is neutralization? Why do neutralizations proceed very nearly to completion? What is the "heat of neutralization"?
29. What is: (a) titration; (b) an indicator; (c) the end-point?
30. Why must the indicator be chosen carefully for every neutralization titration?
31. Distinguish between end-point and point of neutrality.
32. What is the normality of a solution of sulfuric acid, 40.5 ml. of which is required to react with 28.6 ml. of 0.32 N potassium hydroxide?
33. What volume of 0.5 N hydrochloric acid would be required to react with 50 ml. of 0.08 N sodium carbonate solution?
34. What volume of 0.36 N hydrochloric acid is required to react with 4.38 g. of magnesium carbonate which is 80 per cent pure?
35. What weight of pure sodium hydrogen sulfate could be produced from 42 ml. of 2.6 N sulfuric acid?
36. What mass of potassium hydroxide would be contained in 600 ml. of a solution, 40 ml. of which is required to react with 48 ml. of 1.8 N hydrochloric acid?
37. What volume of 0.2 N sodium hydroxide solution should be required to react exactly with 30 ml. of a solution of hydrochloric acid which was prepared by dissolving in 350 ml. of water 50 ml. of a solution of hydrochloric acid whose density is 1.117 g./ml. and which contains 23.3 per cent of hydrogen chloride?
38. What is hydrolysis? What types of salts are most readily hydrolyzed?
39. How will an aqueous solution of ammonium nitrite react to water? $K_{NH_4OH(20°C.)} = 1.8 \times 10^{-5}$. $K_{HNO_2(20°C.)} = 4.6 \times 10^{-4}$.
40. Calculate the numerical value of the hydrolysis constant for sodium acetate.

Exercises for Chapter 18

1. Can silicon be said to be dimorphic? Give reasons for your answer.
2. What may be inferred from the fact that the melting point and boiling point of silicon are much higher than the corresponding constants for the first three elements of the third period?
3. Discuss the occurrence of silicon.
4. Calculate the percentage of silica contained in muscovite.

5. Theoretically, what weight of pure, anhydrous magnesium chloride should one be able to prepare from 2 kg. of soapstone which is 90 per cent pure?

6. What weight of aluminum is required, in theory, to produce 1 kg. of silicon from its dioxide? If aluminum is selling at $.20 per lb., what would the necessary aluminum cost? What name is given to this process for preparing silicon?

7. What weight of ferric oxide (Fe_2O_3) should be required to prepare 100 lb. of ferro-silicon containing 55 per cent iron?

8. What are the uses of ferrosilicon?

9. It is desired to produce 100 cu. m. of dry hydrogen at 740 mm. of pressure and at a temperature of 25° C. by the use of ferrosilicon and aqueous sodium hydroxide. What weight of ferrosilicon containing 60 per cent of silicon should be required?

10. Ten grams of silicon is converted into magnesium silicide, which, in turn, is treated with hydrochloric acid to prepare monosilane. If it is assumed that this is the only silicon-bearing product formed, what volume should it occupy at S.T.P.?

11. In laying down a certain smoke screen, 500 kg. of silicon tetrachloride was used. What weight of sand was ultimately added to the land below as a result of this smoke screen having been formed?

12. At what temperature does the Acheson process for preparing Carborundum operate? At this temperature and standard pressure, what will be the volume occupied by the gas produced along with 4 kg. of Carborundum?

13. What weight of 95 per cent pure Carborundum would be required to produce 1 ton of steel containing 2 per cent by weight of silicon?

14. How could one tell whether a given white powder was silica or alumina?

15. A given sample of alpha-quartz is heated to 1020° C. and held at that temperature for some time. According to theory, what substance ultimately should be formed? Why?

16. List some uses for silica.

17. It is desired to separate a mixture of hydrogen, nitrogen, and helium gases by physical means. How might the task be accomplished?

18. A certain phosphate rock contains 1.5 per cent by weight of fluorine as calcium fluoride. What weight of sodium fluosilicate could be prepared, in theory, from a ton of the rock?

19. Discuss the preparation of: (a) glass; (b) pottery; (c) bricks.

20. Discuss the relationship between the size and charge of an ion and the properties of the chloride which it will form.

Exercises for Chapter 19

1. What is the basis of distinction between a sol and a solution?

2. What are colloids? How did they acquire their name?

3. How may colloid chemistry be defined?

4. What names are given to the components of a colloidal system?

5. Name and characterize the various classes of colloidal systems and give an example of each.

6. What is the difference between sols and gels? What main classes of gels may be noted?
7. Define: (a) syneresis; (b) imbibition; (c) benzosol; (d) alcogel; (e) lyophilic colloid; (f) benzophilic colloid; (g) hydrophobic colloid.
8. What is a reversible colloid, and why is it so named?
9. Given a colorless transparent mixture, how might one determine whether it is a sol or a solution?
10. List the properties which distinguish sols and solutions.
11. What is the Tyndall effect? What is its cause?
12. What is the relationship between the blue sky and colloidal chemistry?
13. Why are rising moons often redder in autumn than in winter?
14. What is the Brownian movement, and how did it get its name?
15. What is dialysis?
16. Give as many reasons as you can why colloidal particles do not settle from their suspensions as rapidly as do suspended coarser particles.
17. It is desired to remove an excess of sodium carbonate from commercial waterglass. How might this be done?
18. How may the high adsorptive power of colloids be explained; and how thick are adsorbed layers believed to be?
19. How may one determine whether given colloidal particles are electrically charged, and if so what the sign of the charge is? What is the source of the charges on many such particles?
20. What is the isoelectric point? Why is a knowledge of it of value?
21. Into what general classes may the methods of preparing colloidal dispersions be grouped? Name several methods of each class.
22. Describe Bredig's method of preparing colloids.
23. How may colloidal dispersions be stabilized?
24. What are agglomerating agents, and how may they produce their effect?
25. How may colloids be precipitated, and why is such knowledge of value?
26. How may crystalline substances be caused to form sols?
27. What is a protective colloid, and how does it protect?
28. How are foams prepared? Make a list of several instances in which foams are: (a) advantageous; (b) a nuisance.
29. How may one break: (a) a foam; (b) an emulsion?
30. Why are fogs and dusts so similar in behavior, and how are dusts most readily "settled"?
31. Why and how does soap act as a cleaning agent?
32. Nitrates are among the most soluble of inorganic salts. Why is it that these salts which are so essential to plant growth are not washed away by hard rains?
33. Discuss the operation and the value of the froth-flotation process.
34. It is nearly impossible to farm land which is either almost pure sand or pure clay. Why?
35. What is humus, and of what value is it?
36. Discuss the importance of colloids and colloidal phenomena in everyday life.

Exercises for Chapter 20

1. Name and briefly characterize the allotropic modifications of phosphorus.
2. Which of the allotropes of phosphorus are most common? What are their respective physical properties, and how may they be interconverted?
3. Which of the allotropes of phosphorus seem to be fundamental? Which of these is the more active?
4. Discuss the natural occurrence of phosphorus. What is its most important ore?
5. How is free phosphorus prepared? Which modification is obtained and how is it preserved? Write equations for the reactions involved.
6. What quantity of phosphorus is theoretically obtainable from 5 kg. of phosphorite which is 80 per cent pure?
7. Discuss the chemical properties of phosphorus.
8. With what element does phosphorus form the greatest number of binary compounds? Might this have been expected?
9. Write equations for the reaction of phosphorus with oxygen, sulfur, chlorine, and calcium, and name the compounds formed.
10. Calculate the percentage of phosphorus in pure chlorapatite.
11. List the differences in preparation and properties of the two common oxides of phosphorus.
12. What is one of the principal laboratory uses of the highest oxide of phosphorus?
13. Give equations for two methods of preparing orthophosphoric acid.
14. It is desired to prepare 100 l. of syrupy orthophosphoric acid. What weight of phosphate rock, 80 per cent pure, would be required to furnish the necessary phosphorus?
15. What volume of nitrogen dioxide (NO_2) would be formed in a room where the temperature is 22° C. and the pressure is 585 mm. of mercury, by the conversion of 300 g. of orthophosphorous acid to orthophosphoric acid by the action of concentrated nitric acid?
16. What volume of ammonia gas will be formed at S.T.P. by the decomposition of 10 g. of microcosmic salt?
17. Given orthophosphoric acid and magnesium carbonate, how could one prepare: (a) magnesium pyrophosphate; (b) magnesium metaphosphate?
18. What is the phosphate bead test, how is it performed, and what is its value?
19. Discuss the solubility of the various phosphate ions, and tell how one may distinguish the various phosphate ions analytically.
20. Discuss the nomenclature of acids and their salts.
21. Give equations for three methods of preparing orthophosphorous acid.
22. Write equations for the reduction of auric chloride ($AuCl_3$), mercuric chloride ($HgCl_2$), and silver nitrate ($AgNO_3$) to the free metal by each of the following compounds: hypophosphorous acid and orthophosphorous acid.
23. What weight of phosphine (PH_3) would be produced, in theory, by the action of aqueous sodium hydroxide on 6.2 g. of yellow phosphorus? What volume would this gas occupy at 20° C. and 760 mm. of mercury?

24. What weight of phosphorus pentoxide should be required to prepare 5 l. of 2.5 N orthophosphoric acid solution?
25. Why is hypophosphorous acid a stronger acid than orthophosphoric acid?
26. Discuss the changes which oxides undergo as one passes from left to right across a period of the periodic table.
27. Discuss the uses of phosphorus and its compounds.
28. Write and balance equations for the reactions which occur in each of the following cases:

(a) phosphorus + magnesium
(b) phosphorus + bromine
(c) phosphorus + sodium
(d) potassium hydroxide + orthophosphoric acid
(e) potassium hydroxide + pyrophosphoric acid
(f) calcium hydroxide + metaphosphoric acid
(g) calcium hydroxide + orthophosphorous acid
(h) potassium hydroxide + metaphosphorous acid
(i) sodium hydroxide + hypophosphorous acid
(j) sulfuric acid + normal barium orthophosphate
(k) dilute nitric acid + metaphosphorous acid
(l) dilute nitric acid + orthophosphorous acid
(m) dilute nitric acid + hypophosphorous acid
(n) potassium permanganate ($KMnO_4$) + hydrochloric acid + orthophosphorous acid
(o) potassium permanganate + hydrochloric acid + potassium hypophosphite
(p) potassium permanganate + hydrochloric acid + potassium metaphosphite

29. Write equations to represent the following oxidation number changes of phosphorus and its compounds:

(a) $0 \rightarrow +3$ (h) $+6 \rightarrow +5$
(b) $0 \rightarrow +5$ (i) $+7 \rightarrow +5$
(c) $+1 \rightarrow +5$ (j) $+5 \rightarrow +3$
(d) $+3 \rightarrow +5$ (k) $+5 \rightarrow 0$

(e) $+4 \rightarrow +5$ (l) $0 \Big\langle \begin{array}{c} +1 \\ -3 \end{array}$

(f) $-3 \rightarrow +5$ (m) $+1 \Big\langle \begin{array}{c} +5 \\ -3 \end{array}$

(g) $0 \rightarrow -3$ (n) $+3 \Big\langle \begin{array}{c} +5 \\ -3 \end{array}$

$$(o) \; +3 \begin{matrix} \nearrow +4 \\ \searrow 0 \end{matrix} \qquad (q) \; +4 \begin{matrix} \nearrow +5 \\ \searrow -3 \end{matrix}$$

$$(p) \; +4 \begin{matrix} \nearrow +5 \\ \searrow +3 \end{matrix} \qquad (r) \; 0 \begin{matrix} \nearrow +3 \\ \searrow +4 \end{matrix}$$

Exercises for Chapter 21

1. Name and briefly characterize the allotropic modifications of sulfur.
2. Which modification of sulfur is stable at about 20° C.? List the principal physical properties of this allotrope.
3. What is "plastic" sulfur, and how is it prepared?
4. Discuss the occurrence of sulfur. How is sulfur mined in the United States?
5. Discuss the chemical properties of sulfur.
6. Write equations for the reaction of sulfur with each of the following: (a) copper; (b) lead; (c) bismuth; (d) carbon; (e) bromine.
7. What volume of hydrogen sulfide at a temperature of 21° C. and at standard pressure could be prepared, in theory, from 10 kg. of ferrous sulfide which is 93 per cent pure?
8. Calculate the molarity of a solution of hydrogen sulfide in water at 10° C. under standard pressure.
9. Discuss the chemical properties of gaseous hydrogen sulfide and of its aqueous solution.
10. How might cupric, ferric, and sodium ions contained in the same solution be separated by the use of hydrogen sulfide?
11. What are polysulfides? How are they made? What is their use?
12. How many oxides does sulfur form? Which are most important? Which is most easily prepared?
13. Calculate the volume of air (assuming it to contain 21 per cent by volume of oxygen) at 20° C. and a pressure of 585 mm. of mercury which should be required to bring about the combustion of 100 kg. of sulfur.
14. Discuss the chemical properties of sulfurous acid.
15. What weight of 60 per cent sulfuric acid could be prepared from 10,000 kg. of zinc sulfide ore which is 80 per cent pure? What would be the normality of this acid if its density is 1.50 g./ml.?
16. List the methods given for the preparation of the oxychlorides of sulfur.
17. What is the molarity and the normality of hydrogen sulfate at 20° C.?
18. Compare the commercial processes for preparing sulfuric acid. Is there any essential difference in the chemistry of the processes?
19. What weight of 65 per cent sulfuric acid should be added to 100 kg. of pyrosulfuric acid to prepare 98 per cent sulfuric acid?
20. What volume of 6 N sulfuric acid could be prepared from 1 l. of constant boiling

sulfuric acid, and what volume of the 6 N acid should be required to convert 10 g. of magnesium carbonate to the sulfate?

21. Name the following salts: $KHSO_4$, K_2SO_4, $K_2S_2O_3$, $K_2S_2O_4$, $K_2S_2O_8$, $K_2S_2O_6$, K_2SO_3, $KHSO_3$, $K_2S_2O_7$, $K_2S_4O_6$, K_2S, and calculate the oxidation number of sulfur in each.

22. Discuss the chemical properties of sulfuric acid.

23. How does one test for: (a) the sulfate ion; (b) the sulfide ion?

24. Given a salt, known to be K_2SO_4, K_2SO_3 or $K_2S_2O_3$, how might one determine quickly which salt he has?

25. What are the uses of: (a) $Na_2S_2O_3$; (b) $Na_2S_2O_4$?

26. Discuss the uses of sulfur.

27. Why is sulfuric acid a stronger electrolyte than sulfurous acid?

28. Write equations to represent the following oxidation number changes of sulfur and its compounds:

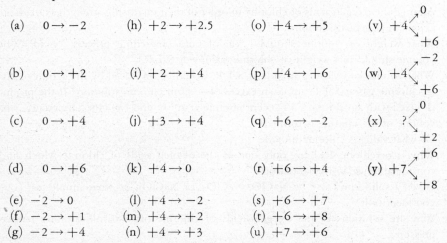

(a) $0 \rightarrow -2$ (h) $+2 \rightarrow +2.5$ (o) $+4 \rightarrow +5$ (v) $+4 \Big\langle \begin{smallmatrix} 0 \\ +6 \end{smallmatrix}$

(b) $0 \rightarrow +2$ (i) $+2 \rightarrow +4$ (p) $+4 \rightarrow +6$ (w) $+4 \Big\langle \begin{smallmatrix} -2 \\ +6 \end{smallmatrix}$

(c) $0 \rightarrow +4$ (j) $+3 \rightarrow +4$ (q) $+6 \rightarrow -2$ (x) $? \Big\langle \begin{smallmatrix} 0 \\ +2 \end{smallmatrix}$

(d) $0 \rightarrow +6$ (k) $+4 \rightarrow 0$ (r) $+6 \rightarrow +4$ (y) $+7 \Big\langle \begin{smallmatrix} +6 \\ +8 \end{smallmatrix}$

(e) $-2 \rightarrow 0$ (l) $+4 \rightarrow -2$ (s) $+6 \rightarrow +7$

(f) $-2 \rightarrow +1$ (m) $+4 \rightarrow +2$ (t) $+6 \rightarrow +8$

(g) $-2 \rightarrow +4$ (n) $+4 \rightarrow +3$ (u) $+7 \rightarrow +6$

29. Write the equation for each of the following metathetical reactions: (1) hydrogen sulfide with (a) zinc chloride, (b) $MnSO_4$, (c) $CoCl_2$, (d) $Ni(NO_3)_2$, (e) $FeCl_2$, (f) $Bi(NO_3)_3$, (g) $SbCl_3$, (h) $SnCl_2$, (i) $AsCl_3$, (j) $Pb(NO_3)_2$, (k) $HgSO_4$, (l) $CuSO_4$, (m) $Cd(C_2H_3O_2)_2$, and (n) $AgNO_3$; (2) sulfuric acid with (a) magnesium carbonate, (b) sodium nitrate, (c) $Cu(C_2H_3O_2)_2$, (d) $BaCl_2$, (e) sodium sulfite, (f) $CaCO_3$, (g) $Sr(NO_3)_2$, (h) sodium carbonate, (i) aluminum "hydroxide," and (j) CaO.

30. Complete and balance the following oxidation-reduction equations:

        (a) $H_2S + HNO_3 \text{ (conc.)} \rightarrow NO_2 +$

        (b) $H_2S + K_2Cr_2O_7 + HCl \rightarrow \underline{S} + CrCl_3 +$

        (c) $H_2S + Ce(SO_4)_2 \rightarrow \underline{S} + Ce_2(SO_4)_3 +$

        (d) $CaSO_4 + C \rightarrow$

        (e) $H_2SO_3 + K_2Cr_2O_7 + H_2SO_4 \rightarrow$

        (f) $H_2SO_3 + Ce(SO_4)_2 + H_2O \rightarrow$

(g) $H_2SO_3 + HNO_3$ (conc.) $\rightarrow NO_2 +$

(h) $H_2SO_3 + HNO_3$ (dil.) $\rightarrow NO +$

Exercises for Chapter 22

1. Give the names and formulas of the oxides of chlorine. What properties do these compounds have in common?
2. Write equations for the decomposition of all of the oxides of chlorine.
3. Describe the variation in properties which occurs in the oxygen acids of chlorine as the oxidation number of the chlorine present increases.
4. Name the following compounds: $Ca(ClO)_2$, $Ca(Cl)OCl$, $Ca(ClO_2)_2$, $MgCl_2$, $Mg(ClO_3)_2$, $Ba(ClO_4)_2$, K_2SiF_6.
5. Give one method of preparing each of the oxygen acids of chlorine.
6. List the uses of the salts of each of the oxygen acids of chlorine.
7. Arrange the oxygen acids of chlorine in order of their increasing strength as oxidizing agents in aqueous solutions.
8. What weight of chlorine should 1 kg. of pure "bleaching powder" yield? What volume should this weight of chlorine occupy at S.T.P.?
9. What volume of chlorine dioxide at S.T.P. would be produced by the action of 20 l. of chlorine gas at S.T.P. upon an excess of sodium chlorite solution? If the product is mixed with air to form a 5 per cent mixture at 20° C. and 730 mm. of mercury, what volume of the mixture is formed?
10. Of what value is chlorine dioxide?
11. Why is perchloric acid the only one of the oxygen acids of chlorine which finds considerable use in the laboratory?
12. Given a solid known to be $NaClO$, $NaClO_3$, or $NaClO_4$, by what simple test could you identify it?
13. Why are solutions of the oxygen acids of chlorine often distilled under reduced pressure?
14. What weight of potassium chlorate would be required to produce 500 ml. of oxygen at 22° C. and 740 mm. of mercury?
15. Calculate the weight of potassium perchlorate which might be prepared by the heat treatment of 2 kg. of potassium hypochlorite.
16. What precautions must be taken in the handling of potassium chlorate? Why?
17. Why is potassium perchlorate often used in preference to potassium chlorate?
18. A sample of a substance known to contain a potassium salt is treated with perchloric acid. If the sample weighed 0.814 g., and if 0.814 g. of potassium perchlorate were formed, what must have been the percentage of potassium in the sample?
19. What weight of sodium peroxide should be required to prepare 800 g. of sodium chlorite?
20. What are odd molecules, and what are their outstanding properties?
21. Write equations to represent the following oxidation number changes of chlorine and its compounds:

26. The existence of water and hydrogen peroxide is an example of the operation of what natural (or scientific) law?
27. Give specific tests for the identification of hydrogen peroxide.
28. Complete and balance the following equations:

(a) $Ca + HOH \rightarrow$ (h) $H_3PO_2 + H_2O_2 \rightarrow$
(b) $CaH_2 + HOH \rightarrow$ (i) $H_3PO_3 + H_2O_2 \rightarrow$
(c) $Ag_2O + H_2 \rightarrow$ (j) $Ca_3P_2 + H_2O_2 \rightarrow$
(d) $CrO_3 + H_2 \rightarrow$ (k) $PtO + H_2O_2 \rightarrow$
(e) $Ba + H_2 \rightarrow$ (l) $HgO + H_2O_2 \rightarrow$
(f) $Fe_2(SO_4)_3 + Ca(OH)_2 \rightarrow$ (m) $KI + HCl + H_2O_2 \rightarrow$
(g) $K_2O_2 + H_2SO_4 \rightarrow$

Exercises for Chapter 24

1. How many liters of nitrogen at S.T.P. should be required to prepare 5 l. of the liquid at its boiling point? What volume of air at 20° C. and 740 mm. of mercury should be required to yield this quantity of nitrogen?
2. Discuss the occurrence, preparation, and physical properties of nitrogen.
3. What quantity of glyceryl trinitrate, $C_3H_5(NO_3)_3$, could be prepared, in theory, from the nitrogen in the air over 1 sq. m. of the earth's surface?
4. What volume of air should be required to be passed with 5 l. of ammonia gas over a copper-cupric oxide mixture so that, after the reaction, the composition of the mixture should be unchanged? Assume both gases to be measured at S.T.P.
5. Assuming stoichiometric conversion, what weight of nitrogen should be required to prepare 12 l. of 8 N nitric acid?
6. How many tons of 85 per cent pure Chile saltpeter must be imported to prepare 100 tons of constant boiling nitric acid?
7. Write equations for the action of both dilute and concentrated nitric acid on zinc. Calculate the volume of 4 N acid required in the first case and the volume of 12 N acid required in the second case to react with 5 g. of zinc.
8. Calculate the normality of a solution of nitric acid whose density is 1.310 g./ml. and which contains 50 per cent of HNO_3.
9. What is: (a) aqua regia; (b) autocatalysis; (c) xanthoproteic acid?
10. Write equations for the pyrolytic decomposition of $Ni(NO_3)_2$, KNO_3, and $AgNO_3$.
11. Discuss the identification of nitrates and nitrites.
12. Calculate the volume of nitrogen dioxide at 22° C. and 585 mm. of mercury evolved by the action of 20 ml. of 12 N nitric acid on copper.
13. Write equations for all steps necessary to convert 100 g. of ammonia into sodium hyponitrite, and calculate the theoretical yield of the latter.
14. Discuss the preparation and physical properties of ammonia.
15. What volume of nitrogen at S.T.P. would be required to produce 100 kg. of calcium cyanamide, and what volume of ammonia at S.T.P. could be prepared from the latter? What would be the mass of this volume of ammonia?

16. Discuss the chemical properties of ammonia.

17. Write equations for the action of hydrazine on mercuric chloride, $HgCl_2$, aurous chloride, $AuCl$, and acidified potassium permanganate.

18. Prepare a chart showing the oxidation states in which each element of the V A family may exist.

19. One gram of a crude sample of realgar is converted to magnesium ammonium arsenate, which, in turn, is converted to magnesium pyroarsenate, $Mg_2As_2O_7$. If this latter substance weighs 0.6868 g., what is the percentage of: (a) realgar in the sample; (b) arsenic in the sample?

20. What weight of arsenic trioxide could be prepared from 50 kg. of 80 per cent pure orpiment?

21. Discuss the properties of the oxides of the V A family.

22. What are thiosalts, how are they formed, and how may they be decomposed?

23. How may one prove that antimonyl and bismuthyl chlorides are not hypochlorites?

24. Discuss the uses of arsenic, antimony, and bismuth, and their compounds.

25. Write equations for the preparation of stibine from antimony trichloride, and for the combustion of the product in air. What weight of the product of combustion should be obtained from 0.12 g. of the trichloride?

26. Write equations for the reactions listed below, and balance them:

    (a) magnesium + nitrogen

    (b) calcium nitride + water

    (c) zinc + dilute nitric acid

    (d) zinc + concentrated nitric acid

    (e) silver + concentrated nitric acid

    (f) sulfur + concentrated nitric acid

    (g) silver nitrate + strong heating

    (h) $Cr(NO_3)_3$ + strong heating

    (i) sulfurous acid + nitrous acid

    (j) hypophosphorous acid + nitrous acid

    (k) orthophosphorous acid + nitrous acid

    (l) normal sodium orthophosphite + nitrous acid

    (m) hydrogen iodide + nitrous acid

    (n) nitrous acid + $K_2Cr_2O_7$ + HCl → $CrCl_3$ + ?

    (o) nitrogen dioxide + sulfur

    (p) hydrogen sulfide + NO_2 → sulfuric acid + ?

    (q) nitric oxide + phosphorus

    (r) NO + $K_2Cr_2O_7$ + H_2SO_4 → HNO_3 + ?

    (s) $NaNO_3$ + Na + HOH → $Na_2N_2O_2$ + ?

    (t) NH_3 + Br_2 → N_2 + ?

    (u) arsenic + conc. nitric acid

    (v) bismuth + conc. nitric acid

    (w) antimony + conc. nitric acid

(x) $As_2O_3 + HOCl + HOH \rightarrow H_3AsO_4 + ?$
(y) orthoantimonic acid + NaOH
(z) $Bi(OH)_3 + NaOH + NaOCl \rightarrow NaBiO_3 + NaCl + ?$

27. Write equations to represent the following changes of oxidation number of nitrogen and its compounds:

(a) $-3 \rightarrow 0$ (h) $+2 \rightarrow -2$ (o) $+3 \rightarrow +5$ (v) $+5 \rightarrow +1$

(b) $-3 \rightarrow +1$ (i) $+2 \rightarrow +3$ (p) $+3 \Big\langle \begin{smallmatrix} +2 \\ +4 \end{smallmatrix}$ (w) $+5 \rightarrow +2$

(c) $-3 \rightarrow +2$ (j) $+2 \rightarrow +4$ (q) $+3 \Big\langle \begin{smallmatrix} +2 \\ +5 \end{smallmatrix}$ (x) $+5 \rightarrow +3$

(d) $-2 \rightarrow 0$ (k) $+2 \rightarrow +5$ (r) $+4 \rightarrow +3$ (y) $+5 \rightarrow +4$

(e) $0 \rightarrow -3$ (l) $+3 \rightarrow -3$ (s) $+4 \Big\langle \begin{smallmatrix} +2 \\ +5 \end{smallmatrix}$

(f) $0 \rightarrow +2$ (m) $+3 \rightarrow +1$ (t) $+4 \Big\langle \begin{smallmatrix} +3 \\ +5 \end{smallmatrix}$

(g) $+1 \rightarrow 0$ (n) $+3 \rightarrow +2$ (u) $+5 \rightarrow -3$

Exercises for Chapter 25

1. What are the principal physical properties of oxygen?
2. Discuss the general trends of the physical properties of the elements of the VI A family of the periodic system.
3. Discuss the occurrence of oxygen. How are small quantities of the element best prepared for the laboratory?
4. What weight of pure potassium chlorate should be required to produce 1 l. of oxygen at 21° C. and at a pressure of 710 mm. of mercury?
5. What volume of oxygen at S.T.P. should be obtained by the decomposition of 12 g. of pure mercuric oxide, HgO?
6. Upon being heated to red heat, which will supply the greater quantity of oxygen, and by how much: 10 g. of potassium nitrate or 10 g. of potassium chlorate?
7. Calculate the percentage of oxygen in each of the following oxides of iron: FeO, Fe_2O_3, Fe_3O_4.
8. What volume of oxygen at 27° C. and standard pressure should be required for the complete combustion of 1 kg. of pure carbon?
9. Discuss the phenomenon of combustion.
10. Why are so few figures on kindling temperatures to be found?
11. What is the "oxygen cycle"?
12. Given 1 l. of a gaseous mixture of oxygen and ozone: upon decomposition of the ozone the volume of gas measured under the same conditions of temperature and

pressure is found to be 1030 ml. What was the percentage by volume of ozone in the original mixture?

13. Two hundred milliliters of a gaseous mixture of oxygen, ozone, and nitrogen are passed first through cinnamon oil, then through a basic solution of pyrogallol. The volume is reduced to 198 ml. by the first treatment and to 158 ml. by the second treatment. What was the percentage by volume of each gas in the mixture?

14. Discuss the preparation of ozone.

15. Discuss the use of ozone.

16. Why is ozone a more active oxidizing agent than oxygen?

17. Discuss the occurrence, production, and use of selenium and tellurium.

18. Discuss the chemical properties of selenium and tellurium.

19. What volume of 8 N nitric acid should be required to convert 5 g. of tellurium into tellurous acid? What volume of 3 N sodium hydroxide would be required to convert the product to normal sodium tellurite?

20. What weight of elementary selenium would be formed by the action of selenous acid on the sulfurous acid prepared from the sulfur dioxide obtained by burning 20 g. of a pyrite ore which is 90 per cent pure?

21. Complete and balance equations for the following reactions:

$$(a) \quad FeTe + HCl \rightarrow$$
$$(b) \quad H_2SeO_3 + KMnO_4 + HCl \rightarrow$$
$$(c) \quad H_2SeO_3 + K_2CrO_4 + H_2SO_4 \rightarrow$$
$$(d) \quad H_2SeO_3 + HNO_3 \text{ (dil.)} \rightarrow$$
$$(e) \quad Se + HNO_3 \text{ (conc.)} \rightarrow$$
$$(f) \quad H_2SeO_4 + H_2S \rightarrow SO_2 + H_2SeO_3 +$$
$$(g) \quad H_2SeO_4 + H_4P_2O_6 + HOH \rightarrow$$
$$(h) \quad H_2SeO_4 + H_3PO_2 \rightarrow$$
$$(i) \quad H_2SeO_4 + HNO_2 \rightarrow$$
$$(j) \quad H_2SeO_4 + H_2SO_3 \rightarrow$$
$$(k) \quad TeO_2 \xrightarrow{\Delta}$$
$$(l) \quad H_6TeO_6 + H_3PO_3 \rightarrow H_2TeO_3 +$$
$$(m) \quad H_6TeO_6 + H_2C_2O_4 \rightarrow CO_2 +$$
$$(n) \quad H_6TeO_6 + FeCl_2 + HCl \rightarrow$$
$$(o) \quad H_6TeO_6 + H_2S \rightarrow + \underline{S}$$

Exercises for Chapter 26

1. In the light of your knowledge of the four common halogens, predict the physical and chemical properties of element 85.

2. What quantity of bromine should be required to saturate 5 l. of water at 20° C.?

3. When bromine water acts as an oxidizing agent, its bromine is reduced to the bromide ion. What is the normality of the solution of problem 2 as an oxidizing agent?

4. How many grams of a sample of fluorspar containing 70 per cent of calcium fluoride should be required to prepare 3 kg. of a 30 per cent solution of hydrofluoric acid?

5. Which contains the larger quantity of fluorine, and by how much: 100 g. of pure calcium fluoride or a like mass of pure cryolite?

6. A certain brine whose density is 1.38 g./ml. contains 2.1 per cent of sodium bromide and 0.42 per cent of magnesium bromide. If recovery is 96 per cent complete, what volume of this water would be required for the preparation of 5 kg. of bromine?

7. How many milliliters of bromine at 20° C. should be required to prepare 10 l. of constant boiling hydrobromic acid?

8. One liter of bromine at 20° C. is added to potassium hydroxide and the solution is warmed. What bromine products will be obtained, and what will be the mass of each?

9. The density of ethylene bromide at 25° C. is 2.17 g./ml. What volume of this liquid could be prepared from 50 g. of bromine?

10. How many grams of water should be required to react with the phosphorus triiodide prepared from 1 g. of iodine?

11. Why is iodine more soluble in a solution of sodium iodide than in water?

12. Discuss the occurrence, preparation, and uses of each of the halogens discussed in this chapter.

13. List the halogens in order of increasing strength as oxidizing agents, their hydrides in increasing strength as acids, their hydroxides in increasing strength as oxidizing agents, and their hydroxides in increasing strength as acids.

14. How can it be shown that chloric acid is less stable than iodic acid?

15. What is the normality of a certain iodine solution, 30.0 ml. of which reacts with 52.3 ml. of 0.6 N sodium thiosulfate solution?

16. A 0.1060-g. sample of arsenic trioxide is oxidized to arsenic acid by 60 ml. of a solution of iodine. What is the normality of the solution?

17. What is the normality of a solution of phosphoric acid of which 30 ml., when added to a mixture of sodium iodide and sodium iodate, liberates sufficient iodine to require for its titration 45 ml. of a solution made by dissolving 5 g. of hydrated sodium thiosulfate in 400 ml. of water?

18. Discuss the relationship of iodine and goiter.

19. Discuss the preparation of the hydrogen halides by direct union.

20. Discuss the detection and identification of halogens as they exist in their binary compounds.

21. Write equations to represent the following oxidation number changes of bromine and its compounds:

(a) $-1 \rightarrow 0$ (c) $+1 \rightarrow -1$ (e) $+5 \rightarrow -1$ (g) $+1 \nearrow^{+5}_{\searrow -1}$

(b) $0 \rightarrow -1$ (d) $+5 \rightarrow 0$ (f) $0 \nearrow^{+1}_{\searrow -1}$

22. Write equations to represent the following oxidation number changes of iodine and its compounds:

(a) $-1 \rightarrow 0$ (d) $+1 \rightarrow -1$ (g) $+5 \rightarrow -1$ (j) $+4 \begin{smallmatrix} \nearrow 0 \\ \searrow +5 \end{smallmatrix}$

(b) $0 \rightarrow -1$ (e) $+5 \rightarrow +4$ (h) $+1 \begin{smallmatrix} \nearrow -1 \\ \searrow +5 \end{smallmatrix}$ (k) $0 \begin{smallmatrix} \nearrow +1 \\ \searrow -1 \end{smallmatrix}$

(c) $0 \rightarrow +5$ (f) $+5 \rightarrow 0$ (i) $+1 \begin{smallmatrix} \nearrow 0 \\ \searrow +5 \end{smallmatrix}$

23. Write and balance equations for the following reactions:
(a) carbon tetrachloride + fluorine
(b) calcium silicate + fluorine and water
(c) sodium iodide + fluorine
(d) sodium silicate + hydrofluoric acid
(e) silicon tetrafluoride + water
(f) bromine + chloric acid
(g) bromine + conc. nitric acid
(h) bromine + hydrogen peroxide
(i) bromic acid + ferrous chloride + $HCl \rightarrow HBr +$?
(j) sodium + iodine
(k) phosphorus + iodine
(l) sodium orthoarsenite + iodine + sodium bicarbonate $\rightarrow$ sodium orthoarsenate + sodium iodide + carbon dioxide + water
(m) hydriodic acid + $KMnO_4 \rightarrow$ free iodine + ?
(n) potassium iodide + nitric acid (dil.)
(o) potassium bromide + H_2SO_4
(p) perchloric acid + iodine
(q) iodine pentoxide heated above 300° C.
(r) periodic acid + phosphorus pentoxide
(s) K_2MnO_4 + iodic acid + acetic acid $\rightarrow KMnO_4 + HI +$?

Exercises for Chapter 27

1. In what respects is carbon's position in the periodic system reflected in its properties?
2. Discuss the physical properties of carbon.
3. Graphite is very easily split into thin plates, while diamond is split only with difficulty. How is this difference usually accounted for?
4. Discuss the natural occurrence of carbon.
5. Write equations to illustrate the chemical behavior of carbon.
6. Why is carbon monoxide a good reducing agent while the dioxide will not so serve?
7. In theory, what volume at S.T.P. should 1 g. of carbon disulfide vapor occupy? What weight of carbon should be required to produce that quantity of the substance?
8. What volume of chlorine at 25° C. and 740 mm. of mercury should be required to prepare 1 l. of liquid carbon tetrachloride at 20° C. from carbon disulfide?

. Suggest a procedure for converting colemanite into pure orthoboric acid.

. Prepare a list of the especially useful compounds of boron, and the uses of each.

. Write equations for the formation of the halides of boron.

. Write an equation for the hydrolysis of: (a) boron nitride; (b) calcium boride.

. Write an equation for the combustion of methyl borate.

. Discuss the hydrides of boron.

. Discuss the family relationships of the elements of the III A family.

. Discuss the occurrence and physical properties of: (a) gallium; (b) indium; (c) thallium.

Discuss the properties of the hydroxides of: (a) gallium; (b) indium; (c) thallium.

Complete and balance the following equations:

(a) $BCl_3 + HI \rightarrow BI_3 +$

(b) $HOBH_3 + SO_2 \rightarrow HBO_2 + \underline{S} +$

(c) $B + C \rightarrow$

(d) $B + F_2 \rightarrow$

(e) $Ga + HCl \rightarrow$

(f) $Ga + Cl_2 \rightarrow$

(g) $Ga + O_2 \rightarrow$

(h) $Ga + HNO_3$ (conc.) $\rightarrow$

(i) $GaCl_3 + NaOH \rightarrow NaGaO_2 +$

(j) $GaCl_3 + K_4Fe(CN)_6 \rightarrow$

(k) $In + O_2 \rightarrow$

(l) $In_2O_3 \xrightarrow{\Delta} In_3O_4 +$

(m) $In_2O_3 + H_2 \xrightarrow{300° C.} In_2O_2 +$

(n) $In(NO_3)_3 + H_2S \rightarrow In_2S_3 +$

(o) $In_2(SO_4)_3 + K_2CrO_4 \rightarrow$

(p) $Tl + Br_2 \rightarrow$

(q) $Tl + S \rightarrow$

(r) $TlOH \xrightarrow{\Delta}$

(s) $TlCl_3 + H_2S \rightarrow$

(t) $Tl(NO_3)_3 + NaI \rightarrow$

(u) $Tl_2S_3 \rightarrow Tl_2S +$

(v) $TlCl + KMnO_4 + HCl \rightarrow TlCl_3 +$

(w) $TlCl_3 + H_2C_2O_4 \rightarrow CO_2 + TlCl +$

(x) $TlCl_3 + H_2S \rightarrow \underline{S} +$

cises for Chapter 29

scuss the common properties of the I A family of elements.

scuss the variations which occur within each of the common properties of the I A

PROBLEMS AND QUESTIONS

9. Give the names and formulas of the oxides of carbon and the names of the acids with which they are most closely related.

10. Given 40 ml. of a gaseous mixture: after being shaken with a stror potassium hydroxide, the volume of the residual gas is found to n This remainder is then passed through an alkaline solution of pyrogall it emerges to measure only 10 ml. Further treatment of the gas with solution of cuprous chloride reduces its volume to 5 ml. This residu to be nitrogen. Assuming that there has been no change of either pressure, calculate the percentage composition of the mixture (by vo the components.

11. Discuss the preparation and use of carbon monoxide.

12. Compare the physical and chemical properties of carbon dioxide and

13. Assuming total conversion, what quantity of limestone which is 97 carbonate should be required to make 100 kg. of sodium bicarbona

14. List several methods for separating a mixture which contains on and the dioxide of carbon.

15. Why are records kept with India ink considered to be more perm written in ordinary inks?

16. What quantity of carbon should be required to prepare 20 g. of sc

17. Discuss the nature and use of fuels.

18. Which should be the better fuel, volume for volume: (a) water g gas? On the basis of the delivery of equal quantities of heat, wl should be the cheaper fuel?

19. When all are burned in the open air, why do benzene and acetylen more soot than alcohol or methane?

20. Ten liters of a mixture which contains 40 per cent CO_2, 50 per c cent oxygen is heated to a high temperature, then restored to the and pressure. What is then the total volume of the mixture; what and what is the percentage of each in the mixture?

21. What is the molarity of an aqueous solution of carbon dioxide pr standard pressure? What should the molarity be if the solutior at 20° C. under a pressure of two atmospheres?

Exercises for Chapter 28

1. What is meant by "the diagonal relationship," and why doe exist?

2. Discuss the physical properties of boron.

3. Calculate the percentage of boron in each of the minerals m assuming complete purity for the minerals.

4. What quantity of pure boron trioxide would be required, in t tion of 150 g. of elementary boron?

5. What quantity of colemanite containing 35 per cent of iner required for the preparation of 1 kg. of orthoboric acid?

family of elements as one passes from elements of lower atomic weight to those of progressively higher atomic weight.

3. Make a list of the properties which you would expect element 87 and its hydroxide and chloride to have.

4. If you were seeking element 87, where and in what condition would you expect to find it?

5. Which of the elements of the I A family should form the most stable fluoride? Give reasons to support your answer.

6. Calculate the percentage of lithium in pure samples of spodumene and amblygonite. What quantity of the former mineral of 93 per cent purity should be required for the preparation of 500 g. of anhydrous lithium chloride?

7. List the respects in which lithium more closely resembles magnesium than it does the other members of its own family. Why does it so behave?

8. Make a table showing for each member of the I A family: (a) date of discovery or isolation; (b) discoverer; (c) occurrence; (d) preparation; (e) uses.

9. How might one easily demonstrate that, of the elements of the I A family, only lithium forms a nitride when burned in the open air?

10. If a current of 20 amp. is supplied at the proper voltage, how long should it flow to liberate 10 gram-molecular weights of potassium from its molten hydroxide?

11. Why is sodium peroxide more commonly encountered than its potassium counterpart?

12. It is desired to prepare a fertilizer which will contain sufficient KCl to give a potassium oxide (K_2O) content of 8 per cent. What weight of KCl would 8 short tons of this fertilizer contain?

13. Can you suggest a reason for KNO_3 being used in the preparation of gunpowder in preference to $NaNO_3$?

14. In theory, what quantity of 85 per cent pure carnallite should be required for the preparation of 500 kg. of pearlash by the LeBlanc process?

15. What is a soap, and how are those which are used as cleaning agents usually prepared? What is the principal difference between potassium and sodium soaps?

16. When sodium cobaltinitrite is added to a certain solution, a yellow precipitate is formed. How may one conveniently determine whether this precipitate is one of potassium, ammonium, rubidium, or cesium?

17. How many liters of sulfuric acid whose density is 1.83 g./ml. should be required to prepare 1,000 kg. of anhydrous ammonium sulfate?

18. Which should make the better fertilizer: (a) ammonium phosphate or (b) ammonium sulfate? Why? Which compound is more commonly used for the purpose, and why?

19. Explain why rubidium and cesium are especially suited for the manufacture of photoelectric cells.

20. What weight of potassium hydroxide is contained in 3 l. of a solution of which 38 ml. is neutralized by reaction with 32 ml. of a 1.65 N solution of sulfuric acid?

21. A solution of potassium carbonate is prepared by dissolving 13.82 g. of the anhydrous salt in sufficient water to make 500 ml. of solution. What volume of this solution should be required to react with 62 ml. of a 2.2 N solution of hydrochloric acid?

22. Complete and balance the following equations:

(a) $Li + O_2 \xrightarrow{\Delta}$

(b) $Li_2O + HOH \rightarrow$

(c) $Li_2O_2 + HOH \rightarrow$

(d) $Li + H_2 \xrightarrow{\Delta}$

(e) $Li + N_2 \xrightarrow{\Delta}$

(f) $LiH + HOH \rightarrow$

(g) $Li_3N + HOH \rightarrow$

(h) $LiCl + NaH_2PO_4 \rightarrow$

(i) $K + O_2 \xrightarrow{\Delta}$

(j) $K + Br_2 \xrightarrow{\Delta}$

(k) $K + S \xrightarrow{\Delta}$

(l) $KNO_2 + K \xrightarrow{\Delta}$

(m) $KO_2 + HOH \rightarrow$

(n) $K_2O_3 + HOH \rightarrow$

(o) $KOH + CO_2 \rightarrow$

(p) $KOH + HI \rightarrow$

(q) $K_2CO_3 + HNO_3 \rightarrow$

(r) $K_2CO_3 + C + N_2 \xrightarrow{\Delta}$

(s) $KCN + S \xrightarrow{\Delta}$

(t) $KCN + Na_2S_2O_3 \rightarrow$

(u) $KNO_3 \xrightarrow{\Delta}$

Exercises for Chapter 30

1. Why are beryllium and magnesium classified with calcium, strontium, and barium rather than with zinc, cadmium, and mercury?

2. Which element of the II A family has properties which differ most widely from those characteristic of the family? Why?

3. Compare the general properties of the elements of the II A family with those of the I A family. In which properties do the greatest similarities occur; in which do the greatest differences occur?

4. Discuss the occurrence, preparation, and use of beryllium.

5. Discuss the occurrence, preparation, and use of calcium.

6. How is calcium oxide prepared commercially? Why must the temperature of the process be controlled carefully?

7. Distinguish between slaked and unslaked lime. List some uses of each.

8. What explanation can you offer for a farmer's adding limestone dust and chips to one of his fields?

9. How does plaster of Paris differ from gypsum? How is it prepared, and how does it set? What are its uses?

10. What weight of water should be evolved when 5 tons of gypsum, 90 per cent pure, are converted into plaster of Paris?

11. List the important salts of calcium, giving their uses and methods of preparation.

12. What is hard water? How may one readily distinguish between hard and soft waters? What are the classes of hard waters? What are the causes of hardness in waters?

13. How may hard waters be softened? Discuss the economic aspects of hard waters and their softening.

14. What quantity of soap (assumed to be sodium stearate) would be wasted in the use of 30 gal. of water which contains 60 p.p.m. of calcium ion?
15. How do the setting of mortar and cement differ?
16. What is Portland cement, and how is it manufactured?
17. Discuss the analytical behavior of: (a) calcium ions; (b) strontium ions; and (c) barium ions.
18. Discuss the occurrence, preparation, and use of strontium and barium.
19. List the important compounds of strontium and barium, and give their uses.
20. What volume of carbon dioxide at S.T.P. would be liberated by the treatment with superheated steam of 5 kg. of witherite of 95 per cent purity?
21. When 50 ml. of a certain solution of sulfuric acid is treated with an excess of barium chloride solution, a precipitate is formed which, upon being collected and dried, is found to weigh 3.2637 g. What was the normality of the acid solution?
22. What weight of $Ba(OH)_2.8H_2O$ would be required to prepare 4.5 l. of a 0.05 N solution of the base? What weight of barium sulfate could be precipitated from 200 ml. of the solution?
23. What weight of lithopone could be prepared from 2 l. of 3 M zinc sulfate solution?
24. A sample of an impure, soluble barium salt is found to weigh 1.1236 g. The sample is dissolved and titrated with standard sulfuric acid solution with tetrahydroxyquinone as an indicator. Thirty milliliters of 0.05 N acid is required for the titration. What is the percentage of barium in the unknown?
25. What is the normality of a solution of barium chloride dihydrate of which 40 ml. reacts with 52 ml. of a 0.22 N solution of silver nitrate? What weight of the salt would 600 ml. of the solution contain?
26. Write equations for the following reactions:

    (a) beryllium + nitrogen
    (b) calcium + hydrogen
    (c) beryllium oxide + carbon
    (d) beryllium hydroxide + sodium hydroxide
    (e) beryllium oxide + potassium oxide
    (f) calcium + nitric acid (dil.)
    (g) potassium beryllate + water
    (h) calcium + oxygen
    (i) calcium sulfide + water
    (j) calcium carbide + water
    (k) calcium silicide + water
    (l) calcium oxide + sulfuric acid
    (m) calcium oxide + hydrochloric acid
    (n) calcium oxide + chlorine
    (o) calcium carbonate + acetic acid
    (p) barium sulfate + carbon
    (q) calcium nitrate + sodium oxalate
    (r) barium oxide + aluminum

(s) barium + water
(t) barium + copper sulfate
(u) strontium + silver nitrate
(v) strontium nitrate + heat

Exercises for Chapter 31

1. Define the terms: (a) metallurgy; (b) mineral; (c) ore; (d) native ore; (e) gangue.
2. Among the important ores, what negative radicals are of greatest importance?
3. Discuss the froth-flotation method of concentrating ores.
4. What is meant by the term "smelting"?
5. Discuss the smelting of: (a) oxide ores; (b) sulfide ores; (c) carbonate ores.
6. List and discuss the commoner methods of refining crude metals. Why is refining desirable?
7. What are alloys, how may they be prepared, and why are they important?
8. What are the general types of alloys?
9. Discuss the general relationships of the elements of the IV A family.
10. Why is the +2 state of oxidation more common to lead than the +4 state which is characteristic of the family?
11. If there were one more member of the IV A family heavier than lead, what physical and chemical properties would you expect it to have?
12. Discuss the occurrence of: (a) germanium; (b) tin; (c) lead.
13. Discuss the recovery and refinement of: (a) tin; (b) lead.
14. Why do not the tin coatings of tin cans turn gray and fall off in the winter?
15. Discuss the uses of: (a) tin; (b) lead.
16. Write equations to represent the characteristic reactions of: (a) tin; (b) lead.
17. How are α- and β-stannic acids prepared, and how do they differ?
18. Why does stannic sulfide dissolve in ammonium sulfide while the polysulfide is required to dissolve stannous sulfide?
19. Calculate the solubility product constant for lead sulfate whose solubility is 4.06 $\times 10^{-3}$ g. per 100 g. of water at 25° C.
20. How are tin and lead confirmed analytically?
21. When is the Betts process used instead of the Parkes process? What are the relative merits and demerits of the two processes?
22. In the Betts process, why are zinc and iron concentrated in the electrolyte while gold and copper collect in the anode mud?
23. Discuss the preparation, properties, and uses of the oxides of lead.
24. Discuss the preparation and use of some of the more important compounds of lead.
25. What is a storage battery? Discuss the operation and recharging of the lead accumulator storage cell.
26. Most home light-plants operate at a potential of 32 v. How many lead storage cells should be required?
27. What weight of lead could be recovered from 5 tons of an ore which contains 16 per cent of lead sulfide if recovery is 88 per cent efficient?

28. What weight of white lead could be prepared from 500 kg. of lead?

29. Write equations for the following reactions:

        (a) germanous chloride + acidified permanganate
        (b) germanium + hydrochloric acid
        (c) germanic chloride + water
        (d) germanic oxide + potassium hydroxide
        (e) $GeHCl_3$ + water
        (f) germanous acid + heat
        (g) germanous acid + potassium hydroxide
        (h) germanous oxide + HCl
        (i) germanic sulfide + heat

30. Write equations for the following reactions:

        (a) tin + conc. nitric acid
        (b) tin + sodium hydroxide
        (c) tin + chlorine
        (d) tin + sulfur
        (e) tin + hydrochloric acid
        (f) sodium stannite + bismuth hydroxide
        (g) stannous oxalate + heat
        (h) tin + oxygen
        (i) tin + gaseous hydrogen chloride
        (j) acidic $SnCl_2$ + ferric chloride
        (k) acidic $SnCl_2$ + silver nitrate
        (l) acidic $SnCl_2$ + $AuCl_3$
        (m) stannous sulfide + ammonium polysulfide
        (n) $SnCl_2$ + H_2S

31. Write equations for the following reactions:

        (a) lead nitrate + sodium hydroxide
        (b) lead + oxygen at 500° C.
        (c) lead + sulfur
        (d) lead + nitric acid (dil.)
        (e) lead nitrate + heat
        (f) litharge + nitric acid
        (g) minium + nitric acid (conc.)
        (h) lead dioxide + sodium hydroxide ·
        (i) sodium plumbite + sodium hypochlorite
        (j) plumbic chloride + heat
        (k) lead dioxide + manganous nitrate + nitric acid
        (l) lead nitrate + potassium chromate

Exercises for Chapter 32

1. Why are transition elements so designated, and how do they differ from regular elements?
2. Discuss the general properties of the transition elements.
3. How do the rare earths differ from other transition elements?
4. Why has study of the rare earths been so difficult?
5. Compare the chemistry of the III B elements with that of the III A elements.
6. Which elements of the IV B family might be produced in quantity, and why have they not been so produced in the past?
7. Discuss the uses of titanium.
8. Would you expect Ti^{+2} and Ti^{+3} compounds to be good reducing agents? Give reasons for your answer.
9. Compare the chemistry of the elements of the V A and V B families.
10. Discuss the chemistry of vanadium. What is its most important state of oxidation, and what are its most important compounds?
11. What are the uses of vanadium and its compounds?
12. What are the uses of: (a) columbium; (b) tantalum?
13. Discuss the occurrence, preparation, and uses of chromium.
14. What states of oxidation does chromium exhibit in its compounds? What are the characteristic colors associated with these states? Which state is most important from a practical standpoint?
15. What are the relationships between chromates and dichromates?
16. How might the following changes be made to occur:

(a) $Cr \rightarrow Cr^{+2}$, (b) $Cr \rightarrow Cr^{+3}$, (c) $Cr^{+2} \rightarrow Cr^{+3}$, (d) $Cr^{+3} \rightarrow Cr^{+6}$, (e) $Cr^{+6} \rightarrow Cr^{+3}$

17. How might one prepare: (a) $CrCl_2$; (b) $CrCl_3$; (c) CrO_2Cl_2?
18. What quantity of sodium dichromate dihydrate could be prepared, in theory, from 1 ton of a chromite ore which assays 48 per cent in chromic oxide? What quantity of chrome yellow could be prepared from the dichromate?
19. Calculate the number of grams of potassium dichromate which should be required to prepare 250 ml. of 0.45 N solution of that salt which is to be used as an oxidizing agent in acid solution.
20. What properties would you expect masurium to possess?
21. Prepare a series of equations which show the relationship between manganese dioxide and the other oxidation states of manganese.
22. What is the normality of a certain potassium permanganate solution as an oxidizing agent in acid solution if 20 ml. of the solution is required to react with 0.2680 g. of anhydrous sodium oxalate? How many grams of manganese are contained in each milliliter of the solution?
23. Twenty-five milliliters of 0.140 N potassium permanganate is required to oxidize from $+2$ to $+3$ the iron contained in an impure sample of Fe_2O_3 which weighs 0.6532 g. What is the percentage of Fe_2O_3 in the sample?

24. What weight of anhydrous manganous sulfate could be prepared from 1 kg. of a pyrolusite ore which contains 38 per cent of manganese dioxide? How might the dioxide be converted to potassium permanganate, and, in theory, what weight of this latter salt should be produced?

25. What weight of potassium permanganate should be required to prepare 5 l. of a solution to be 0.3 N as an oxidizing agent for use in neutral solution?

26. Complete and balance the following equations:

$$\text{(a) } YCl_3 + K \xrightarrow{\Delta}$$
$$\text{(b) } Y + HNO_3 \text{ (dil.)} \rightarrow$$

$$\text{(c) } La + O_2 \xrightarrow{\Delta}$$
$$\text{(d) } Ce(SO_4)_2 + H_2S + H_2SO_4 \rightarrow \underline{S} +$$
$$\text{(e) } Tb_2O_7 + H_3PO_3 + HCl \rightarrow TbCl_3 +$$
$$\text{(f) } EuCl_2 + FeCl_3 \rightarrow EuCl_3 +$$
$$\text{(g) } SmCl_2 + MnO_2 + HCl \rightarrow MnCl_2 +$$
$$\text{(h) } TiO + HCl \rightarrow$$
$$\text{(i) } TiO_2 + HNO_3 \text{ (conc.)} \rightarrow$$

$$\text{(j) } TiO_2 + K_2O \xrightarrow{\Delta}$$
$$\text{(k) } TiCl_4 + NaOH \rightarrow$$
$$\text{(l) } Na_2TiO_3 + HOH \xrightarrow{\text{Boil}}$$

$$\text{(m) } TiCl_4 + H_2 \xrightarrow{\Delta}$$
$$\text{(n) } Ti(OH)_3 + HNO_3 \rightarrow Ti(NO_3)_4 + NH_4NO_3 +$$

27. Complete and balance the following equations:

$$\text{(a) } ZrO_2 + H_2SO_4 \rightarrow$$

$$\text{(b) } V + O_2 \xrightarrow{\Delta}$$

$$\text{(c) } Cb + N_2 \xrightarrow{\Delta}$$

$$\text{(d) } Ta + S \xrightarrow{\Delta}$$

$$\text{(e) } VCl_5 + H_2 \xrightarrow{\Delta}$$
$$\text{(f) } VCl_2 + FeCl_3 \rightarrow FeCl_2 +$$

$$\text{(g) } Cr_2O_3 + Al \xrightarrow{\Delta}$$

$$\text{(h) } Cr + O_2 \xrightarrow{\Delta}$$

$$\text{(i) } CrO + O_2 \xrightarrow{\Delta}$$
$$\text{(j) } CrO + HCl \rightarrow$$
$$\text{(k) } CrSO_4 + K_2CrO_4 + H_2SO_4 \rightarrow$$

(l) $K_2Cr_2O_7 + SO_2 + H_2SO_4 + H_2O \rightarrow KCr(SO_4)_2 \cdot 12H_2O +$

(m) $CrO_3 \xrightarrow{250° C.}$

(n) $Na_2Cb_2F_6 + Na \xrightarrow{\Delta}$

28. Complete and balance the following equations:

(a) $MnO_2 + O_2 \xrightarrow{\Delta}$

(b) $MnO + O_2 \xrightarrow{\Delta}$

(c) $MnS + HCl \rightarrow$

(d) $MnCl_3 + HOH \rightarrow$

(e) $H_2S + K_2MnO_4 + HCl \rightarrow MnCl_2 + \underline{S} +$

(f) $MnO_3 + Na_2CO_3 \rightarrow$

(g) $Mn(NO_3)_2 + HNO_3 + PbO_2 \rightarrow HMnO_4 +$

(h) $KMnO_4 + Na_2C_2O_4 + H_2SO_4 \rightarrow CO_2 +$

(i) $K_2MoO_4 + H_2O_2 \rightarrow H_2MoO_8 +$

(j) $WO_3 + H_2 \xrightarrow{\Delta}$

(k) $Re + O_2 \xrightarrow{\Delta}$

(l) $NaReO_4 + AgNO_3 \rightarrow$

Exercises for Chapter 33

1. What are complex ions, and, in general, what elements tend to form them?
2. Who was the first scientist to propose a general theory of the chemistry of complex compounds?
3. What is the "coördination number" of complex compounds, and what values may it have? What are the commonest coördination numbers?
4. Outline the system of nomenclature used for complex compounds.
5. Name the following compounds by the system outlined in problem 4:

$$K_3[Co(CN)_6]; \quad [Ni(NH_3)_4(H_2O)_2](NO_3)_2; \quad [Co(NH_3)_4(NO_2)_2]Cl.$$

6. Discuss the occurrence of iron and the conversion of iron ores into pig iron.
7. What are the functions of the coke and limestone used in the blast furnace?
8. Considering coke to be pure carbon, calculate the quantity of coke required to furnish sufficient carbon monoxide to reduce 1 ton of a hematite ore which is 90 per cent ferric oxide. (Assume that there is no loss of CO.)
9. If the ore mentioned in problem 8 contains 9 per cent SiO_2 and 0.5 per cent lime (CaO), what quantity of limestone containing 98 per cent $CaCO_3$ would be required to remove as $CaSiO_3$ the silica from 1 ton of it?
10. How do cast iron, wrought iron, and steel differ?
11. What is the difference between white and gray cast iron?

12. List the metals commonly used in the preparation of special steels and note the special properties associated with the presence of each.

13. List the advantages and disadvantages of the Bessemer and open-hearth processes.

14. The iron in an ore sample which weighs 0.9942 g. is reduced to the ferrous condition and reoxidized in the presence of acid to the ferric condition with 0.15 N potassium permanganate solution. If 38 ml. of the permanganate solution is required, what is the percentage of iron in the sample and what is the percentage of pure ferric oxide in the sample?

15. Which is the stronger base, ferrous or ferric hydroxide? On what basis might you have predicted their relative strengths?

16. How is ferrous sulfate used in the clarification of water?

17. Much iron pyrite ore is found in nature. Why is it not considered a good source of iron?

18. How do Prussian blue and Turnbull's blue differ? What use is made of them? Write equations for the formation of these compounds.

19. Discuss the chemistry of blueprinting.

20. How are cobalt and nickel usually separated from each other?

21. Discuss some uses of cobalt and nickel.

22. List some uses for the salts of cobalt.

23. Given a solution containing Co^{+2} and Ni^{+2} ions, how might a separation of these ions be effected?

24. Discuss the occurrence and uses of the platinum metals.

25. Why are platinum and palladium not more widely used as catalysts?

26. Discuss the proper care of platinum laboratory vessels.

27. Compare and contrast the common properties of the elements of the I B and I A families of the periodic system.

28. Which is the stronger base—silver hydroxide or cupric hydroxide? Which is the more stable?

29. Write equations for all reactions which take place when each of the currency metals is treated with each of the following reagents: (a) chlorine; (b) oxygen; (c) sulfur; (d) nitric acid.

30. Compare the chemical properties of copper and zinc.

31. An object whose total surface is 30 sq. cm. is plated with silver. If a current of 0.120 amp. is allowed to pass for one hour, what will be the thickness of the deposit (assuming uniform deposition)?

32. Compare the occurrence and recovery of the currency metals.

33. In what respects are the currency metals unusual?

34. What weight of cupric sulfate pentahydrate could be prepared from 1 ton of ore whose copper content is only 2 per cent?

35. List the essential steps of the photographic process; give the purpose of each; and tell how each is accomplished (general methods).

36. What valences are shown by each of the currency metals? Which of these are the more important?

37. What is the percentage of gold in an ore if 45 g. of solid sodium cyanide is required to remove the metal from a 500-g. sample of the crushed ore?

38. Complete and balance the following equations:

$$\text{(a) Fe + HOH (steam)} \xrightarrow{\Delta}$$

(b) $Fe + HCl \rightarrow$

$$\text{(c) } FeC_2O_4 \xrightarrow{\Delta}$$

$$\text{(d) } Fe_2O_3 + CaO \xrightarrow{\Delta}$$

(e) $FeCl_3 + KI \rightarrow$

(f) $FeCl_3 + SnCl_2 \rightarrow$

(g) $Fe(CN)_3 + KCN \rightarrow$

(h) $CoO + HNO_3 \rightarrow$

$$\text{(i) } CoC_2O_4 + H_2 \xrightarrow{\Delta}$$

(j) $Co(OH)_2 + H_2SO_4 \rightarrow$

(k) $Ni(NO_3)_2 + NH_4OH \text{ (excess)} \rightarrow$

$$\text{(l) } NiO + O_2 \xrightarrow{\Delta}$$

$$\text{(m) } Co(NO_3)_2 \xrightarrow{350° \text{ C.}}$$

(n) $CoCl_2 + NaOCl + HOH \rightarrow$

(o) $Co(NO_3)_2 + NaOI + HOH \rightarrow$

$$\text{(p) } Os + O_2 \xrightarrow{\Delta}$$

(q) $Pd + HNO_3 \rightarrow$

$$\text{(r) } Os + HNO_3 \xrightarrow{\Delta}$$

$$\text{(s) } Ir + O_2 \xrightarrow{1100° \text{ C.}}$$

$$\text{(t) } Cu + H_2SO_4 \xrightarrow{\Delta}$$

(u) $CuCl + Na_2CO_3 + HOH \rightarrow$

$$\text{(v) } CuS \xrightarrow{\Delta}$$

(w) $CuCl_2 + SO_2 + HOH \rightarrow$

(x) $CuSO_4 + KI \rightarrow$

(y) $AgNO_3 + AlCl_3 \rightarrow$

$$\text{(1z) } Au_2S_3 + O_2 \xrightarrow{\Delta}$$

$$\text{(2z) } AuCl_3 \xrightarrow{\Delta}$$

$$\text{(3z) } HAuCl_4 \xrightarrow{120° \text{ C.}}$$

Exercises for Chapter 34

1. Why are zinc, cadmium, and mercury classified as neither transition elements nor elements of the regular families?

2. In what ways are the members of the II B family peculiar?

3. Compare the colors, stabilities, and basicities of the oxides of the $+2$ oxidation state of the metals of the II B family.

4. Discuss the occurrence, preparation, and physical properties of: (a) zinc; (b) cadmium; (c) mercury.

5. If one assumes recovery to be 96 per cent efficient, what quantity of zinc should be obtained from 3 kg. of an ore which contains 65 per cent of zinc carbonate?

6. Assuming no loss, if a coating of zinc 0.01 cm. thick is applied to sheet iron, what area of iron can be coated by 5 kg. of zinc?

7. Distinguish between cold galvanized, hot galvanized, and Sherardized iron.

8. Given equal volumes of solutions of zinc nitrate and zinc acetate whose concentrations in terms of zinc are identical. More zinc sulfide can be precipitated from the latter by the action of hydrogen sulfide. Why?

9. What are the upper and lower limits of temperature for the ordinary use of mercurial thermometers?

10. If one would read a mercurial barometer as exactly as possible, what corrections should be applied to the reading?

11. Why does the addition of magnesium chloride to a solution of mercuric chloride lower the concentration of mercuric ions in the solution?

12. Would hydrogen sulfide in the air cause the darkening of surfaces painted with either cadmium yellow or vermilion? Why, or why not?

13. Discuss the preparation and use of the important salts of: (a) zinc; (b) cadmium; (c) mercury.

14. Compare the stability of mercurous and mercuric salts.

15. When the mercury in a mercurial barometer stands at a height of 585 mm., how high should the water in a water barometer stand? (Neglect all corrections for temperature effects in both cases.)

16. Write equations for all of the preparations mentioned in sections 16, 17, 24, and 25 of this chapter.

17. Given a 0.01 N solution of zinc chloride. If the solubility product constant of zinc sulfide is 1.2×10^{-23}, what concentration of S^{--} would be required to cause precipitation of zinc sulfide to begin?

18. Calculate the weight of mercury vapor at $20°$ C. which would be contained in a room whose dimensions are 10 m. $\times$ 8 m. $\times$ 4 m. What would be the volume of this weight of mercury as a liquid?

19. How might mercury be used to obtain oxygen from the air?

20. How could a mixture of potassium and mercuric chlorides be separated?

21. Write equations to represent the following changes:

$$Hg \rightarrow HgCl_2 \rightarrow Hg_2Cl_2 \rightarrow HgCl_2 \rightarrow Hg \rightarrow Hg_2(NO_3)_2 \rightarrow Hg_2O \rightarrow HgO \rightarrow Hg$$

Exercises for Chapter 35

1. What is radioactivity, and by whom was it discovered?
2. Write a 500-word paper on the discovery of radium.
3. Discuss the occurrence of radium. What is believed to be its origin?
4. Name and characterize the emanations of radium.
5. What is believed to be the origin of radioactive emanations, and why are some elements radioactive while others are not?
6. Why are atoms of another element formed as a result of radioactive changes?
7. A certain element of mass 232 and of atomic number 90 is a member of the IV B group of the periodic system. If an alpha particle is ejected by atoms of this element, what are the atomic number and the atomic weight of the atom formed, and of what element is it an isotope? Give the same information for a second product formed by the ejection of a beta particle from the first product.
8. Of what ordinary element is ionium an isotope?
9. Upon what does the rate of radioactive disintegration depend? Why do changes in physical and chemical conditions have no effect upon this rate?
10. If one had a 1-g. sample of radium B, what quantity of it would remain at the end of 18 hrs.?
11. Given a sample of radium. Why does not the quantity of polonium produced continue to increase throughout the decomposition of the radium?
12. Discuss the use of radium. Why is it more commonly used than are the other naturally occurring radioactive elements?
13. Distinguish between: (a) transmutation and (b) fission.
14. How may transmutation be brought about artificially?
15. How may protons, deuterons, and alpha particles be accelerated? Why can the neutron not be accelerated in like manner?
16. Complete the balancing of the following equations:

$$\text{(a)} \quad _{15}P^{31} + {}_2He^4 \rightarrow Cl + {}_0n^1$$
$$\text{(b)} \quad _{27}Co^{59} + {}_0n^1 \rightarrow Fe + {}_1H^1$$
$$\text{(c)} \quad _{10}Ne^{20} + {}_1D^2 \rightarrow F + {}_2He^4$$

17. Write equations to represent the manner in which the radioactive chlorine obtained in equation 16(a), above, might disintegrate to attain stability.
18. Atoms of $_{25}Mn^{56}$ can be prepared by bombarding with neutrons $_{25}Mn^{55}$, $_{26}Fe^{56}$, and $_{27}Co^{59}$. Write transmutation equations for these changes.
19. Discuss the use of artificial radioactive elements.
20. List some of the effects which you think the general use of sub-atomic energy would have upon your life.

Exercises for Chapter 36

1. In what way did the discovery of the inert gases have an influence upon theories of atomic structure?
2. Give a brief résumé of the history of the discovery of the inert gases.

3. How may the inert gases be identified?
4. Compare the densities and the lifting powers of hydrogen and helium.
5. In what ways, other than by lack of chemical activity, do the members of the VIII A family exhibit their inertness?
6. Discuss the uses of the inert gases
7. What is the origin of the name of each of the inert gases?
8. How and where are helium and argon obtained commercially?
9. Prepare a graph on which the atomic weights of the inert gases are plotted as abscissas and their boiling points as ordinates.
10. What are "neon" signs, and why are they so named?
11. Why is radon more commonly used than radium in the treatment of patients?
12. In terms of the present concept of atomic structure, why is radon capable of spontaneous disintegration though unable to undergo ordinary chemical changes?
13. Calculate the volume of air at 21° C. and 760 mm. of pressure which should be required for the production of 1 lb. of: (a) argon; (b) krypton; (c) xenon. (Assume that 22.4 l. of air at S.T.P. has a mass of 29 g.)
14. In what way was the periodic classification of the elements of importance in the discovery of the inert gases?

TABLE OF INTERNATIONAL ATOMIC WEIGHTS, 1946

Element	Symbol	At. No.	At. Wt.	Element	Symbol	At. No.	At. Wt.
Actinium	Ac	89	227.05	Mercury	Hg	80	200.61
Aluminum	Al	13	26.97	Molybdenum	Mo	42	95.95
Americium	Am	95	241	Neodymium	Nd	60	144.27
Antimony	Sb	51	121.76	Neon	Ne	10	20.183
Argon	A	18	39.944	Neptunium	Np	93	237
Arsenic	As	33	74.91	Nickel	Ni	28	58.69
Astatine	At	85	211	Nitrogen	N	7	14.008
Barium	Ba	56	137.36	Osmium	Os	76	190.2
Beryllium	Be	4	9.02	Oxygen	O	8	16.0000
Bismuth	Bi	83	209.00	Palladium	Pd	46	106.7
Boron	B	5	10.82	Phosphorus	P	15	30.98
Bromine	Br	35	79.916	Platinum	Pt	78	195.23
Cadmium	Cd	48	112.41	Plutonium	Pu	94	239
Calcium	Ca	20	40.08	Polonium	Po	84	210
Carbon	C	6	12.01	Potassium	K	19	39.096
Cerium	Ce	58	140.13	Praseodymium	Pr	59	140.92
Cesium	Cs	55	132.91	Protactinium	Pa	91	231
Chlorine	Cl	17	35.457	Radium	Ra	88	226.05
Chromium	Cr	24	52.01	Radon	Rn	86	222
Cobalt	Co	27	58.94	Rhenium	Re	75	186.31
Columbium	Cb	41	92.91	Rhodium	Rh	45	102.91
Copper	Cu	29	63.57	Rubidium	Rb	37	85.48
Curium	Cm	96	242	Ruthenium	Ru	44	101.7
Dysprosium	Dy	66	162.46	Samarium	Sm	62	150.43
Erbium	Er	68	167.2	Scandium	Sc	21	45.10
Europium	Eu	63	152.0	Selenium	Se	34	78.96
Fluorine	F	9	19.000	Silicon	Si	14	28.06
Francium	Fa	87	223	Silver	Ag	47	107.880
Gadolinium	Gd	64	156.9	Sodium	Na	11	22.997
Gallium	Ga	31	69.72	Strontium	Sr	38	87.63
Germanium	Ge	32	72.60	Sulfur	S	16	32.06
Gold	Au	79	197.2	Tantalum	Ta	73	180.88
Hafnium	Hf	72	178.6	Technetium	Tc	43	99
Helium	He	2	4.003	Tellurium	Te	52	127.61
Holmium	Ho	67	164.94	Terbium	Tb	65	159.2
Hydrogen	H	1	1.0080	Thallium	Tl	81	204.39
Illinium	Il	61	147	Thorium	Th	90	232.12
Indium	In	49	114.76	Thulium	Tm	69	169.4
Iodine	I	53	126.92	Tin	Sn	50	118.70
Iridium	Ir	77	193.1	Titanium	Ti	22	47.90
Iron	Fe	26	55.85	Tungsten	W	74	183.92
Krypton	Kr	36	83.7	Uranium	U	92	238.07
Lanthanum	La	57	138.92	Vanadium	V	23	50.95
Lead	Pb	82	207.21	Xenon	Xe	54	131.3
Lithium	Li	3	6.940	Ytterbium	Yb	70	173.04
Lutecium	Lu	71	174.99	Yttrium	Y	39	88.92
Magnesium	Mg	12	24.32	Zinc	Zn	30	65.38
Manganese	Mn	25	54.93	Zirconium	Zr	40	91.22